RADIOISOTOPES AND THE AGE OF THE EARTH

RESULTS OF A YOUNG-EARTH CREATIONIST RESEARCH INITIATIVE

Edited by

Larry Vardiman
Andrew A. Snelling
Eugene F. Chaffin

Institute for Creation Research
El Cajon, CA

Creation Research Society
Chino Valley, AZ

Radioisotopes and the Age of the Earth
Results of a Young-Earth Creationist Research Initiative

Published by

Institute for Creation Research   Creation Research Society
PO Box 2667   and   6801 N. Highway 89
El Cajon, California 92021   Chino Valley, Arizona 86323

First Printing 2005

Printed in the United States of America

Library of Congress Cataloging-in-Publication Data

Library of Congress Control Number: 2005929150
ISBN 0-932766-81-1

Cover Design by Janell Robertson

Dedication

Scientists' wives need to be understanding. They must forgive the absent stare of a husband when he tries to solve an equation in his head while eating a candlelit dinner. They must endure enthusiastic descriptions of new scientific discoveries couched in foreign terms not even found in *Webster's Dictionary*. They must abide multiple stops at geological road cuts during family vacations to collect rock samples and fill suitcases with chunks of granite.

The wives of the RATE group were particularly understanding. They allowed us to travel to San Diego once a year to meet with our colleagues while they stayed at home and waited by the phone. They permitted us to spend hours on the Internet sending emails to one another. They encouraged us when we were depressed. They calmed us when we were overly optimistic. They provided the encouragement and balance we so desperately needed. We wish to dedicate this book to our wives who made it possible for us to practice our science to the best of our abilities. Thanks to all of you—the wives of the RATE group.

- Brenda Austin
- Mary Baumgardner
- Janette Boyd
- Pamela Chaffin
- Sally DeYoung
- Bonita Humphreys
- Kym Snelling
- Jeannette Vardiman

We also wish to remember Jean, John Baumgardner's first wife, who went to be with the Lord part way through the RATE project. She touched our hearts deeply a few weeks before her death from cancer when she emailed us a beautiful testimony of her faith in the Lord and her confidence in seeing all of us in Glory.

Contents

List of Tables

Table	Title	Page

Isochron Discordances and the Role of Inheritance and Mixing of Radioisotopes in the Mantle and Crust

Accelerated Decay: Theoretical Considerations

Table	Title	Page

List of Figures

Figure	Title	Page

Figure	Title	Page

Figure	**Title**	**Page**

Figure	Title	Page

Do Radioisotope Clocks Need Repair? Testing the Assumptions of Isochron Dating Using K-Ar, Rb-Sr, Sm-Nd, and Pb-Pb Isotopes

Figure	Title	Page

Isochron Discordances and the Role of Inheritance and Mixing of Radioisotopes in the Mantle and Crust

Figure	Title	Page

Figure	Title	Page

Figure	Title	Page

Figure	Title	Page

Accelerated Decay: Theoretical Considerations

**Summary of Evidence for a Young Earth
from the RATE Project**

Figure	Title	Page

The RATE Group

Front row (left to right): Dr. John R. Baumgardner, Dr. Larry Vardiman, Dr. D. Russell Humphreys, Dr. Eugene F. Chaffin.
Middle row (left to right): Dr. Andrew A. Snelling, Dr. Steven A. Austin, Dr. Donald B. DeYoung
Back row (left to right): Dr. John D. Morris (ICR President), Dr. Kenneth B. Cumming (Dean, ICR Graduate School), Mr. William A. Hoesch (Research Assistant), Dr. Steven W. Boyd.

Prologue

John D. Morris, Ph.D.*

Evolution and deep time go hand in hand. Eons of time are required to generate and accumulate rare beneficial mutations into the vast array of life we see today. Natural selection cannot produce them, it only selects from the various mutants present. As the late George Wald, former Harvard biology professor, has said:

> Time is in fact the hero of the plot ... Given so much time, the "impossible" becomes possible, the possible probable, and the probable virtually certain. One has only to wait: time itself performs the miracles
>
> (The origin of life, *Scientific American, 191*(2), p. 49, 1954).

It's as if time heals all wounds. Time shrouds all the problems of evolution from view. But, what if the eons of time are a myth?

The authors of this book are convinced that evolution does not happen today, did not happen in the past, and could not happen ever. In fact, the more time available, the more deterioration of the genome occurs, and extinction will prevail. In reality, time is the enemy of evolution, not its hero. But without deep time, evolution can't even be entertained.

Concepts speculating on the long ago past don't occupy the same tier of credibility as present day observations. The historical sciences may be legitimate exercises, but they are not the same as the science of observable processes.

For instance, we know how a clam lives, assimilates its food, moves around, reproduces and dies. Furthermore, we observe an impressive variety of clams, and in many cases we even know ancestral relationships among some of the varieties, for they developed in observable time. But what non-clam evolved into a clam in the unobserved past? How did it happen? These historical questions can't be answered with certainty

---

* *President, Institute for Creation Research, Santee, California*

in the present. How can we investigate the long-ago past?

Geology students are taught to approach a rock outcrop or laboratory experiment with multiple working hypotheses in mind. Predict the data expected from each hypothesis, and then put them to the test. Gather the data. Gather **all** the data. Then see which hypothesis is best supported by the data. That hypothesis is the one most likely correct.

But time questions differ from others. Lacking a time machine, we can't scientifically observe the past. Today we can only observe and test the remnants of past processes preserved in the present. Thus the past, especially the long-ago past, is inaccessible to science. Even so, deep time has achieved immunity from comparison to any other model. To many, the reality of immeasurably long ages has become such a dogma it never gets questioned at all. The investigator may try to fine tune a date—is the rock 1.35 or 1.37 billion years old?—but no totally different hypothesis merits consideration. Until now, that is.

In 1997 an eight year research initiative to investigate this very issue was launched. Entitled **R**adioisotopes and the **A**ge of **T**he **E**arth (RATE), and staffed by experts qualified in relevant fields, it attempted to test the validity of radioisotope dating of rocks, source of the main evidence for deep time. In the true spirit of multiple working hypotheses, these scientists determined to put the basic concept to the test. They determined to gather data heretofore ignored or censored by adherence to only one idea. They purposed to run experiments never before conceived. They demanded that the deep time way of thinking be put to the test, and results compared to the expectations of both old and young earth models. They were intent on seeing which of the two schools of thought was more likely correct.

It would be inaccurate to claim that the RATE scientists had no bias. All are dedicated Christians and all hold the Bible as correct in all its teachings, even in matters of science and history. They have become convinced that belief in the Bible is a reasonable position, well supported by facts and logic. While scientists often make pronouncements contrary to Scripture, no verified fact of science contradicts any of its teachings, even as it relates to the unobserved past. The Bible doesn't give all the details, but it does provide the overall framework within which historical and scientific data can be interpreted in a robust and intellectually satisfying manner.

The concept of biased scientists may come as a surprise to some, but in reality all investigators have a bias before starting their studies and all experiments are chosen and conducted within that bias. One's thinking can be dominated by generally uniform processes over long ages or by rapid and catastrophic processes over a comparatively short timescale. Since all scientists are locked into the present, studying data and running experiments in the present, limited by their present knowledge, skills and logic, accurately reconstructing the past is virtually impossible. Without a guide, without the big picture provided by a capable and reliable observer of the past, we will all fall short of absolute truth. The RATE scientists are convinced that the Bible's picture of the past is the proper one to inform our present investigation.

The Bible tells of an orderly progression of six 24-hour days only thousands of years ago during which all things were created. Each step was necessary before the next until the earth was fully prepared for animal life and finally man. The oceans, the atmosphere, the continents, the plants, the Sun, Moon, and stars, the animals—each formed by creative processes quite unlike processes of today—each in its place and each accomplishing its purpose. Finally, with man as its steward, it was all "very good" (Genesis 1:31) from the Creator's perspective. But man then chose to reject God's authority over him, immediately precipitating the ruination of creation, followed by a world-restructuring flood in Noah's day. Today we live and do our science in the cursed, flooded, remnant of a once "very good" world, making historical investigations difficult.

If we deny the historicity of these great world-changing events, we have little chance of discerning earth's true past. Without the certainty of a fully-functional earth created by God in the beginning, we might misinterpret that functional maturity for age. Without factoring the great Flood into our thinking, we might assign great time spans to things formed very rapidly in that high energy environment. If we limit our thinking to the processes happening today, at only the rates, scales and intensities we observe today, we cannot arrive at the truth about the earth's past and how it came to be in the state it is in today. With the Bible's big picture as our framework, we have a chance of properly reconstructing the earth's history and understanding its present condition.

During the first three years of the RATE initiative radioisotope dating methods and theory were put to the test. The results of those methods were shown to be discordant, inconclusive and sometimes bizarre. Only by selective reporting of the results, and blind adherence to the underlying unprovable assumptions involved, do they even appear to point in the direction of deep time. In short, it was conclusively shown that the radioisotope dating methods do not unequivocally yield the accurate ages of the items tested. But they were doing something. What were they really showing? Is there a better understanding of them which can replace the failed one? The RATE book published after the first three years revealed the questionable state of the radioisotope dating methods and proposed experiments which could shed some light in the darkness.

The next five years were occupied by conducting those experiments and analyzing the data and theory. This book presents the results. Of course, not every question was asked, thus much more remains to be done. But every investigation attempted yielded a positive result for the Creation/Flood/young earth model. Numerous other investigations were suggested.

Does this work prove the young earth model? Of course not, as no historical reconstruction can be fully proved. But it does show that of the two viewpoints the young earth model is better supported and more consistent with **all** the radioisotope evidence.

Thus this book opens a new chapter in the origins controversy. As never before it calls into question the deep time model and places the Biblically compatible young earth model on a level of scholarship never before achieved and archived. Its pages contain many profound thoughts, which will shake current scientific orthodoxy to its core. It deserves careful consideration by all who value truth.

Acknowledgments

In the acknowledgments to the first RATE book, **Radioisotopes and the Age of the Earth: A Young-Earth Creationist Research Initiative**, the RATE group expressed the following hopes:

> Over the next five years we hope to answer some of the questions which have been raised in this book. At a minimum, we hope to advance our understanding about the age of the earth and possibly resolve the apparent dilemma regarding radioisotopes. We request your continued prayers on our behalf.

This book reports on the findings of the five-year research effort to answer a series of questions about the age of the earth. It is obvious that the supporters of this project have prayed and the Lord has fulfilled the hopes expressed far above our expectations. Not only were the financial needs for this research fully met but the scientists involved in this work were inspired to new heights of creativity and accomplishment. We were provided answers to most of the questions raised in the first book and we made incredible progress toward answering others. The evidence which came from our experimental and theoretical work thrilled us time and again as we reported to one another at our annual meetings. It was exciting being part of a project which honors the Lord and discovers new information about how His world operates. We want to thank our Creator God for all that He has provided and done in making the RATE project possible and in giving us the answers we were seeking.

The RATE group would like to thank the Institute for Creation Research (ICR) and the Creation Research Society (CRS) for supporting and publishing this work. We recognize that some of the statements we have made may not necessarily represent the positions or viewpoints of ICR or CRS. Thank you to Dr. John Morris for his encouragement and support for this effort. Although Dr. Don DeYoung is part of the RATE group, we wish to thank him for his extra work in writing the

"Lay Translation" of the RATE book and coordinating with CRS. Thank you to Dr. Kenneth Cumming, Mr. Don Rohrer, and Mr. Mark Rasche and the staff of ICR for all their support and help behind the scenes. Thank you to ICR for the investment of about $250,000 of indirect costs over and above the direct donations received. Thank you to The Master's College for allowing Dr. Steven Boyd to participate in the RATE project. Thank you to Bill Hoesch for his work as field geologist and laboratory technician in collecting and preparing many of the rock samples. Thank you to Mark Armitage for his help in the work on radiohalos and for contributing photomicrographs of zircons from his electron microscope and of some radiohalos from his optical microscopes. And, we thank Laurel Hemmings for her diligence and accuracy in typesetting this book

Thank you to over 400 donors who supported this project with their prayers and finances. We believe your funds (over $1 million) were wisely and carefully spent in the service of the Lord. We were amazed as time after time the necessary funds arrived just as they were needed. Over forty technical reviewers read and commented on this book. Our reviewers were very busy people who served us well by providing thorough and helpful reviews that improved the presentation of the research results. In accordance with our policy to maintain the identity of our reviewers in confidence, in contrast to releasing them in our first book, we have chosen not to reveal their names here. However, you and the Lord know who you are. Thank you.

Chapter 1

Introduction

Larry Vardiman, Ph.D.*

Abstract. One of the most significant contradictions between the Bible and the prevalent world-view of origins today is the age of the earth. The Bible teaches that the earth is thousands of years old while the current conventional theory of origins says the earth is billions of years old. Many Bible-believing Christians recognize this disparity and are willing to financially support a large-scale research effort to resolve this contradiction. This book is a report of an eight-year project called RATE (**R**adioisotopes and the **A**ge of **T**he **E**arth) designed to resolve the apparent contradiction between the thousands of years taught in Scripture and the billions of years taught by the conventional scientific community. This first chapter gives a summary of the history of the RATE project, tabulates the basic results, comments briefly on the significance of what was found, and offers advice for additional research in the future. The detailed results are reported in the chapters to follow.

1. The Birth of RATE

Radioisotopes are radioactive elements which transform into new daughter elements by nuclear decay while radiating energetic particles. Scientists have long assumed that the decay rates are relatively constant and regular. If this were so, then radioisotopes should be relatively trustworthy clocks. They ought to be reliable chronometers with which to assess the age of rocks, and taken together, the whole earth. However, profound problems have been raised showing that the traditional readings of these "clocks" are problematic.

* *Chief Operating Officer and Astrogeophysics Department Chairman, Institute for Creation Research, Santee, California*

Does the decay of radioisotopes reliably and validly (truthfully) show the earth to be billions of years old? Or is the evidence more consistent with a Biblical chronology suggesting that the earth was formed less than 10,000 years ago? This book focuses on the explanation of existing quantities of daughter elements derived from radioisotopes. While arguments have been constructed showing that the traditional interpretations of radioisotopic methods of geochronology are flawed, proponents of the Biblical chronology have yet to account for the large quantities of daughter isotopes that must have been formed in a short period of time.

To address the foregoing problems, on July 4, 1997 seven young-earth creation scientists—Steve Austin, John Baumgardner, Gene Chaffin, Don DeYoung, Russ Humphreys, Andrew Snelling, and Larry Vardiman—met in San Diego, California. They reviewed the procedures and assumptions used for radioisotope dating of rocks. They found that the variety of radioisotopic methods are not reliable because of the flawed circular reasoning underlying their development and use.

Empirically, the various radioisotopic methods are known to be excessively unreliable in repeated application, commonly in substantial disagreement with each other in dating the very same rocks, and without a coherent theoretical basis. Furthermore, they are often in disagreement with many non-radioactive chronometers which suggest a young earth. Nevertheless, the fact that large quantities of daughter isotopes are found in the vicinity of parent radioisotopes must be accounted for.

The RATE research initiative born at that meeting in 1997 led to an eight-year project designed to investigate the processes that may have produced the known large quantities of daughter elements in a period of about 10,000 years. The vast disparity between the billions of years estimated from conventional radioisotopic methods and the thousands of years derived from a literal* interpretation of the Bible would hopefully be resolved. Rather than merely showing the logical flaws

---

* *To interpret the Bible literally means to read it with a straightforward understanding of the text wherever possible unless there is good evidence for not doing so. This does not rule out the occasional occurrence of poetic or allegorical passages.*

in the conventional assumptions used in dating schemes, the RATE project focused on uncovering the processes that may have led to the observed daughter elements.

The members of the RATE team listed below have been heavily involved throughout the project:

- Dr. Steven A. Austin, Geologist, Institute for Creation Research, California
- Dr. John R. Baumgardner, Geophysicist, Institute for Creation Research, California[1]
- Dr. Steven W. Boyd, Hebraist, The Master's College, California[2]
- Dr. Eugene F. Chaffin, Physicist, Bob Jones University, South Carolina[3]
- Dr. Donald B. DeYoung, Physicist, Grace College and Seminary, Indiana[4]
- Dr. D. Russell Humphreys, Physicist, Institute for Creation Research, California[5]
- Dr. Andrew A. Snelling, Geologist, Institute for Creation Research, California[6]
- Dr. Larry Vardiman, Atmospheric Scientist, Institute for Creation Research, California

Not only was each member of the RATE team trained in different aspects of science, they also had different interests and ideas on how to tackle the relevant problems. Much of the time in the annual meetings was spent in attempting to understand the various member perspectives and in reaching consensus on what experiments to conduct and how to interpret the findings. However, one of the common convictions among the entire team was a high regard for Scripture and its literal interpretation including the acceptance of recent creation and the global Flood, and the trustworthiness of Biblical chronology.

---

[1] *Formerly with Los Alamos National Laboratory*
[2] *Joined the project for the last four years*
[3] *Board member of the Creation Research Society (CRS)*
[4] *Board member of CRS*
[5] *Formerly with Sandia National Laboratories and Board member of CRS*
[6] *Formerly with Answers in Genesis*

2. The Life of RATE

The RATE project was designed to last a total of eight years. The first three years were dedicated to reviewing the literature on radioisotope techniques for dating rocks and proposing what research should be done to develop a better explanation for a young earth. This phase ended with the publishing of the book, **Radioisotopes and the Age of the Earth: A Young-Earth Creationist Research Initiative** [*Vardiman et al.,* 2000] which reported on these two accomplishments. The remaining five years were dedicated to conducting the research proposed in the first phase. The whole project ended with the publishing of this book, **Radioisotopes and the Age of the Earth: Results of a Young-Earth Creationist Research Initiative** [*Vardiman et al.,* 2005]. In addition, a non-technical version of this final book and a video documentary of the project have been prepared by *DeYoung* [2005] and the *Institute for Creation Research* [2005] respectively. These non-technical summaries of results have both been entitled **Thousands not Billions: Challenging an Icon of Evolution**.

When the project was started in 1997 no funds or sponsoring institutions had been identified to support the project. However, the Institute for Creation Research elected to sponsor the first meeting until funding could be obtained. The Creation Research Society joined ICR in soliciting funds and participated in publishing the two main technical reports [*Vardiman et al.,* 2000, 2005]. Answers in Genesis supported Dr. Snelling's participation in the RATE project for his first year on the project, and initially helped distribute fliers and news items to help raise support.

The total cash donations to the RATE project have exceeded $1,000,000 supplemented by about $250,000 in indirect costs paid by ICR. The total expenditure has thus exceeded $1,250,000. Over 400 donors gave gifts of less than $1000. More than fifty contributed $1000 or more, and several individuals gave substantially greater sums. Most of the expenses for the RATE project fell into one of three categories; salaries and overhead for the RATE scientists, charges from laboratories to process and analyze rock samples, and travel, meeting, and publishing expenses. Some of the laboratory costs ran as high as $2000 per sample. Direct laboratory costs exceeded $250,000. Salaries and overhead costs included expenses in literature searches, field work, meeting attendance, interpretation of results, and writing of articles and reports. Travel expenses included the cost of nine annual meetings of the RATE group, participation in the Fifth International Conference on Creationism, and technical society meetings like the American Geophysical Union where RATE results were reported. A portion of the cost to prepare the non-technical book about the project and all of the cost of the video documentary were paid from RATE funds.

Most of the communication among the RATE project scientists occurred by email. Without this form of communication the geographically widespread research conducted from Australia to the east coast of the United States would not have been possible in the time frame of eight years. It was common practice for one scientist to forward an idea or draft report to one or two of the others, with information copies to the remainder of the group, and have written responses back within twenty-four hours. Many times the email discussion would go back and forth multiple times before agreement was reached on how to proceed with a particular phase of the research. The technical books were also reviewed and edited by email. Electronic files of individual chapters were compressed and transmitted over the Internet. In the final stages of the editing, the files became too large to transmit easily because of the intensive graphics, and had to be recorded on discs and mailed by overnight delivery.

Once each year the entire RATE project group met face to face in San Diego to review the research accomplished and to organize ongoing research. These meetings were highlights of the year because of the creativity and motivation they produced. Each scientist was allotted half an hour to report on his research on a particular topic. These reports typically occurred on the first day of the two-day annual meeting. On the second day, special topics and problem areas were addressed followed by administrative decisions concerning such matters as budgets and reporting schedules. Each annual meeting began with a devotional study and prayer. At the end of each annual meeting an evening of fellowship at a local restaurant was a well-deserved reward. A written report containing documents presented during the annual meeting was published each year for the exclusive use of the RATE project group. The purpose of these reports was to provide immediate documentation of what had been accomplished during that meeting and a record for posterity.

Special care was taken in publishing the technical reports of the RATE project. A multi-stage process was used in the review. The first draft of each chapter was forwarded to all members of the group to read and comment on at the annual meeting. After the written and verbal review within the RATE group, a second draft of each chapter was peer reviewed by outside technical experts. These experts were not necessarily all young-earth creationists, but most were Christians. The review process was administered by the three editors—Larry Vardiman, Andrew Snelling, and Eugene Chaffin. When the outside reviews were completed the chapters were revised by the authors and resubmitted to the editors for final review. The last step was to review the third draft which was formatted into its final form for the book. The process took almost two years for each technical book.

A key issue identified early in the RATE project needed immediate attention: How much radioisotopic decay had occurred in the history of the earth? If it was a large amount, how could it be explained? Phase one showed that *a large amount of radioactive decay had indeed occurred.* At least four pieces of evidence made this conclusion inescapable. First, a large quantity of Pb, the end product in the U decay chain, was found in close proximity to the radioactive centers still containing residual U. Second, fission tracks, caused by the passage of high-energy fragments emanating from the fission of U atoms gave evidence of a large amount of nuclear decay. Third, radiohalos were formed around primary and secondary radioactive centers where large concentrations of high-energy α-particles damaged the surrounding crystal structures leaving spherical shells of discoloration. And, fourth, relatively large concentrations of He were still present in the rocks. This He resulted from emitted α-particles having captured two electrons each to become He atoms and coming to rest.

Once the RATE group was certain that a large amount of nuclear decay had actually occurred, the obvious explanation for so much daughter product was accelerated radioactive decay. This hypothesis was reluctantly embraced because conventional wisdom dictates that even under extreme physical conditions like high temperatures and pressures the decay rates typically do not change today by more than a few percent. However, as the evidence began to accumulate during the RATE project it became clear that accelerated nuclear decay was the most promising explanation for the large amount of daughter products. Initially, the concept of accelerated decay was only an hypothesis, but evidence from several different sources resulted in *accelerated decay becoming the primary explanation for the findings of RATE.*

3. The Experiments of RATE

Most of the research proposed in the first RATE project book was addressed during the subsequent five-year research phase. It was never anticipated that all the questions raised initially would be definitively answered. However, the advances achieved were greater than anyone expected. The research findings will be described in detail by each principal investigator in the following chapters and will be summarized in the last chapter. Here only a thumbnail sketch of each of the major research topics will be addressed.

Table 1 lists the principal investigator, a description of the experiment, and the main results of the five RATE project experiments originally identified as **High Priority RATE Experiments** in Chapter 1, Table 1 of *Vardiman et al.* [2000, p. 16]. Significant advances were achieved in all five experiments. It should also be noted that the majority of donated funds, consistent with the stated purpose for raising those funds, were expended in conducting these five high-priority experiments.

Table 2 lists the principal investigator, a description of the experiment, and the main results of three additional studies that also achieved significant results. Two of these experiments—Case Studies in Rock Dating and Biblical Word Studies—had been listed in Table 2 of *Vardiman et al.* [2000, p. 17] as **Low Priority RATE Experiments**.

Table 1. Results of high priority experiments.

Experiment	Principal Investigator	Description	Main Results
He Diffusion	D. Russell Humphreys	An experimental measurement of diffusivity of He in zircon from Precambrian granodiorite from the Jemez Caldera, New Mexico, and the development of a two-dimensional theoretical diffusion model of He through zircon and biotite.	*The measured diffusion rate of He in zircon is five orders of magnitude greater than present U-Pb decay produces He.* The measured diffusivity of He in zircon used in the model estimates the age of the zircons and the granodiorite to be 6000±2000 years.
Isochron Discordance	Steven A. Austin	A detailed chemical analysis of rock samples from the diabase sill at Bass Rapids, Grand Canyon and the Beartooth amphibolite, Wyoming. Whole-rock and mineral isochron comparisons for four isotope pairs.	Isochrons give four different estimates of age for the same rock sample. Estimated age is greater for α-decay than for β-decay. Conventional radioisotope dating techniques display considerable internal inconsistency.
Nuclear Decay Theory	Eugene F. Chaffin	An exploration of theoretical mechanisms which could explain accelerated nuclear decay.	Minor variations in nuclear parameters like potential well width and depth can produce orders of magnitude change in α-decay rates. Beta-decay can be accelerated by different amounts depending on "forbidden modes."
Radiohalos	Andrew A. Snelling	A wide geological and geographical collection and survey of U, Th, and Po radiohalos and an explanation of their formation.	Polonium radiohalos formed rapidly under catastrophic conditions. Their formation follows the decay of U and argues for an accelerated decay rate and rapid cooling of granites formed during the Genesis Flood.
Fission Tracks	Andrew A. Snelling	A geological collection and analysis of fission tracks in zircons from five selected locations. An interpretation of conditions associated with their formation.	The quantity of fission tracks in most samples is consistent with a large amount of nuclear decay during the period of the Genesis Flood, implying that accelerated decay has occurred. Fewer fission tracks in some samples appears to be due to their erasure during hot conditions associated with accelerated nuclear decay.

Table 2. Results of additional significant experiments.

Experiment	Principal Investigator	Description	Main Results
Case Studies in Rock Dating	Andrew A. Snelling	A collection and chemical analysis of ten rock units from recent time to the early Precambrian. Whole-rock and mineral analyses using four isochron dating methods were applied to the samples. A search for evidence of inheritance and mixing of radioisotopes in the mantle and crust was also conducted.	Marked discordance was found among the isochron estimates of ages. *Alpha-decaying radioisotopes gave older isochron ages than β-decayers, and the greater the atomic weight of the isotope the older the estimated age.* It was concluded that radioisotope methods cannot be relied upon for absolute ages of rocks and that the only explanation for this pattern of discordance is accelerated decay at periods in the past. Contamination of recent crustal rocks by inheritance and mixing has occurred, but accelerated decay is the dominant cause of discordance.
Biblical Word Studies	Steven W. Boyd	A statistical study of the difference in verb forms between narrative and poetic passages of the Old Testament.	Preterite, Perfect, Imperfect, and WawPerfect verb forms were found to have significantly different frequency distributions between narrative and poetic passages. These differences are significant at a P-value of less than 0.0001. When applied to the Creation and Flood accounts in Genesis this statistical model indicates that these accounts are narrative and should be interpreted as literal, historical events.
Carbon-14 (^{14}C) in Coals and Diamonds	John R. Baumgardner	A measurement and analysis of ^{14}C in coals and diamonds using accelerator mass spectrometer (AMS) methods. Seventy carbon-rich samples reported in the conventional literature had already been found to contain ^{14}C. Ten new coal samples from different depths in the geologic record and twelve diamonds from widely divergent geographical locations were collected and measured by RATE for their ^{14}C contents. The implications of measurable concentrations of ^{14}C in coals and diamonds for a young earth were explored.	This project was added due to new information offered to the RATE project in 2001 by Dr. Paul Giem. The peer-reviewed radiocarbon literature documents scores of examples of ^{14}C/^{12}C ratios in the range of 0.1–0.5 percent of the modern ^{14}C/^{12}C ratio with uniformitarian ages from 1–500 million years. RATE measurements of coals confirmed these reported concentrations. Measurements in diamonds (which are highly resistant to contamination) found similar ^{14}C concentrations. The values correspond to ^{14}C ages between 44,000 and 57,000 years using conventional assumptions. A lower, more realistic estimate for biospheric ^{14}C prior to a cataclysm which buried all the fossils would yield an estimated age of about 5000 years. This age is consistent with the Biblical account of a global Flood on the planet a few thousand years ago (not billions).

The third experiment—^{14}C in Coal and Diamonds—was a new experiment conceived during phase two and had not been anticipated in earlier plans. The results of all three of these studies, however, were so significant and surprising that they merit special attention in a separate table.

Table 3 lists six other experiments that were also identified in Table 2 of *Vardiman et al.* [2000, p. 17] as **Low Priority RATE Experiments**. It lists the experiment, a description of the experiment, and a brief discussion. With some exceptions, little progress was made on these experiments. The discussion indicates that some were incorporated partially into the higher-priority experiments and some were not addressed at all. A few of them will be included in recommendations for future work to be found in the summary in the last chapter of this book.

4. The Significance of RATE

The geological timescale with its hypothesized billions of years has been regarded by evolutionists as their impregnable stronghold against the Biblical record of Creation. Whenever their other arguments have met with fatal opposition, they have retreated into the claim that billions of years of time could account for primordial conditions on earth accidentally producing life. Whenever they are unable to provide a naturalistic mechanism to account for the transformation of molecules into man by chance, they assert the *fact of evolution*—a drama with an unwritten script supposedly spanning hundreds of millions of years. It is believed by many evolutionists that a great lapse of time can perform "miracles."

The Bible, by contrast, paints a radically different picture of our planet's history. In particular, it describes a time when God catastrophically destroyed the earth and essentially all its air-breathing life. The only consistent way to interpret the geological record in light of this Biblical event is to understand that fossil-bearing rocks are the result of a massive global Flood that occurred only a few thousand years ago and lasted but a year. This Biblical interpretation of the rock

Table 3. Results of low priority experiments.

Experiment	Description	Discussion
U/Th Halos	A geological and geographical collection and analysis of U and Th radiohalos.	Completed as part of the radiohalos study by Snelling. See the description and discussion of radiohalos in Table 1.
Pu in Oklo Reactor	A theoretical study of Pu and other trace elements associated with a natural reactor in a geological formation in Africa.	Considered as part of nuclear decay theory by *Chaffin* [2000].
Allende Meteorite Origin	An exploration of the concentration of radioisotopes in meteorites. Meteorites were not involved in geological processes on the earth but would potentially be affected by accelerated decay of a cosmological nature.	Attention to this subject was postponed because of other more pressing topics. Because of the significance of radioisotopic signatures in meteorites in estimating the age of the universe and the age of the earth as a whole, the study of meteorites should have a high priority in future work.
Diffusion of Ar in Biotite	Experimental measurement and analysis of the diffusion rate of Ar in biotite.	It was found that this effort had already been reported in the literature. Because of the significant findings of RATE about He in zircon and biotite, probably little of value could be learned by examining Ar at this time.
Origin of Chemical Elements	A theoretical study of the cosmogenic origin of the elements. The purpose was to explore a possible alternative to the nucleogenesis model.	A preliminary approach to this topic was started by an associate. However, the work was suspended after a short period of study due to disagreements with the approach.
Cosmology and Nuclear Decay	A theoretical study of the concept of "the stretching of the heavens" stated several times in Scripture with the concept of "a rapid, completed expansion of space".	This effort was suggested by *Humphreys* [2000, pp. 369–374] as a possible explanation for accelerated decay and the associated cooling necessary to explain how large amounts of heat could be removed.

record implies that the animals and plants preserved as fossils were all contemporaries. This means trilobites, dinosaurs, and man all dwelled on the planet simultaneously, and they perished together in a world-destroying cataclysm.

Although creationists have long claimed that the rock formations themselves testify unmistakably to water catastrophism on a global scale, evolutionists generally have ignored this testimony and countered with their theory of a long lapse of time supposedly justified by their interpretation of the decay of radioisotopes. This supposed bastion of evolutionary thinking is owed largely to the doctrine of uniformitarianism passed down from one generation of geologists to the next since the time of Charles Lyell in the early nineteenth century. Uniformitarianism assumed that the vast amount of geological change recorded in the rocks must be the product of slow and uniform processes operating over an immense span of time. This theory rejects a global cataclysm of the type described in the Bible and in other ancient texts as impossible and therefore nonhistorical.

With the discovery of radioactivity about a hundred years ago, evolutionists deeply committed to the uniformitarian outlook believed they finally had irrefutable proof of the immense antiquity of the earth. In particular, they discovered the very slow nuclear decay rates of elements like U while observing considerable amounts of the daughter products from such decay. They interpreted these discoveries as vindicating both uniformitarianism and evolution, which led to the domination of these beliefs in academic circles around the world throughout the twentieth century.

Even when creationists point out that radioisotope dating of rocks is built on three basic assumptions which often cannot be justified, evolutionists would retreat into the stronghold of their prior assumption that the earth has been around for billions of years. This defense rested ultimately on radioisotope dating.

Radioisotope dating techniques are based on three assumptions:

- The rate of radioisotopic decay has always been constant.
- The isotopic abundances in a specimen have not been altered by processes other than radioactive decay. (When evidence suggests this has not been true for a given sample, the results are commonly discarded.)
- The amount of daughter isotopes when the rock was first formed are believed to be small, often negligible, or the original isotopic composition can be determined. (So-called "isochron" methods attempt to date rocks that contain significant initial levels of daughter isotopes.)

However, the RATE project has convincingly shown that the first and most fundamental of these assumptions is invalid, namely that the rate of radioisotopic decay has not always been constant. This conclusion was reached from several independent lines of evidence showing that nuclear decay has been accelerated during brief episodes of earth's history. Furthermore, this increase in decay rate was not a small amount, but was on the order of a billion or more times greater than the rates observed today.

Such change in decay rate obviously calls into question all radioisotope dating methods. The calculation of the age of a rock based on the present-day rate of decay of a radioisotope from the amounts of daughter element is clearly invalid if the rate of decay has been different in the past. Almost certainly the agent that caused a change in decay rate of a single radioisotope affected them all. However, our studies suggest the acceleration has not been uniform for all elements, but was greater for different categories of nuclear decay and also greater for elements with greater atomic weights. This variable change in decay rate appears to be the explanation for isochrons of different parent/daughter isotope pairs *giving divergent ages for the same rock or mineral.*

One line of evidence strongly supporting accelerated decay is associated with two clocks involving the decay of U in zircon crystals in granite. The age of granite calculated from the rate at which He diffuses from imbedded zircons gives an age which is *orders of magnitude less than the millions to billions of years calculated from U decaying to Pb.* The rate of diffusion appears not to have been affected by whatever accelerated the nuclear decay. Consequently, the age of the earth from the diffusion "clock" is on the order of thousands of years, not millions or billions, in agreement with the young age of the earth derived from the genealogies in the Bible. Billions of years thought necessary for evolution to occur never happened. Without these eons of time available, evolution becomes unthinkable. The consistent time frame between the calculations of He diffusion in granite and the Biblical chronology support the Bible's statements of earth history and Creation.

5. The Administration of RATE

The RATE project made breakthroughs not only in the physics of radioisotope dating but also in the way creationist research is administered and funded. The total cost exceeded $1,250,000 and was provided by over 400 donors. The effort was purposely organized as a closed-ended, eight-year project in order for the donors to be able to evaluate the goals, progress, and results in a business-like manner. Many research projects, whether they are sponsored by government or private sources, rarely have clearly specified goals or sensibly bounded time frames for their achievement. Most are open-ended and not subject to sufficient review by the persons paying the bills. Although, funding for most research comes from the government, foundations, or other sources that have built-in procedures for previewing and periodic review to decide if funding should be continued, reports are often published in technical journals and read only by experts in the field. The general public may not even be aware that the research is being conducted on a particular subject or what the results mean when the project is over.

The approach to funding and reporting by the RATE project was significantly different. First, the RATE team recognized that few, if any, normal sources of funding for scientific research were likely to support this effort. There is such a bias against creationist thinking that government agencies and most foundations are not viable sources. Most large private foundations which might have been potential sponsors for this project did not have the technical expertise to evaluate the scientific details of the proposed work. So, the RATE team concluded that most funding would likely come from individuals and small foundations. The project would therefore need to be planned and described in a way that the informed public could comprehend the general concepts, the methods to be applied, and the importance of the potential findings.

A second difference was that technical evaluations of the scientific proposals and reports of the results would need to be made from within the creationist scientific community. It is desirable that at the end of the project summaries of the major findings should be reported in conventional journals and news releases, but in the early stages at least, proposals and reports would need to be made within creationist venues. The battle to report in conventional circles would be so difficult initially that it would detract from other more important efforts to complete the research. Unfortunately, the number of experts who have the knowledge to evaluate the technical details of radioisotopes and nuclear decay is so limited that adequate evaluation is difficult to achieve in any venue. Nonetheless, it was a recognized priority. Without adequate review and evaluation by independent experts, confidence in the proposals and results would be jeopardized. On the other hand, utilizing experts from outside the creationist community would almost certainly incorporate sufficient bias to jeopardize the integrity of the whole RATE project. Scientists with little sympathy to a literal view of Scripture often completely reject creationist work, regardless of its quality, or stubbornly deny that favored assumptions should be open to scrutiny.

Because of the decision to obtain most of the technical reviews and to report the initial results within the creationist community, there have been some concerns expressed about the appropriateness of reporting preliminary research results to the general community in order to raise funds before publishing them. It is common practice in scientific circles to strongly limit public releases of scientific results until the technical reports have had a peer review in one or more of the conventional scientific journals. A number of scientific societies have codes of conduct which include strong statements insisting on such practices. For example, the National Academy of Sciences, the American Geophysical Union, the Geological Society of America, the American Physical Society, the American Chemical Society, the American Mathematical Society, and the American Association for the Advancement of Science, among others, have such standards incorporating strong commitments to independent peer reviews. However, because of the difficulty in publishing creationist research in conventional journals and because of the desirability of making information available for public scrutiny, the RATE project team chose to release critical findings after publishing them in peer-reviewed creationist journals and conferences.

In fact, the RATE project may have been the first creationist research project to generate detailed guidelines for the conduct and ethics of research. Of course, the ethics for creationists should be even higher than the conventional scientific community, but it would be helpful if these guidelines were developed and disseminated explicitly for those who may wish to conduct and report creationist research. To this end, Dr. Henry Morris Jr., founder and President Emeritus of the Institute for Creation Research, has drafted a white paper which attempts to fill this need. It may be found in the Appendix to this chapter entitled, *Peer Evaluation in Scientific Research and Creationism.* We anticipate that his white paper will also be published in one or more of the creationist research journals in the near future.

A third difference was that the RATE project was designed to last eight years. Unlike most funded research, this project had a determined stopping point. It was understood that not all the questions raised initially would be fully answered during the project. But, by specifying a fixed length of time for the project, the donors could more easily assess how much progress was being made and could decide if their investment had been worthwhile. Specified reports at the end of the proposal phase and the research phase would provide the necessary information for evaluation. In addition, the researchers would also have fixed deadlines for the completion of subprojects. Questions not answered during the eight years of the project would need to be addressed in follow-on research. Funding and reporting of the follow-on research would need to be conducted subsequently and separately from the RATE project.

A final difference was that although the RATE project was intended to be conducted according to the highest standards of scientific quality and integrity and reported to the technical community, it was also intended to be comprehensible to the larger community from which the funding came. Unfortunately, an attitude has arisen among many scientists that science is so technical that most of the public are not prepared to understand it and explanations should not be attempted. Many technical journals seem to accept as a matter of course that no effort is needed or justified to explain research objectives, methods, and results in language comprehensible by the general public. This elitism may have developed because funding for science has primarily become a function of government agencies. Scientists are no longer responsible for justifying their sometimes esoteric work to the public at large, but, rather, to a committee of their peers or to faceless administrators. The attitude has become so prevalent that any scientist who attempts to express his excitement for science in a popular format is criticized by his peers as degrading the dignity of science. Carl Sagan was a premiere example of this. Although he was widely praised by the public for having an unusual gift of explaining science in simple terms, his peers generally held him in low esteem for his attempts to communicate scientific ideas at a popular level.

The RATE project could not get funding and also ignore its public, even if such an attitude had developed. It was highly dependent upon its donors and purposely chose to communicate with them throughout the project. Unless the non-technical supporters understood what was planned and what was accomplished, the scientists would not have been able to obtain the funds necessary to complete the experiments. The RATE scientists sincerely believed it was part of their responsibility to clearly inform the supporters what their funds had purchased. The initial proposals were written in a form that a technically literate public could grasp. Also, scientific concepts and world-views dramatically affect the lay public. The RATE scientists attempted to communicate as clearly as possible to them. The concepts and objectives were clearly spelled out. Throughout the project timely non-technical reports were published reporting on new results and plans. And at the end of the project, not only was this final technical report published, but a lay version of the technical report and a video documentary of the RATE project geared to the non-technical public at large were produced. Each scientist also has the responsibility of continuing to interpret and publish his results in peer journals and at appropriate conferences. However, it may be several years before all the results of RATE are fully reported.

We believe that God called the scientists of the RATE project for such a time as this. We pray that the LORD will honor the results of this effort and that whatever valid findings we have discovered will permeate the scientific community and our society. We believe a false confidence in radioisotope dating has been a key factor in undermining confidence in the Bible and faith in God in our society. We pray this work will lead to a new reformation—to the glory of God!

6. The Future of RATE

Although the RATE project has accomplished much in the field of radioisotope dating to show radioisotope data indeed support a young-earth creationist perspective, there are many remaining questions to be clarified and explored. A number of remaining problems are discussed in the final chapter of this book. No doubt some readers will ask, as we have: If the RATE project is ending in 2005, how will these questions be addressed?

The Institute for Creation Research (ICR) has decided to expand its research efforts into a larger domain. Not only has the RATE project identified several questions about radioisotope decay which need further work, but while it was underway several ICR scientists have also pursued other research themes. Geology, paleoclimatology, geophysics, biology, and molecular biology are long-standing topics of interest to the faculty at ICR. The RATE project has shown in a practical way how these efforts can be funded and developed. Because of the scientific and administrative success of the RATE project, ICR has been encouraged to develop a much larger multi-disciplinary research program. It is believed that if strategic research projects are identified and defined, the supporters of ICR will once again recognize their value and commit necessary funding. It is evident that much can be accomplished by following this model in other disciplines.

In December of 2004 a new Research Council was convened at ICR to discuss just such a plan. The intent was to develop procedures for identifying significant research, to raise more funds, perform research, review results, and report findings. Follow-on to the RATE project research would be included as part of this multi-disciplinary program. In addition, some of the research could be conducted as thesis topics by students in the ICR Graduate School. It is recognized that obtaining funds for multiple projects of the magnitude of the RATE project may be a considerable challenge, but there are other projects comparable in significance to the RATE project which have the potential for major advances in defending the Biblical account of earth history.

7. Additional Resources

The following chapters in this book are highly technical in nature, and it may be difficult for some to follow the text because of the nomenclature. An extensive glossary was included in the first RATE book by *Vardiman et al.* [2000] to assist the non-specialist in defining terms. The reader is encouraged to acquire a copy of the first book to accompany this final report. A non-technical book has been written by *DeYoung* [2005] and a video documentary has been produced by the *Institute for Creation Research* [2005] which discuss the RATE project and its results without all the technical nomenclature and details.

8. Acknowledgments

I wish to express my appreciation to all the donors who made the RATE project possible with their gifts. Thanks to over a dozen reviewers who provided detailed comments and suggestions on the drafts of this introductory chapter and the summary chapter, and to over two dozen experts in various fields who helped review the technical chapters. As much as I would like to honor all these reviewers by listing their names, the editors are following standard peer review protocol by keeping the reviewers' identities confidential.

And I wish to thank the LORD for blessing the RATE project team with the insights He gave us and the privilege of doing this research. When the RATE project was started in 1997 we adopted the following statement of David to Goliath as our project inspiration. It expresses how we felt when facing this gigantic problem initially, our dependence on God for insights and funding, and the hope we had for His help. I would like to quote that passage again at the end of this project to remind us how God has provided. As David faced Goliath in the valley of Elah he said to the Philistine:

"Thou comest to me with a sword, and with a spear, and with a shield: but I come to thee in the name of the LORD of hosts, the God of the armies of Israel, whom thou hast defied. This day will the LORD deliver thee into mine hand; and I will smite thee, and take thine head from thee; and I will give the carcasses of the host of the Philistines this day unto the fowls of the air, and to the wild beasts of the earth; that all the earth may know that there is a God in Israel. And all this assembly shall know that the LORD saveth not with sword and spear: for the battle is the LORD's, and he will give you into our hands." 1 Samuel 17:45–47

References

Chaffin, E. F., Theoretical mechanisms of accelerated radioactive decay, in *Radioisotopes and the Age of the Earth: A Young-Earth Creationist Research Initiative*, edited by L. Vardiman, A. A. Snelling, and E. F. Chaffin, pp. 305–331, Institute for Creation Research, El Cajon, California, and Creation Research Society, St. Joseph, Missouri, 2000.

DeYoung, D. B., *Thousands not Billions: Challenging an Icon of Evolution*, a non-technical version of the RATE project report, Master Books, Green Forest, Arkansas, 2005.

Humphreys, D. R., Accelerated nuclear decay: a viable hypothesis?, in *Radioisotopes and the Age of the Earth: A Young-Earth Creationist Research Initiative*, edited by L. Vardiman, A. A. Snelling, and E. F. Chaffin, pp. 333–379, Institute for Creation Research, El Cajon, California, and Creation Research Society, St. Joseph, Missouri, 2000.

Institute for Creation Research, *Thousands not Billions: Challenging an Icon of Evolution*, a video documentary of the RATE project, 50 minutes, Institute for Creation Research, El Cajon, California, 2005.

Vardiman, L., A. A. Snelling, and E. F. Chaffin (editors), *Radioisotopes and the Age of the Earth: A Young-Earth Creationist Research Initiative*, 676 pp., Institute for Creation Research, El Cajon, California, and Creation Research Society, St. Joseph, Missouri, 2000.

Vardiman, L., A. A. Snelling, and E. F. Chaffin (editors), *Radioisotopes and the Age of the Earth: Results of a Young-Earth Creationist Research Initiative*, Institute for Creation Research, El Cajon, California, and Creation Research Society, Chino Valley, Arizona, 2005.

Appendix: Peer Evaluation in Scientific Research and Creationism

Henry M. Morris, Jr., Ph.D.*

It is normally recommended that activities involving scientific research, especially the publication of the results of that research, include what is known as "peer review" prior to publication. This is generally true in the case of the secular academic and industrial research communities, but has not always been the practice in Christian communities. This paper, therefore, will attempt to suggest guidelines for the peer review process in connection with research carried out and/ or published by Bible-believing Christian scientists and organizations, in particular those committed to literal creationism.

It is obviously important that scientific research by Christians be carried out carefully, then analyzed and interpreted judiciously before publishing. Christians and others who are not scientists should be able to have confidence in its accuracy and reliability. A good peer review process is very important for this assurance.

Christian men and women of science should follow even a higher standard in this connection than their secular colleagues, in the sense that they are ultimately required to give an account of their stewardship (of talent, time and opportunity, as well as money) to God Himself:
"Wherefore putting away lying, speak every man truth with his neighbor."
Ephesians 4:25.
"...whatsoever ye do, do all to the glory of God."
1 Corinthians 10:31.
They must, therefore, be scrupulously honest in reporting the results of their research. If certain data points or trends are omitted—or, for some reason, added by interpolation—this must also be reported, with justifying reasons carefully explained.

When an interpretation is applied to the data, perhaps intended to support a Biblical or philosophical position, this may be legitimate and good, provided only that the context clearly acknowledges that it is only

---

* *President Emeritus, Institute for Creation Research, Santee, California*

the writer's interpretation, allowing the reader the option of agreeing or disagreeing.

At the same time, such a process is never infallible and may be difficult to achieve, especially when underlying spiritual motivations could be affecting either the researchers or reviewers or both.

Concerns about the peer-review process commonly in use by secular scientists have been raised not only by Christian creationists but also by non-Christian evolutionists in connection with *their* research. Both of these groups have deplored the clear influence of non-scientific bias in many reviewers. Reviewers should therefore be selected, if possible, who will not allow their personal beliefs to influence their scientific evaluation of the research.

Some may question the above discussion as being too self-serving. However, Christians—especially those who are called "young-earth creationists" (we prefer the term "literal creationist" or, even better, simply "Biblical creationist," since our interpretations are primarily Bible-based) have found by experience that it is almost impossible to get a fair evaluation from scientists whose interpretations are essentially naturalistic and uniformitarian in science.[1] Different premises inevitably lead to conflicting interpretations.

It is also significant that our cautions with respect to the peer-review process are shared by many who are not creationists at all. This includes, for example, such eminent evolutionists as Dr. Lynn Margulis, an honored biologist, Dr. Frank Tipler, world-class specialist in relativistic physics and quantum mechanics, and up-and-coming young British physicist João Magueijo. All of these have written bitter complaints about the peer-review process as it commonly works in secular science,[2] tending to prevent publication of any book or article or funding of any proposal which does not adhere to current majority opinion. One could also mention world-famous astronomer Halton Arp and many others.

Thus, although peer review can be invaluable in limiting the harmful

---

1. This fact has been discussed and documented by numerous creationist scientists. One brief example is a three-page article entitled "Willingly Ignorant" in the ICR newsletter *Acts & Facts* for December 2003.
2. Ibid. Their complaints are quoted in the *Acts and Facts* article, with documentation.

influences of fallacious research, it can also be of deadly influence in screening out valuable discoveries and silencing truth. Reviewers must be selected judiciously!

Another important factor, largely unique to scientific research in young-earth creationism, is that funding is not available from sources accessible to naturalistic scientists (governments, large foundations, industrial coalitions, etc.). Funds must be sought largely from Christian individuals, who are naturally concerned with the possible Biblical and/or moral implications of the proposed research. That means that the purpose and value must be convincingly explained in the proposal, otherwise these funds (usually not large in the first place) will be channeled into more obvious spiritually oriented causes.

Pure research for the sake of pure research may motivate secular scientists and their funding sources, but Christians are expected by God to be careful stewards of their financial resources and thus will require persuasive Biblical reasons for using them to support scientific research. That constraint, therefore, must also be understood by any peer reviewer.

All of the above considerations have made it next to impossible to get reports of creationist research—not to mention creationist reinterpretations of evolutionary naturalistic research—published in secular scientific journals or funded by any source other than Christian individuals. Creationists are often berated for not publishing in such journals, but failure to get creationist research accepted for publication is not necessarily because of their allegedly poor science.

The fact is that many creationist scientists already have extensive publication records based on their research done on strictly secular topics with secular goals. This is certainly true of most of the scientists associated with the Creation Research Society, Answers in Genesis, the Institute for Creation Research, and other such organizations. But scientific studies that may support young-earth creationism (or even just intelligent design) are widely deemed in the secular world to be unworthy even of discussion. Creationists thus often have been forced to establish their own publications and draw peer reviewers from their own ranks (which thankfully have been growing).

Selecting the Peer Reviewers

In view of the above discussion, any "young earth" or "intelligent design" scientific research proposal or publication should, whenever possible, be evaluated and critiqued by at least two or more peer reviewers, chosen in accordance with the following criteria.

- The reviewer should be qualified by both education and experience to give an accurate and knowledgeable evaluation of the proposed or reported research and its treatment in the submitted paper.
- The reviewer should be willing and able to do a fair and impartial evaluation within the available and stated time constraints.
- Whenever possible, the reviewer should be in agreement with—or at least not antagonistic to—the Biblical viewpoint of the researcher, especially if the research is potentially relevant to that perspective.
- A negatively inclined reviewer should be selected only if he or she agrees to limit the critique to scientific questions. It will be understood that interpretations may clash, but that should not be a consideration in the review, unless clearly so stated in the review request.

Finally, if no reviewers can be found satisfying the above criteria, the creationist may, if he believes his work truly should be published, go ahead and publish it with an appropriate note informing readers of the situation.

Chapter 2

Young Helium Diffusion Age of Zircons Supports Accelerated Nuclear Decay

D. Russell Humphreys, Ph.D.*

Abstract. Experiments sponsored by RATE show that helium leakage deflates long half-life radioisotopic ages. In 1982 Robert Gentry found amazingly high retentions of nuclear-decay-generated helium (He) in microscopic zircons ($ZrSiO_4$ crystals) recovered from a borehole in hot Precambrian granitic rock at Fenton Hill, New Mexico. In 2001 RATE contracted with a high-precision laboratory to measure the rate of He diffusion out of the zircons. The measured rates resoundingly confirm a numerical prediction we made based on the reported retentions and a young age. Combining rates and retentions gives a He diffusion age of 6000±2000 (1σ) years. This contradicts the uniformitarian age of 1.5 billion years based on nuclear decay products in the same zircons. These data strongly support our hypothesis of episodes of highly accelerated nuclear decay occurring within thousands of years ago. Such accelerations shrink the radioisotopic "billions of years" down to the 6000-year timescale of the Bible.

In section 13 I discuss, in the light of our diffusion data, one of the problems for the accelerated decay hypothesis, disposal of excess radiogenic heat. Appendices A–C present details of our experimental data. Appendix D is an extensive answer to a critic of this work.

This chapter combines and updates three publications presented at or in: (1) the Fifth International Conference on Creationism in August 2003, (2) an American Geophysical Union annual meeting in December 2003, and (3) the *Creation Research Society Quarterly* in June 2004. When I say "we" below, I am referring to my co-authors for those papers. They are my three colleagues on the He diffusion project from the RATE steering committee:

* *Astrogeophysics Department, Institute for Creation Research, Santee, California*

Steven A. Austin, John R. Baumgardner, and Andrew A. Snelling.

1. Introduction

A significant fraction of the earth's radioactive elements, particularly U and Th, appear to be in the granitic rock of the upper continental crust. In the granites, U and Th tend to be localized inside special minerals such as *zircon* (zirconium silicate, $ZrSiO_4$). Zircon has high hardness, high density, and high melting point, often forming microscopic, stubby, prismatic crystals with dipyramidal terminations (Figure 1), commonly grayish, yellowish, or reddish brown. Atoms of U and Th within cooling magma replace up to 4% of the normal Zr atoms within the lattice structure of zircon as it is crystallizing. In contrast, the products of U and Th decay that are also in the magma do not incorporate themselves into the lattice. In particular, the most common type of lead ions (Pb^{2+}) are too large to fit into the lattice. Thus in a newly formed zircon, the U concentration is much greater than in the magma, while the Pb concentration is much less than in the magma. The radioactive zircon crystals often become embedded in larger crystals, such as mica (particularly biotite), as the magma cools and solidifies.

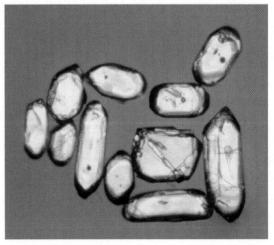

Figure 1. Zircons from the Jemez granodiorite. Photo by R. V. Gentry.

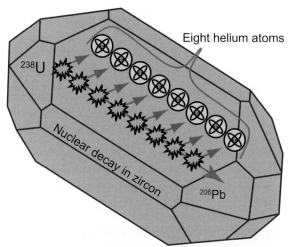

Figure 2. Nuclear decay makes He within zircons.

As the U and Th nuclei in a zircon decay, they produce He (Figure 2). For example, ^{238}U emits eight α-particles as it decays through various intermediate elements to ^{206}Pb. Each α-particle is a ^4He nucleus, consisting of two protons and two neutrons. Each explosively expelled ^4He nucleus eventually comes to a stop, either within the zircon or in the surrounding material. There it quickly gathers two electrons and becomes a neutral He atom.

Helium is a lightweight, fast-moving atom that does not form chemical bonds with other atoms. It can *diffuse* through solids relatively fast, meaning that He atoms wiggle through the spaces between atoms in a crystal lattice and spread themselves out as far from one another as possible. For the same reason it can leak rapidly through tiny holes and cracks, making it ideal for leak detection in laboratory vacuum systems. The diffusion and leakage rates are so great that believers in the billions of years had expected most of the He produced during the alleged 4.5 billion years of the earth's existence to have worked its way out of the crust and into the earth's atmosphere long ago. In this chapter we argue that, in this case and similar cases, the He has not had enough time (less than 8000 years) to escape from the zircons, much less the crust.

2. The Helium is Still in the Zircons

In the 1970s, geoscientists from Los Alamos National Laboratory began drilling core samples at Fenton Hill, a potential geothermal energy site just west of the volcanic Valles Caldera in the Jemez Mountains near Los Alamos, New Mexico (Figure 3). There, in borehole GT-2, they sampled the granitic Precambrian basement rock, which we will refer to as the Jemez granodiorite. It has an assigned radioisotopic age of 1.50 ($\pm$ 0.02) billion years, as determined by various methods using the U, Th, and Pb isotopes in the zircons themselves [*Zartman*, 1979]. The depths of the samples varied from near the surface down to 4.3 km,

Figure 3. Drilling rig at Fenton Hill, New Mexico. Photo by Los Alamos National Laboratory.

with *in situ* temperatures from 20°C to 313°C (measurement accuracy of ±1°C [*Laney and Laughlin*, 1981, p. 502, Table 1]). The Los Alamos team sent some of these core samples to Oak Ridge National Laboratory for isotopic analysis.

Most of the zircons were in biotite [*Gentry*, 1995], a black mica common in granitic rock. At Oak Ridge, Robert Gentry, a creationist physicist, crushed the samples (without breaking the much harder zircon grains), extracted a high-density residue (because zircons have a density of $4.7 \, g/cm^3$), and isolated the zircons by microscopic examination, choosing crystals about 50–75 µm long. The zircon masses were typically on the order of a microgram. The Oak Ridge team then heated the zircons to 1000°C in a mass spectrometer and measured the amount of ^{4}He liberated. In 1982 they published the data in *Geophysical Research Letters* [*Gentry et al.*, 1982]. Table 1 details their results, plus two samples ("2002" and "2003") from the same borehole we analyzed in the years 2002 and 2003.

The first column itemizes the samples analyzed. The second and third columns show the depth and temperature of each sample *in situ*. The fourth column shows the volume (at standard temperature and pressure) of He liberated in the laboratory per microgram of zircon.

Table 1. Helium retentions in zircons from the Jemez granodiorite. $1 \, ncc = 10^{-9} cm^3$.

Sample	Depth (m)	Temperature (°C)	Helium * (ncc/µg)	Q/Q_0	Error
0	0	20	8.2	—	—
2002	750	96	~12.1	~0.80	—
1	960	105	8.6	0.58	±0.17
2003	1490	124	6.3	0.42	±0.13
2	2170	151	3.6	0.27	±0.08
3	2900	197	2.8	0.17	±0.05
4	3502	239	0.16	0.012	±0.004
5	3930	277	~0.02	~0.001	—
6	4310	313	~0.02	~0.001	—

* After consulting with Dr. Gentry, we have corrected, in the fourth column, two apparent typographical errors in the corresponding column of his table. One is in the units of the column (which should have been $10^{-9} cc/µg$ instead of $10^{-8} cc/µg$); the other is in sample 4 of that column. The crucial fractions in column five were correctly reported, as we have confirmed with our data.

The fifth column is the ratio of the observed quantity of He Q (total number of He atoms in the crystal) to the calculated quantity Q_0 that the zircons would have accumulated and retained if there had been no diffusion. The Los Alamos team measured the amount of radiogenic Pb in zircons 2.9 km deep in the same borehole and same granodiorite [*Zartman*, 1979], and the Oak Ridge team confirmed those figures with their ion microprobe [*Gentry*, 1995]. Because the various decay chains generate an average of 7.7 He atoms per Pb atom produced, Gentry and his colleagues were able to calculate Q_0 from the amount of Pb in the zircons. In doing so, they compensated for the estimated loss of α-particles emitted from near the edges of the zircons out into the surrounding material.

The Oak Ridge team estimated that uncertainties in calculating Q_0 might limit the accuracy of the ratio Q/Q_0 to $\pm 30\%$. This is by far the dominant error in the analyses throughout this chapter. We will (very conservatively) regard it as a 1σ random error. Column 6 of the table shows the resulting estimated errors in the ratios.

Samples 1 through 6 came from the granodiorite, but sample zero came from larger zircons in a surface outcrop of an entirely different rock unit. For that rock unit U/Th/Pb information was not available, making an estimate of Q_0 not feasible. Lacking a ratio, we cannot use sample zero in the calculations.

Samples 2002 and 2003 came from the same borehole and same rock unit as did samples 1 through 6, but we acquired the former as core samples from Los Alamos National Laboratory only a few years ago. We sent them to Activation Laboratories in Ontario, Canada, where they extracted biotite and zircons. We did not select sizes of zircons in sample 2002, nor measure their total mass accurately, but we did so for sample 2003. The lengths of the latter were between 50 and 75 μm, and the approximately 1200 selected crystals weighed a total of 216 μg. After extraction, we sent both zircon and biotite samples to our diffusion experimenter (Section 5), where he measured the total quantity of He contained in each sample. We used Gentry's estimate of Q_0 to get our estimate of the fraction retained in sample 2003 (see Section 10 for details). We did the same for sample 2002, though we lacked an accurate measurement of its total mass and so did not accurately know the He liberated per microgram.

Samples 5 and 6 had the same amount of He. Gentry and his colleagues noted that He emerged from those samples in shorter bursts than the other samples, indicating a different distribution of He within those zircons. In Section 7, we will show that the amount of He from sample 5 is just about what would be expected from the trend in the cooler samples. But we allow for the possibility of its error being considerably larger than the cooler samples.

According to the thermal behavior outlined in the next section, we would ordinarily expect that the hotter sample 6 would have much less He than sample 5. The fact that the He content did not decrease suggests that some additional effect may have occurred which limited the outflow of He from the zircon. In Section 7 we suggest a likely explanation.

The above considerations suggest that we can use samples 1 through 5 in a theoretical analysis with ordinary diffusion. We will treat sample 6 as a special case.

Samples 1 through 3 had He retentions of 58, 42, 27, and 17%. The fact that these percentages are high confirms that *a large amount of nuclear decay* did indeed occur in the zircons. Other evidence strongly supports much nuclear decay having occurred in the past [*Humphreys*, 2000, pp. 335–337]. We emphasize this point because many creationists have assumed that "old" radioisotopic ages are merely an artifact of analysis, not really indicating the occurrence of large amounts of nuclear decay. But according to the measured amount of Pb physically present in the zircons, about 1.5 billion years worth—at today's rates—of nuclear decay occurred. Supporting that, sample 1 still retains 58% of all the α-particles (the He) that would have been deposited in the zircon during this decay of U and Th to Pb.

It is the uniformitarian (see Endnote i) assumption of invariant decay rates that leads to the usual conclusion that this much decay required 1.5 billion years. In this chapter we will include the assumption of billions of years of time in the uniformitarian model we construct for diffusion.

Notice that the retention levels decrease as the temperatures increase. That is consistent with ordinary diffusion: a high concentration of He in the zircons diffusing outward into a much lower concentration in the surrounding minerals, and diffusing faster in hotter rock. As the next section shows, diffusion rates increase strongly with temperature.

In later sections, we will show that these large retentions (see Endnote ii) are quite consistent with diffusion taking place over *thousands* of years, not billions of years.

3. How Diffusion Works

If the reader is not very familiar with diffusion and wants to know more, we recommend a very clear little book, **Atomic Migration in Crystals**, written for non-experts [*Girifalco*, 1964]. Figure 4, adapted from that book [*Girifalco*, 1964, p. 39, Figure 23], illustrates how an atom diffuses through a solid crystal lattice of other atoms. Figure 4a shows a He atom initially at position A, surrounded by a cell of lattice

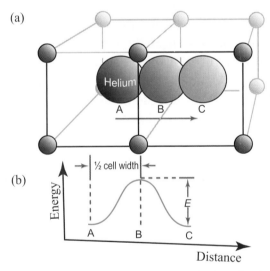

Figure 4. Helium atom moving through a crystal. Usually, lattice cations are smaller than He atoms, but lattice anions are somewhat larger. Here for clarity we show all lattice ions as being small.

atoms. The lattice atoms repel the He atom, tending to confine it to the center of the cell, where the repulsion balances out in all directions. Heat keeps the atoms of the lattice vibrating at its various resonant frequencies. The vibrating atoms continually bump into the He atom from all sides. The higher the temperature, the more vigorous the bumping.

Every now and then, the lattice atoms will bump the He atom hard enough to push it into the "activated" position B, midway between cells. The lattice atoms must give the He enough kinetic energy to overcome the repulsive potential energy barrier between the cells, which we have shown in Figure 4b. This required amount of kinetic energy, E, is called the *activation energy*. If the lattice atoms have given any more energy than E to the He atom, it will not stop at position B. Instead, it will continue on to position C at the center of the adjacent cell. The He atom has thus moved from one cell to the next.

If there is an initially high concentration of He atoms in one part of the crystal, these random motions will eventually spread—that is, diffuse—the He more uniformly though the crystal and out of it. Let us define $C(x, y, z, t)$ as the *concentration*, the number of He atoms per unit volume, at position (x, y, z) at time t. Many textbooks show that when diffusion occurs, the time rate of change of C is proportional to the "sharpness" of the edges of the distribution of He, or more mathematically, proportional to the Laplacian of C, $\nabla^2 C$:

$$\frac{\partial C}{\partial t} = D\nabla^2 C, \quad \text{where } \nabla^2 = \frac{\partial^2}{\partial x^2} + \frac{\partial^2}{\partial y^2} + \frac{\partial^2}{\partial z^2} \qquad \text{(1a, b)}$$

Equation (1a), called the "diffusion equation," occurs frequently in many branches of physics, for example, to describe heat conduction in solids. Specialists in the diffusion of atoms through materials call it "Fick's Second Law of Diffusion." The factor D, the *diffusion coefficient*, or *diffusivity*, has dimensions of cm^2 (or m^2) per second. (Most of the diffusion literature still uses centimeters and calories instead of meters and joules). Very often it turns out that at high temperatures, the diffusion coefficient depends exponentially on the absolute temperature T (degrees Kelvin above absolute zero):

$$D = D_0 \exp\left(-\frac{E_0}{RT}\right) \qquad (2)$$

where R is the universal gas constant, 1.986 calories per mole-Kelvin (8.314 J/mol-K). The constant D_0 is independent of temperature. The "intrinsic" activation energy E_0 typically is between 10 and 100 kcal/mol (about 40 and 400 kJ/mol). Section 11 discusses how these quantities are related to the geoscience concept of *closure temperature*, and it shows why the concept is irrelevant to our conclusions.

If the crystal has *defects*, such as vacancies in the crystal lattice, impurities, dislocations, grain boundaries, or damage from radiation, then the diffusion coefficient equation will have a second term related to the defects:

$$D = D_0 \exp\left(-\frac{E_o}{RT}\right) + D_1 \exp\left(\frac{E_1}{RT}\right) \qquad (3)$$

The defect parameters (D_1 and E_1) are almost always smaller than the intrinsic parameters (D_0 and E_0):

$$E_1 < E_0, \quad D_1 < D_0 \qquad (4)$$

The typical *Arrhenius plot* in Figure 5 shows how the diffusion coefficient D of equation (3) depends on the inverse of the absolute temperature, $1/T$. Because the plot uses a logarithmic scale for D and a linear scale for $1/T$, each term of equation (3) manifests itself as a straight line in the temperature region where it is dominant. (Plotting with T instead of $1/T$ would make the lines curved instead of straight.) The slopes are proportional to the activation energies E_0 and E_1. The intercepts with the vertical axis, where $1/T$ is zero, are the parameters D_0 and D_1.

The intrinsic line has a steep slope and a high intercept, while the defect line has a shallow slope and a low intercept. Starting on the right-hand side of the graph, at low temperatures, let us increase the temperature, moving to the left. When the temperature is high enough, we reach a region, the "knee," where the two terms of equation (3)

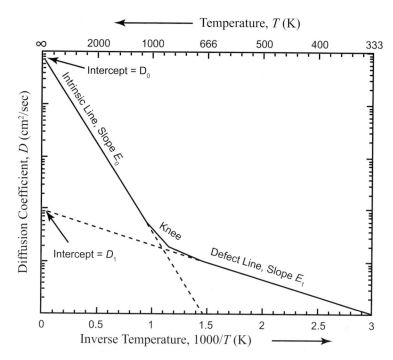

Figure 5. Typical Arrhenius plot.

are about equal. To the left of that region, at high temperatures, the intrinsic properties of the crystal dominate the diffusion. To the right of the knee, at lower temperatures, the defects dominate. Because defects are very common in natural crystals, this two-slope character is typical [*Girifalco*, 1964, pp. 102, 126].

For a given type of mineral, the location of the knee can vary greatly. It depends on the value of D_1, which depends on the amount of defects in the particular crystal. The more defects there are, the higher D_1 is. If we increase the number of defects, the defect line moves upward (keeping its slope constant) on the graph, as Figure 6 illustrates.

In the case of zircons containing radioisotopes, the main cause of defects is radioactivity, so highly radiation-damaged ("metamict") zircons will have a large value of D_1, causing the defect line to be higher on the graph than for a low-radioactivity zircon.

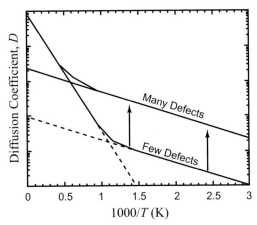

Figure 6. Increasing number of defects slides the defect line upward.

4. I Misunderstood Early Zircon Data

At the beginning of our investigations in 1997, I did not properly understand the only source of He-in-zircon data that was available then, and that influenced the course of the RATE research. My misunderstanding caused us: (a) to think that the main restriction on He outflow from the zircon was not the zircon itself, but rather the biotite surrounding the zircon, and consequently (b) to commission our own experiments. The outcome proved to be very fortunate, because we acquired a much better understanding of the He diffusion *in situ*. Here are more details.

Our initial source of He-in-zircon diffusion data was a 1970 paper by Sh. A. Magomedov, a researcher in Dagestan (then part of the Soviet Union). He published diffusion data for radiogenic Pb and He in highly metamict (radiation-damaged) zircons from the Ural Mountains [*Magomedov*, 1970]. These were the only He-in-zircon diffusion data we could find during an extensive literature search we did in 1999.

Magomedov was mainly interested in Pb diffusion, so he did not list his He data explicitly in a table. Instead he showed them in a small graph, along with data for Pb diffusion and electrical conductivity, σ. His label for the ordinate was not clear to me: "ln(D,σ)." In Western scientific literature "ln" with no further note usually means the *natural logarithm* (base *e*). The common logarithm (base 10) is usually shown as "log." (That is not always so in some Russian articles, but I did not think of that.) I first assumed Magomedov was reporting $\ln_e D$, which made the resulting diffusion coefficients very high, as the triangles and dotted line near the top of Figure 7 show. The previous RATE book shows that interpretation [*Humphreys*, 2000, p. 347, Figure 6]. Another possibility was that Magomedov was reporting $\ln_e (D/a^2)$, where *a* is the effective radius of his zircons, about 75 μm. Figure 7 shows (circles and thin solid line near middle) the resulting diffusion rates for that interpretation. In the temperature range of interest to us, the rates are still rather high.

Based on those supposed high rates, I assumed in my first theoretical model [*Humphreys*, 2000, pp. 346–348] that the zircons were a negligible impediment to He outflow, compared to the minerals around

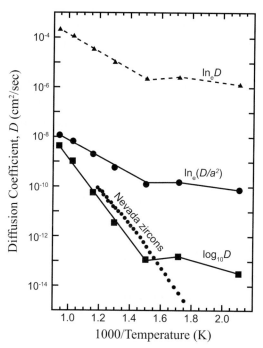

Figure 7. Interpretations of Russian zircon data (hollow symbols and lines) compared with Nevada zircon data (dots). The ordinate is *D* (not D/a^2)

them, such as the biotite. That made the RATE project concentrate our first experiments on He diffusion not in zircon, but rather in biotite, for which we found no previous measurements in the literature.

But in 2001 we received a preprint of a paper [*Reiners et al.*, 2002] listing new He diffusion data in zircons from several sites in Nevada. Figure 7 shows some of that data (Fish Canyon Tuff sample FCT-1) as a line of solid dots. These data were many orders of magnitude lower than our interpretation of Magomedov's graph. The Russian data would agree with the Nevada data if we re-interpret Magomedov's label as meaning "$\log_{10}D$," the *common* logarithm of *D*. Figure 7 shows that interpretation near the bottom (squares and thick solid line). We attribute the small difference between the high-slope "intrinsic" parts of the Russian and Nevada data to differences in estimates of effective radius (Section 5). The nearly horizontal part of the Russian data is probably a "defect" line due to much radiation damage (see end of previous section). That part of the Russian data is about two orders of magnitude higher than data from zircons in Nevada and New Mexico (compare *D* numbers at bottom of Figure 7 with those in Figures 8 and 13). It turns out that the low-temperature "defect" part of the Russian data is about seven orders of magnitude too high to support a uniformitarian interpretation.

The new data and my new interpretation of the old data imply that zircon is a significant impediment to He diffusion, and that we cannot neglect it. In Section 7 of this chapter I report how we changed our theoretical model to account for that fact.

5. Pre-2003 Data for Jemez Granodiorite Minerals

The Nevada zircon data did not extend to low enough temperatures to compare them with the He retentions. Moreover, they were not from the New Mexico site. Measurements of noble gas diffusion in a given type of naturally occurring mineral often show significant differences from site to site, caused by variations in composition and amounts of defects. For that reason it is important to get He diffusion data on zircon and biotite from the same rock unit (the Jemez granodiorite) that was the source of Gentry's samples. Accordingly, in 2001 the RATE project commissioned such experimental studies.

Through a small mining company, Zodiac Minerals and Manufacturing, we contracted with a well-recognized expert on He diffusion measurements in minerals, having many publications related to that field. As we wished, Zodiac did not tell him they were under contract to us, the goals of the project, or the sites of the samples. We have encouraged him to publish his measurements and offered to send him the geologic site information if he does so. Appendices B and C list his data in detail.

We decided to get data on biotites and zircons from the same borehole, GT-2, from which Gentry's zircons came. Los Alamos National Laboratory kindly gave us several GT-2 core samples from a depth of 750 m. That is somewhat shallower than Gentry's samples, but still in the same rock unit. We sent one of them to Activation Laboratories in Ontario, Canada, where they extracted the biotite and zircons. They did not separate the zircons into size groups. They measured the U and Pb isotopes in three of the zircons, getting a U-Pb concordia age of 1439±2 Ma (Appendix A). That is within a few percent of the published age for zircons deeper in the same borehole, 1500±20 Ma [*Zartman*, 1979]. We reserved the rest of the zircons, roughly 0.35 mg, for diffusion measurements.

Then we sent both the biotite and the zircons to our diffusion experimenter. He sieved the biotite sample to get crystals between 75 and 100 μm, but he used all the zircons that Activation Laboratories had extracted, regardless of size. Size of crystals (*effective radius*) is important in converting the raw data into diffusivities. For a description of a typical diffusion experimental apparatus, see an article in *Analytical Chemistry* [*Farley et al.*, 1999]. Our experimenter sent us the raw data in 2002, which is the reason we call the sample "2002" in Table 1.

Figures 8 and 9 are Arrhenius plots of the data we had by early 2002 for zircon and mica, respectively. The zircon data in Figure 8 are from the Jemez granodiorite in New Mexico [from our experimenter, see our Appendix C, Table C1], the Fish Canyon Tuff in Nevada [*Reiners et al.*, 2002], and the Ural Mountains in Russia (re-interpreted from *Magomedov* [1970]). We are assuming their average size was the same

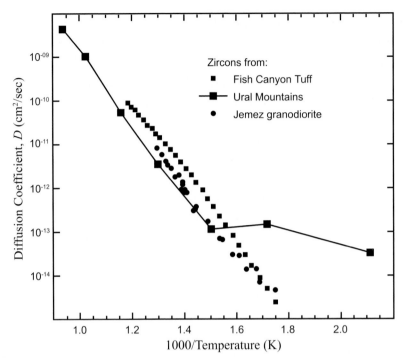

Figure 8. Observed diffusion coefficients in zircons. The ordinate is D (not D/a^2).

as the Nevada zircons (average length ~60 μm, $a \cong 30$ μm, Section 6). The Russian study was for crystals ~150 μm long.

Notice that all the sets of zircon data agree fairly well with each other at high temperatures. At 390°C (abscissa = 1.5), the Russian data have a knee, breaking off to the right into a more horizontal slope for lower temperatures. That implies a high number of defects (see section 4), consistent with the high radiation damage Magomedov reported. The Nevada and New Mexico data (sample 2002) go down to 300°C (abscissa = 1.745) with no strong knee, implying that the data are on the intrinsic part of the curve. Our least-squares linear curve fit [of $\ln(D/a^2)$ from equation (2) versus $1/T$] to these New Mexico (Jemez granodiorite) zircon data gives the following diffusion parameters, and the 1σ error bounds of the fit:

$$E_0 = 34.4 \pm 0.9 \, \text{kcal/mol}, \quad \frac{D_0}{a^2} = 3548^{+3100}_{-1700} \, \text{sec}^{-1} \quad \text{(5a, b)}$$

Figure 9 shows data for two types of mica, biotite and muscovite. The biotite data are from the Jemez granodiorite. Those, and similar data we obtained (see Appendix B) for biotite from the Beartooth amphibolite in Wyoming, are the only data for that mineral we know of. For comparison to the biotite data, we have also included published data for muscovite [*Lippolt and Weigel*, 1988].

The muscovite and biotite data are consistent with each other. In the low temperature range of interest, the New Mexico biotite has diffusion coefficients more than an order of magnitude higher than the zircons in Figure 8. That means the biotite, while not being negligible, did not impede the He outflow as much as the zircon did. That confirmed that the zircon rates were more important.

After that, in the summer and fall of 2002, we tried several times to get lower-temperature zircon data. However, we only discovered

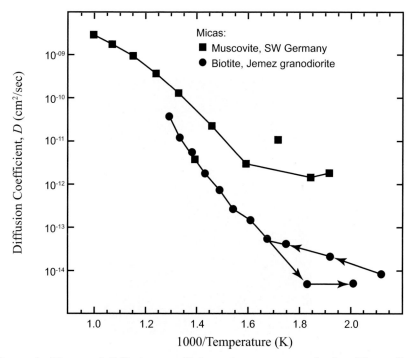

Figure 9. Observed diffusion coefficients in two types of mica. The ordinate is D (not D/a^2).

several wrong ways to make such measurements. First, we asked the experimenter to do new runs on the same batch of zircons, but at lower temperatures. The results were ambiguous, an effect we decided was due to exhaustion of He from the smaller zircons in the batch, thereby increasing the effective radius of the remaining part of the batch [*Fechtig and Kalbitzer*, 1966, section 2.5, p. 72].

Second, we sent the experimenter a new set of zircons from the same depth in GT-2 and asked him to sieve out crystals in the 50–75 μm size range. Before sieving, he decided to leach the crystals in cold concentrated hydrofluoric acid (HF) to remove flecks of biotite clinging to them. Though the technique was new for zircons, it seemed reasonable. However, the values of D/a^2 he then obtained were over fifty times higher than all previous zircon data, both ours and data published by others. Scanning electron microscope images (Figure 10) revealed severe pitting and cracking in the HF-treated zircons. That would allow He to leave the zircons much faster than normally.

These were all the data we had by February 2003, the deadline for the final version of our conference paper [*Humphreys et al.*, 2003a].

Figure 10. Scanning electron microscope photo of a zircon leached in HF. Compare to an untreated zircon in Figure 11. Note 30-μm scale at lower right. Photo by Mark H. Armitage.

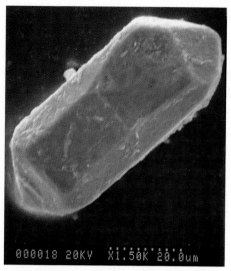

Figure 11. Scanning electron microscope photo of a zircon from size-selected sample 2003. Note 20-μm scale at lower right. Photo by Mark H. Armitage.

6. More Recent Data

In the fall of 2002, we acquired new samples from borehole GT-2, this time from a depth of 1490 m. That is between the depths of Gentry's samples 1 and 2 (see Table 1). We sent them to Activation Laboratories, where they extracted both biotites and zircons. This time they sorted the zircons into several size groups, getting about 1200 crystals in the size range Gentry used, having lengths of 50–75 μm.

Figure 11 shows a scanning electron microscope (SEM) image of one such zircon. Mark Armitage obtained the image in his newly established microscopy laboratory at the Institute for Creation Research, where he also obtained SEM images of the HF-treated zircons the previous section mentioned [*Armitage*, 2004]. In the spring of 2003, we sent our experimenter the 50–75 μm zircons, along with the biotites. This is the sample we labeled "2003" in Table 1 and elsewhere. This time we asked the experimenter (a) not to etch the crystals in HF (unnecessary anyhow because no sieving was needed) and (b) to get zircon diffusivities at lower temperatures. We also asked that he measure more precisely the total He per unit mass in both the zircons and the biotites. In July 2003, one month before the conference, we received his results.

As usual, the experimenter measured the rate of He release at various steps of temperature. Then he put that data into standard formulas to calculate D/a^2, where D is the diffusivity and a is the effective radius of the crystals. The formulas [*Fechtig and Kalbitzer*, 1966, p. 71, equations (5a, b, c), with $R \rightarrow a$] use the fraction (of the total yield) emitted in a given step, the fraction emitted in the previous step, and the duration of the step. The result gives the ratio D/a^2 during that step directly, without the experimenter having to know a specifically. Column 6 of Table 2 shows the resulting values of D/a^2 for the zircons. The experimenter did not report error bounds for D/a^2, but elsewhere he reports:

> In actual practice, we obtain He ages that reproduce to within 6% (2σ), demonstrating some natural variability within grain populations [*Farley*, 2002, p. 833].

The accuracy of such (U-Th)/He ages also reflects the accuracy of the D/a^2 measurement.

The standard formulas assume that the initial distribution of He in the zircons is uniform. But in reality, the zircons would have a "rounded" He-versus-radius profile due to the *in situ* He loss into the biotite. That is, less He would emerge during the initial heating steps than otherwise, because the outer regions of the zircon would be He-depleted. In that case, said the devisers of the standard formulas [*Fechtig and Kalbitzer*, 1966, p. 71],

> The apparent diffusion constants will come out too low, and the activation energies too high.

Also see a similar conclusion by *Reiners et al.,* [2004].

In his report on the 2002 zircon runs (Appendix C), our experimenter advised us that to account for this effect, we should ignore the first set of increasing-temperature steps in his runs. For the 2003 zircons, he reported that we should treat them just the same. Accordingly, we ignored steps 1–9 in calculating D. A more sophisticated analysis could probably extract accurate values of D from the raw He-time data for those steps, but we leave that work for later research.

Diffusion researchers conventionally assume the effective radius a for zircons to be half their length (see next section), which in this case

Table 2. Latest (2003) Jemez zircon diffusion data for about 1200 50–75 μm length zircon crystals from borehole GT-2 at a depth of 1490 m. Column 2 is the temperature at each step, controlled to better than 3°C (Appendix B). Column 3 is the amount of He released (1 ncc = 10^{-9} cm^3 at STP, standard temperature and pressure) at the given temperature step. Column 4 is the time at each step. Column 5 is the cumulative fraction of the total He yield. Column 6 is the value of D/a^2 calculated by the experimenter according to standard formulas, where D is the diffusivity and a is the average effective radius. Column 7 is the value of D assuming $a = 30$ μm, and omitting steps 1–9 according to advice from the experimenter (see text). Total He yield: 1356 ncc at STP (includes fusion step). Total mass = 216 μg. The experimenter did not list results of step 3 because it had "poor temperature control."

Step	Temp (°C)	He (ncc)	Time (sec)	Cumulative Fraction	D/a^2 (sec^{-1})	D (cm^2/sec)
1	50	1.91E-05	3660	1.41E-08	4.73E-21	—
2	100	3.82E-03	3660	2.83E-06	1.91E-16	—
4	200	3.17E-01	3600	0.000256	1.58E-12	—
5	250	1.32E-01	3660	0.000354	1.41E-12	—
6	300	3.43E-01	3660	0.000606	5.78E-12	—
7	350	2.97E+00	3660	0.002798	1.78E-10	—
8	400	9.86E+00	3600	0.010072	2.27E-09	—
9	450	4.28E+01	3660	0.041626	3.89E-08	—
10	500	1.48E+02	3600	0.150546	5.55E-07	4.99E-12
11	475	3.93E+01	3660	0.179567	2.63E-07	2.37E-12
12	425	4.90E+00	3600	0.183185	3.72E-08	3.35E-13
13	375	6.29E-01	3660	0.183649	4.75E-09	4.28E-14
14	325	7.77E-02	3600	0.183706	5.98E-10	5.38E-15
15	275	1.01E-02	3660	0.183714	7.64E-11	6.88E-16
16	225	3.56E-03	7260	0.183716	1.36E-11	1.22E-16
17	175	7.78E-04	7260	0.183717	2.97E-12	2.68E-17
18	205	2.03E-03	7200	0.183718	7.81E-12	7.03E-17
19	255	4.25E-03	3660	0.183722	3.22E-11	2.90E-16
20	305	3.03E-02	3600	0.183744	2.33E-10	2.10E-15
21	355	2.41E-01	3660	0.183922	1.83E-09	1.65E-14
22	405	1.94E+00	3600	0.185352	1.50E-08	1.35E-13
23	455	1.47E+01	3600	0.196188	1.18E-07	1.06E-12
24	505	8.09E+01	3660	0.255886	7.87E-07	7.09E-12
25	460	1.35E+01	3660	0.265832	1.57E-07	1.41E-12
26	410	1.86E+00	3660	0.267207	2.23E-08	2.00E-13
27	360	2.46E-01	3600	0.267389	3.00E-09	2.70E-14
28	310	3.18E-02	3660	0.267412	3.82E-10	3.43E-15

gives us an average value for a of about 30 μm. Multiplying column 6 by the resulting value of a^2 gives us values of the diffusivity D for points 10–28, which we show in column 7 of Table 2. I estimate that the 1σ error in D is less than ±30% (see Endnote iii).

7. A New Creation Model

We need a theoretical framework in which we can interpret the diffusion data of the previous section. As we mentioned at the end of section 4, in our first Creation model we wrongly assumed that the zircons were a negligible impediment to the He diffusion. In this section we construct a new Creation model.

As before, the Creation model starts with a brief burst of accelerated nuclear decay generating a high concentration C_0 of He uniformly throughout the zircon (like the distribution of U and Th atoms), but not in the surrounding biotite. After that the He diffuses out of the zircon into the biotite for a time t. As in our previous model, we chose $t = 6000$ years. The time is short enough that the additional amount of He generated by normal nuclear decay would be small compared to the initial amount. We assume the temperatures to have been constant at today's values. We will show in Section 8 that this assumption is generous to uniformitarians.

Because the biotite diffusion coefficients are not too different from the zircon coefficients, we should have a model accounting for two materials. Diffusion in zircon is, as far as anyone knows, approximately isotropic, with He flowing essentially at the same rate in all three directions. Diffusion in biotite is not isotropic, because most of the He flows two-dimensionally along the cleavage planes of the mica. But accounting for anisotropy in the biotite would be quite difficult, so we leave that refinement to the next generation of analysts. (See Appendix D, Section D4 for estimate of size of the error involved in assuming isotropy in biotite.) To keep the mathematics tractable, we will assume spherical symmetry, with a sphere of zircon of effective radius a inside a spherical shell of material having an outer radius b, as Figure 12 shows. Then the concentration C will depend only on time and the distance r from the center.

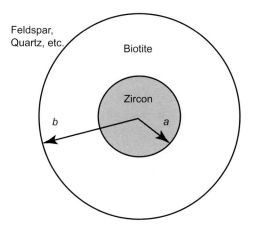

Figure 12. Spherical approximation of the zircon-biotite system.

Let us consider the values we should assign to *a* and *b*. Magomedov's zircons were between 100 and 200 μm long [*Magomedov*, 1970, p. 263], for an average length of about 150 μm. He assigned the crystals an effective radius of half the average length, or 75 μm. Gentry selected zircons between about 50 μm and 75 μm, for an average that we will round off to 60 μm. Half of that gives us an effective radius for our analysis of the Jemez zircons with a 1σ estimate of error (see Endnote iii):

$$a = 30(\pm 1.5)\,\mu\text{m} \qquad (6)$$

This is an average value, representing all the crystals in the size-selected sample. Note that this value is larger than the 22 μm I chose in our first Creation model [*Humphreys*, 2000, p. 347]. See Appendix D, Section D4. Biotite in the Jemez granodiorite is in the form of flakes averaging about 0.2 mm in thickness and about 2 mm in diameter. Because the cleavage planes are in the long direction, and diffusion is mainly along the planes, the diameter is the relevant dimension for diffusion. That gives us a nominal outer radius for the biotite flake of:

$$b \approx 1000\,\mu\text{m} \qquad (7)$$

Because *b* is more than thirty-two times larger than *a*, the disk-like (not spherical) volume of biotite the He enters is more than 1000 (~32^2) times the volume of the zircon. This consideration affects the boundary conditions we choose for $r=b$, and how we might interpret sample 6 (see Section 2), as follows. To predict D in zircon with the equations below, we only need to know the value of b to within an order of magnitude, because it tends to cancel itself out in an analysis of errors. The physical reason for the cancellation is that for large values of b/a, He concentration in the biotite generally remains much lower than the He concentration in the zircon, so that the former would not significantly affect the flow of He from the zircon. That applies to samples 1–5.

However, let us consider sample 6. Suppose that He could not escape the biotite at all. Then as diffusion proceeds, C would decrease in the zircon and increase in the biotite, until the concentration was the same throughout the two materials. After that C would remain essentially constant, at about 0.001 C_0. The fraction Q/Q_0 remaining in the zircon would be about 0.001, which is just what Gentry observed in sample 6.

So a possible explanation for sample 6 is that diffusion into the surrounding materials (feldspar, quartz), and leakage (along grain boundaries) was slow enough (during the relatively short time t) to make the outflow of He from the biotite negligible. For that sample, the temperature and diffusivity were high enough for He to spread uniformly through both zircon and biotite during that time.

Our measurements on sample 2002 (see Appendix B) showed that the He concentration in the Jemez biotite at a depth of 750 m was small, only about 0.32×10^{-9} cm³ STP (standard temperature and pressure) per microgram (μg). Taking into account the difference in density of biotite and zircon (3.2 g/cm³ and 4.7 g/cm³), that corresponds to almost exactly the same amount of He per unit volume as sample 6 contained. Our measurements on sample 2003 (see Section 10) confirm that. This suggests the zircon and biotite were near equilibrium in sample 6, thus supporting our hypothesis.

At lower temperatures, for He retentions greater than 0.001, C in the biotite would be lower than C in the zircon. In that case the boundary at $r=b$ would not significantly affect the outflow of He from the zircon. We will assume this was approximately true for sample 5 also, but not for sample 6. To simplify our analysis for samples 1 through 5, we will assume the usual boundary condition, that the concentration $C(r)$ falls to zero at radius $r = b$:

$$C(b) = 0 \qquad\qquad (8)$$

Choosing a different boundary condition would have little effect on the result, because it turns out that in the short time available, little He could leave the biotite under any circumstances. For the initial conditions, we assume that the concentration is a constant, C_0, inside the zircon, and zero outside it:

$$\text{At } t = 0: \quad C(r) = C_0 \text{ for } r < a, \quad \text{and} \quad C(r) = 0 \text{ for } r > a \qquad (9a, b)$$

After time zero, there also must be continuity of both C and He flow at $r = a$. We need a solution to the diffusion equation, equation (1), in its radial form, for the above boundary conditions. In 1945, Bell published such a solution for the corresponding problem in heat flow [*Bell*, 1945, p. 46, equation (4B)]. His solution, which is mathematically complex, allows for different diffusion coefficients in the two regions. We will simplify the solution considerably by making the diffusion coefficients the same in both regions. Because the diffusion coefficient of biotite is somewhat higher than that of zircon at the temperatures of interest, our solution will have slightly slower (no more than 30% slower) He outflows and correspondingly longer times than the real situation. This approximation is generous to the uniformitarian point of view because it increases the time He could remain in the zircons. For more discussion of the above boundary conditions, and possible alternatives to them, see Appendix D, Section D4.

With the above simplification, Bell's equation reduces to one given by Carslaw and Jaeger [*Carslaw and Jaeger*, 1959, p. 236, equation (19)]. After making the simple changes required to go from heat flow to atomic diffusion [*Crank*, 1975, p. 8, equation (1.21)], and accounting for notation differences (note meanings of a and b), we get the following solution:

$$C(r,t) = \frac{2C_0}{r} \sum_{n=1}^{\infty} \frac{1}{n\pi} \left(\frac{b}{n\pi} \sin\frac{n\pi a}{b} - a\cos\frac{n\pi a}{b} \right)$$
$$\times \sin\frac{n\pi r}{b} \exp\left(-n^2 \frac{\pi^2 Dt}{b} \right) \tag{10}$$

where D is the diffusion coefficient of zircon. Next we need to determine the fraction Q/Q_0 of He retained in the zircon after diffusion takes place for time t. First, note that $Q(t)$ and Q_0 are the volume integrals of $C(r, t)$ and C_0 in the zircon:

$$Q(t) = 4\pi \int_0^a C(r,t)r^2 dr, \quad Q_0 = \frac{4}{3}\pi a^3 C_0 \tag{11a, b}$$

Volume integrating equation (10) as required by equation (11a) and dividing by equation (11b) gives the fraction of He retained in the zircon after time t elapses:

$$\frac{Q(t)}{Q_0} = \sum_{n=1}^{\infty} S_n \exp\left(-n^2 \frac{\pi^2 Dt}{b^2} \right) \tag{12}$$

where we define the function S_n as follows:

$$S_n = \frac{6b^3}{n^4\pi^4 a^3} \left(\sin\frac{n\pi a}{b} - \frac{n\pi a}{b}\cos\frac{n\pi a}{b} \right)^2 \tag{13}$$

To solve equation (12), let us rewrite it in terms of a new variable, x, and a new function, $F(x)$, as follows:

$$F(x) = \frac{Q}{Q_0}, \quad \text{where } F(x) = \sum_{n=1}^{N} S_n \exp(-n^2 x),$$
$$\text{and } x = \frac{\pi^2 Dt}{b^2} \tag{14a, b, c}$$

Now we can use software like *Mathematica* [*Wolfram*, 1991] to find the roots of equation (14a), that is, to find the values of x for which $F(x)$ will give us particular values of the retention fraction Q/Q_0. When the latter and b/a are large, the series in equation (14b) does not converge rapidly. For our value of b/a, 33.3, it was necessary to go out to $N=300$ to get good accuracy. Table 3 lists the resulting values of x, and the values of D necessary to get those values from equation (14c) using a time of 6000 years, $t = 1.892 \times 10^{11}$ seconds. The estimated errors in D essentially result from the reported ±30% errors (which we conservatively assumed to be 1σ random errors) in Q/Q_0. The other errors, such as in the average values of a (less than ±5%) and b (negligible effect), are much smaller. When we take the square root of the sum of the squares of the various errors, the effect of the ±30% error completely dominates.

Table 3. New Creation model.

Sample	T (°C)	Q/Q_0	x	D (cm²/sec)	1σ Error (%)	
1	105	0.58±0.17	5.9973×10^{-4}	3.2103×10^{-18}	+122	-67
2	151	0.27±0.08	2.4612×10^{-3}	1.3175×10^{-17}	+49	-30
3	197	0.17±0.05	4.0982×10^{-3}	2.1937×10^{-17}	+39	-24
4	239	0.012±0.004	3.3250×10^{-2}	1.7798×10^{-16}	+33	-18
5	277	~0.001	1.8190×10^{-1}	9.7368×10^{-16}	—	—

In summary, the fifth column shows the zircon diffusion coefficients that would be necessary for the Jemez zircons to retain the observed fractions of He (third column) for 6000 years at the temperatures listed in the second column. Column 6 gives the (probably overestimated) 1σ error in the predicted values of D.

This new model turns out to be very close to my previous Creation model—within 0.5% for sample 1 and 0.05% for the others—despite the different assumptions and equations. The effect of two changes (going from cavity in biotite to solid in biotite, and increasing the effective radius from 22 μm to 30 μm) almost completely canceled each other out (see Appendix D, Section D4.) Thus my previously published predictions [*Humphreys*, 2000, p. 348, Figure 7] of diffusion coefficients still happen to be numerically valid—no thanks to me! But the numbers should be re-interpreted to apply to zircon, not biotite.

We will compare the data not only to this new model, but also to a uniformitarian model, which we describe in the next section.

8. Uniformitarian Model

In the RATE book [*Humphreys*, 2000, p. 346], we outlined a simple model appropriate for the uniformitarian view, with its billions of years, of the history of the rock unit:

> ... steady low-rate radioactive decay, He production, and He diffusion for 1.5 billion years at today's temperatures in the formation.

Our assumption of constant temperatures is generous to the uniformitarian model. Two geoscientists from Los Alamos National Laboratory constructed a theoretical model of the thermal history of the particular borehole (GT-2) we are concerned with [*Kolstad and McGetchin*, 1978, p. 213, Figure 11]. They started by assuming "a background vertical geothermal gradient of 25°C/km." That means initial conditions with absolute (K) temperatures 16 to 31% lower than today for samples 1 through 6, putting them in the low-slope "defect" range of diffusion. Their model then has an episode of Pliocene-Pleistocene volcanism starting to increase the temperature several megayears ago. It would peak about 0.6 Ma ago at temperatures roughly 50 to 120°C above today's values, depending on depth. After the peak, temperatures would decline steadily until 0.1 Ma ago, and then level off at today's values.

Later studies [*Harrison et al.*, 1986; *Sasada*, 1989] add a more recent pulse of heat and have past temperatures being higher, 110 to 190°C more than today's levels just 24,000 years ago, and higher before that [*Harrison et al.*, 1986, p. 1906, Figure 9]. This would put the samples well into the high-slope "intrinsic" range of diffusion.

The effect of such heat pulses would be great. For several million years, the diffusion coefficients would have been about two to three orders of magnitude higher than today's values. During the previous 1.5 billion years, supposedly at lower temperatures than today, the diffusion rates would have been on the "defect" line (Figure 5) and therefore not much below today's levels. Thus the long time at lower temperatures would not compensate for high losses during the few million years at higher temperatures. This makes our assumption of constant temperatures at today's values quite favorable to the uniformitarian scenario. For further comments, see Section 10 and Figure 16.

As we will see, the long uniformitarian timescale requires zircon diffusion coefficients to be about a million times slower than the measured biotite coefficients. That means the biotite would not be a significant hindrance to the He flow in the uniformitarian model, and the results would not be much different than those for a bare zircon. For further comments on that assumption, see Appendix D, Section D4, change (3). With continuous production of He, the concentration C in the zircon would reach its steady-state level relatively quickly (see Section 11) and remain at that level for most of the alleged 1.5 billion years. Again we assume a spherical zircon of radius a. Carslaw and Jaeger give the corresponding solution for heat flow [*Carslaw and Jaeger*, 1959, p. 232, case VIII)]. Converting to the notation for atomic diffusion shows us how the steady-state concentration C in the zircon depends on the radius r from the center:

$$C(r) = \frac{Q_0}{\frac{4}{3}\pi a^3} \frac{\left(a^2 - r^2\right)}{6Dt}, \text{ for } r \leq a \tag{15}$$

Here Q_0 is the total amount of He that would be produced in time t. That is, Q_0/t is the He production rate. As before, D is the diffusion coefficient of zircon, and a is the effective radius. Using equation (11a) to integrate equation (15) and dividing by Q_0 gives us the fraction of He Q/Q_0 in the zircon in the steady-state condition:

$$\frac{Q}{Q_0} = \frac{a^2}{15Dt} \tag{16}$$

Table 4 gives us the zircon diffusion coefficients required to give the observed retentions for $a = 30\,\mu m$ and $t = 1.50$ (± 0.02) billion years $= 4.7 \times 10^{16}$ sec ($\pm 1.3\%$).

The same reasoning on sample 6 applies for this model as for the Creation model, except that it is less likely the He could remain totally sealed in the biotite for over a billion years. For the other samples, this model is exactly the same as our previously published "evolution" model [*Humphreys*, 2000, p. 348, Figure 7].

Table 4. Uniformitarian model.

Sample	T (°C)	Q/Q_0	D (cm²/sec)	1σ Error (%)
1	105	0.58±0.17	2.1871×10^{-23}	±30
2	151	0.27±0.08	4.6981×10^{-23}	±30
3	197	0.17±0.05	7.4618×10^{-23}	±30
4	239	0.012±0.004	1.0571×10^{-21}	±30
5	277	~0.001	1.2685×10^{-20}	—

9. Comparing Data and Models

Figure 13 shows the new Jemez zircon data of Table 2, plotted with the two models for comparison. The data (blue dots) fall right upon the predicted Creation model (green squares)—as close as errors in the data and approximations in the model would lead us to expect (notice the ±2σ error bars on both models and data in the figure). The data points extend past the "knee" of the model at 197°C (abscissa = 2.13), into the lower-temperature "defect" region determined by radiation damage in the crystals. This was quite important to examine, because the defect part of the curve can vary greatly from site to site (see Sections 3 and 4). Even in the defect region, the data agree quite well with the model. It is not often in science that experimental data so clearly validate a pre-published numerical model.

The data also resoundingly reject the uniformitarian model (red squares). The points of that model are the values of diffusivity required to retain the observed amounts of He for 1.5 billion years at *today's* temperatures in the rock unit. However, as I mentioned in the previous section, uniformitarian thermal models of the rock unit require that the temperatures have been *higher* in the past [*Kolstad and McGetchin*, 1978; *Harrison et al.*, 1986; *Sasada*, 1989]. So the points of our uniformitarian model are below the average temperatures during the alleged eons. A more accurate depiction would slide the uniformitarian model points horizontally leftward to represent the allegedly higher average temperatures. That would make the vertical gap between that model and the data even larger, as the left-hand side of Figure 16 (in

Section 10) shows. Thus the uniformitarian model in Figure 13 is very generous to uniformitarians, minimizing the gap. Even so, the data points are about 100,000 times higher than the model points. At their closest, the lower 2σ bound of the data and the upper 2σ bound of the uniformitarian model are more than twenty-five standard deviations apart. Uniformitarianism has totally failed this experimental test.

We can also compare the new diffusivities with the observed retentions to calculate the age of the zircons. Turning equation (14c) around gives us

$$t = \frac{b^2 x}{\pi^2 D} \qquad (17)$$

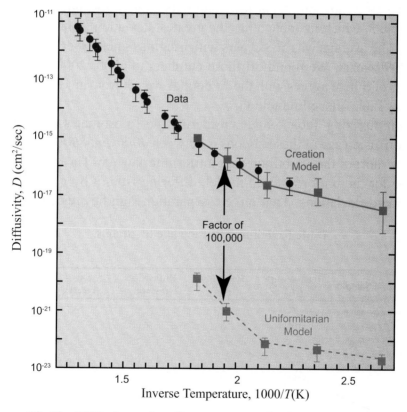

Figure 13. The 2003 zircon data line up very well with the Creation model, and they resoundingly reject the uniformitarian model. The ordinate is D (not D/a^2). Error bars show $\pm 2\sigma$ bounds on data and models.

Using $a/b = 0.03$, the values of D/a^2 from Table 2, and the values of x from Table 3 gives us the length of time diffusion would have been occurring. Table 5 shows the results of doing that.

Diffusivities in this table come from best exponential fits to nearby measured points from Table 2, column 7. Because our lowest measured value for D is at 175°C, we extrapolated 24°C down to the temperature of sample 2 but not further down to those of samples 2003, 1, or 2002. Then we calculated ages (see Endnote iv) as we did in our paper for the Fifth International Conference on Creationism [*Humphreys et al.*, 2003a, Sections 6 and 8], putting the *x*-values of Table 3 and the values of D below into equation (17) to get the values for the age *t* we show above. See our comments in Section 10 (related to Figure 15) about sample 3, which in Table 5 has the greatest deviation from the average age. The average was 5681 years with a sigma (square root of variance) of 1999 years. We round off those numbers to 6000±2000 years. Our value of σ here agrees with the 1σ bounds we get from an error analysis using Table 3 (see Endnote v).

Summarizing Table 5 and considering the 1σ estimates of error, the He diffusion age of these zircons is between *4000 and 8000 years*. This is far short of the 1.5 billion year uniformitarian age. The data offer no hope for the uniformitarian model, differing from it by more than 25 standard deviations. That large a separation signifies rejection of the

Table 5. Helium diffusion age of zircons.

Sample	Temperature (°C)	Retention (%)	Diffusivity (cm²/sec)	Age (years)
2002	96	~80	—	—
1	105	58	—	—
2003	125	42	—	—
2	151	27	1.09×10^{-17}	7270
3	197	17	5.49×10^{-17}	2400
4	239	1.2	1.87×10^{-16}	5730
5	277	~0.1	7.97×10^{-16}	~7330
			Average:	5681
			Sigma:	1999

Table 6. Billion-year uniformitarian retentions versus observed retentions.

Sample	T (°C)	Measured D/a^2 (sec^{-1})	Helium Retentions Q/Q_0	
			After 1.5 billion years	Observed
2002	96	—	—	~0.800
1	105	—	—	0.580
2003	124	—	—	0.420
2	151	1.21×10^{-12}	1.16×10^{-6}	0.270
3	197	6.10×10^{-12}	2.31×10^{-7}	0.170
4	239	2.08×10^{-11}	6.77×10^{-8}	0.012
5	277	8.86×10^{-10}	1.59×10^{-8}	~0.001

uniformitarian hypothesis with an extremely high level of confidence (see Endnote vi). The zircon data show a knee, where the data break off horizontally to the right into a shallow-slope "defect" line. But even if that had not been the case, the high-slope "intrinsic" line would still pass well above the uniformitarian model.

We can also use these observed data to estimate what He retentions Gentry should have found if the zircons were really 1.5 billion years old. If no He could leak out of the biotite during that time, then all of the samples would have had retentions of about 0.001, much less than all samples but number 5 [see Section 7 between equations (7) and (8)]. However, we know that He can diffuse through the surrounding materials, quartz and feldspar (so even sample 5 would retain much less than 0.001). By assuming those materials are comparatively negligible hindrances, we can put the diffusivity data of Table 5 into equation (16) to get the "unrestricted outflow" retentions after 1.5 billion years. Table 6 shows the results.

So the best uniformitarian estimate of retentions for all samples would be somewhere between 0.001 (zero flow into surrounding minerals) and the small numbers in column 4 (unrestricted flow into surrounding minerals). That is not what we observe. In summary, the observed diffusion rates are so high that if the zircons had existed for 1.5 billion years at the observed temperatures, all samples would have retained *much less He than we observe*. That strongly implies they have not existed nearly so long a time. In Appendix D we consider mechanisms that might limit He diffusion and increase He retention. We find no mechanism that is capable of retaining large amounts of He for even a few million years, much less billions of years.

10. Closing Some Loopholes

After stepwise heating the 216 μg of zircons in sample 2003 to get the diffusivity data, our experimenter raised the temperature to a high value and held it there long enough to get the rest of the He out of the crystals. The total yield of He from the zircons was 1356 ncc (1 ncc = 10^{-9} cm³ STP = 0.4462 × 10^{-4} nanomole), or 6.05 × 10^{-2} nmol (1σ error ±3%). Dividing by the mass (±1%) gives us 6.28 ncc/μg, or 303 nmol/g (±3%). Multiplying the latter value by the density of zircon, 4.7 g/cm³ (±2%), gives us the He concentration in the zircon: 1320 nmol/cm³ (± 4%).

For the 5.562 mg (±1%) of biotite, the total yield of He was 257 ncc (±3%), giving 2.06 nmol/g (±3%). Multiplying by the density of biotite, 3.2 g/cm³ (±2%) gives us the He concentration in the biotite: 6.57 nmol/cm³ (±4%).

These data are quite useful in closing possible loopholes in our case. First, the 6.28 ncc/μg yield of these zircons is quite consistent with Gentry's retention data. Gentry's (±30%) estimate of radiogenic He deposited in the zircons, 15 ncc/μg ±30% (1σ), is consistent with our data on radiogenic Pb in the zircons. Dividing our retention by that value gives us a retention fraction of 0.42±0.13. Almost all of that error is systematic, caused by Gentry's ±30% error. That is, if we were to correct all retentions, both Gentry's and ours, with a new estimate of He deposited, our point would move up or down together with Gentry's points. Here we only want to compare our retention with those of Gentry, so I will leave the systematic error out of the comparison. The He measurement error, on the other hand, has a 1σ random error of ±3% (see Endnote iii). These zircons came from a depth of 1490 m, nearly midway between Gentry's samples 1 and 2 in Table 1. The interpolated temperature at that depth would be 124 (±1)°C. Figure 14 shows that our new retention point fits quite well between Gentry's retentions for samples 1 and 2. This supports the validity of Gentry's

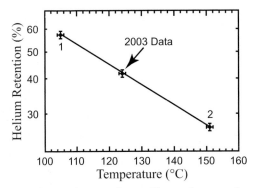

Figure 14. New retention point confirms Gentry's retention data. Error bars show 1σ measurement uncertainties.

retention measurements.

Second, the concentration of He in the zircon, 1320 nmol/cm^3, is about 200 times greater than the concentration in the surrounding biotite, 6.6 nmol/cm^3. Because the laws of diffusion require flow from greater to lesser concentrations, these data mean that He is moving *out* of the zircons *into* the biotite, not the other way around.

Third, because the average volume of the biotite flakes is hundreds of times greater than that of the zircons (Section 7), the amount of He in the biotites is on the same order of magnitude as the amount of He lost by the zircons. That rebuts a uniformitarian conjecture [*Ross*, 2003] that there might have been vast amounts (100,000 times greater than the already-large observed amounts) of non-radiogenic primordial He in the zircons 1.5 billion years ago.

Our new He retention fraction (0.42 at 124°C) can be treated the same way as we treated Gentry's retention data to make a prediction of diffusion rates. That is, we can use our retention figure to calculate what value of D at 124°C would be required if the zircons were 6000 years old. Figure 15 shows how this "retrodiction" point fits very well with the diffusion rate data and the Creation model prediction.

In Figure 15, I have relabeled the abscissa by temperature and have redrawn the lines in accord with the new data. The largest outlier from the lines is the model point at 197°C. The difference suggests the true retention fraction for that sample might have been about half the

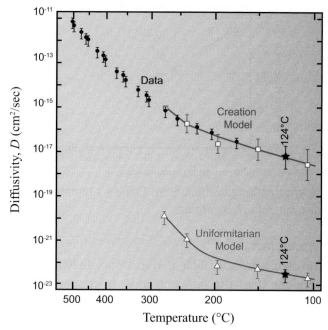

Figure 15. Lines of Figure 13 redrawn in accordance with the 2003 data. Stars with "124°C" above are the diffusivities required by our new retention datum (0.42) and the ages assumed by the two models. Bars show the 2σ error bounds on data and models. Error for leftmost (277°C) Creation model point is undetermined (Section 2).

fraction *Gentry et al.* [1982] reported (Table 1, sample 3). Whatever the cause, a two-fold discrepancy for one point pales into insignificance in light of the enormous 100,000-fold discrepancy between the observed diffusivities and all points of the uniformitarian model.

Some people might wonder if temperatures in the Jemez granodiorite before 6000 years ago were low enough for long enough to make the diffusion coefficients small enough to retain the He. We discussed that possibility in Section 8, but here we point out how low such temperatures are likely to be.

In Figure 15, the right-hand four points, the 175°C experimental point (solid dot) and the three points deduced from retentions and a 6000 year age (hollow squares and star) appear to make a fairly straight line. That suggests that below 175°C, the "defect" slope has established itself. In that case, the best linear fit (to $\ln D$ vs $1/T$) gives parameters (with 1σ error bounds) of the defect line for these zircons from borehole GT-2:

$$E_1 = 10.19^{+0.59}_{-0.62} \text{ kcal/mol}, \quad D_1 = (2.49 \pm 1.69) \times 10^{-12} \text{ cm}^2/\text{sec} \quad (18)$$

Because E_1 is small, the slope of the defect line is small. Figure 16 extrapolates this line and its 1σ error bounds down to very low temperatures. The intercept with $D = 10^{-23} \text{ cm}^2/\text{sec}$ is (note minus sign):

$$T = -78^{+21}_{-14} {}^\circ\text{C}$$

By coincidence, that happens to be the temperature of sublimating *dry ice* (frozen CO_2). The "Cold" uniformitarian model in Figure 16 simply slides the "Present Temperatures" uniformitarian model of Section 8 rightward far enough to meet the dotted line, the diffusivities extrapolated from our data. The amount of shift required means that to get the diffusion coefficients low enough, say on the order of $10^{-23} \text{ cm}^2/\text{sec}$, to allow a billion-year time-scale, the temperature in the granodiorite would have to have been extremely low, about that of dry ice. (In our previous publications, we slid the "Cold" model to even lower temperatures, but the data and fit here are more accurate.) No geoscientist we know would advocate an earth that was *cryogenic* for 1.5 billion years!

Moreover, as we commented in Section 8, uniformitarian models of the thermal history of the rock unit call for much *higher* past temperatures than the ones at present, not lower temperatures. The "Hot" model in Figure 16 slides the "Present Temperatures" model to the left far enough to roughly account for the uniformitarian Pliocene-Pleistocene thermal models. Notice that in that case the discrepancy between data and model increases to a factor of about *100 million*. The alleged hot episode of several million years would have completely wiped out any He that might have accumulated during the alleged previous 1.5 billion years. That is why our assumption of constant temperatures at today's levels is very generous to the uniformitarian model.

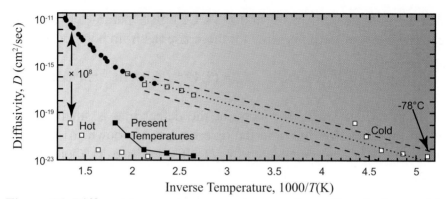

Figure 16. Different temperatures cannot rescue the uniformitarian model. Errors for data and models are the same as in Figure 15. Dotted line is best fit to last four points. Dashed lines are 1σ upper and lower bounds to fit.

11. "Closure Temperature" does not Help the Uniformitarian Model

Some people misunderstand the geoscience concept of *closure temperature*, thinking that zircons cooling below that temperature are permanently closed systems and thereafter would lose no significant amounts of He by diffusion. That argument would not affect our samples 2–5 because they are *above* the closure temperature our experimenter calculated, 128°C (Appendix C). However, our samples below the closure temperature would also not be affected, because it turns out that even well below the closure temperature, zircons can *re-open* and lose large amounts of He. Here we explain closure temperature and re-opening, and show that in the uniformitarian scenario, even the cooler Jemez granodiorite zircons would re-open early in their history.

Consider a hot zircon cooling down in newly formed granite. If the cooling rate is constant, then the seminal article by Martin Dodson [*Dodson*, 1973] on closure temperature shows that the diffusion coefficient D (of He moving out of the zircon) decreases exponentially with a time constant τ given by:

$$\tau = \frac{RT^2}{E_0\left(\dfrac{dT}{dt}\right)} \tag{19}$$

where T is the absolute temperature, dT/dt is the cooling rate, R is the gas constant, and E_0 is the activation energy in the "intrinsic" region (Section 3).

In the uniformitarian scenario, nuclear decay produces He at a nearly constant rate. At the beginning, when the zircon is very hot, He diffuses out of the crystal as fast as nuclear decay produces it. But as the zircon cools, it will eventually reach a temperature below which the *loss rate becomes less than the production rate*. That point is essentially what Dodson meant by the "closure" temperature. He showed that for a constant cooling rate the closure temperature T_c is

$$T_c = \frac{E_0}{R \ln\left(A\tau \frac{D_0}{a^2} \right)} \tag{20}$$

where A is a dimensionless constant (55 for a sphere), D_0 is the "intrinsic" intercept in Figure 5, a is the effective radius of the crystal, and τ is the diffusion time constant given by equation (19). Since τ depends on the cooling rate, hence affecting T_c somewhat, geoscientists imply some conventional cooling rate when they specify a closure temperature. In Appendix C our experimenter assumes a cooling rate of 10°C per million years and finds that the closure temperature of the Jemez granodiorite zircons is 128°C.

After the zircon cools below the closure temperature, He begins to accumulate in it, as Figure 17 shows. Later, as the temperature levels off to that of the surrounding rock, the diffusion coefficient D becomes constant. (The case of changing long-term temperatures is harder to analyze, but there will still be a time of re-opening.) As the amount of He in the zircon increases, Fick's laws of diffusion (Section 3) says the loss rate also increases. Eventually, even well below the closure temperature, the *loss rate approaches the production rate*, an event we call the "re-opening" of the zircon. Then the amount of He in the zircon will level off at a steady-state value, which we called Q in equation (16). After that, the zircon will again lose He as fast as nuclear decay produces it.

Let us estimate the *closure interval*, the length of time t_{ci} the zircon

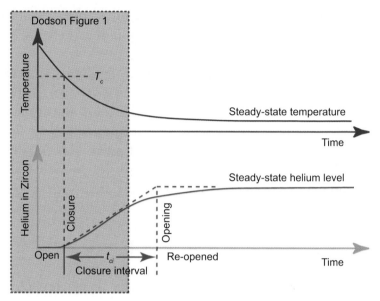

Figure 17. Closure and re-opening of a zircon. Dotted-line box on the left contains the essentials of Dodson's Figure 1, which did not extend far enough in time to show re-opening.

remains closed before re-opening. As we remarked just below equation (15), the He production rate is Q_0/t, where t is the uniformitarian age of the zircon, 1.5 billion years. Assuming a linear rise as a first approximation, the production rate multiplied by t_{ci} is roughly equal to the steady-state value of Q, which is the right-hand side of our equation (16) multiplied by Q_0

$$\left(\frac{Q_0}{t}\right) t_{ci} \approx \left(\frac{a^2}{15Dt}\right) Q_0 \tag{21}$$

Solving for t_{ci} gives us the approximate closure interval:

$$t_{ci} \approx \frac{a^2}{15D} \tag{22}$$

If the closure interval were long compared to the age of the zircon, then the zircon would indeed be a closed system. But would that be the case in the uniformitarian view of the Jemez zircons? Using the effective radius of the zircons, 30 µm, and the measured values of D (Figure 15) in equation (22), gives us t_{ci} values between *a few dozen years and a few thousand years*, depending on the temperature of the sample in the borehole. Those times are very small compared to the uniformitarian age of 1.5 billion years.

So even if the zircons had cooled rapidly and reached closure temperature early in their history, our measured diffusion rates say they would have re-opened shortly after that. During most of the alleged eons the zircons would have been an open system. They would be losing as much He as the nuclear decay produced. Thus, in this case, closure *temperature* does not help the uniformitarian model, because the closure *interval* is brief.

12. Discussion: A Tale of Two Hourglasses

Experiments have strongly vindicated what creationists felt when Gentry reported the high He retentions over twenty years ago. The He indeed could not have remained in the zircons for even a million years, much less the alleged 1.5 billion years. Even more exciting, our more recent experiments give a He diffusion age of 6000 years (with a 1σ error of ±2000 years), which resonates strongly with the date of Creation we get from a straightforward Biblical chronology.

Figure 18 illustrates the contrast between this He age and the radioisotopic age. It shows two different "hourglasses," representing He diffusion and U-Pb nuclear decay. These hourglasses give drastically different dates.

We have much data to show that we have read the He hourglass correctly:

- U-Pb data give us the initial amount of sand (He) in the top half (the zircon).
- Gentry's measurements, confirmed by ours, give us the present amount of sand in the top half.
- Our diffusion rate experiments show how fast sand is presently trickling (diffusing) out of the top half into the bottom half (the biotite).

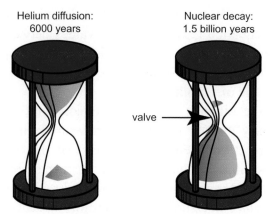

Helium diffusion: Nuclear decay:
6000 years   1.5 billion years

valve ⟶

Figure 18. Two hourglasses representing two methods of dating zircons. "Valve" represents nuclear decay acceleration.

- Our measurements show roughly the right amount of sand in the bottom half (He in the biotite).

For the nuclear decay hourglass, we also know similar things:

- present amounts in the top half (U in the zircon),
- the present trickling rate (nuclear decay rates), and
- the amounts in the bottom half (Pb isotopes in the zircon).

The large amount of He, the actual α-particles from the decays, confirms that a large amount of nuclear decay has taken place.

One way to reconcile these two hourglass readings is to suggest that one of them has a "valve" at its bottleneck controlling the trickling rate, a valve that was adjusted drastically in the past, either by natural mechanisms or possibly by direct intervention from God.

Some might want to imagine that the valve is on the He hourglass, and that for billions of years, diffusion rates were over 100,000 times slower until a few thousand years ago. In Sections 8 and 10, we discussed the possibility that *in situ* temperatures might have been low enough for long enough to accomplish that reduction by natural means. But we found that such scenarios (such as having "dry ice" temperatures deep underground for 1.5 billion years) do not seem at all feasible. In Appendix D we examine all the other conceivable natural ways we know of that the diffusion rates might have been much lower. None of them appears to be significant.

Another possibility is that God may have changed diffusion rates by some drastic means, say by adjusting the laws of atomic physics which control diffusion. But the laws of atomic physics also control the biochemical processes that sustain life. It is difficult to imagine (although God is not at all restricted by our weak imaginations) any such change in atomic physics that would have allowed life on earth to exist. Certainly the theorist would have a very large number of complicated consequences to explain.

On the other hand, it is much simpler to imagine that the valve is on the nuclear decay hourglass. Nuclear forces affect only a tiny region at the center of the atom. They have very little effect on the outer electronic structure of the atom or its chemical interactions. Moreover, a relatively small change in nuclear forces can cause a billion-fold acceleration of nuclear decay rates [*Chaffin*, 2000, 2003; *Humphreys*, 2000]. Finally, the preponderance of Biblical and geoscience evidence for a young world [*Humphreys*, 2000, pp. 337–339] points to a change that would only affect dating methods which depend on slowly-decaying nuclei.

Thus our new diffusion data support the hypothesis we proposed in our first book [*Vardiman*, 2000, pp. 3–5], that God drastically accelerated the decay rates of long half-life nuclei during the earth's recent past. For a feasibility study of this hypothesis—including God's possible purposes for such acceleration, Biblical passages hinting at it, disposal of excess heat, preserving life on earth, and effects on stars— see *Humphreys* [2000, pp. 333–379]. The last three problems are not yet fully resolved, but we expect to see progress on them in future papers. The next section gives some of our thinking about the heat problem.

13. Disposing of Excess Heat

In the previous RATE book [*Humphreys*, 2000, pp. 337, 369–370], my feasibility study of the accelerated decay hypothesis pointed out and discussed one of the obvious problems: nuclear decay generates heat! I wrote that without long periods of time in which the heat could dissipate by normal mechanisms, or without some new and faster mechanism, crustal rocks would melt many times over if decay rates were accelerated.

I also pointed out that heat is not merely a problem for accelerated decay, but also for all Creation or Flood models I know of.

There is simply too much geological work to be done in too short a time. So the solution I outline here should be useful to *any* creationist geological model.

The RATE initiative has found several lines of evidence implying that *rapid cooling* occurred along with accelerated nuclear decay, resulting in a smaller rise of temperature than would have occurred without such cooling. Andrew Snelling's successful model for the formation of Po radiohalos requires rapid cooling. He and Mark Armitage concluded,

... the timescale for cooling of the granitic plutons was also extremely short, measured in half-lives of these isotopes (days, not years) [*Snelling and Armitage*, 2003, p. 260].

John Baumgardner solved a long-standing geothermal mystery by assuming a burst of heat from accelerated decay accompanied by rapid cooling [*Baumgardner*, 2000, pp. 80–86]. In both these cases, most of the cooling could not be by the normal processes of conduction, convection, or radiation. Instead, the process would have to cool the entire volume of material simultaneously ("volume" cooling) and abnormally fast.

The diffusion data in this chapter imply that after the zircons acquired their He, they were never very much hotter than they are now, nor were they hot for very long. For a simplified illustration of this, imagine that the zircons experienced a high temperature T_h for a short time Δt, after which the temperature dropped abruptly to today's level, T, and remained at that level for a time t until now. Let us say that during the hot period, the zircons did not lose more than 30% of their He, thus having a retention fraction of 0.70. (Otherwise, t would have to be quite a bit less than 4000 years to allow the large retentions we observe.) Solving equation (14a) for a retention fraction Q/Q_0 of 0.70 gives us the value of x that would apply to the hot period:

$$x_h = 2.9169 \times 10^{-4} \qquad (23)$$

Then equation (14c) gives us the diffusivity D_h required to retain 70%

of the He during time Δt:

$$D_h = \left(\frac{b}{\pi}\right)^2 \frac{x_h}{\Delta t} \tag{24}$$

Dividing equation (24) by a similar equation using D, x, and t gives us the ratio of the "hot" diffusivity D_h to today's diffusivity D:

$$\frac{D_h}{D} = \frac{x_h}{x} \frac{t}{\Delta t} \tag{25}$$

If today's diffusivity is on the "intrinsic" part of the curve, then we can use equation (2) and a little algebra to give us the temperature T_h during the hot spell in terms of the present temperature T:

$$T_h = \frac{T}{1 - \dfrac{RT}{E_0} \ln\left(\dfrac{x_h}{x} \dfrac{t}{\Delta t}\right)} \tag{26}$$

Here R is the universal gas constant, 1.986 cal/mol/K, and E_0 is the activation energy given in equation (5a). Let us take as an example the x-value and temperature (197°C = 470K) of point 3 in Table 3, and a t of 6000 years. Then for a Δt of 1 year, T_h would be about 90°C above today's temperature. For a Δt of 1 month, T_h would be about 140°C hotter than today. If the heat pulse had been much hotter or longer than those typical values, the diffusion age we calculate would have been significantly less than 4000 years, an age not correlating to any known geological event in the formation. In other words, our data and model are consistent with at most a short, moderate pulse of heating during and just after the accelerated decay episode.

It is very likely water was flowing through the cleavage planes of the biotite while it was hot [Snelling, 2005a, p. 133]. That would keep these zircons cooler than zircons in a material like tuff [Snelling, 2005b, p. 276ff] without clear channels for water flow. But probably that mechanism alone would not be enough to keep the temperature increase as low as 90°C. Also, the heat carried by the water has to go somewhere else on earth, and that heat would be more than enough to melt the earth's crust globally. Thus we require significant volume cooling to compensate for the otherwise large amount of heat from accelerated nuclear decay.

Now let us explore a way such volume cooling might occur. In my feasibility study, I pointed out [*Humphreys*, 2000, pp. 370–373] a little-known and less-understood phenomenon in standard General Relativity theory that seems quite relevant. The mechanism causes photons and moving material particles in an expanding cosmos to lose energy [*Robertson and Noonan*, 1968, pp. 343–344, 354–356; *Landau and Lifshitz*, 1983, pp. 374–375; *Ohanian and Ruffini*, 1994, pp. 582–583; *Rindler*, 2001, p. 369]. The equations clearly show the loss of energy, but where and how the energy goes is less clear. From the similarity of one of the equations to the thermodynamic conservation of energy in an expanding gas, Robertson and Noonan conclude (speaking of photons):

> Therefore, the radiation energy which is lost in an expanding universe is used up as work in aiding the expansion.

But they do not specify how. Other writers say even less, leaving even relativity experts in considerable confusion about whether the lost energy goes somewhere or simply disappears.

This mechanism offers good potential for removing heat on a large scale. We do not need to resolve the experts' confusion about where the energy goes in order to utilize this mechanism. However, for those who would like some understanding of the phenomenon, I offer the following very simplified explanation of my own.

If we take some Biblical and scientific clues seriously and think of space as being an actual but non-perceived *material* [*Humphreys*, 1994, pp. 66–68, 84, 89], then there is a way to understand the energy loss mechanism. Spacetime would be a "fabric" of three space dimensions and one time dimension, a deformable surface in a "hyperspace" of *four* space dimensions and one time dimension [*Humphreys*, 1994, pp. 93–96; *Humphreys*, 2002, pp. 100–101]. The fabric would be bent in the fourth (unperceived) direction with various curvatures. Particles can move along the surface unhindered, but the surface constrains the particles to follow curved paths conforming to the bends in the surface. For example, if the "fabric" constrains a particle of mass m moving with non-relativistic velocity v to follow a path whose radius of curvature is

R, as in Figure 19, then the particle will in turn exert a centrifugal force F on the fabric:

$$F = m\frac{v^2}{R} \tag{27}$$

This force would be in the direction of bending (the "R-direction") perpendicular to the surface of the "fabric," which as I implied above is a fourth spatial direction we cannot perceive directly. If the radius of curvature increases with a rate R, then the particle will lose kinetic energy E at a rate E given by the product of the force and the fabric's speed in the R-direction:

$$\dot{E} = -F\dot{R} = -m\frac{v^2}{R}\dot{R} \tag{28}$$

The dots signify the rate of change with respect to proper time (physical clock time) τ at the point in question. Dividing equation (25) by the kinetic energy gives us a simple result for the fractional loss rate:

$$\frac{\dot{E}}{E} = -2\frac{\dot{R}}{R} \tag{29}$$

In relativistic cosmologies, the fractional rate of change of the large-scale radius of curvature turns out to be the Hubble parameter H, so in that case equation (26) becomes

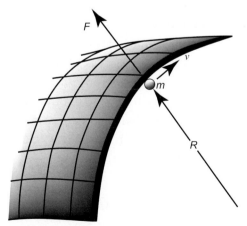

Figure 19. Particle motion in curved space.

$$\frac{\dot{E}}{E} = -2H \tag{30}$$

For photons and material particles of relativistic speeds, the result is similar, but with a different numerical factor. This result is exactly the same as the more rigorous general relativistic calculations give. This derivation shows us where the energy of a particle goes—it aids the expansion of the fabric, adding slightly to its kinetic energy. The particle and photon energy losses are by no means the main cause of the expansion, but the losses are very significant compared to their own energies. Eventually, the textbooks say, a free particle having mass will lose all its kinetic energy and come to rest relative to the "fabric."

Materialist academics will not like my derivation above because they do not like ascribing physical reality to "hyperspace" (although they do allow it as a mathematical convenience) or ascribing physical substance to spacetime. There appear to be deep-seated religious reasons for their dislike, as I pointed out in my cosmology book [*Humphreys*, 1994, pp. 94–95]. But, as I mentioned above, it is not necessary to accept my explanation to accept the loss mechanism itself.

As far as I can tell, the loss mechanism would apply not only to free particles, but also to particles under the influence of electromagnetic forces (such as forces between atoms), because such forces would operate entirely in the surface of the fabric, not adding vectorially to forces in the R-direction perpendicular to the surface. (The loss mechanism might not apply to particles orbiting in local gravitational fields, which come from local curvatures in the fabric superposed on the cosmic curvature [*Cooperstock et al.*, 1998].) That means that atoms and electrons moving thermally in a solid should also experience such a loss of kinetic energy, that is, thermal energy. If there were no other inputs or outputs of energy to or from the particles, the temperature T of the material would decrease in the same way as the energy in equation (30):

$$\frac{\dot{T}}{T} = -2H \tag{31}$$

When the other inputs and outputs of heat are significant, this equation would not apply. Instead, we would have to include equation (30) as one of the heat losses in the usual heat transport equations.

This mechanism would be insignificant if the Hubble parameter H has always had its present very small value. However, H would have a much higher value during periods of high time dilation, because it is the fractional rate of expansion as measured by *proper* time, time as measured by local, physical, clocks. In contrast, we would expect the rate of expansion to be governed by global parameters, which are in turn most closely related to ideal clocks synchronized with distant clocks. As a first approximation, we could say that the expansion rate as measured by distant clocks would be roughly constant during the periods of interest. But our local clocks would be very slow relative to distant clocks during periods of high time dilation locally, so the rate of expansion as measured by our local clocks would then be very large. As I suggested in my cosmology book [*Humphreys*, 1994, p. 68] and in my previous RATE chapter [*Humphreys*, 2000, pp. 367–368, 372–373], the Bible implies that two such episodes of expansion occurred, one during early Creation week and one during the Genesis Flood. These are the same two periods that seem most likely to have experienced accelerated nuclear decay, and there is probably a connection, as I pointed out [*Humphreys*, 2000, 367–369].

The fact that we see destructive events (apparently occurring after the Fall of Adam) in the distant cosmos would be explained by a many-fold (at least an order of magnitude) expansion/time-dilation episode during the year (as measured by our clocks) of the Genesis Flood. That would make H during the Flood billions of times higher than today's value, and we would easily be able to get rid of all the excess radiogenic heat.

The real problem is how to keep non-radioactive materials from getting *too cold* at the same time. I have not had time to pursue this part of the idea further, so here I can only outline a speculation that may turn out to provide a good explanation later.

If the "fabric" of space is a real material, as Scripture implies [*Humphreys*, 1994, pp. 67–68], then it must have a *temperature*. I speculate that its temperature might set a minimum on how much heat could be transferred to the fabric during rapid expansion. For example, equation (31) might become:

$$\dot{T} = -2H(T - T_{min}) \tag{32}$$

where T_{min} is a minimum temperature that might depend on the amount of time dilation occurring at the moment. If T_{min} were about $300\,K$ during the Genesis Flood, then creatures aboard the Ark could stay warm. Though this is sheer guesswork now, I am confident that a good explanation exists (whether or not we can find it). That is because (a) the evidence convinces me that accelerated nuclear decay did indeed occur, and (b) as one of Noah's descendants, I know that his family did not freeze to death aboard the Ark!

To summarize the heat problem, we have several lines of physical evidence for volume cooling having occurred, and there is at least one promising theoretical approach we can try. When we can devote more time to the problem, we may see good progress on it.

14. Conclusion

The experiments the RATE project commissioned have clearly confirmed the numerical predictions of our Creation model (updated slightly in Section 7), which we published beforehand [*Humphreys*, 2000, p. 348, Figure 7]. Other experimental data published since the beginning of our experiments agree with our data. The data also clearly reject the uniformitarian model. The data and our analysis show that over a billion years worth of nuclear decay has occurred very recently, between 4000 and 8000 years ago. This strongly supports our hypothesis of recent episodes of highly accelerated nuclear decay.

These diffusion data are not precise enough to reveal details about the acceleration episodes. Were there one, two, or three? Were they during early Creation week, after the Fall, or during the Flood? Were there only 500 to 600 million years worth of acceleration during the year of the Flood, with the rest of the acceleration occurring before that? We cannot say from this analysis. However, the fact that these zircons are from a Precambrian rock unit sheds some light on various creationist models about when strata below the Cambrian formed. We can say that the "diffusion clock" requires a large amount of nuclear decay to have taken place within thousands of years ago, after the zircons became solid. At whatever time in Biblical history Precambrian rocks came into existence, these data suggest that "1.5 billion years" worth of nuclear decay took place after the rocks solidified not long ago. Since the Phanerozoic strata usually give nuclear dates of 545 Ma or less, our zircons started accumulating He a significant time before the Genesis Flood began depositing the major fossil layers.

Previously we have presented the technical data in this chapter in three different scientific venues. The first was at the Fifth International Conference on Creationism in Pittsburgh, Pennsylvania, U. S. A., August 4–9, 2003, and archived in its *Proceedings* [*Humphreys et al.*, 2003a]. Then we presented new results in a poster and an abstract at the American Geophysical Union Annual Fall Meeting in San Francisco in December 2003, with the abstract being published in the *Transactions* of that organization [*Humphreys et al.*, 2003b]. Last, the *Creation Research Society Quarterly* documented the new data and results in its June 2004 issue [*Humphreys et al.*, 2004].

Our most important result is this: *He diffusion casts doubt on uniformitarian long-age interpretations of nuclear data and strongly supports the young world of Scripture.*

Acknowledgments

Many people and institutions have contributed to collecting and interpreting these data. In particular, we would like to express our appreciation to Robert Gentry for his seminal research and good advice, to Los Alamos National Laboratory for giving us the Fenton Hill samples, to Yakov Kapusta and Activation Laboratories, Ltd., for processing them, to Mark Armitage for his microscope work, to William (Bill) Hoesch for his laboratory work, to Roger Lenard and Majdah Al-Qutani of Zodiac Mining and Manufacturing, Inc., for its services as intermediary, and especially to the donors whose generosity made this work possible.

Appendix A: Isotopic Analysis of Jemez Zircons

Here we summarize a report by Dr. Yakov Kapusta (Activation Laboratories, Ltd., in Ontario, Canada) on an isotopic analysis he made on three zircons from Los Alamos National Laboratories core sample GT-2480 from borehole GT-2 in the Jemez granodiorite at a depth of 750 m. Dr. Kapusta separated zircons from the core sample using heavy liquids and magnetic separation. He picked three crystals from the zircon concentrate for analysis. Table A1 shows his results and notes.

Table A1. U-Pb analysis of three zircons from the Jemez granodiorite.

#	Mass (μg) (a)	Concentrations			Ratios			
		U (ppm)	Pb (ppm)	Pb(com.) (pg) (b)	$\frac{^{206}Pb}{^{204}Pb}$ (c)	$\frac{^{208}Pb}{^{206}Pb}$ (d)	$\frac{^{206}Pb}{^{238}U}$ (e)	Error (2σ%)
z1	0.8	612	106.1	13.6	241.2	0.633	0.102828	.50
z2	1.0	218	59.6	1.4	2365.1	0.253	0.236433	.23
z3	1.7	324	62.7	1.7	3503.6	0.218	0.172059	.11

#	Ratios				Ages			
	$\frac{^{207}Pb}{^{235}U}$ (e)	Error (2σ %)	$\frac{^{207}Pb}{^{206}Pb}$ (e)	Error (2σ %)	$\frac{^{206}Pb}{^{238}U}$	$\frac{^{207}Pb}{^{235}U}$	$\frac{^{207}Pb}{^{206}Pb}$	Correlation Coefficient
z1	1.2744	.56	0.08989	.23	631.0	834.4	1423.2	0.912
z2	2.9535	.26	0.09060	.12	1368.1	1395.7	1438.2	0.887
z3	2.1456	.13	0.09044	.07	1023.4	1163.6	1434.9	0.828

Notes:
(a) Sample weights are estimated by using a video monitor and are known to within 40%.
(b) Total common-Pb in analyses
(c) Measured ratio corrected for spike and fractionation only.
(d) Radiogenic Pb.
(e) Corrected for fractionation, spike, blank, and initial common Pb.
Mass fractionation correction of 0.15%/amu±0.04%/amu (atomic mass unit) was applied to single-collector Daly analyses and 0.12%/amu±0.04% for dynamic Faraday-Daly analyses. Total procedural blank less than 0.6 pg for Pb and less than 0.1 pg for U. Blank isotopic composition: $^{206}Pb/^{204}Pb$ = 19.10±0.1, $^{207}Pb/^{204}Pb$ = 15.71±0.1, $^{208}Pb/^{204}Pb$ = 38.65±0.1. Age calculations are based on the decay constants of *Steiger and Jäger* [1977]. Common-Pb corrections were calculated by using the model of *Stacey and Kramers* [1975] and the interpreted age of the sample. The upper intercept of the concordia plot of the $^{206}Pb/^{238}U$ and $^{207}Pb/^{238}U$ data was 1439.3 Ma±1.8 Ma. (The published Los Alamos radioisotope date for zircons from a different depth, 2900 meters, was 1500±20 Ma [*Zartman*, 1979].)

Appendix B: Diffusion Rates in Biotite

Following are two reports by our diffusion experimenter (with our comments in brackets) on his measurements of He diffusion in biotite from two locations. As far as we know, these are the only He-in-biotite diffusion data that have been reported. The first sample, BT-1B, was from the Beartooth amphibolite near Yellowstone National Park. The second sample, GT-2, was from the Jemez granodiorite, borehole GT-2, from a depth of 750 m. The geology laboratory at the Institute for Creation Research extracted the biotite from both rock samples by crushing, density separation with heavy liquids, and magnetic separation. The experimenter sieved both samples to get flakes between 75 and 100 μm in diameter. Taking half of the average diameter to get an effective radius of 44 μm, we plotted the resulting diffusion coefficients for the GT-2 sample in Figure 9. We plotted the muscovite data in Figure 9 using the effective radius recommended in the report [*Lippolt and Weigel*, 1988], 130 μm.

Results of He Diffusion on Zodiac Biotite, BT-1B
(Beartooth Amphibolite) October 18, 2000

Experiment:

Approximately 10 mg of biotite BT-1B, sieved to be between 75 and 100 μm, was subjected to step heating. Steps ranged in temperature from 50°C to 500°C in 50°C increments, with an estimated uncertainty on T of < 3°C. Durations ranged from 6 to 60 minutes, with longer durations at lower temperatures; uncertainty on time is < 1% for all steps. After the ten steps the partially degassed biotite was fused to establish the total amount of He in the sample. Helium was measured by isotope dilution quadrupole mass spectrometry, with an estimated precision of 2%. Helium diffusion coefficients were computed using the equations of *Fechtig and Kalbitzer* [1966] assuming spherical geometry.

Data:

Table B1. Diffusion of He from biotite sample BT-1B

Step	Temperature °C	Minutes	Cumulative Fraction	ln e (D/a^2)
1	50	61	3.45E-06	-35.80
2	100	61	1.16E-04	-28.76
3	150	61	1.37E-03	-23.83
4	200	61	6.34E-03	-20.81
5	250	30	1.76E-02	-18.15
6	300	30	5.33E-02	-15.88
7	350	16	1.02E-02	-14.11
8	400	16	2.11E-01	-12.54
9	450	10	3.38E-01	-11.25
10	500	6	4.74E-01	-10.11
Remainder Fusion			5.26E-01	
Total			1.00000	

[In a later addendum to this report, the experimenter told us that the total amount of He liberated was about $0.13 \times 10^{-9}\,cm^3$ (at STP) per µg of biotite.]

Interpretation:

Helium diffusion from this biotite defines a remarkably linear Arrhenius profile, fully consistent with thermally activated volume diffusion from this mineral. The first two data points lie slightly below the array; this is a common feature of He release during step heating of minerals and has been attributed to "edge effects" on the He concentration profile [*Fechtig and Kalbitzer*, 1966; *Farley*, 2000]. Ignoring those two data points, the activation energy and diffusivity at infinite T based on these data are 25.7 kcal/mol and 752 [cm²/sec] respectively. At a cooling rate of 10°C/Ma, these parameters correspond to a closure temperature of 39°C.

[After this the experimenter added a "Recommendations" section wherein he discussed the possibility of vacuum breakdown of the biotite at high temperatures, the relevant effective radius for biotite (probably half the sieved flake diameter), and the source of He in the biotite (probably U and Th in zircons that had been in the flakes before separation). We decided none of these questions were important enough to investigate in detail for now, since this sample was not from a site we were interested in at the time. It merely happened to be on hand at the Institute for Creation Research geology laboratory, making it ideal for an initial run to look for possible difficulties in experimental technique.]

Results of He Diffusion Experiment on Zodiac Biotite, GT2 [Jemez Granodiorite] March 24, 2001

Experiment:
   Approximately 10 mg of biotite GT-2, sieved to be between 75 and 100 μm, was subjected to step heating. Steps ranged in temperature from 50°C to 500°C in 50°C increments, with an estimated uncertainty on T of <3°C. Durations ranged from seven to 132 minutes, with longer durations at lower temperatures; uncertainty on time is <1% for all steps. After eleven steps of increasing T, the sample was brought back to lower temperature, and then heated in six more T-increasing steps. After the seventeen steps the partially degassed biotite was fused to establish the total amount of He in the sample. Helium was measured by isotope dilution quadrupole mass spectrometry, with an estimated precision of 2% (steps 12 and 13 are much more uncertain owing to low gas yield). Helium diffusion coefficients were computed using the equations of *Fechtig and Kalbitzer* [1966] assuming spherical geometry.

Data:
   See Table B2. [In a later addendum to this report, the experimenter told us that the total amount of He liberated was about $0.32 \times 10^{-9}\,\mathrm{cm^3}$ (at STP) per μg of biotite.]

Interpretation:
   Helium diffusion in this sample follows a rather strange pattern, with a noticeable curve at intermediate temperatures. I have no obvious explanation for this phenomenon. Because biotite BT-1B did not show this curve, I doubt it is vacuum breakdown. I ran more steps, with a

Table B2. Diffusion of He from biotite sample GT-2.

Step	Temperature °C	Minutes	Cumulative Fraction	ln e (D/a^2)
1	50	61	1.61E-05	-32.72
2	50	60	2.79E-05	-32.01
3	100	60	2.39E-04	-27.32
4	150	61	1.91E-03	-23.18
5	200	61	4.70E-03	-21.54
6	250	31	6.81E-03	-20.59
7	300	31	9.69E-03	-19.92
8	350	16	1.35E-02	-18.63
9	400	15	2.44E-02	-17.03
10	450	9	4.90E-02	-15.05
11	500	7	1.07E-01	-13.13
12	225	132	1.07E-01	-22.12
13	275	61	1.07E-01	-21.07
14	325	61	1.07E-01	-19.70
15	375	60	1.10E-01	-18.07
16	425	55	1.24E-01	-16.15
17	475	61	1.99E-01	-14.22
Fusion			8.00E-01	
Total			1.00000	

drop in temperature after the 500°C step, to see if the phenomenon is reversible. It appears to be, that is, the curve appears again after the highest *T* step, but the two steps (12, 13) that define this curve had very low gas yield and high uncertainties. It is possible that we are dealing with more than one He source (multiple grain sizes or multiple minerals?). [We think it is likely there were some very small He-bearing zircons still embedded in the biotite flakes, which would be one source. The other source would be the He diffused out of larger zircons no longer attached to the flakes.] This sample had about twice as much He as BT-1B. Note that despite the strange curvature in GT-2, the two biotite samples have generally similar He diffusivity overall.

[The similarity the experimenter remarks upon made us decide that the biotite data were approximately correct. Because these data below 300°C were also about an order of magnitude higher than our creation model, we supposed that zircon might be a more significant hindrance to He loss than biotite, so we turned our attention to zircon. It turned out that our supposition was correct, which makes it less important to have exact biotite data.]

Appendix C: Diffusion Rates in Zircon

Below is a report by the diffusion experimenter (again with our comments in brackets) on his measurements of He diffusion in zircons extracted by Yakov Kapusta from Los Alamos National Laboratories core sample GT-2480 from borehole GT-2 in the Jemez granodiorite at a depth of 750 m. Appendix A gives Kapusta's radioisotopic analysis of three of the zircons. The rest, unsorted by size and labeled as sample YK-511, were forwarded to the experimenter for diffusion analysis. In this chapter we call the sample "2002". In Figure 8 of this chapter, we assumed an effective radius of 30 μm (or length 60 μm) and plotted the points (numbers 15–44) which the experimenter concludes below are the most reliable. These points only go down to 300°C, but the later ones in Table 2 (sample 2003) go down to 175°C.

Report on Sample YK-511
[Jemez Granodiorite, sample 2002] May 14, 2002

We step heated 0.35 mg of zircons from the large vial supplied by Zodiac. We verified that the separate was of high purity and was indeed zircon. The step heat consisted of forty-five steps so as to better define the He release behavior. The first fifteen steps were monotonically increasing in temperature, after that the temperature was cycled up and down several times.

Results:
See Table C1. The first fourteen steps lie on a linear array corresponding to an activation energy of ~46 kcal/mol and a closure temperature of ~183°C assuming a cooling rate of 10°C/Ma. However steps 15–44 [shown in Figure 8 of this chapter], which were cycled from low to high temperature and back, lie on a shallower slope, corresponding to $E_a = 34.5$ kcal/mol and $T_c = 128$°C. This change in slope from the initial

Table C1. Diffusion data for zircon sample YK-511.

Step	Temperature °C	Helium-4 (nnc)	Time (seconds)	Fraction	Cumulative Fraction	D/a^2 (sec^{-1})
1	300	5.337083	3660	0.001259	0.001259	3.78E-11
2	300	1.316732	3660	0.000311	0.001570	2.10E-11
3	300	0.935963	3660	0.000221	0.001791	1.77E-11
4	325	3.719775	3660	0.000878	0.002669	9.34E-11
5	350	7.910044	3660	0.001867	0.004536	3.21E-10
6	375	18.12294	3660	0.004278	0.008815	1.36E-09
7	400	36	3660	0.008498	0.017313	5.29E-09
8	425	73.10049	3660	0.017256	0.034569	2.13E-08
9	450	106.0761	3660	0.025040	0.059609	5.85E-08
10	460	78.89137	1860	0.018623	0.078232	1.27E-07
11	470	96.99925	1860	0.022897	0.101130	2.08E-07
12	480	117.2479	1800	0.027677	0.128807	3.40E-07
13	490	146.8782	1860	0.034671	0.163479	5.38E-07
14	500	171.5538	1800	0.040496	0.203976	8.46E-07
15	453	149.5962	7200	0.035313	0.239290	2.31E-07
16	445	66.45767	7260	0.015687	0.254978	1.16E-07
17	400	9.589814	6840	0.002263	0.257241	1.86E-08
18	420	10.64711	3600	0.002513	0.259755	3.98E-08
19	440	23.19366	3660	0.005475	0.265230	8.69E-08
20	460	52.3035	3660	0.012346	0.277577	2.05E-07
21	480	102.7062	3660	0.024244	0.301821	4.38E-07
22	325	0.357828	3660	8.45E-05	0.301906	1.61E-09
23	350	0.718240	3660	0.000170	0.302075	3.23E-09
24	375	1.690889	3660	0.000399	0.302475	7.62E-09
25	400	4.246082	3660	0.001002	0.303477	1.92E-08
26	425	8	3660	0.001888	0.305365	3.64E-08
27	450	21	3660	0.004957	0.310323	9.70E-08
28	460	22.0839	1860	0.005213	0.315536	2.05E-07
29	470	33	1800	0.007789	0.323326	3.26E-07
30	480	45	1860	0.010622	0.333948	4.47E-07
31	490	62.39899	1800	0.014729	0.348678	6.75E-07
32	500	82.65262	1800	0.019510	0.368189	9.59E-07
33	475	120.222	7260	0.028379	0.396569	3.80E-07
34	445	45	7260	0.010622	0.407191	1.53E-07
35	400	5.879406	7260	0.001387	0.408579	2.05E-08
36	300	0.075983	3660	1.79E-05	0.408597	5.26E-10
37	320	0.685076	21660	0.000162	0.408759	8.02E-10
38	340	1.122111	18060	0.000265	0.409024	1.58E-09
39	360	1.986425	14460	0.000469	0.409493	3.49E-09
40	380	3.413768	10860	0.000806	0.410299	8.01E-09
41	400	5.752365	7260	0.001357	0.411657	2.03E-08
42	420	6.126626	3660	0.001446	0.413103	4.30E-08
43	440	13.67016	3600	0.003226	0.416330	9.85E-08
44	460	30.37821	3660	0.007171	0.423501	2.19E-07

run-up to the main body of the experiment is occasionally observed and attributed to either:

(1) A rounded He concentration profile in the zircons, such that the initial He release is anomalously retarded. In other words, the He concentration profile is shallower than the computational model used to estimate diffusivities assumes. This effect goes away as the experiment proceeds and the effects of the initial concentration profile become less significant. This rounding could be due to slow cooling or possibly to recent reheating.

(2) The change in slope might be due to changes in the zircons during the heating experiment. For example, it is possible that annealing of radiation damage has occurred. This sample has a very high He yield (540 nmol/g) so radiation damage is likely. However the zircons were only marginally within the window where radiation damage is thought to anneal in zircons, so this hypothesis is deemed less likely.

Consideration of geologic history and/or further experiments are necessary to firmly distinguish between these possibilities.

Conclusion:

The most reasonable conclusion from the data is that the main body of the experiment, steps 15–44, yields the best estimate of the closure temperature, about 130°C. This is somewhat cooler than we have observed before in zircons though the database is not large. Radiation damage may be important in the He release kinetics from this He-rich sample.

[End of report by diffusion experimenter.]

Appendix D: Effects of the Interface and of Model Variations

Recently a critic sought very hard to find loopholes in our arguments. While his critique is unpublished and none of his points had any significant impact on our conclusions, it is worthwhile to review the specifics of his critique and answer them here. The critic felt a crucial issue was the possibility that the interface between zircon and biotite might slow or stop He diffusion because of He having different *chemical potentials* or *solubilities* in those two minerals, or because of *interface resistance* between them due to other causes. In the next three sections we will explain those terms and quantify their effects.

D.1 Differences in Chemical Potential

A diffusion theorist [*Manning*, 1968, section 5-3, p. 180, equation 5-36] expresses the *chemical potential*, μ, for He atoms constituting a fraction N of all the atoms in a crystal at temperature T as the sum of two parts:

$$\mu = kT \ln N + \mu'$$ (D1)

where k is the Boltzmann constant. The first term on the right, the "entropy of mixing," contains no information related to the forces between atoms. The second term, μ', is the one we are interested in. It is the contribution from all other factors, particularly the interaction energy between He and the other atoms of the crystal.

The same theorist [*Manning*, 1968, section 5-3, p. 180, equations 5-37 and 5-39] then expresses the flux J of He atoms in the x-direction through a region with diffusivity D as:

$$J = -D \frac{\partial C}{\partial x} - \frac{DC}{kT} \frac{\partial \mu'}{\partial x}$$ (D2)

The first term on the right represents ordinary diffusion. It is the second term that represents an additional flux due to a driving force, the gradient of μ'. This force originates in whatever chemical attraction the He atom might have for the atoms of the crystal in which it resides. Inside the crystal, these forces average to zero, but at the interface with another crystal, there may be a jump in μ'. If a He atom were to have greater chemical attraction for the atoms of zircon than for the atoms of biotite, that would result in a force at the interface hindering its outward motion into the biotite. The question we need to address is, "Just how great is the effect?"

Because He is one of the noble gases, we might suspect that it would have very little chemical attraction for any other atoms. In fact, He is the least chemically active of all the noble gases [*Holloway*, 1968,

p. 45, Table 2.1]. Nevertheless it does exhibit a faint attraction for other atoms. Theory and experiments [*Wilson et al.*, 1988, p. 936, Table XI] show that He atoms adhere very slightly to the surfaces of alkali halide crystals, with interaction potentials on the order of a few hundred calories per mole of He. The largest estimated potential is 293.4 cal/mol, at the "saddle point" between the Na and F ions at the surface of NaF. The smallest potential listed is beside a Cl ion at the surface of NaCl, 111.7 cal/mol.

The difference of those potentials provides an estimate of the difference of μ' at an interface between NaF and NaCl: 181.7 cal/mol, or 0.00788 eV per He atom. Because noble gases have a greater chemical affinity for halides [*Holloway*, 1968, p. 89] than for most other ions, the above number is almost certainly greater than the corresponding number for the silicate minerals we are considering. So at the interface between zircon and biotite, we can take the following value as a generous upper bound on the magnitude (absolute value) of the difference in μ':

$$\left|\Delta\mu'\right| < 0.0079 \,\text{eV/atom} \tag{D3}$$

Now we need to quantify the effect of that difference on the flux of He atoms in equation (D2). As we did in Sections 7 and 8, we assume for simplicity that the diffusivity D is the same for biotite as for zircon, and therefore constant across the interface. Because the observed value of C in the biotite is hundreds of times smaller than in the zircon (this chapter, Section 10), the magnitude of the change in concentration, ΔC, across the interface is nearly equal to the concentration C in the zircon:

$$\left|\Delta C\right| \approx C \tag{D4}$$

Assuming that the changes ΔC and $\Delta\mu'$ both occur within roughly the same small distance δx, the width of the interface, the He flux J in equation (D2) becomes:

$$J \approx -D\frac{\Delta C}{\delta x} - D\frac{\Delta C}{\delta x}\frac{\Delta\mu'}{kT} \tag{D5}$$

To make this mechanism a viable possibility for rescuing the uniformitarian scenario, the second term on the right-hand side must be: (1) of opposite sign to the first ($\Delta\mu'$ must be negative, meaning He is more attracted to zircon than biotite), and (2) large enough to reduce J to a level about 100,000 times lower than what the first term alone would give. That could reduce the He flow enough to let the zircon retain the He for 1.5 billion years. In the coolest sample we analyzed, at 100°C, the average thermal energy kT of the atoms was 0.0321 eV. Then $|\Delta\mu'/kT|$ would be less than 0.246 for that sample, and even smaller for the hotter samples. That makes the magnitude of the second term less than 25% of that of the first term for all the samples we analyzed. However, our upper bound on the value of $\Delta\mu'$ based on the chemical affinity of He with alkali halides is likely at least an order of magnitude larger than the actual value. So a magnitude of the second term less than 2.5% of the first term is probably more realistic. The second term obviously does not provide the large reduction of He flow the uniformitarian scenario requires.

However, an even more basic consideration shows our measurement procedures have already accounted for such differences. We note that the magnitude of $\Delta\mu'$ is several times greater for a zircon-vacuum interface than for a zircon-biotite interface. That is, the attraction of a He atom for the biotite it is entering partly cancels its attraction for the zircon it is leaving. But our experimenter measured the diffusivities of zircons in a *vacuum*. So the zircon diffusivities we report in Table 2 already include the effect of a *stronger* interface reflection than would exist for the zircons in their natural biotite setting. So however strong or weak the "chemical potential" interface effect may be, our measured diffusivities already account for it in a way that is generous to the uniformitarian model.

D.2 Solubility

Solubility in this context corresponds to the maximum number of He atoms one gram of crystal can absorb per bar of pressure [*Weast*, 1986, p. 101]. The critic used the term as a measure of the difficulty with which a He atom could enter biotite. As a hypothetical example, if all the spaces between atoms in biotite were much smaller than the diameter of a He atom, then He could never enter the crystal, so He would be completely insoluble in biotite. If an α-decaying nucleus inside the biotite were to generate a He atom therein, then the atom could distort the lattice and push its way out. The crystal would have a small but non-zero He diffusivity and zero solubility.

However, real minerals have non-zero solubilities. The solubilities of He in obsidian and basaltic glass between 200° and 300°C, for example, are on the order of 50 nmol/g per bar [*Jambon and Shelby*, 1980, Figure 2c] and on the same order in other minerals [*Broadhurst et al.*, 1992]. The solubility of He in biotite has not been measured (we were the first to measure even diffusivity for that pair of substances), so we must find a way to estimate its effect in this case.

One way is to consider the interaction potential part μ' of the chemical potential we mentioned in the previous section. For a He atom near the surface of a crystal, the gradient of the potential is negative, making the force attractive. But the force can become repulsive for a He atom entering a tightly packed crystal. For example, imagine that a He atom has to come very close to an O atom. If their nuclei are closer together than 2.94 Å (1 Å = 1 angstrom = 1×10^{-8} cm ≈ diameter of a neutral H atom), the force between the two atoms is repulsive [*Kar and Chakravarty*, 2001, Table I, σ_{os} column and gradient of their equation 2].

However the space between silicate sheets in biotite is much larger than that [*Deer et al.*, 1962, Vol. 3, pp. 1–3, 55; *Dahl*, 1996, Figure 1 and Table 4]. The large spacing is the reason the diffusivity of He in biotite (section 5, Figure 9) is about ten times higher than in zircon, which has tighter spacing [*Deer et al.*, 1962, Vol. 1, pp. 59–68]. The relative spacings and diffusivities imply the solubility of He in biotite is greater than in zircon, so the force related to solubility, included in the gradient of μ', would tend to push He atoms out of zircon and into biotite. Hence their respective solubilities would not hinder He outflow from the zircon but rather enhance it.

D.3 Interface Resistance

Our critic also postulated some type of *interface resistance* arising from special distortion of the crystalline lattices at the interface between zircon and biotite. We can model such hypothetical interface resistance [*Crank*, 1975, p. 40, section 3.4.1] as a very thin layer of very low diffusivity between the zircon and biotite. The concentration of He would drop rapidly across the layer, approximating a discontinuous change of concentration between zircon and biotite. Such a layer might consist of physically or chemically altered zircon or biotite. Typical interface layers, such as oxides on metals, range from a few dozen angstroms to hundreds of angstroms in thickness.

Let us estimate how low the diffusivity D of the interface would have to be in order to retain the He in the zircon for 1.5 billion years. Since D is supposed to be much lower than the diffusivities of both zircon and biotite, we can approximate the situation as a hollow sphere with a wall of diffusivity D having an inner radius a and outer radius b. A source (representing nuclear decay) inside the sphere generates He at a steady rate q_0, and the He diffuses through the wall out into a vacuum outside the sphere. Textbooks show [*Carslaw and Jaeger*, 1959, section 9.2, p. 231, equation (7), $Q_0 \rightarrow q_0$, $K \rightarrow D$, $v_1 \rightarrow C$, $v_2 \rightarrow 0$] that the steady-state He outflow q_0 is

$$q_0 = 4\pi DC \frac{ab}{b-a} \qquad (D6)$$

where C is the steady-state concentration of He inside the sphere. Taking the wall thickness δ ($b=a+\delta$) to be small compared to a ($\delta \ll a$), integrating q_0 for time t, and C over the sphere volume (Section 7, equation 16) gives us the ratio of He retained, Q, to total He generated, Q_0:

$$\frac{Q}{Q_0} \approx \frac{a\,\delta}{3D\,t} \qquad (D7)$$

Turning this around gives us the interface diffusivity D required to retain a fraction Q/Q_0 of He for time t in a zircon of effective radius a

surrounded by an interface of thickness δ:

$$D \approx \frac{a\,\delta}{3(Q/Q_0)\,t} \qquad (D8)$$

For example, with a (large) interface thickness of 300 Å, $a = 30\,\mu m$, and a time of 1.5 billion years, the 17% retention of sample 3 requires an interface diffusivity of

$$D \approx 3.8 \times 10^{-25}\,cm^2/sec \qquad (D9)$$

This is over *one billion times lower* than the diffusivities we measured in biotite (Section 5, Figure 9) and zircon (Section 5, Figure 8) at the same temperature, 197°C. To see whether this is an achievable value or not, let us examine an example the critic gave for physical alteration of the minerals at the zircon-biotite interface.

The critic suggested that when biotite crystallizes around a zircon, it possibly forms with its silicate sheets (along which are the cleavage planes) everywhere parallel to the surface of the zircon, so that the biotite wraps up the zircon like layers of cellophane. But in the hundreds of thousands of zircon-containing biotite flakes that we ourselves have observed under the microscope [*Snelling and Armitage*, 2003; *Snelling et al.*, 2003; *Snelling*, 2005a], the silicate sheets remain parallel all the way to the edge of the zircon crystal and do not wrap around the included zircons. A Los Alamos report has a photo of a radiohalo in biotite from borehole GT-2 showing the biotite cleavage staying parallel to itself, running right up against the zircon, and not becoming parallel to the zircon surface [*Laughlin and Eddy*, 1977, Figure 6, p. 18]. There is simply no observational support for the critic's hypothesis that layers of biotite totally envelop an included zircon.

However, for the sake of having a specific illustration of interface resistance, let us indulge the critic and imagine that a few dozen of the biotite layers closest to the zircon wrap around it, having a total interface thickness of 300 Å. We will even imagine that there are no openings in the biotite wrapping at the edges and corners of the zircon faces. In that case, diffusion in the interface would have to take place in the harder direction, perpendicular to the silicate sheets rather than parallel to them.

Let us estimate the diffusivity in that harder direction. Measurements show that in biotite, "Ar diffusion is ~500 times faster parallel to the silicate sheets than perpendicular to the silicate sheets" [*Onstott et al.*, 1991, section 7, p. 166]. Because a He atom has a smaller diameter, 2.28 Å, than an Ar atom, 3.35 Å [*Kar and Chakravarty*, 2001, Table I; σ_{ss} column], then for He there should not be as great a difference between "parallel" diffusivity $D_{||}$ and "perpendicular" diffusivity $D_{\perp}$. So for He in biotite, the ratio $D_{||}/D_{\perp}$ should be less than 500. Our measurements for He in biotite (Section 5, Figure 9) gave, for example, $D_{||} = 8.6 \times 10^{-15}$ cm²/sec at 200°C. Dividing that diffusivity by 500 gives us a lower bound on the diffusivity in the difficult direction:

$$D_{\perp} > 1.7 \times 10^{-17} \text{cm}^2/\text{sec} \qquad (D10)$$

That is over *40 million times greater* than the maximum diffusivity, equation (D9), that a 300 Å interface could have and still retain the He for 1.5 Ga. Hence such a hypothetical mechanism fails to account for the high He retention we document. Moreover, as we have already indicated, there is no observational support for the sort of interface crystallographic structure our critic speculates might exist.

D.4 Effects of Model Assumptions

The critic also explored the effects of several changes in the assumptions of our models:
(1) inserting a large interface resistance,
(2) increasing the Creation model D for biotite to infinity,
(3) decreasing the uniformitarian model D for biotite from infinity down to that of zircon,
(4) accounting for anisotropy of biotite and zircon, and
(5) changing the effective radius a from our early value of 22 μm [*Humphreys*, 2000, p. 347] to our more recent and more appropriate value of 30 μm (Section 7, after equation 9).
We have discussed change (1) in the preceding section, showing that

it is unrealistic. Change (2) increases the He loss rate from the zircons by a factor of six, making it less realistic than our assumption, which had a worst-case effect of 30% (Section 7, after equation 9). Change (3) decreases the loss rate from zircons by a factor of six, but we think it is unrealistic for uniformitarians to demand an extremely low value of D for the biotite as well as the zircon.

Regarding mineral anisotropies (4), we point out two things:

- switching from sphere to cylinder geometry (roughly approximating anisotropy effects) for the most important mineral (zircon) would alter the results by less than a factor of two, and
- even a factor-of-ten reduction in the modeled diffusivity of the surrounding mineral (biotite) would change our results by less than 30% (Section 7, after equation 9). Thus, accounting for biotite anisotropy would affect our results by much less than 30%.

As for zircon, anisotropy in it is probably just as negligible as it is in many other similarly shaped crystals, such as quartz. Both our experimenter and other diffusion experts have not assigned a high priority to investigating that possibility.

Change (5), the increase in effective radius a required by our better knowledge of zircons, by itself would have increased the model-required D's by a factor of about two. But our better knowledge also required another model change, from a "bubble" in biotite to a solid in biotite. This second change reduced the Ds by about a factor of two. Because the two effects nearly cancelled each other out, the *net* change in predicted D was less than 0.5%. We explained these things in our Fifth International Conference on Creationism paper [*Humphreys et al.*, 2003a, section 6], but perhaps not clearly enough.

The critic acknowledged that changes (2–5) would not come anywhere close to eliminating the 100,000-fold discrepancy between our data and any reasonable uniformitarian scenario. But he asserted that the several-fold sensitivity to changes in assumptions means that the close agreement between the Creation model and the data was merely accidental. That may be a possibility, but it may also mean we exercised good theoretical judgment in choosing the simplifying assumptions for our prediction.

D.5 Closing Criticisms

Finally, the critic proposed we postpone publication until (a) further theoretical and experimental investigations would close all alleged loopholes, and (b) until we have much more data supporting our case from boreholes all over the world. We disagree with him. On point (a), detractors can allege loopholes eternally, and we think we have addressed all the so-far-alleged loopholes well enough to place the burden of proof on the detractors.

On point (b), the critic was not clear as to what he meant. If he wanted diffusion rate data on zircons from more sites, it is doubtful that such data would be much different than what we measured. Our zircon data give essentially the same intrinsic parameters, E_0 and D_0, as those of several other experimenters (Section 5, Figure 8). As for the defect parameters, E_1 and D_1, there is no reason to expect them to generally give defect lines more than one or perhaps two orders of magnitude different from ours. That is because the radiation levels in our zircons are fairly typical (in contrast to those of Magomedov, see our Section 4). Defect lines for zircons at future sites would have to be more than five orders of magnitude lower than ours in order to have even a chance of rescuing the uniformitarian scenarios.

Possibly the critic meant his point (b) to imply that the high He retentions in the Jemez granodiorite could be unusual, so we would need to do similar studies on a large amount of sites to assure ourselves that high retentions are normal. Of course it would be good to do more such studies, but we feel that the data in this chapter are so well established that it would be wrong to withhold them for the several years required for other site studies. In fact, our data here may stimulate more such studies.

As an encouragement to creationists considering such work, we offer the following opinion: *high He retentions are probably the rule*, not the exception. Otherwise the large amount of geoscience literature reporting great (U-Th)/He chronometry ages (Section 9) would not exist. That is because the method essentially divides the amount of He retained by today's nuclear decay rate, so large retentions of He are necessary to get great ages. If their zircons had lost most of their He by diffusion, their dates would be in great disarray, and usually rather young. Because their zircons are often of similar size as ours [*Reiners*, 2002], the He loss rates will be similarly fast. That suggests young diffusion ages such as ours will turn out to be common.

I would like to take this opportunity to thank Roger Lenard, a physicist at Sandia National Laboratories in Albuquerque, New Mexico, for his expert advice on chemical thermodynamics, which helped me to prepare Sections D2 and D3 above.

Endnotes

i   Uniformitarianism is the conscious or unconscious assumption that "all continues just as it was from the beginning" [2 Peter 3:4], omitting the possibility of any large-scale physical interventions by God into the natural realm. Often scientists do this because, whether they are aware of it or not, they have accepted "methodological naturalism," the incorrect teaching that scientists must ignore scientific evidence for non-natural phenomena. The teaching is incorrect because such an *a priori* naturalism would lead to incorrect interpretations of the data if God has in fact intervened in the natural world in a way that leaves physical evidence of the intervention. Many uniformitarians interpret scientific data to support their preconception of cosmic and biological evolution occurring during supposed billions of years. Such interpretations misunderstand clear observational data all around us [*Humphreys*, 2000, p. 339]. The Bible predicted [2 Peter 3:5–6] that a time would come when many thinkers would ignore "elephant in the living room" evidence for a recent Creation and a worldwide catastrophic Flood.

ii   Note that the large retentions are not what uniformitarian geoscientists mean by "excess He" [*Baxter*, 2003]. In the context of these zircons, "excess" He would correspond to retentions *greater than 100%* of the amount nuclear decay could produce in 1.5 Ga. We are not claiming such "excess" He at all. The uniformitarian method of "He dating," called *(U-Th)/He chronometry* [*Reiners*, 2002] is entirely different from the He *diffusion* dating we are employing here. (See Endnote iv.) (U-Th)/He chronometry would not call attention to the large He *retentions* we are concerned with (in fact, it depends upon large retentions, Appendix D, section D4), so it may turn out that sites like borehole GT-2 are common throughout the world.

iii   Half the cited 2σ experimental reproducibility error of 6% in D/a^2 gives us a 1σ error of $\pm 3\%$. I estimate the 1σ error in the average value of a^2 for these size-selected zircons is less than $\pm 10\%$. A possible shape factor error [*Fechtig and Kalbitzer*, 1966, p.72, Section 2.4] for the shape distribution in our Figure 1 could add a 1σ error in a^2 of $\pm 25\%$. (I measured the length/width ratio of each zircon in Figure 1 and used the resulting ratios in this analysis.) That error is systematic, shifting the whole $D(T)$ curve up or down by the same factor. Also, it cancels itself out in comparisons with the predictions based on the same value of a^2 for crystals of the same size from the same site. But here I will regard it as random. Taking the square root of the sum of the squares of those errors gives us 27.0%, which I round upward to 30%. So in Table 2, multiplying D/a^2 in column 6 by a^2 gives values of the diffusivity D in column 7 whose 1σ error I estimate as $\pm 30\%$.

iv   Our diffusion dating method in Section 9 differs entirely from the "He dating" of (U-Th)/He chronometry [*Reiners*, 2002]. Very crudely, the difference is this: (U-Th)/He chronometry divides the number of He atoms *in* a crystal by *nuclear* decay rate. Diffusion dating divides the number of He atoms *lost* from the crystal by the *diffusion* rate. Some practitioners of (U-Th)/He chronometry, in their unpublished comments about our work, have not yet understood this distinction.

v   Because b is nominal and ultimately cancels itself out of the analysis (see paragraph under equation (7) in Section 7), the 1σ error bounds on D/b^2 in equation (17) are the same as those of D/a^2, $\pm 3\%$, as Endnote iii above shows. The error for extrapolation between data points with the curve fit is smaller than that. The effects of those errors are small compared to the effect of the (assumed 1σ) $\pm30\%$ error in Q/Q_0 on x in Table 3 and equation (17). The resulting bounds on x (and D) in samples 2–4 of Table 3 (the age calculation does not use sample 1 and the error in sample 5 is indeterminate) average out to $\pm32\%$. That correlates well with the error of $\pm(2000$ years/6000 years$) = \pm33\%$ from the statistics of the individual age calculations in Table 5.

vi The probability that a single data point could be separated by more than 25 standard deviations on a given side away from the mean of the normal distribution governing the data is less than 6×10^{-8} [Abramowitz and Stegun, 1967, p.933, equation (26.2.25), using $1 - P_4(x)$ and $x = 25$].

References

Abramowitz, M., and I.A. Stegun, *Handbook of Mathematical Functions*, sixth printing, National Bureau of Standards, Washington, DC, 1967.

Armitage, M.H., Helium retention in deep-core zircons, *American Laboratory*, *36*(14), 17–20, 2004.

Baumgardner, J.R., Distribution of radioactive isotopes in the earth, in *Radioisotopes and the Age of the Earth: A Young-Earth Creationist Research Initiative*, edited by L. Vardiman, A.A. Snelling, and E.F. Chaffin, pp.49–94, Institute for Creation Research, El Cajon, California, and Creation Research Society, St. Joseph, Missouri, 2000.

Baxter, E.F., Quantification of the factors controlling the presence of excess ^{40}Ar or ^{4}He, *Earth and Planetary Science Letters*, *216*, 619–634, 2003.

Bell, R.P., A problem of heat conduction with spherical symmetry, *Proceedings of the Physical Society* (London), *57*, 45–48,1945.

Broadhurst, C.L., M.J. Drake, B.E. Hagee, and T.J. Bernatowicz, Solubility and partitioning of Ne, Ar, Kr, and Xe in minerals and synthetic basaltic melts, *Geochimica et Cosmochimica Acta*, *56*, 709–723, 1992.

Carslaw, H.S., and J.C. Jaeger, *Conduction of Heat in Solids*, second edition, Clarendon Press, Oxford, 1959.

Chaffin, E.F., Theoretical mechanisms of accelerated nuclear decay, in *Radioisotopes and the Age of the Earth: A Young-Earth Creationist Research Initiative*, edited by L. Vardiman, A.A. Snelling, and E.F.

Chaffin, pp. 305–331, Institute for Creation Research, El Cajon, California, and Creation Research Society, St. Joseph, Missouri, 2000.

Chaffin, E. F., Accelerated decay: theoretical models, in *Proceedings of the Fifth International Conference on Creationism*, edited by R. L. Ivey, Jr., pp. 3–15, Creation Science Fellowship, Pittsburgh, Pennsylvania, 2003. See *http://www.icr.org/research/icc03/pdf/RATE_ICC_Chaffin.pdf*.

Cooperstock, F. I., V. Faraoni, and D. N. Vollick, The influence of the cosmological expansion on local systems, *Astrophysical Journal*, *503*, 61–66, 1998.

Crank, J., *The Mathematics of Diffusion*, second edition, Oxford University Press, Oxford, 1975.

Dahl, P. S., The crystal-chemical basis for Ar retention in micas: inferences from interlayer partitioning and implications for geochronology, *Contributions to Mineral Petrology*, *123*, 22–39, 1996.

Deer, W. A., R. A. Howe, and M. A. Zussman, *Rock-Forming Minerals,* vol. I, *Ortho- and Ring Silicates*, vol. III, *Sheet Silicates*, Longmans, Green, and Company, London, 1962.

Dodson, M. H., Closure temperature in cooling geochronological and petrological systems, *Contributions to Mineralogy and Petrology*, *40*, 259–274, 1973.

Farley, K. A., Helium diffusion from apatite: general behavior as illustrated by Durango fluorapatite, *Journal of Geophysical Research*, *105*(B2), 2903–2914, 2000.

Farley, K. A., (U-Th)/He dating: techniques, calibrations, and applications, in *Noble Gases in Geochemistry and Cosmochemistry*, edited by D. Porcelli, C. J. Ballentine, and R. Wieler, pp. 819–844, Mineralogical Society of America, Washington, DC, Reviews in Minerology and Geochemistry, vol. 47, 2002.

Farley, K. A., P. W. Reiners, and V. Nenow, An apparatus for high-precision helium diffusion measurements from minerals, *Analytical Chemistry*, *71*(10), 2059–2061, 1999.

Fechtig, H., and S. Kalbitzer, The diffusion of argon in potassium-bearing solids, in *Potassium-Argon Dating*, edited by O. A. Schaeffer and J. Zähringer, pp. 68–107, Springer-Verlag, New York, 1966.

Gentry, R. V., private communication, December 31, 1995.

Gentry, R. V., G. J. Glish, and E. H. McBay, Differential helium retention in zircons: implications for nuclear waste management, *Geophysical Research Letters*, *9*(10), 1129–1130, 1982.

Girifalco, L. A., *Atomic Migration in Crystals*, Blaisdell Publishing Company, New York, pp. 39, 89, 1964.

Harrison, T. M., P. Morgan, and D. D. Blackwell, Constraints on the age of heating at the Fenton Hill site, Valles Caldera, New Mexico, *Journal of Geophysical Research*, *91*(B2), 1899–1908, 1986.

Holloway, J. H., *Noble-Gas Chemistry*, Methuen, London, 1968.

Humphreys, D. R., *Starlight and Time: Solving the Puzzle of Distant Starlight in a Young Universe*, Master Books, Green Forest, Arkansas, 1994.

Humphreys, D. R., Accelerated nuclear decay: a viable hypothesis?, in *Radioisotopes and the Age of the Earth: A Young-Earth Creationist Research Initiative*, edited by L. Vardiman, A. A. Snelling, and E. F. Chaffin, pp. 333–379, Institute for Creation Research, El Cajon, California, and Creation Research Society, St. Joseph, Missouri, 2000.

Humphreys, D. R., Our galaxy is the centre of the universe, 'quantized' red shifts show, *TJ*, *16*(2), 95–104, 2002. See *http://www.answersingenesis. org/home/area/magazines/tj/docs/TJv16n2_CENTRE.pdf*

Humphreys, D. R., S. A. Austin, J. R. Baumgardner, and A. A. Snelling, Helium diffusion rates support accelerated nuclear decay, in *Proceedings of the Fifth International Conference on Creationism*, edited by R. L. Ivey, Jr., pp. 175–195, Creation Science Fellowship, Pittsburgh, Pennsylvania, 2003a. See *http://www.icr.org/research/icc03/pdf/Helium_ICC_7-22-03.pdf*.

Humphreys, D. R., S. A. Austin, J. R. Baumgardner, and A. A. Snelling, Recently measured helium diffusion rate for zircon suggests inconsistency with U-Pb age for Fenton Hill granodiorite, *EOS, Transactions of the American Geophysical Union, 84*(46), Fall Meeting Supplement, Abstract V32C-1047, 2003b. Poster at *http://www.icr.org/research/ AGUHeliumPoster_Humphreys.pdf*.

Humphreys, D. R., S. A. Austin, J. R. Baumgardner, and A. A. Snelling, Helium diffusion age of 6,000 years supports accelerated nuclear decay, *Creation Research Society Quarterly*, *41*(1), 1–16, 2004. See *http://www. creationresearch.org/crsq/articles/41/41_1/Helium_lo_res.pdf*.

Jambon, A., and J. E. Shelby, Helium diffusion and solubility in obsidians and basaltic glass in the range 200–300°C, *Earth and Planetary Science Letters, 51*, 206–214, 1980.

Kar, S., and C. Chakravarty, Diffusional anisotropy of simple sorbates in silicalite, *Journal of Chemical Physics A, 105*, 5785–5793, 2001.

Kolstad, C. D., and T. R. McGetchin, Thermal evolution models for the Valles Caldera with reference to a hot-dry-rock geothermal experiment, *Journal of Volcanology and Geothermal Research, 3*, 197–218, 1978.

Landau, L. D., and E. M. Lifshitz, *The Classical Theory of Fields*, fourth English edition, Pergamon Press, Oxford, 1983.

Laney, R., and A. W. Laughlin, Natural annealing of pleochroic halos in biotite samples from deep drill holes, Fenton Hill, New Mexico, *Geophysical Research Letters, 8*(5), 501–504, 1981.

Laughlin, A. W., and A. C. Eddy, Petrography and geochemistry of Precambrian rocks from GT-2 and EE-1, *Los Alamos Scientific Laboratory Report LA-6930-MS*, 1977.

Lippolt, H. J., and E. Weigel, ^{4}He diffusion in ^{40}Ar-retentive minerals, *Geochimica et Cosmochimica Acta, 52*, 1449–1458, 1988.

Magomedov, Sh. A., Migration of radiogenic products in zircon, *Geokhimiya, 1970*(2), 263–267 (in Russian), 1970. English abstract in *Geochemistry International, 7*(1), 203, 1970. English translation available from D. R. Humphreys.

Manning, J. R., *Diffusion Kinetics for Atoms in Crystals*, Van Nostrand, Princeton, 1968.

Ohanian, H. C., and R. Ruffini, *Gravitation and Spacetime*, second edition, W. W. Norton and Company, New York, 1994.

Onstott, T. C., D. Phillips, and L. Pringle-Goodell, Laser microprobe measurement of chlorine and argon zonation in biotite, *Chemical Geology, 90*, 145–168, 1991.

Reiners, P. W., (U-Th)/He chronometry experiences a renaissance, *EOS, Transactions of the American Geophysical Union, 83*(3):21, 26–27, 2002.

Reiners, P. W., K. A. Farley, and H. J. Hickes, He diffusion and (U-Th)/He thermochronometry of zircon: initial results from Fish Canyon Tuff and Gold Butte, Nevada, *Tectonophysics, 349*(1–4), 297–308, 2002.

Reiners, P. W., T. L. Spell, S. Nicolescu, and K. A. Zanetti, Zircon (U-Th)/He thermochronometry: He diffusion and comparisons with ^{40}Ar/^{39}Ar dating,

Geochimica et Cosmochimica Acta, 68(8), 1857–1887, 2004.

Rindler, W., *Relativity: Special, General, and Cosmological*, Oxford University Press, Oxford, 2001.

Robertson, H. P., and T. W. Noonan, *Relativity and Cosmology*, W. B. Saunders Company, Philadelphia, 1968.

Ross, H. N., *Reasons to Believe* radio broadcast, September 18, 6 to 8 p.m. Pacific time, 2003. Moderator: Krista Bontrager. Studio participants: Hugh Ross, Fazale Rana, and Marge Harmon. Telephone participant: Roger Wiens. Broadcast archive web link and response at *http://www.icr.org/headlines/rate-hughross.html* .

Sasada, M., Fluid inclusion evidence for recent temperature increases at Fenton Hill hot dry rock test site west of the Valles Caldera, New Mexico, U. S. A., *Journal of Volcanology and Geothermal Research, 36*, 257–266, 1989.

Snelling, A. A., Radiohalos in granites: evidence for accelerated nuclear decay, in *Radioisotopes and the Age of the Earth: Results of a Young-Earth Creationist Initiative*, edited by L. Vardiman, A. A. Snelling, and E. F. Chaffin, pp. 101–207, Institute for Creation Research, El Cajon, California, and Creation Research Society, Chino Valley, Arizona, 2005a.

Snelling, A. A., Fission tracks in zircons: evidence for abundant nuclear decay, in *Radioisotopes and the Age of the Earth: Results of a Young-Earth Creationist Initiative*, edited by L. Vardiman, A. A. Snelling, and E. F. Chaffin, pp. 209–324, Institute for Creation Research, El Cajon, California, and Creation Research Society, Chino Valley, Arizona, 2005b.

Snelling, A. A., and M. H. Armitage, Radiohalos—a tale of three granitic plutons, in *Proceedings of the Fifth International Conference on Creationism*, edited by R. L. Ivey, Jr., pp. 243–267, Creation Science Fellowship, Pittsburgh, Pennsylvania, 2003. See *http://www.icr.org/research/icc03/pdf/ICCRADIOHALOS-AASandMA.pdf* .

Snelling, A. A., J. R. Baumgardner, and L. Vardiman, Abundant Po radiohalos in Phanerozoic granites and timescale implications for their formation, *EOS, Transactions of the American Geophysical Union, 84*(46), Fall Meeting Supplement, Abstract V32C-1046, 2003. Poster at *http://www.icr.org/research/AGURadiohaloPoster_Snelling.pdf* .

Stacey, J. S., and J. D. Kramers, Approximation of terrestrial lead isotope evolution by a two-stage model, *Earth and Planetary Science Letters*, *26*, 201–221, 1975.

Steiger, R. H., and E. Jäger, Subcommission on geochronology: convention on the use of decay constants in geo- and cosmochronology, *Earth and Planetary Science Letters*, *36*, 359–362, 1977.

Vardiman, L., Introduction, in *Radioisotopes and the Age of the Earth: A Young-Earth Creationist Research Initiative*, edited by L. Vardiman, A. A. Snelling, and E. F. Chaffin, pp. 1–25, Institute for Creation Research, El Cajon, California, and Creation Research Society, St. Joseph, Missouri, 2000.

Weast, R. C. (editor), *Handbook of Chemistry and Physics*, sixty-seventh edition, CRC Press, Boca Raton, Florida, 1986.

Wilson, J. W., J. H. Heinbockel, and R. A. Outlaw, Atomic forces between noble gas atoms, alkali ions, and halogen ions for surface interactions, *Journal of Chemical Physics*, *89*(2), 929–937, 1988.

Wolfram, S., *Mathematica*, second edition, Addison-Wesley, New York, 1991.

Zartman, R. E., Uranium, thorium, and lead isotopic composition of biotite granodiorite (Sample 9527-2b) from LASL Drill Hole GT-2, *Los Alamos Scientific Laboratory Report LA-7923-MS*, 1979.

Chapter 3

Radiohalos in Granites: Evidence for Accelerated Nuclear Decay

Andrew A. Snelling, Ph.D.*

Abstract. The ubiquitous presence of ^{238}U and ^{210}Po, ^{214}Po, and ^{218}Po radiohalos in the same biotite flakes within granitic plutons formed during the Flood falsifies the hypothesis that all granites and Po radiohalos were created, but testifies to the simultaneous formation of these radiohalos. Thus if the Po radiohalos were formed in just a few days while the fully-formed ^{238}U radiohalos were simultaneously generated by at least 100 million years worth (at today's rates) of radioactive decay, radioisotope decay had to have been accelerated. Therefore, conventional radioisotope dating of rocks based on assuming constancy of decay rates is grossly in error. Accelerated radioisotope decay of ^{238}U in zircons within the biotites rapidly formed the ^{238}U radiohalos and produced large quantities of the short-lived ^{222}Rn and Po isotopes. Hydrothermal fluids released by the cooling granitic magmas then transported those isotopes along the biotites' cleavage planes to deposit the Po isotopes in chemically conducive, adjacent lattice defect sites, on average only 1 mm or less distant. The hydrothermal fluids progressively replenished the supply of Po isotopes to the deposition sites as the Po isotopes decayed to form the Po radiohalos. Because of the annealing of α-tracks above 150°C, all the radiohalos only formed below 150°C. However, the U-decay and hydrothermal fluid transport started while the granitic rocks were crystallizing at higher temperatures. Therefore, the granitic magmas must have cooled rapidly or else the short-lived Po isotopes would have decayed before radiohalos could have formed. It is thus estimated that granitic plutons must have cooled within 6–10 days, and that the various Po radiohalos formed within hours to just a few days. The heat generated

* *Geology Department, Institute for Creation Research, Santee, California*

by accelerated radioisotope decay and tectonic processes during the Flood would have annealed all radiohalos in Precambrian (pre-Flood) granitic rocks at that time, so the few radiohalos now observed in these granitic rocks had to have formed subsequently by secondary hydrothermal fluid transport of ^{222}Rn and Po isotopes in their biotites during the Flood. While convective flows of hydrothermal fluids moved and dissipated heat from granitic plutons in days, that mechanism alone would not seem capable of removing the enormous quantities of heat generated by accelerated radioisotope decay over that brief timescale. Other mechanisms must have operated to allow for the survival of the biotites and their ^{238}U and Po radiohalos. The discovery of plentiful Po radiohalos in metamorphic rocks extends the application of the hydrothermal fluid transport model for Po radiohalo formation to these rocks. This confirms that hydrothermal fluids transformed deeply-buried sedimentary rocks to regional metamorphic complexes, which then had to have cooled within days for the Po radiohalos to have formed. Additionally, the prolific Po radiohalos found in granitic and metamorphic rocks and veins that host metallic ore lodes reflect the passage of the hydrothermal fluids that transported and deposited the metallic ores. This suggests such hydrothermal ore veins formed rapidly, and that Po radiohalos could provide an exploration tool for locating new ore lodes. Thus Po radiohalos provide powerful evidence of many rapid geological processes consistent with both the year-long catastrophic global Biblical Flood, and a young earth.

1. Introduction

Radiohalos (abbreviated from radioactive halos) are minute circular zones of darkening surrounding tiny central mineral inclusions or crystals within some minerals. They are best observed in certain minerals in thin microscope sections of rocks, notably in the black mica, biotite, where the tiny inclusions (or radiocenters) are usually zircon crystals. The significance of radiohalos is due to them being a physical, integral historical record of the decay of radioisotopes in the radiocenters over a period of time. First reported between 1880 and 1890, their origin was a mystery until the discovery of radioactivity. Then in 1907 *Joly* [1907] and *Mügge* [1907] independently suggested that the darkening of the minerals around the central inclusions is due to the alpha (α) particles produced by α-decays in the radiocenters. These α-particles damage the crystal structure of the surrounding minerals, producing concentric shells of darkening or discoloration (Figure 1). When observed in thin sections these shells are concentric circles with diameters between 10 and 40 µm, the circles simply resulting from planar sections through the concentric spheres centered around the inclusions [*Gentry*, 1973].

Many years of subsequent investigations have established that the radii of the concentric circles of the radiohalos as observed in thin sections are related to the α-decay energies. This enables the radioisotopes responsible for the α-decays to be identified [*Gentry*, 1974, 1984, 1986, 1988; *Snelling*, 2000]. Most importantly, when the central inclusions, or radiocenters, are very small (about 1 µm) the radiohalos around them have been unequivocally demonstrated to be products of the α-emitting members of the ^{238}U and the ^{232}Th decay series. The radii of the concentric multiple spheres, or rings in thin sections, correspond to the ranges in the host minerals of the α-particles from the α-emitting radioisotopes in those two decay series [*Gentry*, 1973, 1974, 1984]

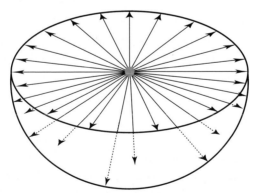

Figure 1. Sunburst effect of α-damage trails. The sunburst pattern of α-damage trails produces a spherically colored shell around the halo center. Each arrow represents approximately 5 million α-particles emitted from the center. Halo coloration initially develops after about 100 million α-decays, becomes darker after about 500 million, and very dark after about 1 billion (after *Gentry* [1988]).

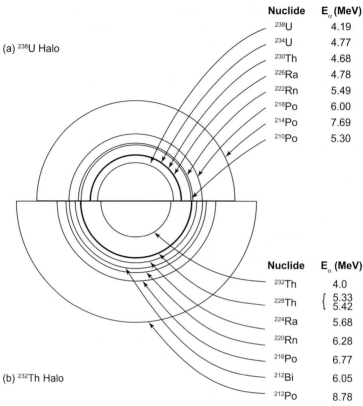

Nuclide E_α (MeV)

Nuclide	E_α (MeV)
^{238}U	4.19
^{234}U	4.77
^{230}Th	4.68
^{226}Ra	4.78
^{222}Rn	5.49
^{218}Po	6.00
^{214}Po	7.69
^{210}Po	5.30

(a) ^{238}U Halo

Nuclide	E_α (MeV)
^{232}Th	4.0
^{228}Th	5.33 / 5.42
^{224}Ra	5.68
^{220}Rn	6.28
^{216}Po	6.77
^{212}Bi	6.05
^{212}Po	8.78

(b) ^{232}Th Halo

Figure 2. Schematic drawing of (a) a ^{238}U halo, and (b) a ^{232}Th halo, with radii proportional to the ranges of α-particles in air. The nuclides responsible for the α-particles and their energies are listed for the different halo rings (after *Gentry* [1973]).

(Figure 2). Uranium-235 radiohalos have not been observed. This is readily accounted for by the scarcity of ^{235}U (only 0.7% of the naturally-occurring U), since large concentrations of the parent radionuclides are needed to produce the concentric ring structures of the radiohalos.

Ordinary radiohalos can be defined, therefore, as those that are initiated by ^{238}U or ^{232}Th α-decay, irrespective of whether the actual halo sizes closely match the respective idealized patterns (Figure 2). In many instances the match is very good, the observed sizes agreeing very well with the ^{4}He ion penetration ranges produced in biotite, fluorite and cordierite [*Gentry*, 1973, 1974]. Uranium and Th radiohalos usually are found in igneous rocks, most commonly in granitic rocks and in granitic pegmatites. While U and Th radiohalos have been found in over forty minerals, their distribution within these minerals is very erratic [*Ramdohr*, 1933, 1957, 1960; *Stark*, 1936]. Biotite is quite clearly the major mineral in which U and Th radiohalos occur. Wherever found in biotite they are prolific, and are associated with tiny zircon (U) or monazite (Th) radiocenters. The ease of thin section preparation, and the clarity of the radiohalos in these sections, have made biotite an ideal choice for numerous radiohalo investigations, namely, those of *Joly* [1917a, b, 1923, 1924], *Lingen* [1926], *Iimori and Yoshimura* [1926], *Kerr-Lawson* [1927, 1928], *Wiman* [1930], *Henderson and Bateson* [1934], *Henderson and Turnbull* [1934], *Henderson et al.* [1934], *Henderson and Sparks* [1939], *Gentry* [1968, 1970, 1971], and *Snelling and Armitage* [2003]. Uranium, Th and other specific halo types in most of these studies have been observed mainly in Precambrian rocks, so much remains to be learned about their occurrence in rocks from the other geological periods of the strata record. However, some studies have shown that they do exist in rocks stretching from the Precambrian to the Tertiary [*Holmes*, 1931; *Stark*, 1936; *Wise*, 1989; *Snelling and Armitage*, 2003]. Unfortunately, in most instances the radiohalo types are not specifically identified in these studies.

Some unusual radiohalo types that appear to be distinct from those formed by ^{238}U and/or ^{232}Th α-decay have been observed [*Gentry*, 1970, 1971, 1973, 1984, 1986; *Gentry et al.*, 1973, 1976a, 1978; *Snelling*, 2000]. Of these, only the Po (polonium) radiohalos can presently be identified with known α-radioactivity [*Gentry*, 1967, 1968, 1973, 1974; *Gentry et al.*, 1973, 1974]. There are three Po isotopes in the ^{238}U-decay chain. In sequence they are ^{218}Po (half-life of 3.1 minutes), ^{214}Po (half-life of 164 microseconds), and ^{210}Po (half-life of 138 days). Polonium halos contain only rings produced by these three Po α-emitters (Figure 3). They are designated by the first (or only) Po α-emitter in the portion of the decay sequence that is represented. The presence in Po radiohalos of only the rings of the three Po α-emitters implies that the radiocenters

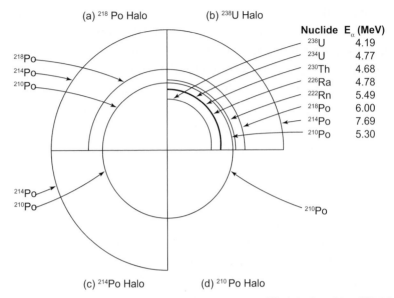

Figure 3. Composite schematic drawing of (a) a ^{218}Po halo, (b) a ^{238}U halo, (c) a ^{214}Po halo, and (d) a ^{210}Po halo, with radii proportional to the ranges of α-particles in air. The nuclides responsible for the α-particles and their energies are listed for the different halo rings (after *Gentry* [1973]).

which produced these Po radiohalos initially contained only either the respective Po radioisotopes that then parented the subsequent α-decays, or a non-α-emitting parent [*Gentry*, 1971; *Gentry et al.*, 1973]. These three Po radiohalo types occur in biotites within granitic rocks [*Gentry*, 1968, 1971, 1973, 1974, 1984, 1986, 1988; *Gentry et al.*, 1973, 1974; *Wise*, 1989; *Snelling and Armitage*, 2003].

Joly [1917b, 1924] was probably the first to investigate ^{210}Po radiohalos and was clearly baffled by them. Because *Schilling* [1926] saw Po radiohalos located only along cracks in fluorite from Wölsendorf in Germany, he suggested that they originated from preferential deposition of Po from U-bearing solutions. *Henderson* [1939] and *Henderson and Sparks* [1939] invoked a similar but more quantitative hypothesis to explain Po radiohalos along conduits in biotite. However, those Po radiohalos found occurring along much more restricted cleavage planes, similar to those found by *Gentry* [1973, 1974], have been more difficult to account for. The reason for these attempts to explain the origin and formation of the Po radiohalos by some secondary process is simple—the half-lives of the respective Po isotopes are far too short to be reconciled with the Po having been primary, that is, originally in the granitic magmas which are usually claimed to have slowly cooled to form the granitic rocks that now contain the Po-radiohalo-bearing biotites. The half-life of ^{218}Po, for example, is 3.1 minutes. However, this is not the only formidable obstacle for any secondary process that transported the Po into the biotites as, or after, the granitic rocks cooled. First, there is the need for isotopic separation of the Po isotopes, or their β-decay precursors, from parent ^{238}U [*Gentry et al.*, 1973]. Second, the radiocenters of very dark ^{218}Po radiohalos, for example, may need to have contained as much as 5×10^9 atoms (a concentration of greater than 50%) of ^{218}Po [*Gentry*, 1974]. But these ^{218}Po atoms must migrate or diffuse from their source at very low diffusion rates through surrounding mineral grains to be captured by the radiocenters before the ^{218}Po decays [*Fremlin*, 1975; *Gentry*, 1968, 1975].

Studies of some Po radiohalo centers in biotite (and fluorite) have shown little or no U in conjunction with anomalously high ^{206}Pb/^{207}Pb and/or Pb/U ratios, which would be expected from the decay of Po without the U precursor that normally occurs in U radiohalo centers [*Gentry*, 1974; *Gentry et al.*, 1974]. Indeed, many ^{206}Pb/^{207}Pb ratios were greater than 21.8 reflecting a seemingly abnormal mixture of Pb isotopes derived from Po decay independent of the normal U-decay chain [*Gentry*, 1971; *Gentry et al.*, 1973]. Thus, based on these data, Gentry advanced the hypothesis that the three different types of Po radiohalos in biotites represent the decay of primordial Po (that is, original Po not derived by U-decay), and that the rocks hosting these radiohalos, that is, the Precambrian granites as he perceived them all to be, must be primordial rocks produced by fiat creation, given that the half-life of ^{214}Po is only 164 microseconds [*Gentry*, 1979, 1980, 1982, 1983, 1984, 1986, 1988, 1989].

As a consequence of Gentry's Creation hypothesis, the origin of the Po radiohalos has remained controversial and thus apparently unresolved.

Snelling [2000] has thoroughly discussed the many arguments and evidences used in the debate that has ensued over the past two decades, and concluded that there were insufficient data on the geological occurrence and distribution of the Po radiohalos for the debate to be decisively resolved. Of the twenty-two locations then known where the rocks contained Po radiohalos, *Wise* [1989] had determined that six of the locations hosted Phanerozoic granitic rocks, a large enough proportion to severely question Gentry's hypothesis of primordial Po in fiat created granitic rocks. Many of these Po radiohalo occurrences are also in proximity to higher than normal U concentrations in nearby rocks and/or minerals, suggesting ideal sources for fluid separation and transport of the Po. Furthermore, *Snelling* [2000] found that there are now significant reports of ^{210}Po as a detectable species in volcanic gases, in volcanic/hydrothermal fluids associated with subaerial volcanoes and fumeroles, and associated with mid-ocean ridge hydrothermal vents and chimney deposits [*LeCloarec et al.*, 1994; *Hussain et al.*, 1995; *Rubin*, 1997], as well as in groundwaters [*Harada et al.*, 1989; *LaRock et al.*, 1996]. The distances involved in this fluid transport of the Po are several kilometers (and more), so there is increasing evidence of the potential viability of the secondary transport of Po by hydrothermal fluids during pluton emplacement, perhaps in the waning stages of the crystallization and cooling of granitic magmas [*Snelling and Woodmorappe*, 1998; *Snelling*, 2000]. Indeed, as a result of this present study, *Snelling and Armitage* [2003] investigated the Po radiohalo occurrences in three Phanerozoic granitic plutons and logically argued for a model of Po radiohalo formation involving secondary transport of Po by hydrothermal fluids during crystallization and cooling of the granitic magmas. Their data from the present study and details of this hydrothermal fluid transport model have been published [*Snelling et al.*, 2003], but full details encompassing these results will be elaborated upon in this report.

Whereas Po radiohalos would appear to indicate extremely rapid geological processes were responsible for their production (because of the extremely short half-lives of the Po isotopes responsible), ^{238}U and ^{232}Th radiohalos appear to be evidence of long periods of radioactive decay, assuming decay rates have been constant at today's rates throughout earth history. Indeed, it has been estimated that dark, fully-formed U and Th radiohalos require around 100 million years worth of radioactive decay at today's rates to form [*Gentry*, 1973, 1974; *Humphreys*, 2000; *Snelling*, 2000]. Thus the presence of mature U and Th radiohalos in granitic rocks globally throughout the geological record would indicate that at least 100 million years worth of radioactive decay at today's rate has occurred during earth history. As proposed by *Humphreys* [2000] and *Vardiman et al.* [2000], these observable data require that within the Biblical young-earth time framework radioisotope decay therefore had to have been accelerated, but just by how much needs to be determined. If, for example, mature U and Th radiohalos were found in granitic rocks that were demonstrated to have formed during the Flood year, then that would imply about 100 million years worth of radioisotope decay at today's rates had occurred at an accelerated rate during the Flood year [*Baumgardner*, 2000; *Snelling*, 2000]. Furthermore, if Po radiohalos were alongside U and Th radiohalos in the same Flood-related granitic rocks, then that would have implications as to the rate of formation and age of these granitic rocks formed during the Flood year within the Biblical timescale. Similarly, there is insufficient data on the distribution of all radiohalo types in the vast Precambrian geological record. Indeed, the distribution pattern of all radiohalo types in Precambrian granitic rocks might well be significant, providing clues about the earth's early history within the Biblical framework.

2. Rationale of the Present Study

A systematic effort was initiated to investigate the occurrence and distribution of all radiohalo types in granitic rocks throughout the geological record globally [*Vardiman et al.*, 2000]. The initial focus was on granitic plutons that intrude strata interpreted as having been deposited during the Flood, the plutons themselves thus being considered to have formed also during the Flood. In conventional terms these are granitic plutons that are designated as Paleozoic (Cambrian-Permian) and Mesozoic (Triassic-Cretaceous). As a picture began to emerge of the occurrence and distribution of all radiohalo types in those granitic rocks, investigations were then extended to also focus on Precambrian granitic rocks. These are interpreted as having formed during the pre-Flood era, some perhaps even being remnants of the Creation week itself. Some more recent granitic rocks, belonging to the Tertiary of the geological record, which tentatively represent post-Flood granitic intrusions, were also studied. Because the U and Th radiohalos are a physical record of α-decay of U and Th, and of how much α-decay has occurred, it was important to use in this study samples of granitic rocks from as many different levels in the geological record as possible to be representative of the full span of earth history, to thus obtain the best detailed overview of the history of radioisotope decay through the geological record. Furthermore, because the Po radiohalos have the potential to be direct physical evidence of rapid geological processes, it is crucial to know their distribution in the geological record. If the model for Po radiohalo formation by secondary transport of Po in hydrothermal fluids during the cooling of intruded granitic magmas [*Snelling and Armitage*, 2003] is sustained by all the relevant evidence, then that would not only have time implications for the intrusion and cooling of granitic magmas during the Flood, but also potentially throughout the other periods of earth history.

The advantage of radiohalos is not only do they represent a visible, physical record of nuclear decay, but that record is wiped away if a rock recrystallizes or if subsequent to its initial formation the rock is heated again to above the temperature at which previously-formed radiohalos are annealed. This means that the problem of inheritance of parent/daughter correlations (radioisotope ratios) that complicates standard isochron methods is avoided, and the radiohalos only record the nuclear decay that has occurred since the last heating event to which the host rocks were subjected. This has direct implications for Precambrian (pre-Flood) granitic rocks, because it is highly likely that many of them could have been reheated during the Flood due to the tectonic upheavals and the catastrophic deposition of thick sequences of sedimentary strata on those crystalline basement rocks. Should there be an absence of mature (fully-formed) U and Th radiohalos in

Phanerozoic granitic rocks, this would present a powerful argument that very little nuclear decay has taken place since multi-celled life was buried and fossilized at the onset of the Flood year. Ages of hundreds of millions of years as commonly determined by the standard radioisotope isochron methods could thus primarily be a consequence of inheritance of parent/daughter correlations (radioisotope ratios) from Precambrian sources in the earth's crust and mantle. On the other hand, if mature U and Th radiohalos are present in granitic rocks that were intruded, crystallized and cooled during the Flood year, then that would be direct physical evidence that at least 100 million years worth (at today's rates) of nuclear decay must have occurred during the Flood year only 4500 or so years ago, implying that the nuclear decay rates had to have been accelerated. Thus all types of radiohalos, wherever found in the granitic rocks of the geological record, have the potential to place constraints and implications on the history of nuclear decay through the earth's history, and to place time constraints upon the intrusion and cooling of granitic rocks and associated geological processes. This may also include time constraints on the sedimentary rocks that have been metamorphosed, some of those being so affected by the increasing temperatures and pressures that their metamorphism generated granitic magmas which subsequently crystallized *in situ* and cooled as the temperatures and pressures decreased again.

3. Collection of Samples

Granitic rocks are of course ubiquitous in the earth's crust and are frequently exposed at the earth's surface across large areas. Ease of access to suitable outcrops of granitic rocks is not uniform, so it was logical to target regions with easy access in proximity to those involved in the sampling program. Suitable Phanerozoic granitic rocks are well exposed in outcrops throughout southeastern Australia in the Lachlan, New England and Adelaide Fold Belts (Orogens) and are readily accessible in road cuts along the major highways linking the major cities of Brisbane, Sydney, Melbourne, and Adelaide, as well as along subsidiary roads branching from them. The conventional ages of these granitic rocks are Ordovician to Triassic, so to supplement the conventional timespan covered by those granitic rocks, samples were collected of the Cretaceous granitic rocks that outcrop extensively and are readily accessible in the Peninsular Ranges of southern California east and northeast of San Diego, as well as in the Sierra Nevada Ranges of the Yosemite area of central California. Precambrian granitic rocks were also sampled in the Grand Canyon along the Colorado River corridor accessed by raft. With the assistance of others, samples of other Precambrian and Phanerozoic granitic rocks were collected in Western Australia, Arizona, New Mexico, Colorado, Wyoming, Georgia, and North and South Carolina in the U.S.A., in Cornwall and the Lake District of England, and in parts of Scandinavia. Cretaceous and Tertiary granites were also sampled in Washington state, Montana, Idaho, Utah, and Arizona. Both the geographical coverage of these many samples, and their span of the geological record, provided an excellent representative sample set for the purposes of this study.

The space limitations of this report preclude a detailed description of each granitic pluton sampled, and of the samples collected for this study. Descriptions of three sampled granitic plutons and the results of the search for radiohalos in those samples have already been reported by *Snelling and Armitage* [2003]. The details of other selected granitic plutons sampled and the significance of the radiohalos found in them will be reported in other papers published elsewhere. For the purposes of this report the focus is on the overall study of the radiohalos found in all the granitic rock samples collected, so only general sample location details need to be provided. Of course, the key component of these granitic rocks for this study was the presence of biotite in them visible to the naked eye, and if possible trace amounts of zircon.

Most of the samples were obtained from road cuts through outcrops of granitic plutons along highways and subsidiary roads, but a few were collected along hiking trails, and in the case of the Grand Canyon, along the Colorado River corridor. Every effort was made to obtain the freshest samples. Fist-sized (1–2 kg) pieces of granitic rock were collected at each location, and when possible the details of the precise area sampled were recorded using a hand-held G.P.S. unit.

4. Experimental Procedures

A standard petrographic thin section was obtained for each sample. In the laboratory, a scalpel and tweezers were used to prize flakes of biotite loose from sample surfaces, or where necessary portions of the samples were crushed to liberate the constituent mineral grains. Biotite flakes were then hand-picked and placed on the adhesive surface of a piece of clear Scotch™ tape fixed to a bench surface with its adhesive side up. Once numerous biotite flakes had been mounted on the adhesive surface of this piece of clear Scotch™ tape, a fresh piece of clear Scotch™ tape was placed over them and firmly pressed along its length so as to ensure the two pieces of clear Scotch™ tape were stuck together with the biotite flakes firmly wedged between them. The upper piece of clear Scotch™ tape was then peeled back in order to pull apart the sheets composing the biotite flakes, and this piece of clear Scotch™ tape with thin biotite sheets adhering to it was then placed over a standard glass microscope slide so that the adhesive side had the thin mica flakes adhered to it. This procedure was repeated with another piece of clear Scotch™ tape placed over the original Scotch™ tape and biotite flakes affixed to the bench, the adhering biotite flakes being progressively pulled apart and transferred to microscope slides. As necessary, further hand-picked biotite flakes were added to replace those fully pulled apart. In this way tens of microscope slides were prepared for each sample, each with many (at least twenty to thirty) thin biotite flakes mounted on them. This is similar to the method pioneered by Gentry. A minimum of thirty (usually fifty) microscope slides was prepared for each sample to ensure good representative sampling statistics. Thus there was a minimum of 1000 biotite flakes mounted on microscope slides for each sample.

Each thin section for each sample was then carefully examined under a petrological microscope in plane polarized light and all radiohalos present were identified, noting any relationships between the different radiohalo types and any unusual features. The numbers of each type of radiohalo in each slide were counted by progressively moving the slide backwards and forwards across the field of view, and the numbers recorded for each slide were then tallied and tabulated for each sample. Only radiohalos whose radiocenters were clearly visible were counted. Because of the progressive peeling apart of many of the same biotite flakes during the preparation of the microscope slides, many of the radiohalos appeared on more than one microscope slide, so this procedure ensured each radiohalo was only counted once.

5. Results

All results have been compiled in three tables. Table 1 lists the results from all the Precambrian granites, Table 2 all the Paleozoic-Mesozoic granites, and Table 3 all the Tertiary granites. This grouping of samples was chosen as an approximation of what might constitute pre-Flood granitic rocks (the Precambrian granitic rocks of Table 1), Flood granitic rocks (the Paleozoic-Mesozoic granitic rocks of Table 2), and what tentatively might be designated as post-Flood granitic rocks (the Tertiary granitic rocks of Table 3). Some examples of typical radiohalos found in these granitic rocks are shown in the photomicrographs of Figure 4. Typically the U and Th radiohalos were found to be overexposed, that is, there has been so much α-decay of U and Th in the radiocenters that all the inner rings have been obliterated, so that all the areas inside the ^{218}Po and ^{216}Po rings respectively are dark (Figures 2 and 4). Similarly, in many of the samples the ^{210}Po radiohalos were also overexposed, clearly implying that there had been so much α-decay of the ^{210}Po in the radiocenters darkening all of the area inside the single ^{210}Po ring (Figures 3 and 4c). Even many of the ^{214}Po radiohalos in the samples in which they occur are overexposed, all of the area inside the ^{210}Po ring being darkened because of all the α-decay of ^{210}Po in the radiocenters (Figures 3 and 4f). However, the few ^{218}Po radiohalos observed in just a few samples (only in some of the Paleozoic-Mesozoic granitic rocks in Table 2) are all "normal" radiohalos, with all three Po rings visible (Figures 3 and 4g), except for the example in Figure 4h. Similarly, in some samples some of the ^{210}Po and ^{214}Po radiohalos are also "normal" (not overexposed) (Figure 4d and e).

A perusal of Tables 1, 2 and 3 unmistakably reveals that in most

Table 1. Radiohalos recorded in Precambrian (pre-Flood) granitic rocks.

Rock Unit	Location	"Age"	Samples (Slides)	Radiohalos					Number of Radiohalos per Slide	Number of Po Radiohalos per Slide	Ratios			
				^{210}Po	^{214}Po	^{218}Po	^{238}U	^{232}Th			^{210}Po:^{238}U	^{210}Po:^{214}Po	^{210}Po:^{218}Po	^{238}U:^{232}Th
Granite (Methrow)	Washington (USA)	600 Ma(?)	1 (50)	1	0	0	0	0	0.02	0.02	—	—	—	—
Pikes Peak Granite	Colorado (USA)	1080 Ma	1 (51)	80	2	0	8	0	1.8	1.6	10.0:1	40.0:1.0	—	—
Lake George Granite	Colorado (USA)	1080 Ma	1 (51)	12	0	0	14	0	0.5	0.24	1.0:1.2	—	—	—
Sherman Granite	Wyoming (USA)	1400 Ma	1 (50)	4	0	0	0	0	0.1	0.1	—	—	—	—
Ruin Granite	Arizona (USA)	1430 Ma	1 (41)	176	1	0	10	0	4.6	4.3	17.6:1	176.0:1.0	—	—
Jemez granodiorite	New Mexico (USA)	1500 Ma	1 (33)	29	1	0	14	0	1.3	0.91	2.1:1	29.0:1.0	—	—
Granite (Unaweep Canyon)	Colorado (USA)	1500 Ma (?)	1 (50)	19	0	1	0	0	0.4	0.4	—	—	19.0:1.0	—
Orbicular granite (Shoup)	Idaho (USA)	1500 Ma	1 (50)	9	0	1	4	0	0.3	0.2	2.3:1	—	9.0:1.0	—
Helsinki Granite	Helsinki, Finland	1800 Ma	3 (150)	107	1	0	241	0	2.3	0.72	0.44:1	107.0:1.0	—	—
Ruby Pluton		1716 Ma	3 (150)	486	0	0	16	0	3.35	3.24	30.4:1	—	—	—
Trinity Granodiorite		1730 Ma	3 (150)	74	2	0	0	0	0.5	0.5	—	37.0:1.0	—	—
Pipe Creek Pluton	Grand Canyon, Arizona (USA)	1690–1740 Ma	1 (50)	132	0	0	0	0	2.6	2.6	—	—	—	—
Elves Chasm Granodiorite		1840 Ma	5 (250)	53	0	0	0	0	0.2	0.2	—	—	—	—
Owl Creek granite	Wyoming (USA)	2500 Ma	1 (50)	5	0	0	0	0	0.1	0.1	—	—	—	—
Namban Granite	Yilgarn (Western Australia)	2670–	1 (41)	318	16	0	120	3	10.7	8.15	2.7:1	19.9:1.0	—	40.0:1.0
Badja Granite		2689 Ma	1 (43)	188	0	0	58	0	5.7	4.37	3.2:1	—	—	—
Rattlesnake granite	Wyoming (USA)	2800–	1 (50)	10	0	0	25	0	0.7	0.2	1.0:2.5	—	—	—
Bighorn granite		2900 Ma	1 (50)	0	0	0	0	0	0	0	—	—	—	—
Granite (tonalite)	Ilomantsi, Finland	Archean	3 (150)	85	0	0	0	0	0.6	0.6	—	—	—	—

Table 2. Radiohalos recorded in Paleozoic-Mesozoic (Flood) granitic rocks.

Rock Unit	Location	"Age"	Samples (slides)	Radiohalos					Number of Radiohalos per Slide	Number of Po Radiohalos per Slide	Ratios			
				^{210}Po	^{214}Po	^{218}Po	^{238}U	^{232}Th			$^{210}Po{:}^{238}U$	$^{210}Po{:}^{214}Po$	$^{210}Po{:}^{218}Po$	$^{238}U{:}^{232}Th$
Bitterroot Batholith	Idaho (USA)	70–90 Ma	4 (200)	38	0	0	18	0	0.28	0.19	2.1:1.0	—	—	—
Joseph Pluton, Idaho Batholith	Montana (USA)	70–90 Ma	1 (50)	0	0	0	0	0	0	0	—	—	—	—
Mt. Stuart Granite	Washington (USA)	88 Ma	1 (50)	0	0	0	0	0	0	0	—	—	—	—
Black Peak Batholith	Washington (USA)	Late Cretaceous	1(50)	1	0	0	2	0	0.06	0.02	0.5:1.0	—	—	—
Golden Horn Granite	Washington (USA)	Cretaceous	1(50)	7	0	0	1	0	0.2	0.14	7.0:1.0	—	—	—
Indian Hill granites	San Diego County, CA	90 Ma	4 (180)	279	11	0	45	0	1.86	1.61	6.2:1.0	25.4:1.0	—	—
La Posta Pluton	CA	93 Ma	8 (383)	96	4	0	8	0	0.3	0.26	8.0:1.0	24.0:1.0		—
Granodiorite of Mono Dome	Yosemite, CA	93 Ma	1 (50)	6	0	0	0	0	0.1	0.1	—	—	—	—
San Jacinto Pluton	Palm Springs, CA	Late Cretaceous	9 (450)	96	0	0	9	0	0.22	0.21	10.7:1.0	—	—	—
Bass Lake Tonalite	Yosemite, CA	114 Ma	1 (50)	84	0	0	0	3	1.7	1.68	—	—	—	—
Ward Mountain Trondhjemite	Yosemite, CA	115 Ma	1 (50)	63	0	0	0	0	1.26	1.26	—	—	—	—
Granodiorite of Arch Rock	Yosemite, CA	114–117 Ma	2 (100)	106	0	7	10	0	1.23	1.13	10.6:1.0	—	15.1:1.0	—
Tonalite of the Gateway	Yosemite, CA	114–117 Ma	2 (100)	1	0	0	0	0	0.01	0.01	—	—	—	—
Wheeler Crest Granodiorite	Mammoth, CA	200–215 Ma	1 (50)	58	0	12	1	0	1.42	1.4	58.0:1.0	—	4.8:1.0	—
Lee Vining Canyon Granite	Yosemite, CA	200–215 Ma	1 (50)	108	0	2	13	0	2.46	2.2	8.3:1.0	—	54.0:1.0	—
Stanthorpe Adamellite	Qld, Australia	232 Ma	1 (48)	520	4	15	68	19	13.04	11.23	7.6:1.0	130.0:1.0	34.7:1.0	3.6:1.0

Table 2. (continued)

Rock Unit	Location	"Age"	Samples (slides)	Radiohalos					Number of Radiohalos per Slide	Number of Po Radiohalos per Slide	Ratios			
				^{210}Po	^{214}Po	^{218}Po	^{238}U	^{232}Th			^{210}Po:^{238}U	^{210}Po:^{214}Po	^{210}Po:^{218}Po	^{238}U:^{232}Th
Royken/Drammen Granite	Spikkestad, Norway	267±4 Ma	1 (100)	225	0	0	5	0	2.3	2.25	45.0:1.0	—	—	—
Finnamarka Granite	Gulsrudsetra, Norway	268±3 Ma	1 (50)	0	0	0	6	0	0.12	0	—	—	—	—
Land's End Granite	Cornwall, England	274 Ma	1 (32)	3307	485	27	5364	10	287.3	119.3	0.6:1.0	6.8:1.0	122.5:1.0	536.4:1.0
Stone Mountain Pluton	Atlanta, GA	291±7 Ma	6 (291)	1109	93	2	88	0	4.44	4.14	12.6:1.0	12.0:1.0	554.5:1.0	—
Liberty Hill Pluton	Lancaster, SC	299±48 Ma	3 (150)	180	0	0	0	0	1.2	1.2	—	—	—	—
Bathurst Granite	NSW, Australia	330 Ma	1 (51)	45	0	0	3	0	0.94	0.88	15.0:1.0	—	—	—
Spruce Pine pegmatites	Spruce Pine, NC	~340 Ma	3 (150)	1451	71	182	66	0	11.8	11.36	22.0:1.0	20.4:1.0	8.0:1.0	—
Mt Airy Granite	Mt Airy, NC	~350 Ma	2 (100)	1271	22	0	120	0	14.13	12.93	10.6:1.0	57.8:1.0	—	—
Stone Mountain Granite	Stone Mountain, NC	~350 Ma	2 (100)	1543	4	174	5	0	17.26	17.21	309.0:1.0	386.0:1.0	8.9:1.0	—
Harcourt Granite	Vic., Australia	369 Ma	1 (31)	107	130	0	198	0	14.03	7.65	1.0:1.5	1.0:1.2	—	—
Strathbogie Granite	Vic., Australia	374 Ma	1 (50)	1366	232	1	1582	10	63.82	31.98	1.0:1.2	5.9:1.0	1366.0:1.0	158.2:1.0
Shap Granite	Lake District, England	393 Ma	3 (157)	1334	14	4	394	41	11.38	8.61	3.4:1.0	95.0:1.0	333.0:1.0	9.6:1.0
Shannons Flat Granite	NSW, Australia	417–443 Ma	1 (101)	9	18	0	38	0	0.64	0.27	1.0:4.2	1.0:2.0	—	—
Jillamatong Granite	NSW, Australia	417–443 Ma	1 (31)	120	118	0	137	0	12.1	7.68	1.0:1.1	1.0:1.0	—	—
Cootralantra Granite	NSW, Australia	417–443 Ma	1 (43)	230	75	0	276	2	13.56	7.1	1.0:1.2	3.1:1.0	—	138.0:1.0
Cooma Granodiorite	NSW, Australia	433 Ma	1 (41)	373	44	0	418	37	21.27	10.17	1.0:1.1	8.5:1.0	—	11.3:1.0
Encounter Bay Granite	South Australia	487–490 Ma	1 (45)	362	8	0	1586	161	47.04	8.22	1.0:4.4	45.3:1.0	—	9.9:1.0
Palmer Granite	South Australia	490 Ma	1 (51)	1352	17	0	631	3	39.3	26.84	2.1:1.0	79.5:1.0	—	210.3:1.0

Table 3. Radiohalos recorded in Tertiary (tentatively post-Flood) granitic rocks.

Rock Unit	Location	"Age"	Samples (slides)	Radiohalos					Number of Radiohalos per Slide	Number of Po Radiohalos per Slide
				^{210}Po	^{214}Po	^{218}Po	^{238}U	^{232}Th		
Kingston Granite	Kingston Range, CA	Miocene	1 (50)	0	0	0	0	0	0	0
Granite	Phoenix, AZ	Early Miocene-Oligocene	1 (50)	0	0	0	0	0	0	0
Index Granite	Cascades, WA	Oligocene (33 Ma)	1 (50)	9	0	0	2	0	0.22	0.18
Spry Granite	Panguitch, UT	Oligocene	1 (50)	0	0	0	0	0	0	0
Granite	Salt Lake, UT	Tertiary	1 (50)	0	0	0	0	0	0	0
Chelan Granite	Pateros area, WA	Paleocene/Cretaceous	2 (100)	0	0	0	0	0	0	0
Granite	Phoenix, AZ	Late Cretaceous/Early Tertiary	1 (50)	0	0	0	0	0	0	0

samples prolific radiohalos were found, the number of ^{210}Po radiohalos often being very much greater than any other radiohalo type. As expected, all but one of the Tertiary granites in Table 3 contained no radiohalos, due undoubtedly to there having been insufficient time since these granitic rocks were intruded and cooled for enough α-decays to have accumulated enough damage to register as radiohalos (100 million years worth, at today's rates, of α-decays are regarded as being required to produce a mature, fully-formed ^{238}U radiohalo). Yet the sample from

Figure 4 (right). Some typical examples of the different radiohalos found in granitic rocks in this study. (a) An overexposed ^{238}U radiohalo (Cooma Granodiorite, diameter ~70 μm, center) and a ^{210}Po radiohalo (diameter ~39 μm, right). (b) A reversed ^{238}U radiohalo (Shap Granite, diameter ~70 μm). (c) An overexposed ^{210}Po radiohalo (migmatite adjacent to Palmer Granite, diameter 39 μm, lower right). (d) A normal ^{210}Po radiohalo (Stone Mountain Granite, diameter ~39 μm). (e) A normal ^{214}Po radiohalo (Encounter Bay Granite, diameter ~68 μm. (f) Another ^{214}Po radiohalo (centered on a crack) (Land's End Granite, diameter ~68 μm, right) and an overexposed ^{238}U radiohalo (diameter ~70 μm, left).

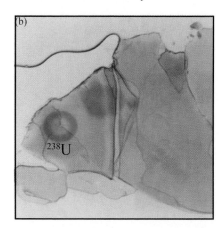

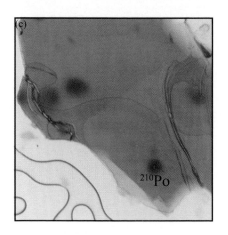

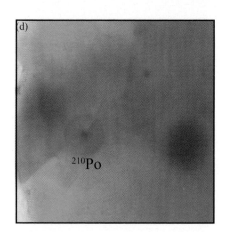

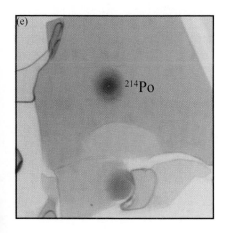

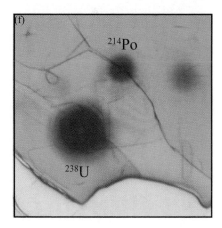

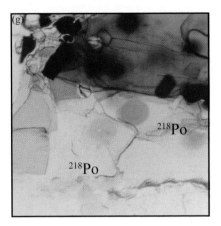

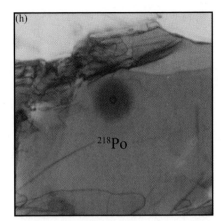

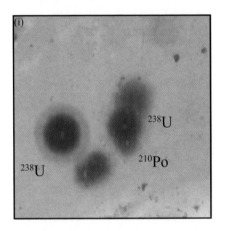

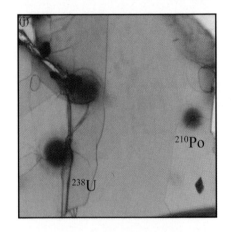

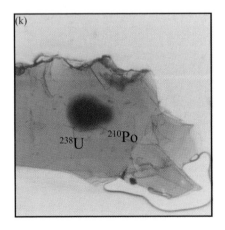

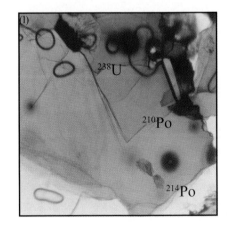

the Index Granite in the Cascades region of Washington state, with a geological age of Oligocene and a radioisotope age of 33 Ma, contained two mature U radiohalos, which suggests that perhaps considerably less than 100 million years worth (at today's rates) of α-decays were needed to form them (or the granite may be older in conventional terms than currently designated/determined).

Another observation is that radiohalos appear to be more prolific in Paleozoic-Mesozoic (Flood) granitic rocks than in Precambrian (pre-Flood) granitic rocks. Because more than one sample was obtained from some granitic plutons and more slides were made from some samples than from others, there needs to be another way of comparing how prolific the radiohalos are in each sample than by looking at the absolute numbers of radiohalos listed in Tables 1 and 2. Thus in those tables appear two columns listing the numbers of radiohalos and Po radiohalos observed in each granitic rock per microscope slide. Thus the Precambrian granitic rocks yielded from 0 to 10.7 radiohalos per slide (per sample), with most samples yielding 1–5 radiohalos per slide (Table 1). On the other hand, the Paleozoic-Mesozoic (Flood) granitic rocks can be seen to have yielded from 0.01 to over 250 radiohalos per slide (per sample), with most samples yielding 1–12 radiohalos per slide (Table 2). These details are shown graphically in Figure 5. Similarly, the Precambrian (pre-Flood) granite rocks yielded from 0 to 8.15 Po radiohalos per slide (per sample) (Table 1), while the Paleozoic-Mesozoic (Flood) granitic rocks yielded from 0 to 119.3 Po radiohalos per slide (per sample) (Table 2). These details are also shown graphically in Figure 6. Perhaps the dataset is not yet large enough to be adamant,

Figure 4 (left). Some typical examples of the different radiohalos found in granitic rocks in this study. (g) Two faint normal ^{218}Po radiohalos (Land's End Granite, diameter ~70 μm, center). (h) An overexposed ^{218}Po radiohalo (Shap Granite, diameter ~70 μm). (i) Overexposed adjacent and overlapping ^{238}U and ^{210}Po radiohalos (Cooma Granodiorite). (j) Overexposed ^{238}U and ^{210}Po radiohalos in the same biotite grain (Encounter Bay Granite). (k) Overlapping overexposed ^{238}U and ^{210}Po radiohalos in the same biotite flake (Land's End Granite). (l) ^{238}U (upper center), ^{214}Po (lower right) and ^{210}Po (right) radiohalos together in the same biotite grain (Land's End Granite).

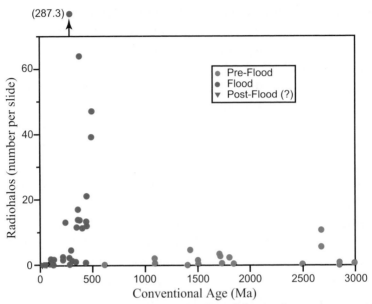

Figure 5. Plot of the conventional age (in millions of years) versus the total number of radiohalos per slide (per sample) for each granitic pluton listed in Tables 1, 2, and 3. The outlier of 287.3 radiohalos per slide is the Land's End Granite, Cornwall, England.

but from these data it would appear that all types of radiohalos are generally more prolific in Paleozoic-Mesozoic (Flood) granitic rocks, as is evident by the number of the granitic rocks in Table 2 containing more than 20 radiohalos per slide, many more than the Precambrian granitic rocks with the best radiohalo yield at just over 10 radiohalos per slide.

In most of these granitic rocks ^{210}Po radiohalos are more abundant than ^{238}U radiohalos (see the ratios columns in Tables 1 and 2). Generally, ^{210}Po radiohalos are 6–12 times more abundant than ^{238}U radiohalos. But there are higher and lower abundance ratios, and in some of these granitic rocks ^{238}U radiohalos are more prevalent than ^{210}Po radiohalos. There just does not seem to be any clear pattern that stands out. In some granitic rocks only ^{210}Po radiohalos are found. Indeed, all but one of the Paleozoic-Mesozoic (Flood) granitic rocks contain ^{210}Po radiohalos even when ^{238}U radiohalos are absent, whereas some of the Precambrian (pre-Flood) granitic rocks contain no radiohalos at all, even when tiny zircon crystals are included within the biotite flakes in them. It is likely, therefore, that ^{238}U radiohalos were originally present in those Precambrian granitic rocks but have since been annealed (that is, the α-particle damage was "healed" by subsequent heating of the rocks energizing the biotites' atoms to move back into their normal crystal lattice positions). Polonium-214 and ^{218}Po radiohalos are rare and only present in some of these granitic rocks (Tables 1 and 2). In the Paleozoic-Mesozoic (Flood) granitic rocks ^{214}Po radiohalos are often present, with or without ^{218}Po radiohalos. In two instances (Table 2) ^{214}Po radiohalos are more abundant than ^{210}Po radiohalos, but otherwise the latter outnumber the former generally by 5–40 to 1. Also, ^{210}Po radiohalos always outnumber the few ^{218}Po radiohalos that sometimes are present, with or without ^{214}Po radiohalos. When both ^{214}Po and ^{218}Po

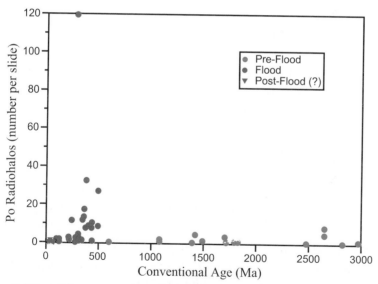

Figure 6. Plot of the conventional age (in millions of years) versus the number of Po radiohalos per slide (per sample) for each granitic pluton listed in Tables 1, 2, and 3. The 119.3 Po radiohalos per slide is again the Land's End Granite, Cornwall, England.

radiohalos are present the former always outnumber the latter, except in one instance, the Stanthorpe Adamellite (see Table 2). Consequently, there again does not appear to be a consistent pattern in the occurrence and abundances of the three Po radiohalo types. Furthermore, there does not appear to be any major difference in the pattern of occurrence of the three Po radiohalo types in the Precambrian (pre-Flood) granitic rocks compared to the Paleozoic-Mesozoic (Flood) granitic rocks, except that the Po radiohalos would seem to be more abundant in the Paleozoic-Mesozoic granitic rocks. Even the ^{238}U radiohalos appear to be more abundant in the Paleozoic-Mesozoic (Flood) granitic rocks compared to the Precambrian (pre-Flood) granitic rocks, even though tiny zircon grains would appear to be just as prevalent in all these biotite-bearing granitic rocks. Where ^{232}Th radiohalos occur surrounding monazite (thorium phosphate) inclusions, they are invariably and overwhelmingly outnumbered by the ^{238}U radiohalos around zircon inclusions.

6. Discussion

6.1 Pre-Flood and Flood Granites

Perhaps the most critical issue that needs to be first resolved is the question of the distinction between pre-Flood and Flood granites. This is particularly necessary in the light of Gentry's Creation hypothesis that, because of the brief half-lives of ^{218}Po and ^{214}Po, the granites in which these Po radiohalos are found must be primordial rocks produced by fiat creation [*Gentry*, 1979, 1980, 1982, 1983, 1984, 1986, 1988, 1989]. This claim has been regarded by many as justified, because most of the granitic rocks and related pegmatites and veins that yielded the Po radiohalos studied by Gentry are designated as Precambrian and thus recognized as pre-Flood, and maybe even Creation week when fiat creation did occur, as testified by the eyewitness account given by the Creator Himself in Genesis 1. The Precambrian designation of those granitic rocks is of course based on the observation that they intrude into, or are associated with, other Precambrian rocks, including Precambrian sedimentary strata and especially Precambrian metamorphic rocks. It is a moot point, but very much still under investigation and discussion, as to just how much of the Precambrian geologic record and the granitic rocks it contains should be consigned to the Creation week, and therefore how much of it pertains to the pre-Flood era from the end of the Creation week until the initiation of the Flood event. Even though some would place the pre-Flood/Flood boundary among the uppermost Precambrian (Upper Proterozoic) strata only a small distance below the Precambrian/Cambrian boundary [*Austin and Wise*, 1994], there is a widespread consensus that the evidence for the commencement of the Flood in the geologic record is where the strata containing fossilized multi-cellular organisms begin, and that is confirmed by the associated evidence of catastrophic deposition of those and other sedimentary strata. Thus the granitic rocks sampled and listed in Table 1 would be widely accepted as pre-Flood because they meet the necessary criteria for being so identified. The only exception might be the first listed granite, from Washington, U.S.A., because its radioisotope "age" could indicate that it formed very early in the Flood during and after the catastrophic deposition of fossiliferous sedimentary strata with similar or earlier "age" designations. This is of course based on the assumption that the radioisotope "age" provides a guide to the relative position of the dated rock unit in the geologic record. But in any case, there is some uncertainty as to the radioisotope "age" of this granite, and its relative position in its local geological context would favor its pre-Flood designation.

Not all the granitic rocks in which Gentry (and others) found Po radiohalos are designated as Precambrian. Tables 4 and 5 in *Snelling* [2000], which were extracted from *Wise* [1989], show that at only fifteen of the twenty-two localities where Po radiohalos had previously been found are those Po radiohalos designated as being hosted by Precambrian granitic and other rocks. Among the six localities listed where the Po radiohalos are hosted by conclusively-identified Phanerozoic granitic rocks is the Conway Granite of New Hampshire, which has been radioisotope dated as Jurassic [*Foland et al.*, 1971; *Foland and Faul*, 1977; *Foland and Allen*, 1991]. Indeed, the biotite flakes in which Gentry found the Po radiohalos had been separated by

Foland for the K-Ar radioisotope dating of the granite. As argued by *Wise* [1989] and *Snelling* [2000], the Conway Granite which hosts these Po halo-bearing biotite grains intrudes Paleozoic (or older Flood) schists and gneisses with distinct contact metamorphic zones, indicating that the host granite was hot when it intruded into the schists and gneisses. Furthermore, *Boucot et al.* [1958] had reported metamorphosed fossils in the schists and gneisses intruded by this granite, so undoubtedly these host rocks originally were fossiliferous Flood-deposited sediments that were subsequently metamorphosed and then intruded by this granite during the Flood (with nearly all fossils obliterated during the process). However, *Gentry* [1989] responded by suggesting that the granite is still a created rock dating back to the Creation week, and instead was tectonically intruded as a solid body into the schists and gneisses during the Flood, the contact metamorphic zone being produced by the heat and pressure generated during this tectonic movement, plus hot fluids from depth. In this way, even though Po radiohalos are found in the biotite in this granite which intrudes metamorphosed fossil-bearing sedimentary rocks, Gentry would still claim the granite and the Po were primordial (created). Indeed, *Gentry* [2003] argues that because the Scriptures repeatedly refer to God creating the foundations of the earth, and because deep drilling into the earth's crust at a number of sites has only found granitic rocks at such depths under the continents, granitic rocks must be the earth's foundation and therefore created by God. However, such an application of the Scriptures presumes the foundations of the earth have been correctly identified only as the granitic rocks at those depths in the earth's crust, when other rocks such as high-grade metamorphic granulites, which can be of granitic composition, have been demonstrated to occur at even greater depths in the earth's crust than where granitic rocks are found [*Müller*, 1977; *Wedepohl*, 1991, 1995]. Furthermore, the mantle rocks below could instead be interpreted as the foundation rocks of the earth implied by Scripture, because both the continents (continental crust) and the ocean basins (oceanic crust) sit on top of the mantle rocks.

To support his claim [*Gentry*, 2003] that all granitic rocks, as well as other hard crystalline rocks such as diorite, syenite, and gabbro, are all earth's primordial created rocks, Gentry has repeatedly challenged the geological community to synthesize granite in the laboratory containing biotite with Po radiohalos, all of which should be identical to the natural radiohalos, biotites and granites that he has studied from the various field locations [*Gentry*, 1979, 1983, 1984, 1986, 1988, 1989, 2003]. Gentry has maintained that if he is correct in identifying granitic rocks as primordial and created by God, then man will not be able to duplicate what God has created. Unfortunately, he has interpreted the apparent silence to his challenge as proving that granites have not been produced in laboratory experiments, and so the "parentless" Po radiohalos and the granites containing them did not form by natural processes. Nevertheless, *Wakefield* [1988b], *Wilkerson* [1989], *Wise* [1989], and *Snelling* [2000] have all responded with details of the experimental work that has been done to produce large crystals of the minerals found in granites, and also granitic textures, but Gentry continues to maintain that his challenge has never been, and therefore cannot be, met [*Gentry*, 2003]. However, as *Brown et al.* [1988] have pointed out, the ability to synthesize granite in the laboratory may have little to do with Creation, the argument basically being a *non sequitur.* Whether certain rocks or minerals can or cannot be synthesized in the laboratory may just reflect how sophisticated or not are laboratory procedures, equipment, etc. Indeed, minerals which could not be produced artificially in the past can now be synthesized—for example, diamonds and opals. Therefore, because all the basic minerals found in granites have already been synthesized in the laboratory [*Jahns and Burnham*, 1958; *Winkler and Von Platen*, 1958; *Mustart*, 1969; *Swanson et al.*, 1972], it would seem unwise to pose a challenge to the geological community on the basis of whether or not a hand-sized piece of granite is synthesized, since future developments in science are unpredictable. In any case, Gentry's insistence that his challenge has not been met is not only with respect to a piece of granite being produced in a laboratory, but the granite must contain Po radiohalos. However, the fact that the geological community has in general ignored Gentry's challenge is, in spite of continuing discussions over minor details, probably not due only to the geological community regarding the natural formation of granites by the crystallization and cooling of molten magma as already well proven from laboratory and field studies [*Pitcher*, 1993; *Hall*, 1996; *Johannes and Holtz*, 1996; *Bouchez et al.*, 1997; *Barbarin et al.*, 2001; *Best and Christiansen*, 2001], but because the Po radiohalos can be dismissed as a "very tiny mystery," as was done by Dalrymple in the 1981 Arkansas court case [*Gentry*, 1988, p. 122].

Even though some of the earliest Precambrian granites ultimately had to have been created by fiat during the Creation week with an automatic appearance of age, there is still the need to come to terms with those younger granites that were intruded into fossil-bearing and therefore Flood-deposited sedimentary strata, with all the appearance of clearly having formed as a result of the processes of intrusion of hot magmas that then crystallized and cooled. Granitic rocks listed in Table 2 fall into this category. So it is necessary to review the evidence that these granitic rocks have formed by the intrusion and cooling of hot magmas during the Flood, and that therefore the timescale for these processes is not in conflict with the timescale of the Flood event and the accumulation of its geological record. Indeed, it has already been shown by *Snelling and Woodmorappe* [1998] that it doesn't necessarily take long periods of time to form and cool large bodies of granitic rock. Furthermore, it is now clear that it previously was a misconception that the large crystals found in granitic rocks required slow cooling rates [*Wampler and Wallace*, 1998]. Indeed, the huge crystals sometimes found in granitic pegmatites indicate their rapid crystallization from fluids saturated with the components for those minerals.

6.2 Evidence for the Intrusion of Granitic Magmas

The experimental work on artificial silicate systems by *Tuttle and Bowen* [1958] is still regarded as a classic, groundbreaking study that settled the argument over the magmatic origin of granites. In the laboratory they melted powdered mixtures of the same compositions as natural granites and then allowed them to cool and crystallize. Significantly, the path of crystallization in the three-component system, quartz-orthoclase-albite (plagioclase), the three major mineral components of granitic rocks, reached its minimum temperature of 660–700°C when the components were in equal proportions (one-third each). When *Tuttle and Bowen* [1958] also plotted on triangular three-component compositional diagrams the normative mineral compositions (calculated from the whole-rock, major-element analyses) of 1269 granites and the modal compositions (as observed and determined from microscope thin sections) of 260 eastern U. S. granites, the quartz, orthoclase, and plagioclase percentages clustered around the small central areas of the diagrams representing a composition of one-third of each component. The point on the three-component compositional diagram where the minimum temperature plotted as the three minerals crystallized from the artificial molten magma in the laboratory coincided exactly with the tight clusters of both normative and modal analyses of the natural granites on the same diagram (the only slight variations being due to the use of different pressures and amounts of water in the laboratory experiments). The overwhelmingly obvious consensus was that these experiments had artificially reproduced natural granites from a hot granitic magma, and the strikingly unmistakable coincidence of the eutectic (minimum) point in the quartz-orthoclase-albite-water system with the exact normative and modal mineral compositions of thousands of granitic rocks analyzed then and subsequently, conclusively demonstrate that most natural granites must have therefore been derived by the cooling of hot granitic magmas. The granitic rocks listed in Table 2 have mineral compositions that are totally consistent with these results—for example, the Bathurst Granite [*Snelling*, 1974]. Lest it be argued that the grain sizes of the artificially produced granites are not exactly identical to those found in natural granites, it needs to be recognized that reproducing in the laboratory the natural conditions found inside the earth is extremely difficult because of their complexity, but many features of natural granites have been produced in the laboratory and it could only be a matter of time before granites absolutely identical to their natural counterparts are simulated in the laboratory. Most of the results of the experimental formation of granitic rocks and the application of those to the formation of natural granites have been compiled by *Johannes and Holtz* [1996].

In many sedimentary basins the deposited sediments with fossils buried in them can be thousands of meters thick. At depths of 5–10 km, especially in tectonically active zones, the pressures and temperatures can reach 5 kbar and 735°C respectively. Under those conditions, the phase equilibria laboratory studies [*Tuttle and Bowen*, 1958; *Johannes and Holtz*, 1996] have demonstrated that the fossiliferous sediments would partially melt, that is, the quartz (SiO_2), orthoclase ($KAlSi_3O_8$), and albite ($NaAlSi_3O_8$) components of the sediments melt leaving behind an unmelted residue of other components that have higher melting temperatures. Because the sedimentary rocks only partially melt to produce these three minerals in the melt, the result is that granitic (quartz-orthoclase-albite) magmas form. Granitic magmas are less dense than the surrounding residues and so, aided by the pressures at those depths, they then are forced to rise through fractures to intrude into the fossiliferous sediments near the top of the accumulated strata in the sedimentary basins, where they rapidly crystallize and cool [*Clemens and Mawer*, 1992; *Petford et al.*, 1993, 2000; *Petford*, 1995; *Brandon et al.*, 1996; *Harris et al.*, 2000]. The specialists researching these processes have themselves been surprised by the evidence they are accumulating that the magma transport processes from the depths where melting has taken place to the shallow depths where the intrusions form are far more rapid than previously envisaged, and once intruded the crystallization and cooling processes are likewise extremely rapid because of the water content of the granitic magmas and because of the role of circulating groundwaters in convective flows into the plutons to carry the heat away [*Cathles*, 1977; *Spera*, 1982; *Ingebritsen and Hayba*, 1994; *Hayba and Ingebritsen*, 1997; *Snelling and Woodmorappe*, 1998]. Subsequent erosion (primarily at the end of the Flood) has exposed at the earth's surface these cooled granitic plutons intruded into the fossiliferous sediments that surround them. This relationship can be readily observed in the field for a number of the granitic plutons listed in Table 2—for example, the Bathurst Granite [*Snelling*, 1974], the Harcourt Granite, Shap Granite, and Encounter Bay Granite.

Regional relationships also provide evidence of the hot magmatic origin of granites. In the sedimentary basins where thick sequences of fossiliferous sediments accumulated rapidly during the Flood, the progressively deeper burial of these sedimentary strata resulted in them being subjected to increasing pressures and temperatures so that they were metamorphosed on a regional scale. As already indicated, when the temperatures and pressures reach critical levels at the highest grades of metamorphism partial melting begins to form granitic magmas. Of course, the fossils and any other organic material that were buried in these sediments were obliterated by the processes of regional metamorphism, so that eventually in the highest grade and partial melting zones all trace of them has gone. Nevertheless, because subsequent erosion at the end of the Flood may have eroded deeply into these rocks, it is now sometimes possible in the field to literally walk over the outcrops from the fossiliferous sedimentary rocks through the zones of progressively metamorphosed sedimentary rocks. The mineral constituents in these zones reflect the increasing temperatures and pressures of regional metamorphism, these temperatures and pressures being verified by many phase equilibria experiments [*Spear*, 1993; *Bucher and Frey*, 2002]. Walking further towards the center of the regional metamorphic complex one comes to where the felsic minerals (quartz, orthoclase, and plagioclase) in the metasedimentary rocks have melted to form migmatites (rocks in which *in situ* partial melting has caused segregation into separate bands within the rock of the felsic melt and mafic residues), and then finally to where the temperatures had been at around 735°C and pressures of 5 kbar and above, so that melting formed granitic rocks (with a mineral composition of approximately 30% quartz, 35% orthoclase, and 35% albite). Some of the granites listed in Table 2 are situated in just such a context with these regional relationships, the classic textbook example being the Cooma Granodiorite in the center of the Cooma Metamorphic Complex in southeastern Australia [*Hall*, 1996], as described and discussed by *Snelling and Armitage* [2003]. Other examples include the Stone Mountain Pluton and La Posta Pluton [*Snelling and Armitage*, 2003], and the Palmer Granite.

The local boundaries between granites and the rocks they have intruded also argue for a hot magmatic origin of granites. In the field, and in three dimensions within mines (both open cast and underground), the effects on the host rocks of the intrusion of hot granitic magmas can be observed, including veining, stoping (extensive veining so that blocks of host rock are surrounded and thus included in the granitic rock), and contact metamorphism. Unfortunately, however, outcrops of the contact zones are often poorly exposed or absent due to the alteration of both the margins of the granitic plutons and their immediately adjacent host rocks having facilitated deeper weathering of them. Nevertheless, where granite/host rock contacts are exposed there is abundant evidence of the effects on the host rocks of the intrusion of the hot granitic magmas. The most spectacular examples of such contact metamorphism are skarns, where granitic magmas have metamorphosed limestones to produce new minerals under the high temperature and pressure conditions consistent with the intruding granitic magmas being responsible, which have been verified by many phase equilibria experiments. Furthermore, in some instances the hot magmatic fluids from the granites have introduced metals into the resultant skarns, such as W at Grassy, King Island, Tasmania [*Kwak*, 1978a, b; *Wesoloski*, 1984; *Brown*, 1990] and Cu at Santa Rita, New Mexico [*Nielson*, 1970; *Ahmad and Rose*, 1980]. At the margins of the Bathurst Granite (Table 2) contact metamorphism of limestone has produced calc-silicate hornfels, with the contact zone between the granite and its host fossiliferous sedimentary strata exposed in outcrops, road cuts, and railroad cuttings, where veining, stoping, and late-stage granitic dikes vividly attest to the intrusion of the molten granitic magma [*Snelling*, 1974]. Some of these contact effects are also observable in outcrops at the margins of the Shap Granite and Encounter Bay Granite (Table 2).

Thus there is field evidence, both locally and regionally, that each of the granites listed in Table 2 was generated, intruded, crystallized, and cooled during the year-long catastrophic global Flood event. Space precludes describing and documenting in detail all the relevant field evidences for each listed granitic pluton, but these details for the Stone Mountain Pluton, the La Posta Pluton, and the Cooma Granodiorite have already been documented by *Snelling and Armitage* [2003].

Planned future papers will describe and document the field and other evidences for the generation and intrusion during the Flood of some more of the granites listed in Table 2—the Bathurst Granite, the Shap Granite, the Encounter Bay Granite, and the Palmer Granite. It is crucial here, though, to establish the Flood origin of these granitic plutons, because it then places time limits not only on the process of formation of these granitic plutons, but on the radiohalos contained in them and reported in Table 2. Indeed, some of the evidence that shows how the formation and cooling of granitic plutons could be achieved within the time limits of the Flood year has already been documented by *Snelling and Woodmorappe* [1998], while the radiohalo evidence that further constrains the time limits on the formation and cooling of granitic plutons to only days and weeks has been presented by *Snelling and Armitage* [2003], and *Snelling et al.* [2003].

6.3 The Po Radiohalo Formation Model

Snelling and Armitage [2003] proposed a hydrothermal fluid transport model for the secondary formation of the Po radiohalos. This model is shown schematically in Figure 7 (from *Snelling et al.* [2003]), and is described and explained in more technical detail in Appendix A.

Tiny zircon crystals containing ^{238}U are found included between the sheets in the biotite crystal structure. As the ^{238}U decays some of the ^{238}U decay products (^{222}Rn and the Po isotopes) diffuse out of the zircon crystals. These are then transported by hydrothermal fluids flowing along the cleavage planes between the biotite sheets distances of 1 mm or less to sites where the Po isotopes precipitate with S (or other) atoms. At temperatures above 150°C the α-tracks along the flow path are annealed and no ^{238}U or Po radiohalos form around either the zircon or the Po radiocenters respectively. However, once the temperature drops below 150°C, with continued hydrothermal fluid flow both ^{238}U and Po radiohalos form concurrently. The Po that α-decays in the Po radiocenters to form the radiohalos is replaced by more Po isotopes from the flowing hydrothermal fluids. Once the flow stops no further Po radiohalo development occurs.

(a)

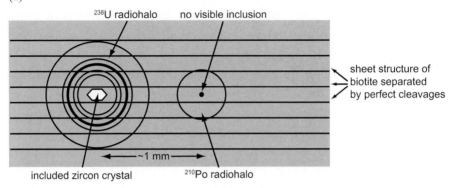

(b)

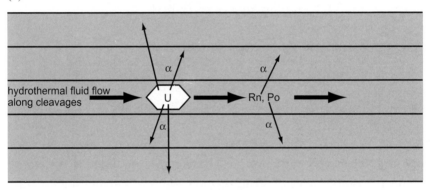

(c)

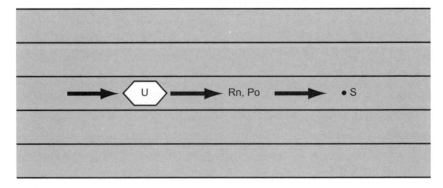

Figure 7 (left). Time sequence of diagrams to show schematically the formation of ^{238}U and ^{210}Po radiohalos concurrently as a result of hydrothermal fluid flow along biotite cleavage planes. (a) Diagrammatic cross-section through a biotite flake showing the sheet structure and perfect cleavage. A tiny zircon crystal has been included between two sheets and its ^{238}U content has generated a ^{238}U radiohalo. A ^{210}Po radiohalo has also developed around a tiny radiocenter between the same two sheets. Its radiocenter contains no visible inclusion, being just a bubble-like "hole" left behind by loss of the inclusion, probably by dissolution of the solid phases. (b) Enlarged diagrammatic cross-section through a biotite flake that has crystallized from a granite magma to 300°C. The U in an included zircon crystal is emitting α-particles, while hydrothermal fluids released from the cooling magma are flowing along the cleavage plane dissolving Rn and Po decay products from the zircon and carrying them downflow where they also emit α-particles. (c) However, at temperatures >150°C the α-tracks are annealed, so no radiohalos form and there is no α-track record of the hydrothermal fluids containing Rn and Po flowing at a rate of up to 5 cm per day along the cleavage plane. A few S atoms are in lattice defects downflow of the zircon crystal.

There are two important implications of this model. First, because of the short half-lives of the Po isotopes (only 3.1 minutes for ^{218}Po), the Po radiohalos had to form in a few hours to a few days. Second, because the full development of ^{238}U radiohalos requires the equivalent of at least 100 million years worth (at today's rates) of radioisotope decay, the concurrent formation of ^{238}U and Po radiohalos implies that at least 100 million years worth of radioisotope decay had to have occurred in no more than a few days. Thus radioisotope decay had to be accelerated, otherwise the decay of ^{238}U would not have supplied sufficient Po isotopes in the short time required to form the Po radiohalos. Furthermore, it can be demonstrated that all the processes involved in the model together place a limit of 6–10 days for the cooling of the host granitic plutons. All the technical details justifying these claims are in Appendix A.

Snelling and Armitage [2003] stressed that the secondary hydrothermal fluid transport model for the generation of the Po-rich radiocenters and subsequently the Po radiohalos was at that time tentative, awaiting

(d)

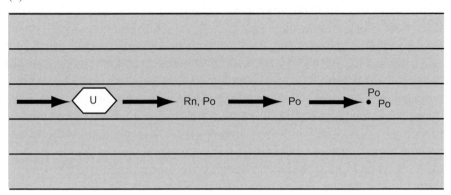

(e)

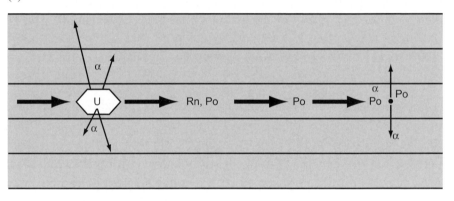

(f)

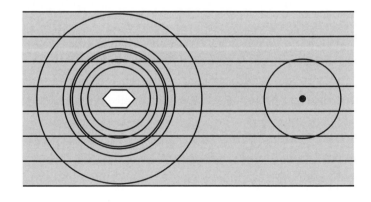

Figure 7 (left). Time sequence of diagrams to show schematically the formation of ^{238}U and ^{210}Po radiohalos concurrently as a result of hydrothermal fluid flow along biotite cleavage planes. (d) As the temperatures approach 150°C and ^{222}Rn decays to ^{218}Po, the Po isotopes in the hydrothermal fluids which have a geochemical affinity for S precipitate to form PoS as the fluids flow by the S in the lattice defects. The U in the zircon continues to decay and replenish the supply of Rn and Po in the fluids. (e) Once the temperature drops to below 150°C, the α-tracks produced by continued decay of U in the zircon and of Po in the PoS are no longer annealed and so start discoloring the biotite sheets. More Po isotopes in the flowing hydrothermal fluids replace the Po in the PoS as it decays to Pb, which also scavenges yet more Po. (f) With further passing of time and more α-decays both the ^{238}U and ^{210}Po radiohalos are fully formed, the granite cools completely and hydrothermal fluid flow ceases. Note that both radiohalos have to form concurrently below 150°C. The rate at which these processes occur must therefore be governed by the 138 day half-life of ^{210}Po. To get ^{218}Po and ^{214}Po radiohalos the processes would have to have occurred even faster.

further data collection and analysis. Their study reported results from only three granitic plutons, whereas this report provides the data from more than 50 granitic plutons ranging in conventional age from Archean to Tertiary (Tables 1, 2 and 3). These observations of the occurrence and distribution of the Po radiohalos in these granitic rocks are totally consistent with this secondary model for Po radiohalo formation. This model for Po radiohalo formation would also seem to be valid regardless of whether the granitic rocks are Precambrian (pre-Flood), Paleozoic-Mesozoic (Flood), or Tertiary (post-Flood?).

6.4 The Implications of the Annealing Temperature for Precambrian Granitic Rocks

The thermal annealing temperature of α-tracks and radiohalos is absolutely crucial to our understanding of the significance of all types of radiohalos, because it is only below that temperature that the radiohalos are preserved. Early observations on the annealing of radiohalos were based on heating experiments in the laboratory. *Poole*

[1928a, b] found that after fifteen minutes heating of both radiohalos and the host biotite at 610°C the halos had completely disappeared and the biotite very rapidly darkened. Similarly, *Armitage and Back* [1994] found that heating Po radiohalo-bearing biotite from 250° to 750°C for up to five hours causes variable but significant changes in damage to biotite, and can erase both structural defects and radiohalos. However, the most crucial and significant observations bearing on this question of the annealing temperature of radiohalos are those made in samples of granitic rocks taken from different depths in the deep drill-hole at Fenton Hill, New Mexico [*Laney and Laughlin*, 1981]. These observations are crucial because they involve granitic rocks under natural conditions. Uranium-238 radiohalos were found associated with every recognizable type of zircon inclusion in the biotite grains in the granitic rocks traversed by the drill-hole. The majority of the observed radiohalos were fully developed and somewhat overexposed. The present equilibrium down-hole temperatures were carefully measured and found to be 104°C at 870.8 m, 135.6°C at 1824.5 m, 153.7°C at 2164.7 m and 283°C at 4057.8 m. Zircons were found in the biotites throughout this temperature and depth range. Partial annealing of radiohalos was first observed at a depth of 1850 m (134°C present temperature). By a depth of 2120 m (151°C present temperature) the annealing of the radiohalos was total. Further down the hole there were zircon inclusions in the biotites as before, but the radiohalos had been totally annealed (obliterated). It was concluded that the present, elevated geothermal gradient had been sufficient to completely anneal the radiohalos at temperatures above about 150°C (at depths below 2115 m).

These observations are a guide to the temperature at which radiohalos are annealed under natural conditions. The temperature of 150°C is low from a geological perspective, and is towards the low end of the scale of temperatures over which hydrothermal fluids flowed in granitic rocks. All the samples of granitic rocks used in this study were collected from surface outcrops that aren't currently exposed to temperatures beyond 50°C, so the radiohalos found in them are not currently being annealed. However, it must be concluded, and this is crucial, that the radiohalos currently observed in these granitic rocks can only have formed and survived at temperatures below 150°C. A corollary to this is that if these granitic rocks have, since their formation, been subsequently exposed to temperatures of 150°C or greater, any radiohalos that were previously generated in them during or since their formation would have been annealed and obliterated during such a heating event.

The implications of these conclusions are highly significant, because they are fatal to Gentry's fiat Creation hypothesis for the origin of the Po radiohalos. Because the radiohalos we observe today, even in Precambrian granitic rocks, could only have formed since those rocks were last below 150°C, then the only circumstances under which currently observed radiohalos in Precambrian granitic rocks could have been generated at the time those rocks formed includes restriction of temperatures since their formation to less than 150°C. Such restriction would have to be regarded as not only highly improbable, but most likely impossible; because since their formation these Precambrian granitic rocks have usually been buried under thousands of meters of sediments deposited catastrophically during the global Flood event, subjecting them to elevated temperatures and pressures, particularly in tectonically active zones.

For example, the 1730–1840 Ma granitic rocks in the Precambrian crystalline basement of the Grand Canyon (Table 1) are estimated to have originally been buried under 3.5 km or more of Mesozoic-Paleozoic (Flood) sedimentary strata, and apatite fission track data indicate that these rocks were subjected to temperatures of at least 130–140°C [*Dumitru et al.*, 1994]. Indeed, apatite from a sample of the Elves Chasm Granodiorite yielded a fission track age of only a little more than 70 Ma [*Naeser et al.*, 1989] compared with that rock's zircon U-Pb radioisotope age of 1840 Ma [*Hawkins et al.*, 1996], indicating thermal annealing of the fission tracks in the apatite. Total annealing of fission tracks in apatite has been shown to occur at temperatures of between 105°C and 150°C [*Naeser*, 1981]. In the same drill-hole at Fenton Hill in New Mexico where the thermal annealing temperature of radiohalos was determined as being 150°C, it was found that the total annealing of fission tracks in apatite occurred at a temperature of 135°C [*Naeser and Forbes*, 1976]. However, equally significant is the zircon fission track data obtained from a granitic rock of the 1736 Ma Diamond Creek Pluton [*Karlstrom et al.*, 2003], which together with three samples of the Middle Proterozoic Dox Formation that is older than the overlying 1100 Ma Cardenas Basalt [*Larson et al.*, 1994; *Hendricks and Stevenson*, 2003], yielded a zircon fission track age of only 1038 Ma [*Naeser et al.*, 1989]. This would indicate that zircon grains in the granitic rocks of the Grand Canyon's Precambrian crystalline basement were partially thermally annealed by their burial, even under Precambrian sedimentary rocks, prior to deposition of the overlying Paleozoic-Mesozoic (Flood) sedimentary rocks. The temperature at which fission tracks in zircons are totally annealed has been estimated at 200±40°C [*Harrison et al.*, 1979; *Hurford*, 1985; *Zeitler*, 1985]. This implies that granitic rocks in the Precambrian basement of the Grand Canyon have been subjected to temperatures approaching 200°C since their formation. Consequently, even though these granitic rocks may have formed during the Creation week [*Austin*, 1994], the Po radiohalos currently observed in them (Table 1) cannot have been produced at that time, and thus are not (unfortunately) evidence of fiat creation.

It is highly likely, and almost certain, that the thermal history of the other granitic rocks listed in Table 1 is similar to that for the granitic rocks of the Grand Canyon's Precambrian crystalline basement. Indeed, the sample of Jemez granodiorite in Table 1 was obtained from the same deep drill-hole at Fenton Hill, New Mexico, in which *Laney and Laughlin* [1981] determined the annealing temperature of radiohalos. This sample came from a shallower depth than that at which the present temperature is 150°C. This does not imply that the ^{210}Po, ^{214}Po and ^{238}U radiohalos in this sample were generated at the time this granitic rock formed, contemporaneously with radiohalos in the same rock deeper in the drill-hole that have been obliterated by the current thermal regime. To the contrary, *Harrison et al.* [1986] found that ^{40}Ar/^{39}Ar analyses of microcline (potassium feldspar) from five samples of this 1500 Ma granodiorite, ranging in drill-hole depth from 1.13 to 4.56 km, and *in situ* temperatures from 110°C to 313°C, indicated thermal events affected the granodiorite at around 1030 and 870 Ma, well before the very recent development of the surrounding volcanic caldera responsible for the present geothermal gradient. The maximum $^{40}Ar/^{39}Ar$ age of 1030 Ma for the microcline grains from the 1500 Ma Jemez granodiorite was interpreted to represent the time at which the rock cooled below ~200°C [*Harrison and McDougall*, 1982], while the 870 Ma age was interpreted to be the time the regional temperature fell below about 130°C, perhaps because of a substantial amount of crustal uplift and erosion. This would appear to represent the earliest time since the formation of this granodiorite after which the ambient temperatures would be conducive to the radiohalos being generated also being preserved. But this doesn't take into account the granodiorite's subsequent burial by a sequence of Mesozoic and Paleozoic (Flood) sedimentary rocks [*Smith et al.*, 1970] prior to the recent (post-Flood) volcanic activity responsible for the present geothermal gradient and the present annealing of radiohalos at depth. So again, a thorough investigation of the geological history and context of this Precambrian granitic rock reveals that the radiohalos presently observed in it are not related to the formation of the granitic rock, but were probably generated subsequently, during and after the Flood.

6.5 The Generation of the Present Po Radiohalos in Precambrian Granitic Rocks

However, if the Po radiohalos in these Precambrian granitic rocks (Table 1) were not generated at the time these granitic rocks formed, but were generated much later during and after the Flood, then how were they generated? It has already been shown that the secondary hydrothermal fluid transport model can explain the formation of Po radiohalos during the late stage of cooling of granitic rocks as they formed during the Flood, so if the Po radiohalos in these Precambrian (pre-Flood) granitic rocks were generated subsequent to, and much later than, the formation and cooling of these granitic rocks, then how could these Po radiohalos be generated? These questions can be simply answered by first determining from the earlier description what are the essential components of the secondary hydrothermal fluid transport model, and whether these components would still be present in these

Precambrian granitic rocks during the Flood.

The first requirement is the presence of zircons as a source of ^{222}Rn and Po isotopes from α-decay of the ^{238}U in them. The second requirement for modeling Po radiohalo formation is that the ^{238}U decay was accelerated, so that a very large quantity of ^{222}Rn and Po atoms would be generated in a very short time frame. The third requirement is flow of hydrothermal fluids through the granitic rocks, including along the biotite cleavage planes, to rapidly transport the ^{222}Rn and Po isotopes. And a fourth essential requirement is suitable Po deposition sites between the biotite cleavage planes. Throughout their existence these granitic rocks have had zircon grains containing ^{238}U and its decay products, and suitable sites for Po deposition between biotite cleavage planes. The zircon grains can still be seen in these granitic rocks under the microscope, as can the Po radiocenters around which Po radiohalos currently exist.

The missing essential component is flow of hydrothermal fluids. The present absence of hydrothermal fluids in these granitic rocks doesn't necessarily preclude their presence in these rocks at times subsequent to their formation, such as during the Flood event. Present-day hydrothermal systems on the ocean floors derive most of their hydrothermal fluids from seawater circulating through the permeable oceanic crust down into the hot rocks surrounding shallow magma chambers [*Scott*, 1997]. Similarly, groundwaters deep within sedimentary basins are heated and dissolve salts and metals to become hydrothermal fluids within the sedimentary strata themselves, and in the Precambrian crystalline basement rocks beneath [*Garven and Raffensperger*, 1997]. Indeed, it has been demonstrated by computer simulations that the warm basinal brines, which have scavenged U from sedimentary and volcanic strata, can become hydrothermal fluids that may penetrate along fracture zones down into the Precambrian crystalline basement beneath. Upon encountering reducing conditions there the U precipitates and concentrates as hydrothermal unconformity-type U deposits, which are high grade and account for more than 25 percent of the world's proven U reserves. There is much evidence that hydrothermal fluids can be generated in diverse geological environments; and that the water content of these fluids can be derived not only from magmatic sources, but also from ground and meteoric waters, and even during regional metamorphism [*Taylor*, 1997]. These relationships between the sources of hydrothermal fluids and the ore deposits the hydrothermal fluids have produced have been firmly established by oxygen and hydrogen isotope studies of the different water sources, and of fluid inclusions in minerals in ore deposits and other geological environments.

There are thus many potential sources of hydrothermal fluids to circulate through Precambrian granitic rocks subsequent to their initial formation and cooling. This would be particularly so during the global catastrophic Flood event, when many of these granitic rocks would have been buried under thick sequences of Flood-deposited sedimentary strata, and when catastrophic tectonics would have greatly accelerated and concentrated the flow of heat from the earth's mantle into the crust [*Austin et al.*, 1994]. Accelerated nuclear decay would have produced heat that augmented these catastrophic geological processes. This accelerated nuclear decay would have generated heat *in situ* at the sites within these Precambrian granitic rocks where ^{222}Rn and Po isotopes were being generated from ^{238}U in zircon grains within biotites. Renewed hydrothermal fluid flow would thus carry these isotopes along the biotite cleavage planes to replenish deposition sites with Po isotopes to form radiocenters and generate new Po radiohalos.

Indeed, there is evidence within these Precambrian granitic rocks of more than one period of hydrothermal fluid flow through them. For example, *Sasada* [1989] investigated the fluid inclusions within the quartz grains of the Jemez granodiorite in the drill-hole at Fenton Hill, New Mexico, and the fluid inclusions in calcite veins within the granodiorite. It was found that the fluid inclusions in both the calcite veins and the quartz grains in the Jemez granodiorite indicated a heating event involving hydrothermal fluids subsequent to formation and cooling of the granitic rocks, and this was followed by cooling and the formation of the calcite veins, before heating of the rocks again to the present temperature by the recent volcanic activity. Furthermore, it was found that the hydrothermal fluids responsible for precipitating the calcite veins in the waning stage of the earlier thermal event are probably similar to the present geothermal fluids in and around the Fenton Hill area of the Valles Caldera. Thus hydrothermal fluids were active in the Jemez granodiorite during a thermal event long after its formation, and the same hydrothermal fluids that deposited the calcite veins would have been capable of transporting ^{222}Rn and Po isotopes from zircon inclusions in biotite grains as they flowed along the biotite cleavage planes to then deposit the Po isotopes in radiocenters that generated new Po radiohalos, concurrently with the formation of new ^{238}U radiohalos around the zircon inclusions. It can therefore be demonstrated that the secondary hydrothermal fluid transport model for the generation of Po radiohalos applies to the Po radiohalos currently found in these granitic rocks. These radiohalos were most probably generated as a result of hydrothermal fluid flows during and after localized thermal events associated with the catastrophic global Flood, long after the granitic rocks and any original Po radiohalos had been formed and then annealed by subsequent thermal events.

6.6 Why the Variations in Abundances of the Radiohalos?

It is apparent from the data in Tables 1, 2, and 3 that there are wide variations in the abundances of radiohalos in those granitic rocks. Furthermore, *Gentry* [1968] estimated there were as many as 20,000–30,000 ^{218}Po and ^{210}Po radiohalos per cm^3 in biotite in a Norwegian granitic pegmatite, while he [*Gentry*, 1999] estimated there are more than one billion U and Po radiohalos in fluorite in a German vein. And there doesn't seem to be a consistent pattern in the abundances of the three types of Po radiohalos.

In Appendix B an attempt is made to explain these abundance variations in terms of three key factors within the hydrothermal transport model for Po radiohalo formation. The first factor is the volume of hydrothermal fluid flow, the second is the quantity of available U-decay products, and the third is the availability of sufficient numbers of sites chemically conducive to Po isotope deposition. Related to the second factor are the varying abundances of zircon grains in the granitic rocks; the more zircon grains there are, the more U-decay products are available to form more Po radiohalos. Several additional factors might explain the different abundances of the Po radiohalos. These include the distances between the zircon grains and the Po radiocenters; the greater the distance the more likely only ^{210}Po radiohalos will form. Also, there is the overall state of crystallinity of the zircon grains and the diffusion of the ^{222}Rn and Po isotopes out of them. If ^{222}Rn diffuses out into the hydrothermal fluids, ^{218}Po radiohalos may form. However, because of the short half-lives of ^{218}Po and ^{214}Po, if only Po isotopes diffuse out of the zircons, only ^{210}Po radiohalos will probably form.

6.7 The Heat Problem

Radioisotope decay generates heat, so accelerated radioisotope decay would have generated enormous quantities of heat in a very short time. Furthermore, if granitic magmas cooled in 6–10 days during the Flood, there is also the heat they released that needed to be removed along with the heat generated by the simultaneous accelerated radioisotope decay. This problem is discussed further in Appendix C. Convective flows of hydrothermal fluids might be capable of moving and dissipating heat from granitic plutons, but an additional, as yet unknown mechanism would have been needed to remove the heat generated by the accelerated radioisotope decay.

6.8 Other Applications and Their Implications

Because there are other sources of hydrothermal fluids apart from cooling granitic magmas, *Snelling and Armitage* [2003] predicted that there may be other geological contexts in which hydrothermal fluids may have transported available U-decay products to generate Po radiohalos. Thus in this study the search for Po radiohalos was extended to metamorphic rocks, and plentiful Po radiohalos were found (Table 4, p. 188). These results and their implications are discussed fully in Appendix D. The hydrothermal fluids responsible for the Po radiohalos confirm the model that regional metamorphic complexes could have been produced by hydrothermal fluid transformation of the minerals in deeply-buried sedimentary rocks. This sets a rapid timescale of only days on both the formation and cooling of metamorphic complexes.

The higher abundance of Po radiohalos in the Land's End Granite of Cornwall, England (Table 2 and Figure 6) was concluded to be due to that granite hosting hydrothermal ore lodes, including those containing U (Appendix D). Thus Po radiohalos associated with deposition of metallic ores by hydrothermal fluids in lodes hosted by granitic and metamorphic rocks could imply their rapid deposition and formation. Additionally, Po radiohalos could therefore provide an exploration tool for the discovery of new metallic ore lodes in prospective host rocks.

7. Conclusions

The evidence from the discovery of the three types of Po radiohalos in the biotites within granitic plutons that can be demonstrated to have formed during the Flood year falsifies the hypothesis for the formation of these Po radiohalos and their host granitic rocks during the Creation week. Furthermore, the presence of dark, mature (fully-formed) ^{238}U and ^{232}Th radiohalos in the same biotites in these same granitic rocks may be interpreted as physical evidence for at least 100 million years worth (at today's rates) of radioactive decay occurring during those parts of the Flood year represented by these granitic rocks. Accordingly, conventional radioisotope dating of rocks based on the assumption of the constancy of decay rates is grossly in error.

The hydrothermal fluid transport model for the secondary formation of the Po radiohalos as proposed by *Snelling and Armitage* [2003] is overwhelmingly confirmed by the evidence gathered in this study from more than fifty granitic plutons. Because the zircon inclusions in the biotite grains contain large amounts of U, ^{238}U decay products readily diffuse out of the zircon crystal lattices. Radon-222 and Po isotopes released from the zircon inclusions are carried by the hydrothermal fluids flowing along the cleavage planes of the biotite grains. These isotopes are carried only short distances (an average of 1 mm) to be deposited at sites where the chemical environment was suitable for concentration of the Po isotopes before they α-decayed. The radiocenters thus formed generated the Po radiohalos. However, due to the annealing temperature of α-tracks being 150°C, even though the transport of these isotopes in the hydrothermal fluids would have been occurring above that temperature, the radiohalos could only form once cooling had reached that temperature. Thus the short half-lives of ^{218}Po and ^{214}Po require the hydrothermal fluid transport and chemical concentration time frames to have been extremely short, less than ten half-lives of these Po isotopes, and calculated to be on the order of hours to just a few days for complete radiohalo formation. Which Po radiohalos form and the abundances of them were determined by the supply of ^{222}Rn and Po isotopes to the hydrothermal fluids (dependent on the U concentrations in the zircons and the diffusion rates), the volume of hydrothermal fluid flow, the distances from the zircon sources to the radiocenters, and the numbers of Po radiocenters that developed (dependent on the metal and other ions available, the numbers of lattice defect sites, and the locally conducive chemical environment). The implication that the short-lived ^{222}Rn and Po isotopes must survive in the cooling granitic magma until the temperature drops below the α-track annealing temperature of 150°C for the Po radiohalos to then form means that the timescale for the cooling of granitic plutons was extremely short, calculated at between six and ten days. And it should be noted that this timescale is constrained by the half-lives of these isotopes, and not by the assumption that these granites formed during the Flood year.

It is also concluded that this hydrothermal fluid transport model for the secondary formation of Po radiohalos also applies to Precambrian (pre-Flood) granitic rocks, whereas in Tertiary (post-Flood?) granitic rocks there has generally been insufficient nuclear decay for enough α-tracks to register as radiohalos. However, because of the annealing temperature of α-tracks being so low at 150°C, even the radiohalos presently observed in the Precambrian granitic rocks had to have formed below that temperature. Thus it is unlikely that the presently observed radiohalos in these rocks were generated at the time when these pre-Flood rocks formed, even if some of them represent Creation week rocks. The heat generated by the accelerated nuclear decay during the Flood, and the catastrophic tectonic and geological processes during the Flood that were driven by heat, might have raised the temperatures in these Precambrian granitic rocks above 150°C, and thus annealed all previous radiohalos. Certainly heat from accelerated radioactive decay would have annealed all previous radiohalos. Connate fluids and groundwaters in granitic and other rocks heated to become hydrothermal fluids would have circulated through pre-Flood granitic rocks and transported ^{222}Rn and Po isotopes from zircons to replenish the Po radiocenters down flow along biotite cleavage planes to generate new Po radiohalos. Thus the thermal annealing temperature of α-tracks at 150°C falsifies the hypothesis that the Po radiohalos we observe in Precambrian granitic rocks were generated by Po created at the same time as those granitic rocks were.

The accelerated nuclear decay, that may be presumed on the basis of concurrent formation of the ^{238}U and Po radiohalos, would have generated enormous quantities of heat. On the basis of present parameters this heat may be estimated to have been sufficient to vaporize the rocks completely. The fact that the zircon inclusions and the biotites with their contained U and Po radiohalos did not vaporize is evidence that the supposed heat generated did not cause a perceived problem. While the convective flows of hydrothermal fluids were capable of moving and dissipating heat from granitic plutons, that mechanism alone would not seem capable of removing the calculated enormous quantities of heat over the brief timescale required to avoid vaporization of granitic rocks due to the accelerated nuclear decay in them. Another mechanism needs to be explored, such as the volume cooling effect of a sudden expansion of the fabric of space.

The discovery of plentiful Po radiohalos in metamorphic rocks extends the application of the hydrothermal fluid transport model for Po radiohalo formation to these rocks, with powerful and far-reaching implications. The required hydrothermal fluid flows dictated by the formation of the Po radiohalos could confirm the model that regional metamorphic complexes were produced by hydrothermal fluid transformation of the minerals in deeply-buried sedimentary rocks. This model would set a rapid timescale on the formation and cooling of regional metamorphic complexes. Only a few days would be required for the temperatures to drop to 150°C and the Po radiohalos then formed. It is also evident that Po radiohalos could be associated with deposition of metallic ores by hydrothermal fluids in lodes hosted by, and associated with, granitic and metamorphic rocks. If preliminary observations of Po radiohalos in association with such hydrothermal ore deposits are confirmed, there is implication for their rapid deposition and formation. Polonium radiohalos can also provide an exploration tool for the discovery of new metallic ore lodes in prospective host rocks. Rather than falsification of the Creation hypothesis for the Po radiohalos in granitic rocks being a disappointment, the Po radiohalos provide powerful evidence for many rapid geological processes consistent with both the year-long catastrophic global Biblical Flood, and a young earth.

8. Further Work

While this study has produced abundant evidence of the widespread occurrence of Po radiohalos in granitic rocks throughout the geologic record, consistent with, and confirming, the hydrothermal fluid transport model for the secondary formation of the Po radiohalos, much further work needs to be done. Many more Precambrian granitic plutons need to be sampled to fill gaps in the coverage of the Precambrian geologic record. The Po radiohalos evidence thus accumulated may help in our understanding of the pre-Flood geologic record, perhaps even helping to define where the Creation week ends in that record. Further sampling of Tertiary granitic plutons would be advisable so as to confirm the general absence of radiohalos in such rocks as due to insufficient nuclear decay having occurred in them. Most importantly, it is desirable that some detailed case studies be undertaken on a moderate number of granitic plutons, involving numerous samples from each pluton so as to increase our understanding of the distribution and abundance of the different radiohalo types. This would particularly include revisiting some of the rocks in which Gentry and others found huge numbers of Po radiohalos. There should be sampling not only of granitic rocks, but also of associated pegmatites and veins. It would be predicted that there could be a higher frequency of Po radiohalos in such pegmatites and veins which form from the late stages of crystallizing granitic magmas (see Appendix B.2). Our understanding of radiohalos is still in its infancy.

With such potential further implications in mind, it is extremely important that the radiohalo studies be extended to metamorphic rocks of all different types, including not only regional metamorphic complexes, but also contact metamorphic rocks where hydrothermal fluid flows have contributed to the transformation of the host rocks in contact with the cooling granitic plutons. Such studies should involve careful sampling of selected regional metamorphic complexes and the metamorphic zones within them to ascertain the distribution and abundances of the Po radiohalos, and also U and Th radiohalos. Such studies could elucidate the hydrothermal fluid flow paths and thus confirm the role of hydrothermal fluids in the formation of the regional metamorphic complexes by the transformation of the original minerals in the precursor sedimentary rocks, as well as confirming the extremely short timescale for the formation of the metamorphic complexes and their cooling.

Polonium radiohalo studies should be extended to the rocks hosting metallic ores that have been deposited by hydrothermal fluid flows which also altered the host rocks. If the preliminary evidence of Po radiohalos being associated with hydrothermal ore veins and lodes is confirmed, then the formation of the Po radiohalos would likewise constrain the deposition of these ore veins and lodes to the rapid timescale for the hydrothermal fluid flows responsible. Such investigations should include some of the hydrothermal ore veins where abundant Po radiohalos were previously documented by Gentry. Furthermore, appropriate studies need to be undertaken to confirm the possibility of Po radiohalos being an exploration tool for the discovery of hydrothermal ore deposits in new districts, and where such ore deposits are so deeply buried that they may not be detected by other exploration methods. Such confirmation of Po radiohalos as an exploration tool would bring them to the attention of the conventional geological community, as well as elaborate their far-reaching implications for the rapid timescale of many geological processes that are usually regarded as taking millions of years.

Acknowledgments

Full acknowledgment is given to the groundbreaking pioneer work on Po radiohalos by Robert Gentry. The training and counsel he provided on radiohalos enabled this research project to be accomplished. Time was spent with Bob in the field, and he also gave personal instruction on the technique of mounting biotite flakes onto microscope slides. It is disappointing that the outcome of this research did not corroborate Bob's hypothesis, but the Po radiohalos still remain profound objective evidence for the rapid formation of granitic rocks, and also probably metamorphic rocks and hydrothermal ore deposits, consistent with a created young earth and the Biblical Flood. In disagreeing with Bob, however, it is important that his essential pioneering research, that was foundational to the research reported here, be recognized and emphasized.

Many people contributed to this research effort, particularly in the provision of the many samples of granitic rocks, either independently or in assisting in the necessary fieldwork. These people include, in alphabetical order, Steve Austin, John Baumgardner, Danny Faulkner, Carl Froede, Paul Garner, Chris Henschke, William (Bill) Hoesch, Peter Klevberg, Mike Oard, Vesa Palonen, Darry Stansbury, Tom Vail, Larry Vardiman, Sandy Waresak, and Kurt Wise. Without the help of these people there would not have been the large number of granitic rock samples that this study reports.

The help of Mark Armitage in the crucial work of preparing microscope slides and then scanning them for radiohalos must be emphasized and gratefully acknowledged. Mark was responsible for processing most of the U.S. and Scandinavian rock samples, while the author was responsible for the processing of all Australian and British samples. Nevertheless, the responsibility for all the results and the interpretation of them rests solely with the author. This research would not have been possible without the gifts of the donors to the RATE project. Those gifts are acknowledged and the donors thanked. The support and helpful advice of the other members of the RATE group are also acknowledged and appreciated.

Appendix A: The Po Radiohalo Formation Model

A.1 A Detailed Description of the Model

Snelling and Armitage [2003] presented a logical argument for the secondary formation of Po radiohalos by transport of ^{222}Rn and Po isotopes in the hydrothermal fluids released by the crystallizing and cooling granitic magmas below 150°C, the thermal annealing temperature of radiohalos in biotite [*Laney and Laughlin*, 1981; *Armitage and Back*, 1994]. This model is shown schematically in Figure 7, from *Snelling et al.* [2003]. The absolutely critical observation on which this model is based is that ^{238}U and Po (most often ^{210}Po) radiohalos are consistently found in the same biotite flakes (Figures 4i-1 and 7a). Whereas the ^{238}U radiohalos have tiny zircon inclusions as their radiocenters, almost all the Po radiohalos in these granites have no visible central inclusions as their radiocenters, just tiny empty "holes" or what looks like "bubbles." Because the biotite flakes have been pulled apart along their cleavage planes to be mounted for microscope examination and identification of the radiohalos in them, this implies that when the ^{238}U and Po radiohalos are observed in the same biotite flakes under the microscope, the radiocenters of these radiohalos are all sitting on the same cleavage planes, which of course means that the radiocenters were originally between the same two sheets of the biotite crystal structure (Figure 7a and b). Now because the thermal annealing temperature of radiohalos in biotite is 150°C [*Laney and Laughlin*, 1981; *Armitage and Back*, 1994), this implies that both the ^{238}U and Po radiohalos together in these biotite flakes could only have formed concurrently below that temperature since the last heating of the biotite above 150°C. The formation of both ^{238}U and Po radiohalos would have to have been concurrent, because as the ^{238}U decays and forms its radiohalo, it also supplies the Po required to form the Po radiohalos (see below). However, at the present rate of ^{238}U decay it has been estimated that to develop a fully-formed (mature) ^{238}U radiohalo requires 100 million years worth of such slow radioisotope decay [*Gentry*, 1973, 1974; *Humphreys*, 2000; *Snelling*, 2000]. On the other hand, the Po isotopes that are the daughters produced by ^{238}U decay only have fleeting half-lives, 138 days for ^{210}Po but only 164 microseconds for ^{214}Po. The latter is particularly critical to the situation where ^{214}Po radiohalos are found in the same biotite flakes as ^{238}U radiohalos, implying that they formed concurrently. Thus if 100 million years worth of ^{238}U decay had to have occurred while the Po radiohalos were forming, then this implies the ^{238}U decay had to have been grossly accelerated so that the 100 million years worth of ^{238}U decay could be fitted into the hours and days over which the Po isotopes accumulated in the radiocenters from which the Po radiohalos concurrently formed. This suggests that the Po transport (or infusion) would have been extremely rapid, so modeling this process is necessary. Of course, the obvious implication is that all conventional radioisotope dating of these rocks, based on the assumption of constant decay at today's slow rates, thus would be grossly in error.

Research in experimental igneous petrology has shown that the temperatures required for melting of rocks to form granitic magmas are significantly lowered by increasing water activity up to saturation, and the amount of temperature lowering increases with increasing pressure [Ebadi and Johannes, 1991]. A corollary to this is that water solubility in granitic magmas increases with pressure, and therefore depth, so that whereas at 1 kbar pressure (3–4 km depth) the water solubility is 3.7 wt% [Holtz et al., 1995], at 30 kbar pressure (100 km depth) the water solubility is approximately 24 wt% [Huang and Wyllie, 1975]. Indeed, water is generally recognized as the most important magmatic volatile component, both for its abundance and for its effects on physical and chemical properties of magmas. Furthermore, the role of water in the crystallization of magmas is fundamental. Indeed, plutons with considerable amounts of magmatic water cool much faster than do those which don't. For example, for a granodiorite pluton 10 km wide and emplaced at 7 km depth, the cooling time from liquidus to solidus temperatures decreases almost ten-fold as the water content increases from 0.5 wt% to 4 wt%, other factors remaining constant [Spera, 1982]. Following the emplacement of a granitic magma in the upper crust, crystallization occurs by the irreversible loss of heat to the surrounding country rocks [Candela, 1992]. As crystallization proceeds, the water dissolved in the magma that isn't incorporated in the minerals crystallizing stays in the residual melt, so the water concentration there increases. When the saturation water concentration is lowered to the actual water concentration in the residual melt, first boiling occurs and water (as superheated steam) is expelled from solution in the melt, which is consequently driven towards higher crystallinities as the temperature continues to fall. Bubbles of water vapor then nucleate and grow, causing second (or resurgent) boiling within the zone of crystallization just underneath the solidus boundary and the already crystallized magma (Figure 8). As the concentration and size of these vapor bubbles increase, vapor saturation is quickly reached, but initially the vapor bubbles are trapped by the immobile crystallized magma crust [*Candela*, 1991]. The vapor pressure thus increases and

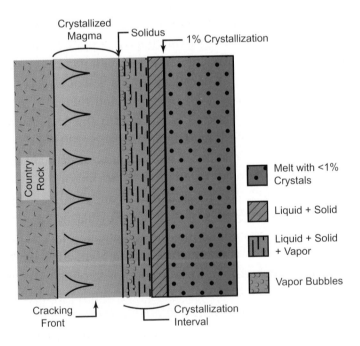

Figure 8. Cross-section of the margin of a magma chamber traversing (from left to right): country rock, cracked pluton, uncracked pluton, solidus, crystallization interval, and bulk melt (after *Candela* [1991]).

the aqueous fluid can then only be removed from the sites of bubble nucleation through the establishment of a three-dimensional critical percolation network, with advection of aqueous fluids through it or by means of fluid flow through a cracking front in the crystallized magma and out into the country rocks (Figure 8). Once such fracturing of the pluton has occurred (and the cracking front will go deeper and deeper into the pluton as the solidus boundary moves progressively inwards towards the core of the magma chamber), not only is magmatic water released from the pluton carrying heat out into the country rocks, but the cooler meteoric water in the country rocks is able to penetrate into the pluton and thus establish hydrothermal circulation. The more water dissolved in the magma, the greater will be the pressure exerted at the magma/rock interface [*Knapp and Norton*, 1981].

Thus by the time the temperature has fallen to 300°C at the core of a granitic pluton the solidus boundary and cracking front have both reached the core of the pluton as well. This means that the magma has totally crystallized into the constituent minerals of the granite. It also means that a fracture network has been established through the total volume of the pluton and out into the surrounding country rocks through which a vigorous flow of hydrothermal fluids has been established. These hydrothermal fluids thus carry heat by convection through this fracture network away from the cooling pluton, ensuring the temperature of the granitic rock mass continues to rapidly fall. The amount of water involved in this hydrothermal fluid convection system is considerable, given that a granitic magma has enough energy due to inertial heat to drive roughly its mass in meteoric fluid circulation [*Norton and Cathles*, 1979; *Cathles*, 1981]. However, there would be even more heat available to drive the circulation of the hydrothermal fluids if accelerated nuclear decay was occurring simultaneously. With such a large volume of hydrothermal fluids percolating through the cooling rock mass, the fluids would also find their way around the grain boundaries of the constituent minerals, and in the case of biotite along its cleavage planes (Figure 7b). Indeed, the heat-driven hydrothermal fluids would force their way along cleavage planes, opening them up to the fluid flow. Between some of the cleavage planes in some of the biotite flakes within the granitic rock are included zircon crystals, and these contain large quantities of trace U, sometimes as much as several hundred ppm. Because of the accelerated nuclear decay occurring concurrently with crystallization of the granitic pluton, the zircons would also contain relatively large concentrations of the ^{238}U decay daughter isotopes, including ^{222}Rn and the three Po isotopes. In fact, it is because ^{238}U decay in the zircons is required as the source of the Po isotopes to produce the Po radiohalos that the ^{238}U and Po radiohalos had to have formed concurrently.

Now Rn is an inert gas, meaning that its atoms have no chemical affinity that would attract them and/or attach them to atoms of other elements, and meaning that its atoms have so much vibrational energy that they neither cohere to form a liquid or link to one another to form a solid. Because of these properties, and because of the heat still in the granite, the ^{222}Rn easily diffuses out of the zircon crystal lattice in spite of the large size of its atoms and dissolves in the hydrothermal fluid flowing along the biotite cleavage planes past the zircon crystal. As it is then carried down flow along the cleavage planes from the zircon crystal the ^{222}Rn eventually α-decays through ^{218}Po, that then subsequently α-decays to ^{214}Po and finally ^{210}Po, while the ^{238}U still in the zircon crystal also α-decays. However, at temperatures above 150°C all α-tracks are annealed [*Laney and Laughlin*, 1981; *Armitage and Back*, 1994], so no radiohalos form and there is no α-track record of the hydrothermal fluids containing the Rn and Po flowing along the cleavage planes (Figure 7c). Similarly, above 150°C α-recoil traces are also annealed. Of course, the hydrothermal fluids would also carry in solution various metals, usually in trace amounts (but sometimes in sufficient quantities to be deposited and concentrated as economic hydrothermal ore deposits). Sulfur is a key component of such ore deposits and granitic rocks, which even when not hosting or associated with hydrothermal sulfide ore deposits contain trace to minor amounts of S. Because the S atoms in granitic rocks are not always found in discrete sulfide minerals it is not unusual for them to be incorporated in the silicate minerals in lattice defects. This could have been accomplished by S atoms being incorporated in mineral lattices at the time those minerals were crystallizing, but it can also result subsequently, such as in biotite, when these late-stage hydrothermal fluids flow along the cleavage planes (Figure 7c).

As the temperature of the granite continues to fall towards 150°C, and ^{222}Rn that has diffused out of the zircon and been included in the hydrothermal fluids flowing past continues to decay to ^{218}Po, the Po isotopes in the hydrothermal fluids would precipitate to form PoS as the fluids flow by the S atoms in the lattice defects, because Po has a geochemical affinity for S [*Bagnall*, 1957] (Figure 7d). The ^{238}U in the zircon also continues to decay and therefore replenish the supply of ^{222}Rn and Po isotopes in the hydrothermal fluids flowing along the cleavage planes in the biotite past the zircon. All α-tracks being produced by the α-decays in the ^{238}U series, whether surrounding the zircon, around the fluid flow paths along the cleavage planes, or around the S atoms where Po isotopes had precipitated, continued to be annealed so there is no preserved record of either those α-decays or the hydrothermal fluid flow along the cleavage planes, except for pervasive chloritization of the biotite. As the Po in the PoS α-decays the S atoms are then available to attract more Po isotopes from the hydrothermal fluids flowing past to reform the PoS radiocenters. Additionally, as the Po eventually decays to Pb, the Pb will also assist in the further concentration of new Po from the passing hydrothermal fluids into the radiocenters, because Pb also has a geochemical affinity for Po (forming PbPo or lead polonide) [*Bagnall*, 1957].

Once the temperature drops to below 150°C, the α-tracks produced by the continued α-decay of the ^{238}U in the zircon and of the Po isotopes in the PoS are no longer annealed, and so the α-tracks produced by α-decay start discoloring the biotite sheets surrounding the zircon crystal and the tiny PoS accumulations (Figure 7e). With the passage of time these processes continue so that more α-decays of both the ^{238}U in the zircon radiocenters and the Po isotopes in the PoS radiocenters produce α-tracks that continue discoloring the surrounding biotite sheets until the resultant ^{238}U and Po radiohalos are fully formed (Figure 7f). Eventually, the hydrothermal fluid flow ceases as the granite cools completely within weeks (see below). Thus if there is no further replenishment of the Po radiohalos centers, there is no further darkening of the Po radiohalos. Nevertheless, Po radiohalos might conceivably form for as long as water continued to diffuse through any mineral that contained U. Within two to three years of Po radiohalo formation commencing U-bearing minerals would be the only potential source of solution-transportable Po. But the problem would then be whether there is sufficient Po available to be dissolved, another reason why visible Po radiohalos would not have formed after the Flood. On the other hand, the ^{238}U in the zircons continues to α-decay so that the resultant ^{238}U radiohalos continue to darken right through until the present time.

It is important to note that both ^{238}U and Po radiohalos (Figure 7) have to form concurrently and are evidenced by halos only when the granite has cooled to below 150°C. The upper limit for the rate at which these processes occur must therefore be governed by the 138 day half-life of ^{210}Po when ^{238}U and ^{210}Po radiohalos are found in the same biotite flakes. Of course, for ^{218}Po and ^{214}Po radiohalos to be generated in the same biotite flakes in which ^{238}U radiohalos around zircon grains also occur, these processes would have to have occurred at very much faster rates, as governed by their very much shorter half-lives. However, because this model for Po radiohalo formation requires ^{238}U decay to have been grossly accelerated by a factor of at least 10^6, it might be expected that the decay of the Po isotopes and their precursors would likewise have been accelerated by a similar factor, thus placing even tighter time strictures on these processes described above. This may not be the case. *Austin* [2005] and *Snelling* [2005] have argued that the discordances between the isochron ages obtained on the same rocks by the different radioisotope systems can only be resolved if the acceleration factor was a function of the decay half-life (and perhaps the atomic weight), such that the longer the half-life of a radioisotope, the more its decay was accelerated. If this were the case, because the half-lives of the Po isotopes and ^{222}Rn are so fleetingly short compared to the half-life of ^{238}U, the decay of the Po isotopes and ^{222}Rn would hardly have been effected by the acceleration of ^{238}U decay. In contrast, those ^{238}U decay products that presently have longer half-lives, such as ^{234}U (248,000 years), ^{230}Th (75,000 years), ^{226}Ra (1662 years), and ^{210}Pb (22 years), would have had their decay accelerated by different factors, but very much lower than that for ^{238}U decay.

A.2 The Source of the ^{238}U Decay Products

There are a few essential components of this Po radiohalo formation model that were dealt with by *Snelling and Armitage* [2003], but which need to be reiterated here. First is the question of the source of the ^{238}U decay products, principally the three Po isotopes. *Snelling and Armitage* [2003] argued that in the three granitic plutons they studied the only common plausible source of ^{238}U decay products was the zircon grains in these granitic rocks that commonly contained tens to hundreds of ppm U. Tiny zircon grains containing large quantities of trace U are also present in all the granitic rocks listed in Tables 1, 2, and 3. These are the U contents of the zircons at the present time, after hundreds of millions of years worth (at today's rates) of ^{238}U decay has occurred to produce the conventional radioisotope ages for these granitic rocks. So this not only implies even greater U contents in these zircons when the granitic rocks formed, but this ^{238}U decay would have produced hundreds of millions of years worth of decay products, including ^{222}Rn and the three Po isotopes. Because the ^{238}U and Po radiohalos had to form concurrently this ^{238}U decay had to have been occurring at a greatly accelerated rate, so even before hydrothermal fluids began transporting these isotopes, large quantities of them would be generated in the zircon grains.

A.3 Hydrothermal Fluid Transport

The radiohalos would only be preserved in biotites after the temperature of the newly-formed granitic plutons falls below 150°C, because above that temperature the α-tracks would have been erased. Such temperatures correspond to the middle of the regime of hydrothermal fluids. Depending on the depth of emplacement during magma intrusion, 150°C is well below the temperature of second boiling and magma degassing (about 370°C depending on the confining pressure), when the water and volatiles held in solution within the magma are released [*Burnham*, 1997; *Giggenbach*, 1997].

Of course, the hydrothermal fluid transport of U-decay products such as ^{226}Ra, ^{222}Rn, and the three Po isotopes would have started as soon as the hydrothermal fluids were generated at above 300°C, so the ^{226}Ra, ^{222}Rn, and ^{218}Po could already have been transported by the hydrothermal fluids some distance before the temperature fell to 150°C without leaving any α-track record of their passage. However, by the time the temperature dropped below the α-track thermal erasure threshold at around 150°C in biotite, only the three Po isotopes can have been incorporated in new radiocenters, as there is no evidence of any other α-emitters in the resultant Po radiohalos [*Gentry*, 1971; *Gentry et al.*, 1973]. Thus, it would seem more plausible to postulate that ^{226}Ra and/or ^{222}Rn would have been the isotopes initially transported by the hydrothermal fluids, because their half-lives of 1622 years and 3.8 days respectively (the latter especially not appreciably effected by the acceleration of ^{238}U decay) would have allowed more time and thus greater distances for the transport process than the 3.1 minute half-life of ^{218}Po (which was initially regarded as a major obstacle to any secondary transport process). Of course, the transport process could also have started with ^{210}Po because of its 138 day half-life, but only ^{210}Po radiohalos would have resulted.

Brown [1997] favored ^{226}Ra to allow the most time for transport over the required distances, yet he calculated that given a constant supply of ^{226}Ra in a hydrothermal fluid the equilibrium concentrations in the fluid of all three Po isotopes would require, beginning at the zero level, about 100 years. *Snelling and Armitage* [2003] therefore discounted ^{226}Ra transport in the hydrothermal fluids as the primary isotope responsible for supply of the Po isotopes to the Po radiohalo centers, because that time frame is longer than the time frame allowable for the cooling of the granitic rocks from the temperatures at which the magmas were intruded. Indeed, because granitic magmas were generated by the partial melting of fossiliferous Flood-deposited sediments, and those magmas then intruded into overlying fossiliferous sediments deposited later in the Flood, to then cool in time for erosion at the end of the Flood to expose the resultant plutons at the earth's surface today, the time frame for cooling of the granitic rocks and the hydrothermal fluid transport of the U-decay products has to have been very much less than a year. Additionally, ^{222}Rn is favored over ^{226}Ra as the start of the hydrothermal fluid transport process because there are two α-decay steps from ^{226}Ra to ^{218}Po, but only one α-decay step from ^{222}Rn to ^{218}Po. Due to α-track annealing there is no observable α-track record along the biotite cleavage planes where the hydrothermal fluids have flowed, so ^{222}Rn is preferred because there would be fewer α-tracks to be annealed. In any case, as an inert gas ^{222}Rn would have more readily diffused out of the zircon crystal lattice than ^{226}Ra, which because of its ionic charge and chemical bonding is more likely to be slower at diffusing out of the zircon crystal lattice. Radon-222 is readily soluble in water and has a diffusion coefficient of 0.985 cm^2 per day (1.14×10^{-5} cm^2 sec^{-1}) at a water temperature of only 18°C [*Bagnall*, 1957], so its diffusion rate would be much faster in water at 100–200°C. Furthermore, because the source of the ^{222}Rn is the zircon crystals within the same biotite flakes as the resultant Po radiohalos, the transport distances are in the micron (μm) to millimeters (mm) range. Therefore, these distances could easily have been accomplished within the flowing hydrothermal fluids along the biotite cleavage planes within the 3.8 day half-life of ^{222}Rn.

However, *Gentry* [1989, 1998] has maintained that the Po radiohalos do not occur along cracks or conduits in biotite, pointing to photographic evidence [*Gentry*, 1967, 1968, 1971, 1973, 1974, 1984, 1988]. This assertion is emphatically incorrect. Biotite flakes are peeled apart along their cleavage planes when mounting them for observation and photography, which is why cracks or defects are not usually seen. Thus radiohalos in biotites are always on cleavage planes, which are "ready made" cracks in the biotite's crystal structure that provide conduits for the flow of fluids. Nevertheless, Po radiohalos have been observed along fractures in biotite flakes, such as the group of ^{218}Po radiohalos and the ^{214}Po radiohalo in Figure 9. Even *Gentry* [1996] has conceded that secondary ^{210}Po radiohalos do occur in biotites along cracks where there are also discoloration lines and bands that follow the cracks, evidence of the passage of fluids with α-particle radioactivity in solution. Similar observations were first made by *Henderson and Sparks* [1939] who published photomicrographs illustrating this phenomenon. *Meier and Hecker* [1976] recorded such U and ^{210}Po bands along conduits in

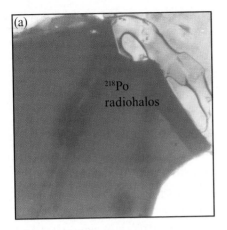
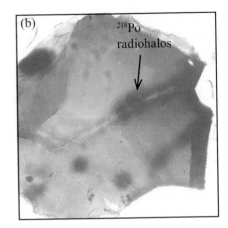
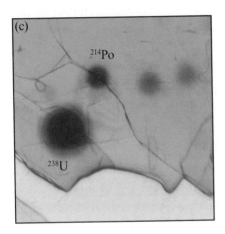
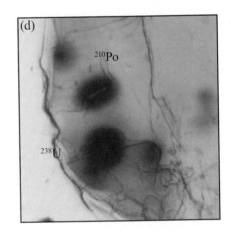

Figure 9. ^{218}Po radiohalos centered along a crack in a biotite flake along which hydrothermal fluids containing ^{218}Po have flowed: (a) color image, (b) black and white image (Stanthorpe Adamellite, the diameter of the radiohalos is ~68 μm). A ^{214}Po radiohalo centered on an apparent crack in a biotite flake (c), and continuous overlapping overexposed ^{210}Po radiohalos (d) in which the radiocenters are connected along a line, suggesting a linear fluid inclusion contained ^{210}Po (Land's End Granite, radiohalo diameters ~68 μm and ~39 μm respectively). Both (c) and (d) also show adjacent overexposed ^{238}U radiohalos (diameters ~70 μm).

biotite. Furthermore, *Gentry et al.* [1974] also noted that single halos are observed around discrete inclusions lodged in conduits or cleavage cracks, while vein halos formed from a continuous distribution of radioactivity apparently deposited from hydrothermal solutions along conduits.

A.4 Supply of Sufficient Polonium

Gentry [1974] calculated that the radiocenters of very dark ^{218}Po radiohalos may have needed as many as 5×10^9 atoms of ^{218}Po each to have produced the ^{218}Po radiohalos, so would hydrothermal fluid transport of ^{222}Rn be able to supply enough ^{218}Po atoms to the radiocenters within the required time frame? Of course, similar numbers of ^{214}Po and ^{210}Po atoms would thus have been needed in radiocenters to produce the respective radiohalos. In Gentry's fiat Creation model all 5×10^9 atoms of Po (a concentration of more than 50%) need to be in the radiocenters all at once at the time of their formation in order to subsequently produce the Po radiohalos. However, *Snelling and Armitage* [2003] have argued that because some granites containing Po radiohalos can be demonstrated to have formed during the Flood event neither the granites nor the Po are primordial (created by fiat). This conclusion is supported by the very much larger dataset here in Table 2. On the other hand, *Snelling and Armitage* [2003] argued that the ^{222}Rn hydrothermal fluid transport model does not require all 5×10^9 atoms of Po to be delivered to each radiocenter at the same time, because the fluid flow can progressively supply this quantity over a period of days, the Po in the fluids replacing the Po in each radiocenter after it α-decays. All that is required is a steady hydrothermal fluid flow with a constant supply of ^{222}Rn and Po isotopes, together with favorable conditions at the deposition sites that became the radiocenters.

Furthermore, given that 1 g of ^{238}U contains 2.53×10^{21} atoms and in radioactive equilibrium with them at present decay rates are 5.8×10^9 atoms of ^{222}Rn and 3.22×10^6 atoms of ^{218}Po [*Friedlander et al.*, 1964], even when the zircon grains in the biotites of the granitic rocks only have U concentrations of hundreds of ppm, the relative numbers of

^{222}Rn and ^{218}Po atoms would still be sufficient to progressively deliver the needed concentrations of Po isotopes to the new radiocenters. This would be especially so if during the transport process there was accelerated nuclear decay of ^{238}U, which would supply even greater numbers of atoms of the decay products than at the present decay rate. Additionally, for every 2.53×10^{21} ^{238}U atoms there are 2.12×10^{11} ^{210}Po atoms, so that given the longer half-life of ^{210}Po (138 days compared with the 3.8 days of ^{222}Rn), its probably similar diffusion rate to ^{222}Rn [*Frey et al.*, 1981; *Snelling and Armitage*, 2003], and the fact that Po is also readily transported in hydrothermal fluids as halide and sulfate complexes [*Bagnall*, 1957], concurrent hydrothermal fluid transport of ^{210}Po would likely have occurred. This would in part explain the consistently high numbers of observed ^{210}Po radiohalos in the granitic rocks listed in Table 2 compared with the numbers of other Po radiohalos. Such hydrothermal fluid transport of ^{210}Po has already been documented, being measured over distances of up to several kilometers and transit times of 20–30 days [*Hussain et al.*, 1995; *Snelling*, 2000].

A.5 Transport Timescale

It is difficult to determine the precise timescale for the hydrothermal fluid transport of ^{222}Rn and for the establishment of the new radiocenters for subsequent Po radiohalo development. The rarity of ^{218}Po radiohalos in the biotites of most of these granitic rocks would seem to be significant. Transport was evidently slow enough for most ^{218}Po atoms to decay in transit before reaching the sites where ^{210}Po was deposited to generate ^{210}Po radiohalos. The extremely short half-life of ^{214}Po (164 microseconds) gives it a lower probability of surviving transport than ^{210}Po has. In most of these granitic rocks ^{210}Po radiohalos outnumber all other radiohalo types. Even though there is not a consistent abundance pattern, the quantities of the different Po radiohalos must be related to the transport mode, distance, and time. This observation alone lends support to the secondary transport model of separation of the Po isotopes from their parent ^{238}U in the formation of the three discrete types of Po radiohalos.

Given the measured diffusion coefficient of ^{222}Rn of 0.985 cm^2 per day in water at 18°C [*Bagnall*, 1957] and its 3.8 day half-life, it may be possible to quantify, or set limits on, the timescale for the hydrothermal transport of ^{222}Rn and the generation of Po radiohalos. It is reasonable to assume that the diffusion coefficient of ^{222}Rn would be much greater in water temperatures of 100–200°C (compared with 18°C), possibly even an order of magnitude higher (as determined by other diffusion measurements, such as for He [*Humphreys et al.*, 2003, 2004; *Humphreys*, 2005]). But this diffusion coefficient was measured in a stationary body of water, whereas the hydrothermal fluids in these cooling granitic rocks have flowed along fractures, around grain boundaries, and along the cleavage planes in biotite grains. Indeed, the fluid flow would likely be a greater factor in Rn transport than diffusion in the water. Even though hydrothermal fluid transport of ^{210}Po has been measured over distances of up to several kilometers over transit times of 20–30 days [*Hussain et al.*, 1995; *Snelling*, 2000], in that example the hydrothermal fluids were flowing through major fractures in basalts on the ocean floor. In contrast, the hydrothermal fluid transport being modeled in this instance requires flow into and along the cleavage planes of biotite grains, which are very much "tighter" than fractures, or even grain boundaries, and thus much more resistant to fluid penetration. Therefore, a more appropriate, conservative estimate of the diffusion of ^{222}Rn in hydrothermal fluids at 100–200°C might be 20 cm^2 per day, which would equate to a linear diffusion rate of the order of 5–6 cm per day. If the average distance of separation is 1 mm between the zircon source of the ^{222}Rn and Po isotopes and the site of deposition of the Po isotopes in a radiocenter to form a Po radiohalo, then at that diffusion rate a ^{222}Rn atom would travel 1 mm in approximately 30 minutes. Because the diffusion coefficient of Po appears to be similar to that of ^{222}Rn, the Po isotopes would also be transported in the flowing hydrothermal fluids at those temperatures over a distance of 1 mm in approximately 30 minutes.

So even though the half-lives of ^{218}Po and ^{214}Po are 3.1 minutes and 164 microseconds respectively, the ^{222}Rn atoms that α-decay just as they arrive near the radiocenter deposition site will contribute to either a [218]Po radiohalo or a [214]Po radiohalo. Because [222]Rn has a half-life of 3.8 days, each [222]Rn atom has more than three days to diffuse out of the crystal lattice of the zircon before being picked up by the hydrothermal fluids flowing past. Atoms of [218]Po and/or [214]Po that were at the surface of the zircon grain could dissolve into the hydrothermal fluids flowing past, so that by the time those atoms reached and were deposited in the radiocenter 1 mm distance away they would have α-decayed to [210]Po and a [210]Po radiohalo would therefore be generated. This would explain the much larger numbers of [210]Po radiohalos in the majority of these granitic rocks, particularly if most of the Po atoms were the [210]Po isotope by the time they diffused out of the zircon crystal lattice and were transported by the flowing hydrothermal fluids. Of course, these estimates are conservative, so this transport timescale could be much shorter, perhaps short enough for [218]Po atoms to be carried from the surface of the zircon crystal to the radiocenter before α-decaying and thus generate a [218]Po radiohalo.

The next issue is the question as to whether, and over what timescale, this hydrothermal fluid transport rate would deliver the 5×10^9 atoms of Po to the radiocenter in time for it to generate the relevant Po radiohalo. If it is postulated that the flowing hydrothermal fluids deliver Po atoms to the new radiocenter at a rate of 10^6 atoms per second, the 5×10^9 atoms of Po required to produce a very dark Po radiohalo would be delivered in approximately three hours. Five $\times 10^9$ atoms represents a concentration of more than 50%, so 10^6 atoms of Po in the hydrothermal fluids coming in contact with the radiocenter each second represents a concentration of just over 100 ppm Po, which is not excessive given the ease with which Po dissolves in hydrothermal fluids as halide and sulfate complexes, and the concentrations of hundreds of ppm of the parent [238]U in the zircon crystals. Polonium-218 or [214]Po atoms delivered to the new radiocenter would α-decay within minutes or fractions of a second, respectively. As Po atoms are progressively delivered to the radiocenter over three hours, the [218]Po or [214]Po radiohalo would be fully formed approximately within the same timescale. Of course, the complete timescale for formation of these Po radiohalos would also include the transport of atoms from the surface of the zircon crystal to the radiocenter. Transport at a rate of 1 mm every thirty minutes would allow delivery of the required concentration of atoms to the radiocenter within that three hours.

However, an equally important factor would be the timescale for the diffusion of ^{222}Rn and Po atoms from inside the crystal lattice of the zircon grain to the grain surface. The zircon grains in the centers of ^{238}U radiohalos are typically 1–10 µm wide, so the distances the ^{222}Rn and Po atoms have to diffuse are very tiny. Larger zircon grains (up to 150 µm long) are often also present in these granitic rocks [*Humphreys*, 2005]. Their relatively larger surface areas (compared with those of the 1–10 µm wide zircons in the ^{238}U radiohalo centers) would also provide an abundant ready supply of ^{222}Rn and Po atoms that also only had to diffuse very tiny distances (< 10µm) out of those zircon crystals. Furthermore, the diffusion of ^{222}Rn and Po atoms out of the zircon grains would have commenced in the hot crystallized granitic rock at temperatures as high as 400°C, so many of these atoms would begin reaching the surfaces of the zircon grains in the time taken for the granitic rock to cool from 400°C to below 150°C. The higher temperatures also cause higher diffusion rates.

These considerations would suggest that ^{222}Rn and even Po atoms would be available at the surface of the zircon grains as soon as hydrothermal fluids were available to begin transporting them, which would have been at temperatures as high as 300°C. On the other hand, this could also put constraints on the timescale for the temperature of the cooling granitic rock to fall from 400°C to 150°C, given the 3.8 day half-life of ^{222}Rn. Indeed, even with a continuous supply of ^{222}Rn from accelerated ^{238}U decay, many of the ^{222}Rn atoms would have already α-decayed to the Po isotopes (principally ^{210}Po) if the timescale for this cooling temperature interval was too long, equal to or greater than 3.8 days. Given that there is only a limited, finite amount of ^{238}U in the zircon grains and thus potential ^{238}U decay products, to maximize the likelihood of Po radiohalo formation it would be optimal for much of the ^{222}Rn to not have decayed to the Po isotopes while still in the zircon grains and in the hydrothermal fluids as the temperatures fall from 400°C to 150°C.

Thus these calculations, which are somewhat conservative, would suggest that the existence of ^{218}Po and ^{214}Po radiohalos in these granitic rocks might require the granitic rocks to cool from 400°C to 150°C in three days or less, and these Po radiohalos would then be generated within three hours subsequent to the temperature falling to 150°C. Transport distances between the zircon grains and the new radiocenters very much greater than 1 mm would favor the generation of only ^{210}Po radiohalos, because of the longer half-life (138 days) of that isotope. This is clearly consistent with the greater number of ^{210}Po radiohalos in these granitic rocks. Another implication of these calculations is that if these granitic rocks cooled from a temperature of 400°C to 150°C in less than three days, and even if there were an exponential decline in the temperature, the time frame for further cooling from 150°C to the ambient temperatures at the intrusion depths of 2–4 km (40–80°C depending on the geothermal gradient) would have to have been less than a further three to seven days. This then would be the time frame for the window in which hydrothermal fluid flow would be occurring below the annealing temperature of α-tracks in biotite to produce all the Po radiohalos, because once hydrothermal fluid flow ceased no further transport of Po isotopes to the radiohalo deposition sites would be occurring.

Furthermore, there are two other implications of these timescale calculations. First, they provide an absolute and objective timescale for the cooling of granitic plutons independent of the assumption that these granitic rocks formed during the Flood event. Because the existence of the ^{218}Po and ^{214}Po radiohalos can only be explained in a timescale for their generation during cooling of these granitic plutons from above 400°C to below 150°C, whereupon the α-tracks generated by Po isotope decay are retained in the biotite crystals to register as radiohalos, then the calculated timescale for generation of these Po radiohalos automatically becomes a measure of the timescale for the cooling of granitic plutons. And that timescale for cooling of granitic plutons from 400°C to 150°C to near-surface crustal temperatures has been calculated here conservatively as a total of only six to ten days! The second implication directly follows. This extremely short timescale for cooling of the granitic plutons and therefore the concurrent flow of hydrothermal fluids automatically precludes ^{226}Ra, with its half-life of 1622 years, as the precursor isotope to the Po isotopes that is transported in the hydrothermal fluid flows. Put simply, if the time window for hydrothermal fluid flow in the cooling granitic plutons is only six to ten days, there is insufficient time for α-decay of enough ^{226}Ra, to even begin generating any Po radiohalos.

For comparison with all the calculations here, it is instructive to review the detailed analysis of the fluid transport of these radionuclides by *Feather* [1978], of the Department of Physics at the University of Edinburgh. In summary, Feather found that if a hydrothermal fluid is assumed to take up ^{226}Ra preferentially from a U source, and if two types of inclusion are present in the biotite, one type providing deposition centers for the Po isotopes, and other centers for deposition of Bi (or Pb) isotopes; then ideal situations may be identified in which Po radiohalos of each of the three types might develop. Basically, he calculated that the discriminating factor is the time of transit of the hydrothermal fluid from the U source to the deposition sites. Transit times ranging upwards from about 20 days favor the development of ^{210}Po radiohalos, transit times of less than five days are required for the development of ^{218}Po radiohalos, and even shorter transit times are necessary (five hours or less) if ^{214}Po radiohalos are to be formed. To this extent Feather was satisfied that the fluid transport hypothesis achieves formal success in producing secondary Po radiohalos.

Note that Feather's transit times are longer because he starts with ^{226}Ra rather than ^{222}Rn, and his model relies only on the flow of the hydrothermal fluids to carry the isotopes over those transit times. On the other hand, in the model calculations here, ^{222}Rn is instead the starting isotope, and atoms of both ^{222}Rn and the Po isotopes also diffuse within the flowing hydrothermal fluids. Thus the transit times are very much shorter. Furthermore, *Feather* [1978] did not take into account either the time constraints the cooling of the granites placed on the overall transit times, or the effect of the limitation of α-track and radiohalo formation to temperatures below 150°C. Therefore it is confidently asserted that the transit times and timescales for Po radiohalo development and granite cooling calculated here are well constrained by all the relevant factors, and thus are very reasonable.

A.6 Establishment of New Radiocenters

There needs to be a mechanism by which the Po isotopes are concentrated at particular (seemingly random) locations to become discrete radiocenters. Most of the hydrothermal fluid transport would be as ^{222}Rn, an inert gas that has no chemical affinity with other species, and no propensity to concentrate by precipitating at discrete locations. Thus, as *Snelling and Armitage* [2003] concluded, it would appear that the radiocenters could only have been formed by the Po atoms resulting from the decay of ^{222}Rn. Polonium behaves geochemically similar to Pb, with an affinity for S, Se, and halides, and even forms polonides with other metals including Pb [*Bagnall*, 1957]. Indeed, *Gentry et al.* [1976b] have demonstrated that where Pb, S, and Se were available in coalified wood, Po transported through the coalified wood by groundwaters became attached to these species, and became concentrated enough in such radiocenters to produce ^{210}Po radiohalos.

Ilton and Veblen [1988] discovered that some biotite grains in granitic rocks that host hydrothermally-produced porphyry Cu ore deposits have inclusions of native Cu 0.002–0.01 μm thick and up to 1.0 μm in diameter in favored lattice planes. They concluded that these tiny Cu inclusions had been deposited from the Cu-bearing hydrothermal fluids that flowed along the cleavage planes within the biotite crystals. *Snelling and Armitage* [2003] therefore concluded that it is thus reasonable to expect that the same hydrothermal fluids that transported Rn and Po isotopes would also have transported metal and other ions [*Giggenbach*, 1997, *Seward and Barnes*, 1997]. Because Po isotopes are readily transported in hydrothermal fluids as halide and sulfate complexes [*Bagnall*, 1957], which are common in hydrothermal fluids [*Giggenbach*, 1997], all that is required for the development of Po radiocenters is for sulfate ions to be reduced at lattice defect sites within the biotite cleavage planes so PoS (polonium sulfide) is precipitated. Similarly, other metals and elements would also be deposited as tiny inclusions along the cleavage planes within the biotites. *Collins* [1992] has correctly noted that the crystal lattice of biotite contains sites where negatively charged halide or hydroxyl ions can be accommodated. Thus *Snelling and Armitage* [2003] concluded that these lattice sites and other imperfections found along cleavage planes in biotites, being relatively large, would provide space for metal and other ions such as Po to enter and take up lattice positions or to be concentrated at particular discrete places along the cleavage planes where the chemical environment was conducive. Indeed, *Collins* [1992] also contended that the Po radiohalos formed as a result of diffusion of ^{222}Rn in "ambient" fluids within the crystallizing granitic rocks.

Another factor in this process is the effect the hydrothermal fluids have directly upon the biotite itself. Invariably, because the hydrothermal fluids contain many dissolved ions such as halides and sulfate they are highly reactive, and thus as they flow along the biotite cleavage planes they interact with the biotite crystal lattice changing its structure by exchange and addition of ions to partly change the biotite into the mineral chlorite. Thus primary evidence that hydrothermal fluids have flowed along the cleavage planes of the biotites in these granitic rocks is the universal observation of the chloritization of all biotite flakes (Figure 10a and c). Equally compelling evidence of the hydrothermal fluid flow along the biotite cleavage planes is the preservation in some of the biotites of the remains of what were fluid-filled inclusions (Figure 10b and d). Fluid inclusions may even have formed radiocenters (Figure 9d), which may explain the bubble-like "holes" and the absence of visible inclusions in almost all Po radiohalos. It is now well established that the chlorite alteration caused by hydrothermal fluids concurrently accompanies the process of deposition of metals and other ions from the hydrothermal fluids, primarily including the precipitation of sulfides [*Reed*, 1997]. Once the center of nucleation is established a sulfide crystal can grow rapidly from the components precipitated and scavenged from the hydrothermal fluids flowing by. *Snelling and Armitage* [2003] concluded that in this way Po was incorporated in discrete radiocenters along the cleavage planes in the biotite flakes where other suitable ions such as S had been concentrated in the lattice sites and crystal

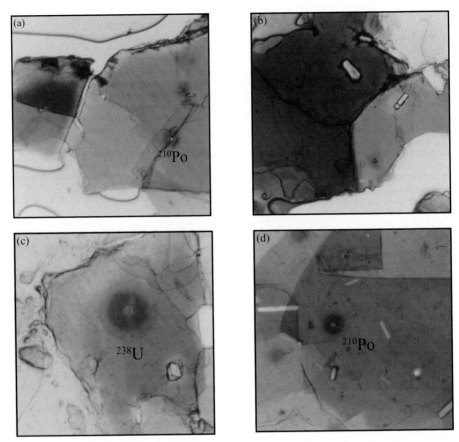

Figure 10. The effects of hydrothermal fluids on biotite. (a) (c) chloritization (b) (d) fluid inclusions (bubbles) in the cleavage planes between biotite sheets. Note the ^{210}Po radiohalos (diameter ~39 μm) centered on the crack in (a) and near fluid inclusions in (d), and the normal well-exposed ^{238}U radiohalo diameter ~70 μm) in (c). The fluid inclusions are ~50 μm long in (b) and up to ~100 μm in (d) (Shap Granite).

imperfections, and where the chemical environment was conducive to Po being concentrated to form discrete radiocenters. Furthermore, as the above calculations have shown, concentrations of ions such as S of only 10^6 atoms would have been required to combine with the Po isotopes being transported in the hydrothermal fluids to hold sufficient Po isotopes in the radiocenters to generate the Po radiohalos. Such an accumulation of S atoms, for example, would form a sub-microscopic inclusion in the biotite, similar to the native Cu inclusions observed by *Ilton and Veblen* [1988]. This would explain why almost all observed Po radiohalo centers appear to be simply empty minute spots. As the concentrated Po atoms subsequently α-decayed, further fluid flow delivered more Po atoms to the radiocenters where the S, metal and/or other ions that had scavenged the Po from the passing fluids had become free to scavenge more Po. Thus as discussed earlier, the required ring density is reached by accumulation over a period of time, calculated to be approximately 1.5 hours or more, during which fluid flow continues, the supply of Po atoms is available, and the chemical environment is conducive to the Po being concentrated in the radiocenters.

The end product of the ^{238}U decay chain, including the three Po isotopes, is ^{206}Pb, which is therefore present in the radiocenters of Po radiohalos [*Gentry*, 1974; *Gentry et al.*, 1974]. Because Po also has a geochemical affinity for Pb [*Bagnall*, 1957], this Pb would also have assisted the concentration of further Po. Once all the Po α-decayed, the Pb and S atoms left in the radiocenters should have formed PbS (galena). So why is such galena not still visible in the Po radiohalo centers? As already indicated, the quantity of S and Pb atoms involved is relatively small, so that the resultant PbS radiocenters would be sub-microscopic and thus not readily visible. However, there could be an alternative explanation. As long as there was an abundant supply of Po in the hydrothermal fluid flow the S atoms would have preferentially bonded with the Po, because Po has a higher electron affinity than Pb [*Aylward and Findlay*, 1971]. Any Pb atoms not bonded to Po atoms would have been dissolved in the passing hydrothermal fluids and removed from the radiocenters. Once the supply of Po in the hydrothermal fluids diminished as the decay of ^{238}U decelerated, PbS would rarely have formed in the radiocenters. Instead, the Pb and S ions would have been flushed out of the radiocenters by being dissolved in the flowing hydrothermal fluids. Whereas the chemical environment in coalified wood was conducive for the Pb, S, and Se to be retained in the Po radiohalo centers [*Gentry et al.*, 1976b], without Po present in the radiocenters the biotite cleavage planes in granitic rocks were no longer able to retain the Pb and S atoms. Even at very low temperatures the chemistry of hydrothermal fluids enable them to dissolve and transport S, Pb, and other metals [*Garven and Raffensperger*, 1997]. This could be the likely explanation for the absence of mineral inclusions in almost all Po radiohalo centers.

Appendix B: Why the Variations in Abundances of the Radiohalos?

B.1 The Observed Abundances of the Radiohalos

It is immediately evident from Tables 1, 2, and 3 that there are enormous differences in the abundances of radiohalos between the different granitic rocks, ranging from no radiohalos at all to more than 10 radiohalos per slide in the Precambrian (pre-Flood) granitic rocks (Table 1); from no radiohalos at all to more than 250 radiohalos per slide in Paleozoic-Mesozoic (Flood) granitic rocks (Table 2); and almost no radiohalos in the Tertiary (post-Flood?) granitic rocks (Table 3). Of course, the lack of radiohalos in the Tertiary granitic rocks is probably due to there being insufficient time for sufficient α-tracks to accumulate and register as radiohalos. Given that a fully-formed radiohalo requires up to an estimated 100 million years worth (at today's rates) of nuclear decay, observable radiohalos would not be expected in Tertiary, and even latest Cretaceous (Table 2), granitic rocks. However, the question remains as to why there are such variations in the abundances of radiohalos in all the earlier granitic rocks.

Indeed, *Gentry* [1968] estimated that there may be as many as 20,000–30,000 ^{218}Po and ^{210}Po radiohalos per cm^3 in biotite in a Norwegian Precambrian granitic pegmatite (without any ^{214}Po radiohalos). *Gentry* [1975] stated that as many as 1000–50,000 ^{214}Po and ^{218}Po radiohalos often occur in some minerals, while he [*Gentry*, 1999] estimated that there are more than one billion U and Po radiohalos in the fluorite of the Phanerozoic vein at Wölsendorf in Germany. *Gentry* [1998] also pointed out that if the Po radiohalos formed by a secondary process from U-decay products, because of the different Po-isotope half-lives there would be greatly different quantities of each isotope co-existing. The amounts existing should be proportional to the respective half-lives. At any given time the atomic ratio of ^{210}Po to ^{218}Po should be 67,000:1, and thus there should be about 67,000 ^{210}Po radiohalos for each ^{218}Po radiohalo. Such proportions are not found. In the granitic rocks listed in Tables 1 and 2, there are always more ^{210}Po radiohalos than ^{218}Po radiohalos (the ^{210}Po:^{218}Po ratios varying from 4.8:1 to 1366:1). Clearly, the proportions of the different Po radiohalos vary from sample to sample. Compared to the granitic rock samples listed in Tables 1 and 2, *Meier and Hecker* [1976] found a distribution in a Norwegian biotite they studied of more than 1000 ^{210}Po radiohalos, 90 ^{218}Po radiohalos, and only one ^{214}Po radiohalo, yet Gentry reported to *Feather* [1978] that abundance ratios for other samples of biotite were ^{218}Po>^{210}Po>^{214}Po, and even ^{214}Po>^{218}Po or ^{210}Po.

So how can these different abundances and proportions of radiohalos be explained? In the one instance where Gentry demonstrated that ^{210}Po radiohalos had formed as a result of secondary fluid transport [*Gentry et al.*, 1976b], 100 or more ^{210}Po radiohalos were sometimes evident in a single thin section (2 cm by 2 cm) of coalified wood, and they occurred quite generally in the thin sections examined. Such an abundance is similar to that found in the Permian Land's End Granite of Cornwall in England, and not unlike the abundance of radiohalos found in the Devonian Strathbogie Granite of Victoria, Australia, and the Ordovician Encounter Bay and Palmer Granites of South Australia (Table 2). It should be noted that all the samples of this study (Tables 1 and 2) are just normal granitic rocks with a biotite abundance of 1–5%, and with the small biotite flakes evenly scattered through the fabric of the rocks. However, in contrast, the spectacular abundances of radiohalos of thousands or more per cm^3 reported by *Gentry* [1968, 1975, 1999] are found in large (10 or more cm^3) biotite and fluorite crystals in granitic pegmatites and calcite-biotite, calcite-fluorite, or fluorite veins (see Tables 4 and 5 of *Snelling* [2000] after *Wise* [1989]).

B.2 Why the Huge Radiohalo Abundances in Granitic Pegmatites and Veins?

Unlike the granitic plutons sampled for this study, that typically extend over areas of $100–1000\,km^2$, granitic pegmatites occur as dike-like bodies that are 1–50 m wide and 100–1000 m long, while veins are generally far more restricted in size. Both granitic pegmatites and veins form from the fluids in a residual melt late in the crystallization of a granitic pluton; and also form from local melting and recrystallization in high-grade metamorphic terranes [Cerny, 1982; Jahns, 1982; London, 1996]. They are characterized by large crystals (large concentrations) of rare minerals that contain volatile elements such as F, and rare elements such as the rare earth elements, Y, Th, U, Zr, Hf, Nb, Ta, Sn, etc., that precipitated from large volumes of hydrothermal fluids saturated in these elements. In the past it was frequently assumed that the presence of these large crystals in pegmatites and veins implied slow growth over long periods of time. This is now known to be a total misconception [Luth, 1976, pp. 405–411; Wampler and Wallace, 1998]. In fact, it has been demonstrated that the rate of nucleation is the most important factor in determining growth rates and eventual sizes of crystals [Lofgren, 1980; Tsuchiyama, 1983]. At the point of aqueous vapor saturation of a granitic melt, crystal fractionation can occur, so that volatiles are concentrated in a mobile vapor (hydrothermal)-residual melt phase which readily migrates into open fractures within the wall-rocks immediately adjacent to a granitic pluton, sometimes within the granite itself, or within host high-grade metamorphic rocks [Jahns and Burnham, 1969]. There the giant crystals (sometimes meters long) in pegmatites grow rapidly at rates of more than $10^{-6}\,cm$ per second [London, 1992] from the hydrothermal fluid in the residual melt phase saturated in volatiles, as the wide pegmatite vein rapidly cools [Chakoumakos and Lumpkin, 1992].

Thus, the formation of granitic pegmatites in wide veins with large crystals requires large volumes of hydrothermal fluids, which are also capable of transporting large quantities of U-decay products, such as ^{222}Rn and the Po isotopes. The first factor that would be responsible for the variations in the abundances of the Po radiohalos would be the volume of hydrothermal fluid flow. The larger the volume of hydrothermal fluids, the more radiocenters that could potentially be supplied with Po isotopes. A meager hydrothermal flow would produce few Po radiohalos.

There also must be a sufficient supply of U-decay products. As first noted by *Wise* [1989], all of the granitic pegmatites and veins that Gentry reported as containing such huge numbers of Po radiohalos in their large biotite (and fluorite) crystals are associated with large concentrations of U in visible mineralization and economic ore bodies (see Tables 4 and 5 of *Snelling* [2000] after *Wise* [1989]). *Wakefield* [1988a, b] and *Wilkerson* [1989] reported that the calcite-fluorite vein hosting the Po radiohalo-bearing biotite at the Fission Mine in Ontario, Canada, also contained cubic crystals and irregular masses of uraninite (primarily UO_2). This uraninite was found in cavities with the biotite in which the large numbers of Po radiohalos were found. The granitic pegmatite hosting the Po radiohalo-bearing biotite at the Faraday Mine, Ontario, Canada, also hosts uraninite and other U minerals. At the Silver Crater Mine, also in Ontario, Canada, the calcite-biotite vein with the Po radiohalo-bearing biotite also contains betafite (a complex U, rare earth element and F-bearing mineral). The betafite is often found as small crystals in close association with clusters of books of biotite, and even within the books themselves [*Wakefield*, 1988b]. Furthermore, the Wölsendorf fluorite district in northeast Bavaria, Germany, is well known for the U mineralization it contains, the fluorite veins being considered hydrothermal in origin and hosting uraninite, pitchblende, and coffinite [*Strunz and Seeliger*, 1960; *Ziehr*, 1980; *Dill*, 1983; *Carl and Dill*, 1985]. All the known fluorite veins with U mineralization occupy major joint systems that are tectonically controlled, and provide easy access for hydrothermal fluids [*Fürst and Bandelow*, 1982]. Finally, even the Kragero Precambrian granitic pegmatite in Norway in which *Meier and Hecker* [1976] reported large numbers of [210]Po radiohalos also has evidence within the biotites of high concentrations of U. They documented fractures along which there was evidence of both U and [210]Po having been transported by flow of hydrothermal fluids. Thus, in each of these instances of reported occurrences of high numbers of Po radiohalos, it can be shown that there were high concentrations of U, and therefore its decay products, adjacent to the host biotite and the fluorite crystals. Where there are higher numbers of Po radiohalos there was a ready source of an associated larger amount of U-decay products.

The third and final factor that could have a bearing on the huge numbers of Po radiohalos reported in some granitic pegmatites and veins is the availability of sufficient numbers of sites chemically conducive to Po isotope deposition. As already indicated, granitic pegmatites typically contain minerals, sometimes in large crystals, containing metals and other elements that are of economic importance. There are many elements in trace amounts that would be carried by the hydrothermal fluids into lattice defects and other sites along biotite cleavage planes to locations that would serve as depocenters for Po isotopes. An element common to the Canadian veins as well as the Wölsendorf vein is the halide F, which is sufficiently abundant to form fluorite crystals. It is significant that not only does Po dissolve in hydrothermal fluids with halides, but halides such as F can be accommodated in the biotite crystal lattice adjacent to the cleavage planes where it could serve as a scavenger of Po isotopes from hydrothermal fluids passing by. Furthermore, in the case of the Wölsendorf fluorite veins, which probably contain the greatest abundance of Po radiohalos, as well as U minerals per unit volume, the veins contain significant quantities of other metals and elements including Se [*Dill*, 1983]. This is significant because Se is an element with which Po has a geochemical affinity, and it was Se that *Gentry et al.* [1976b] found in the radiocenters of the [210]Po radiohalos in the coalified wood, radiohalos that Gentry agrees are of secondary origin due to fluid transport of Po. Thus there is good evidence that in each instance where there are extremely high numbers of Po radiohalos, there was an ample supply of suitable other elements to form the required nucleation centers. Therefore, all three essential components necessary for hydrothermal fluid transport of [222]Rn and Po isotopes to generate the abundant Po radiohalos in each of these geological contexts were in place.

B.3 Why the Lower Radiohalo Abundances in Granitic Rocks?

The conclusion from the foregoing discussion is that the abundance of Po radiohalos will be determined by the availability of ^{238}U and its decay products, the volume of hydrothermal fluid flow, and the availability of depocenters. In the examples just discussed where there are huge numbers of Po radiohalos, there are large concentrations of nearby U in mineralization and in oxide minerals from which the ^{238}U decay products are easily removed. There also were huge volumes of hydrothermal fluids able to transport the abundant ^{238}U decay products. On the other hand, in the granitic rocks in this study, as far as is known, the only source of ^{238}U decay products is the zircon grains whose U contents, and therefore the availability of ^{238}U decay products, is much lower than in U oxide minerals. So no matter how large a volume of hydrothermal fluids is available, if there is a poor supply of ^{238}U decay products, there will be a lower abundance of Po radiohalos. This could especially apply to the Precambrian (pre-Flood) granitic rocks in which the abundances of Po radiohalos are generally lower than their abundances in the Paleozoic-Mesozoic (Flood) granitic rocks (compare Tables 1 and 2). One possible explanation is the longer history of these Precambrian granitic rocks. Uranium-238 decay products could have originally been transported by hydrothermal fluids in the waning stages of the formation of these rocks, but when the Po radiohalos formed then were annealed by a subsequent heating event during the Flood, there was a lower residual abundance of ^{238}U decay products from which replacement Po radiohalos could be generated. The zircon grains in the Paleozoic-Mesozoic granitic rocks have suffered from only one "flushing" by hydrothermal fluids removing their ^{238}U decay products during the Flood. So if the zircons in the Paleozoic-Mesozoic granitic rocks that formed during the Flood had a greater availability of ^{238}U decay products than the Precambrian granitic rocks had at the time of the Flood event, there is a ready explanation for the general greater abundance of Po radiohalos in the Paleozoic-Mesozoic granitic rocks compared to the Precambrian granitic rocks.

The higher abundance of Po radiohalos in one of the Paleozoic-

Mesozoic granitic plutons, namely, the Land's End Granite in Cornwall, England (Table 2), is particularly significant, and further details of the geological context of that pluton are illustrative of how the Po radiohalo abundance is affected by the availability of the ^{238}U decay products and the volume of hydrothermal fluid flow. The Sn deposits of Cornwall in lodes within fracture systems in, and associated with, granitic plutons are well known and famous, but it is not as well known that there are also base metal and U deposits associated with these granitic plutons [*Willis-Richards and Jackson*, 1989; *Jackson et al.*, 1989]. There is a large list of occurrences of U minerals (uraninite, pitchblende, and many secondary U minerals) in these granitic rocks, including the Land's End Granite [*Rumbold*, 1954], and these have been used to U-Pb date the Sn and base metal lodes containing them [*Darnley et al.*, 1965]. Indeed, the Land's End Granite is now regarded as a chemically specialized granite that was emplaced at the end of the development of the Cornubian Batholith, and its Sn, base metal and U lodes developed from the hydrothermal fluid flow generated during the cooling of the pluton [*Chesley et al.*, 1993]. Furthermore, fluid inclusion studies of the mineralized veins have shown that large volumes of hydrothermal fluids circulated through the granitic plutons of the batholith and through fractures into the surrounding host rocks, generating the mineralized veins over a protracted period [*Gleeson et al.*, 2000, 2001]. Hydrogen and oxygen isotope studies of the granites and hydrothermally-altered minerals associated with the mineralized lodes indicate that the hydrothermal fluids were derived both from the magmatic waters of the granitic intrusions and from meteoric waters in the host rocks [*Sheppard*, 1977]. The picture that emerges from all of these studies is that the Land's End Granite, and the other granitic plutons of the Cornubian Batholith, when emplaced contained significantly elevated levels of not only Sn and base metals, but also U, and the prolonged hydrothermal activity that circulated through these granitic plutons carried the U with them to precipitate U minerals in the lodes within fracture zones. The circulating hydrothermal fluids would also have carried ^{238}U decay products together with the dissolved U. There is then a ready explanation for the significantly higher number of Po radiohalos in the Land's End Granite compared to the other Paleozoic-Mesozoic (Flood) granitic rocks in Table 2.

Several other observations and considerations are also relevant. First, another factor that could result in differences in the abundances of the Po radiohalos in the granitic rocks in this study is the abundance of zircon grains in them. Though the Po radiohalos usually outnumber the ^{238}U radiohalos, it is still evident that where there are more ^{238}U radiohalos there are also more Po radiohalos. The abundance of ^{238}U radiohalos is an indication of the abundance of zircon grains in the granitic rock; the more zircon grains there are, the more ^{238}U decay products are available to the hydrothermal fluids, and the more Po radiohalos are formed.

Second, several other factors could explain the different abundances of the various Po radiohalos in these granitic rocks. A primary factor would have to be the distance between the zircon source and the radiocenter where the Po isotopes are deposited. The greater the distance, the more likelihood that only ^{210}Po would survive hydrothermal fluid flow. Generally there are more ^{214}Po radiohalos than ^{218}Po radiohalos. Evidently the emission of a 7.69 MeV ^{214}Po α-particle (average 164 microseconds) immediately after a ^{218}Po α-decay often leaves the previous 6.00 MeV α-track indiscernible. Another factor that must affect the abundances of ^{218}Po and ^{214}Po radiohalos is the timing of both the arrival of the ^{222}Rn and ^{218}Po at the surfaces of the zircon grains after their diffusion out of their crystal lattices, and of the α-decay of ^{222}Rn into ^{218}Po along the hydrothermal fluid flow path within the biotite cleavage planes. If a ^{222}Rn atom has diffused to the surface of the zircon grain within one day of its coming into existence by α-decay of ^{226}Ra, then on average it will still have 2.8 days in which to transit in the hydrothermal fluid flow before α-decaying to ^{218}Po that is then deposited at a radiocenter to generate a ^{218}Po radiohalo. On the other hand, if it has taken the ^{222}Rn three days from the beginning of its existence to diffuse out of the zircon crystal, then it only has on average less than a day for transit in the hydrothermal fluid flow before α-decaying to a ^{218}Po atom. Obviously, because α-decay is a statistical process there will be ^{222}Rn atoms diffusing out of the zircon grains at all different times in their half-lives, but this will affect, in combination with the transit distances to the Po radiocenters and the rate of hydrothermal fluid flow, just which Po isotope will be deposited at the radiocenters and thus generate the respective Po radiohalos. Of course, an allied factor will be the overall state of crystallinity of the zircon grains, because if the zircon crystal structure has suffered radiation damage and become metamict, then diffusion will be more rapid. Indeed, if ^{238}U decay was accelerated there would be dramatically increased stress on the zircon crystal structure so that severe radiation damage would be quickly produced, thus allowing even greater diffusion rates. So variations in the amount and extent of radiation damage and metamictization will determine the rate at which ^{222}Rn and ^{218}Po atoms diffuse out of the zircon grains, and this then relates to the considerations discussed immediately above. Thus all these factors taken together will affect the resultant abundances of the different Po radiohalos, and of course all these factors will be different in each of these granitic rocks.

Appendix C. The Heat Problem

As has been shown already in Appendix A.5, the existence of the Po radiohalos in these granitic rocks, especially the ^{218}Po and ^{214}Po radiohalos because of the extremely short half-lives of these isotopes, has a direct implication as to the timescale for cooling of these granitic plutons. The survival of the Po isotopes and formation of these Po radiohalos places a severe timescale limit of six to ten days on the cooling of granitic plutons from 400°C or more down to the ambient temperatures at the near-surface crustal levels at which these plutons have been emplaced. This results in the problem of removing the enormous quantity of heat involved from the huge volume (specifically of the order of 200–500 km^3) of each granitic pluton within six to ten days. Such removal requires heat dissipation at least six orders of magnitude greater than currently postulated by conventional wisdom [*Petford et al.*, 2000]. However, the existence of the Po and ^{238}U radiohalos together, if generated concurrently, implies nuclear decay had to have been accelerated, by probably at least six orders of magnitude during the Flood year. The enormous amount of heat generated by this accelerated nuclear decay adds considerably to the heat problem.

To put this heat problem in perspective we can quickly do a rough estimate of the effect of just the accelerated nuclear decay, say 500 million years worth (at today's rates), but instead taking place in a single year (the Flood year). The following values of the relevant parameters were obtained from *Stacey* [1992]:

- the typical heat production in a granitic pluton from radioactive decay of U, Th, and K is $\sim 10^{-9}$ W/kg,
- the specific heat of granite is ~ 700 J/kg-K, and
- the number of seconds in 500 million years is $\sim 1.6 \times 10^{16}$ sec.

Thus the adiabatic temperature rise =

$$\left(\frac{(1.6 \times 10^{16}\, \text{sec}) \times (10^{-9}\, \text{W/kg})}{700\, \text{J/kg-K}} \right)$$

$$= 22,400 \text{K}$$

This is equivalent to a temperature rise of more than 22,000°C, which is sufficient, of course, to vaporize a granitic pluton many times over!

Another approach is to assess the heat production in the zircons themselves within the granitic rocks. Note that the U concentrations in the zircon grains can be on the order of 1% by mass of the grains. If the mass of a zircon grain relative to the mass of the biotite crystal that includes it is 0.01, then with the current heat production from radioactive decay of U of 10^{-4} W/kg, the average heat production in the biotite enclosing that zircon grain is 10^{-8} W/kg, which is only an order of magnitude higher than the value used above for a typical granite. Thus the adiabatic temperature rise in the biotite as a result of 500 million years worth of accelerated radioactive decay is an order of magnitude higher than the value obtained for the granitic rock as a whole. Of course, the biotite crystal and the zircon grain included in it would be vaporized! So whichever way the calculation is made, there is no denying that there is a genuine heat problem associated with accelerated nuclear decay.

However, the reality of the existence of the Po and ^{238}U radiohalos in biotite crystals in granitic rocks is evidence that removal of all this heat has not been an insurmountable problem if there has been accelerated decay. Incredible amounts of heat must have somehow been removed rapidly by a process or processes that we have not yet discovered or understood, for otherwise these rocks and the radiohalos in them would have been vaporized!

This potential problem was already anticipated by *Humphreys* [2000], and had previously been highlighted by *Baumgardner* [1986]. All creationist models of young earth history have serious problems with heat disposal, because there is simply too much geological work that has to be done in too short a time. Of course, the perception that there is a problem with disposal of heat is based on our present understanding and observations of heat production from radioactive decay and of heat flow, which are then applied using uniformitarian assumptions to geological processes in the past. But if geological processes have not been uniform in their rate and operation in the past, the uniformitarian assumption to project the present back into the past does not apply. In a nutshell, the perception that there is a heat problem is based solely on our understanding of these processes in the present, our ignorance of what actually happened during the catastrophic upheaval of the Flood year, and the Scriptural restriction to young earth modeling.

However, we need to wrestle seriously with this heat problem, in case we are able to decipher what process or processes may have been operating in concert with the catastrophic geological processes of the Flood year, such as rapid cooling of granitic magmas. *Humphreys* [2000] has suggested a potential solution that involves the expansion of the fabric of space within the cosmos, a process that makes energy disappear! As *Humphreys* [2000, 2005] has explained, there is a well-understood but poorly publicized mechanism in general relativity that could account for this loss. The result of the relevant calculations used in that mechanism is that the radiation energy which is lost in an expanding universe is used up as work in aiding the expansion [*Robertson and Noonan*, 1968]. Further explanation and discussion of this potential solution is provided by *Humphreys* [2005]. Obviously, these issues require further eludication, but the fact remains that in a young earth model radiohalos provide evidence of accelerated nuclear decay and rapid cooling of granitic rocks.

Appendix D. Other Applications and Their Implications

D.1 Other Sources of Hydrothermal Fluids and Their Environments

As discussed earlier, hydrothermal fluids are not only generated in crystallizing granitic plutons that release magmatic fluids, but may incorporate connate and meteoric waters that are heated by magmatic intrusions and are mixed with magmatic fluids. Similarly, hydrothermal fluids can be generated by the deep burial of connate waters within sedimentary basins, and by regional metamorphism as minerals containing water react under increasing temperatures and pressures to produce new minerals and release that water. The hydrothermal fluids associated with magmatic intrusions, particularly granitic plutons, also involve heat from the intrusions that causes contact metamorphism in the host rocks immediately surrounding the plutons. In all of these geological situations involving hydrothermal fluids the extremely active nature of those fluids, due to what they carry in solution, transports metals down flow in rock strata and fractures to locations where the chemical environment is conducive to precipitation of metals and gangue minerals to form ore deposits. Thus the hydrothermal fluids encompass a wide spectrum of fluid sources, and have operated within many geological contexts throughout those periods of earth's history in which the strata record was accumulating. Thus there may be other geological contexts apart from granitic plutons in which hydrothermal fluids may have been responsible for the transport of ^{238}U decay products and the generation of Po radiohalos.

D.2 Metamorphism, Hydrothermal Fluids, and Radiohalos

Snelling and Armitage [2003] have already predicted these potential applications of the hydrothermal fluid transport model for the secondary formation of Po radiohalos to a wide spectrum of geological contexts. They predicted that Po radiohalos should be found not only in granitic plutons, but also in regional metamorphic rocks. As argued here, many granitic plutons containing Po radiohalos were derived from partial melting as a result of regional metamorphism during the Flood. In some instances, for example, the Cooma Granodiorite [*Snelling and Armitage*, 2003], the regional metamorphic rocks from which the granitic plutons were derived are still to be found adjacent to them, or associated with them. *Snelling and Armitage* [2003] demonstrated that the zircons, which were the source of the ^{238}U decay products that were transported by hydrothermal fluids to form the Po radiohalos, were originally detrital zircons in the sediments that were regionally metamorphosed to form the granitic plutons. In the case of the Cooma Granodiorite, ^{238}U and ^{232}Th radiohalos have been observed around zircon and monazite inclusions respectively in biotites within the surrounding high-grade metamorphic rocks [*Williams*, 2001]. These zircon and monazite grains evidently contain sufficient quantities of ^{238}U, ^{232}Th, and their decay products for formation of radiohalos. Therefore, if hydrothermal fluids have flowed through these metamorphic rocks during the regional metamorphism, during the generation of the granitic magma, and during the cooling of both the granitic pluton and the metamorphic terrane, then the passage of those hydrothermal fluids through the biotite crystals in the metamorphic rocks could easily have transported the ^{238}U decay products for generation of Po radiohalos. *Snelling* [1994a, b] has argued that the process of regional metamorphism can be explained by the circulation of hydrothermal fluids through sediment layers of differing mineralogy and composition. The minerals in the sediments were thereby transformed into new metamorphic minerals that are characteristic of each regional metamorphic zone observed in metamorphic complexes today. Such regional metamorphic zones are usually explained in terms of only temperature and pressure conditions operating over millions of years. Thus if Po radiohalos are present in regionally metamorphosed rocks, especially alongside of ^{238}U radiohalos in the same biotite grains, this would provide definitive evidence of the role of hydrothermal fluids in regional metamorphism, and of the timescale involved.

The presence of ^{238}U and ^{232}Th radiohalos in metamorphic rocks has been documented by *Rimsaite* [1967], *Nasdala et al.* [2001], and *Williams* [2001]; but so far there has only been tentative documentation of Po radiohalos in one high-grade metamorphic rock (a gneiss) [*Mahadevan*, 1927; *Gentry*, 1971; *Wise*, 1989]. Thus it would be worthwhile for a concerted systematic effort to be made to verify and document the geological distribution and occurrence of all types of radiohalos in all types of metamorphic rocks, given that hydrothermal fluids are also involved in contact metamorphism. The critical component required would be that the metamorphic rocks contain biotite grains, because these readily host radiohalos. But many other minerals are known to host radiohalos [*Ramdohr*, 1933, 1957, 1976; *Stark*, 1936]; so metamorphic rocks of differing mineral assemblages would need to be examined. While the focus of this study has been granitic rocks, in the course of fieldwork a few metamorphic rocks have been sampled because of their close association with, or relationship to, nearby granitic rocks. The radiohalos found in those samples are recorded in Table 4. These results demonstrate conclusively that Po radiohalos are present in metamorphic rocks in similar abundances and similar proportions of the different types, as in granitic rocks. Metamorphic rocks therefore warrant focused systematic studies, particularly where the rocks in the different metamorphic zones surrounding a granitic pluton are readily accessible, such as in the Cooma Metamorphic Complex surrounding the Cooma Granodiorite [*Browne*, 1914; *Joplin*, 1942; *Hopwood*, 1976; *Johnson et al.*, 1994]. The observations of Po radiohalos in these metamorphic rocks suggest that they too were formed as a result of hydrothermal fluid transport of ^{238}U decay products, in the same way that the Po radiohalos form in granitic rocks. Tiny zircon grains with ^{238}U radiohalos around them are observed in most of these rocks; so there is an adequate supply of ^{238}U decay products. This also implies that hydrothermal fluids were actively circulating through these rocks, at least during the cooling phase of the metamorphism below 150°C.

Although further verification obviously requires more detailed studies, these observations are consistent with the model for regional metamorphism proposed by *Snelling* [1994a, b], that involves the circulation of hydrothermal fluids through deeply-buried sedimentary rocks to transform their minerals into those in the metamorphic rocks. As with the cooling of granitic plutons, because the formation of the Po

Table 4. Radiohalos recorded in regional metamorphic rocks.

Rock Unit	Location	"Age"	Samples (slides)	Radiohalos					Number of Radiohalos per slide	Ratios			
				^{210}Po	^{214}Po	^{218}Po	^{238}U	^{232}Th		^{210}Po:^{238}U	^{210}Po:^{214}Po	^{210}Po:^{218}Po	^{238}U:^{232}Th
Migmatite adjacent to Palmer Granite	South Australia	Ordovician	1 (51)	234	8	0	507	3	14.7	1.0:2.2	29.3:1.0	—	1690:1.0
Biotite Garnet Eclogite	Stordal, Norway	Late Proterozoic	1 (50)	7	0	0	0	0	0.14	—	—	—	—
Metamorphic pegmatite	Steiggjelselva, Norway	Middle to Late Proterozoic	1 (50)	30	0	0	0	0	0.6	—	—	—	—
Gneiss (and pegmatite)	Hegland, Norway	Early Proterozoic	2 (100)	0	0	0	0	0	—	—	—	—	—
Gneiss (and pegmatite)	Arendal, Norway	Proterozoic	2 (100)	65	33	0	0	0	0.98	—	1.97:1.0	—	—
Gneiss	Sandbraten, Norway	Proterozoic	1 (50)	78	0	0	0	0	1.56	—	—	—	—
Gneiss	Gravfoss, Norway	Proterozoic	1 (50)	0	0	0	0	0	0	—	—	—	—
Vishnu Schist	Grand Canyon (USA)	1690–1710Ma	8 (400)	7904	12	4	2376	0	25.7	3.3:1.0	659.0:1.0	1976.0:1.0	—
Rama Schist	Grand Canyon (USA)	1690–1710Ma	2 (100)	574	0	0	54	0	6.3	10.6:1.0	—	—	—
Dyrkorn Gneiss	Sunnmore, Norway	Archean	1 (50)	24	0	7	5	0	0.7	4.8:1.0	—	3.4:1.0	—
Gneiss	Ilomantsi, Finland	Archean	1 (50)	83	0	0	29	0	2.2	2.9:1.0	—	—	—

radiohalos requires extremely rapid cooling and extremely rapid flows of hydrothermal fluids, the similar presence of Po radiohalos in these metamorphic rocks must equally imply that they also cooled extremely rapidly, during which time there were extremely rapid hydrothermal fluid flows through them. During regional metamorphism temperatures can reach as high as 600°C or more; and at those temperatures connate waters contained in the original sediments and water derived from mineral reactions become hydrothermal fluids that would be driven by the heat originating in the center of the metamorphic complex. Up to these temperatures zircon grains will survive intact [*Williams*, 2001]; so as soon as the hydrothermal fluids flow past zircon grains they will transport ^{238}U decay products. As long as the temperatures in the newly formed metamorphic rocks are above 150°C there will be no α-tracks recorded or formation of radiohalos. Because of the 3.8 day half-life of ^{222}Rn and the brief half-lives of 3.1 minutes and 164 microseconds for ^{218}Po and ^{214}Po respectively, temperatures from the peak of metamorphism have to fall extremely rapidly to below 150°C for the Po radiohalos to form before the supply of ^{222}Rn and Po isotopes from the zircons is exhausted, and the hydrothermal fluid flow ceases. Because of these constraints, similar to those with granitic rocks, the time involved for this cooling process from the peak temperatures of metamorphism to ambient temperatures would have to be of the order of 6–10 days. Distances over which the ^{222}Rn and Po isotopes have to be transported must be short enough, and the hydrothermal fluid flows fast enough, for the Po isotopes to be deposited in the radiocenters. If only ^{210}Po radiohalos were in these rocks it could be argued that the cooling and transport process could have taken more time and been over longer distances; but the presence of ^{214}Po radiohalos (Table 4) restricts the time frame. Furthermore, as in the granitic rocks, the fact that both the ^{238}U and Po radiohalos must have formed concurrently after the temperatures had fallen below 150°C implies accelerated nuclear decay during the formation process. The observed fully-formed ^{238}U radiohalos represent up to 100 million years worth of ^{238}U decay at present rates.

It would seem to be very disappointing that the fiat Creation hypothesis for the formation of the Po radiohalos and their host granitic rocks has been falsified. However, the timescale considerations for the formation of Po radiohalos still remain, and they have implications for both the cooling of granitic plutons and metamorphic complexes that contain Po radiohalos. With accelerated nuclear decay the hydrothermal fluids that transport the ^{222}Rn and Po isotopes to form the Po radiohalos must also rapidly transfer an immense amount of heat from crystallizing granitic magmas, and away from the high-grade metamorphic zones to the outer limits of the metamorphic complexes [*Snelling*, 1994a; *Snelling and Woodmorappe*, 1998]. Thus it is contended that the presence of Po radiohalos in granitic and metamorphic rocks implies an extremely short timescale for their formation and cooling—just a few days, not weeks or years—a timescale consistent with the year of the catastrophic global Flood. Similar granite formation and metamorphic processes may have been associated with the Creation week. As with the Precambrian granitic plutons, metamorphic rocks that may date back to the Creation week most likely suffered from the heat flow evident during the tectonics of the Flood; and thus the ^{238}U and Po radiohalos now observed in these rocks may well date only from the Flood event.

D.3 Hydrothermal Ore Deposits and Radiohalos

Hydrothermal fluids have been also responsible for the deposition of many metallic ore deposits—fluids associated with emplacement of granitic magmas, and also fluids associated with regional metamorphism deep within sedimentary basins [*Barnes*, 1997]. Because the occurrence of Po radiohalos in granitic and metamorphic rocks implies rapid convective flows of hydrothermal fluids and also rapid cooling of those rocks, Po radiohalos found associated with hydrothermal metallic ore deposits imply rapid deposition of those ore deposits. For example, the higher abundance of Po radiohalos in the Land's End Granite of Cornwall, England (Table 2 and Figure 6), is not simply due to the large numbers of tiny zircon inclusions in the biotites of that granite. Other granites such as the Strathbogie Granite of Victoria, Australia, also have large numbers of zircon inclusions and ^{238}U radiohalos. Rather, the Land's End Granite radiohalos are also due to the additional U, and therefore also ^{238}U decay products, in the hydrothermal fluids carrying the Sn, Pb, Zn, Cu, etc. through the granite and out into the fractures where the metals were deposited in economic lodes. Similarly, the several pegmatitic veins (in Ontario, Canada) containing biotites with huge abundances of Po radiohalos also host economic U ore deposits, testimony to the hydrothermal fluid flows responsible for both the U ore and the Po radiohalos.

Thus the presence of Po radiohalos associated with such metallic ore deposits has the potential to show that these deposits were formed rapidly. This is a far-reaching implication, because it encompasses all major classes of metallic ore deposits, ranging from porphyry Cu±Au±Mo deposits hosted by granitic rocks to vein deposits of gold and other metals (such as in Cornwall, England), and to massive sulfide deposits containing base and other metals. Such deposits range in size from small to giant, and are found at many distinctive levels throughout the global geological record. Furthermore, a corollary to this is that in new areas that are being explored for hydrothermal metallic ore deposits it may be possible to use the presence and abundance of Po radiohalos as a guide to where there have been hydrothermal fluid flows in favorable host rocks to produce ore deposits. In areas where hydrothermal metallic ore deposits have already been found Po radiohalos could be used as an exploration tool to locate new ore deposits.

The presence of Po radiohalos has powerful and far-reaching implications—implications for the rapid formation of granitic plutons and regional metamorphic complexes, and also for the rapid deposition of metallic ore deposits. These processes would have occurred catastrophically on a global scale within the Flood year. It is possible that metallic ore deposits were also formed during Creation week, and in the pre-Flood world. The "fountains of waters" that operated in the pre-Flood world could have been outlets for hydrothermal fluids flowing deep within the earth's crust which could have deposited metallic ores both at depth and in near-surface locations.

References

Ahmad, S. N., and A. W. Rose, Fluid inclusions in porphyry and skarn ore at Santa Rita, New Mexico, *Economic Geology, 75*, 229–250, 1980.

Armitage, M. H., and E. Back, The thermal erasure of radiohalos in biotite, *Creation Ex Nihilo Technical Journal, 8*(2), 212–222, 1994.

Austin, S. A. (editor), *Grand Canyon: Monument to Catastrophe*, Institute for Creation Research, Santee, California, 1994.

Austin, S. A., Do radioisotope clocks need repair? Testing the assumptions of isochron dating using K-Ar, Rb-Sr, Sm-Nd and Pb-Pb isotopes, in *Radioisotopes and the Age of the Earth: Results of a Young-Earth Creationist Research Initiative*, edited by L. Vardiman, A. A. Snelling, and E. F. Chaffin, pp. 325–392, Institute for Creation Research, El Cajon, California, and Creation Research Society, Chino Valley, Arizona, 2005.

Austin, S. A., and K. P. Wise, The pre-Flood/Flood boundary: as defined in Grand Canyon, Arizona and eastern Mojave Desert, California, in *Proceedings of the Third International Conference on Creationism*, edited by R. E. Walsh, pp. 37–47, Creation Science Fellowship, Pittsburgh, Pennsylvania, 1994.

Austin, S. A., J. R. Baumgardner, D. R. Humphreys, A. A. Snelling, L. Vardiman, and K. P. Wise, Catastrophic plate tectonics: a global Flood model of earth history, in *Proceedings of the Third Conference on Creationism*, edited by R. E. Walsh, pp. 609–621, Creation Science Fellowship, Pittsburgh, Pennsylvania, 1994.

Aylward, G. H., and T. J. V. Findlay, *SI Chemical Data*, John Wiley & Sons, Sydney, 1971.

Bagnall, K. W., *Chemistry of the Rare Radioelements*, Butterworths, London, 1957.

Barbarin, B., W. E. Stephens, B. Bonin, J.-L. Bouchez, D. B. Clarke, M. Cuney, and H. Martin (editors), *Fourth Hutton Symposium: The Origin of Granites and Related Rocks*, Geological Society of America, Special Paper 350, 2001.

Barnes, H. L. (editor), *Geochemistry of Hydrothermal Ore Deposits*, third edition, John Wiley & Sons, New York, 1997.

Baumgardner, J. R., Numerical simulation of the large-scale tectonic changes accompanying the Flood, in *Proceedings of the First International Conference on Creationism*, edited by R.E. Walsh, C.L. Brooks, and R.S. Crowell, vol. 2, pp. 17–30, Creation Science Fellowship, Pittsburgh, Pennsylvania, 1986.

Baumgardner, J.R., Distribution of radioactive isotopes in the earth, in *Radioisotopes and the Age of the Earth: A Young-Earth Creationist Research Initiative*, edited by L. Vardiman, A.A. Snelling, and E.F. Chaffin, pp. 49–94, Institute for Creation Research, El Cajon, California, and Creation Research Society, St. Joseph, Missouri, 2000.

Best, M.G., and E.H. Christiansen, *Igneous Petrology*, Blackwell Science, Malden, Massachusetts, 2001.

Bouchez, J.-L., D.H.W. Hutton, and W.E. Stephens (editors), *Granite: From Segregation of Melt to Emplacement Fabrics*, Kluwer Academic Publishers, Dordrecht, The Netherlands, 1997.

Boucot, A.J., G.J.F. Macdonald, C. Milton, and J.B. Thompson, Jr., Metamorphosed Middle Paleozoic fossils from central Massachusetts, eastern Vermont, and western New Hampshire, *Bulletin of the Geological Society of America, 69*, 855–870, 1958.

Brandon, A.D., R.A. Creaser, and T. Chacko, Constraints on rates of granitic magma transport from epidote dissolution kinetics, *Science, 271*, 1845–1848, 1996.

Brown, R.H., The nature and evidence of the activity of supernatural intelligence, as illustrated by polonium radiohalos, *Origins, 24*, 65–80, 1997.

Brown, R.H., H.G. Coffin, L.G. Gibson, A.A. Roth, and C.L. Webster, Examining radiohalos, *Origins, 15*, 32–38, 1988.

Brown, S.G., King Island scheelite deposits, in *Geology of the Mineral Deposits of Australia and Papua New Guinea*, edited by F.E. Hughes, pp. 1175–1180, The Australasian Institute of Mining and Metallurgy, Melbourne, 1990.

Browne, W.R., The geology of the Cooma district, N.S.W., Part I, *Journal and Proceedings of the Royal Society of New South Wales, 48*, 172–222, 1914.

Bucher, K., and M. Frey, *Petrogenesis of Metamorphic Rocks*, seventh edition, Springer-Verlag, Berlin, 2002.

Burnham, C.W., Magmas and hydrothermal fluids, in *Geochemistry of Hydrothermal Ore Deposits*, third edition, edited by H.L. Barnes, pp.63–123, John Wiley & Sons, New York, 1997.

Candela, P.A., Physics of aqueous phase evolution in plutonic environments, *American Mineralogist, 76*, 1081–1091, 1991.

Candela, P.A., Controls on ore metal ratios in granite-related ore systems: an experimental and computational approach, *Transactions of the Royal Society of Edinburgh, Earth Sciences, 83*, 317–326, 1992.

Carl, C., and H. Dill, Age of secondary uranium mineralization in the basement rocks of northeastern Bavaria, F.R.G., *Chemical Geology, 52*, 295–316, 1985.

Cathles, L.M., An analysis of the cooling of intrusives by ground-water convection which includes boiling, *Economic Geology, 72*, 804–826, 1977.

Cathles, L.M., Fluid flow and genesis of hydrothermal ore deposits, in *Economic Geology: 75th Anniversary Volume*, edited by B.J. Skinner, pp.424–457, The Economic Geology Publishing Company, 1981.

Cerny, P., Petrogenesis of granitic pegmatites, in *Granitic Pegmatites in Science and Industry*, edited by P. Cerny, pp.405–461, Mineralogical Association of Canada, Short Course Handbook 8, 1982.

Chakoumakos, B.C., and G.R. Lumpkin, Pressure-temperature constraints on the crystallization of the Harding pegmatite, Taos County, New Mexico, *Canadian Mineralogist, 28*, 287–298, 1990.

Chesley, J.T., A.N. Halliday, L.W. Snee, K. Mezger, T.J. Shepherd, and R.C. Scrivener, Thermochronology of the Cornubian Batholith in southwest England: implications for pluton emplacement and protracted hydrothermal mineralization, *Geochimica et Cosmochimica Acta, 57*, 1817–1835, 1993.

Clemens, J.D., and C.K. Mawer, Granitic magma transport by fracture propagation, *Tectonophysics, 204*, 339–360, 1992.

Collins, L.G., Polonium halos and myrmekite in pegmatite and granite, in *Expanding Geospheres*, edited by C.W. Hunt, pp.128–140, Polar Publishing, Calgary, Canada, 1992.

Darnley, A.G., T.H. English, O. Sprake, E.R. Preece, and D. Avery, Ages of uraninite and coffinite from south-west England, *Mineralogical Magazine, 34*, 159–176, 1965.

Dill, H., On the formation of the vein-type uranium "yellow ores" from the Schwarzach area (NE-Bavaria, Germany) and on the behaviour of P, As, V and Se during supergene processes, *Geologische Rundschau, 72*(3), 955–980, 1983.

Dumitru, T.A., I.R. Duddy, and P.F. Green, Mesozoic-Cenozoic burial, uplift and erosion history of the west-central Colorado Plateau, *Geology, 22*, 499–502, 1994.

Ebadi, A., and W. Johannes, Beginning of melting and composition of first melts in the system Qz-Ab-Or-H_2O-CO_2, *Contributions to Mineralogy and Petrology, 106*, 286–295, 1991.

Feather, N., The unsolved problem of the Po-haloes in Precambrian biotite and other old minerals, *Communications to the Royal Society of Edinburgh, 11*, 147–158, 1978.

Foland, K.A., and J.C. Allen, Magma sources for Mesozoic anorogenic granites of the White Mountain magma series, New England, USA, *Contributions to Mineralogy and Petrology, 99*, 195–211, 1991.

Foland, K.A., and H. Faul, Ages of the White Mountain intrusives—New Hampshire, Vermont and Maine, USA, *American Journal of Science, 277*, 888–904, 1977.

Foland, K.A., A.W. Quinn, and B.J. Giletti, K-Ar and Rb-Sr Jurassic and Cretaceous ages for the intrusives of the White Mountain magma series, northern New England, *American Journal of Science, 270*, 321–330, 1971.

Fremlin, J.H., Spectacle haloes, *Nature, 258*, 269, 1975.

Frey, G., P.K. Hopke, and J.J. Stekel, Effects of trace gases and water vapor on the diffusion coefficient of polonium-218, *Science, 211*, 480–481, 1981.

Friedlander, G., J.W. Kennedy, and J.M. Miller, *Nuclear and Radiochemistry*, second edition, John Wiley & Sons, New York, 1964.

Fürst, M., and F.-K. Bandelow, Strukturelle und szintillometrische Aufnahmen im Ostteil des Wölsendorfer Flußspatreviers, Bayern, sowie Untersuchungen über eine Pechblendevererzung bei Altfalter, *Geologische Rundschau, 71*(2), 549–578, 1982.

Garven, G., and J.P. Raffensperger, Hydrogeology and geochemistry of ore genesis in sedimentary basins, in *Geochemistry of Hydrothermal Ore Deposits*, third edition, edited by H.L. Barnes, pp. 125–189, John Wiley & Sons, New York, 1997.

Gentry, D., Polonium halos: a closer view, *Bible-Science News, 34*(4), 1–6, 1996.

Gentry, R. V., Extinct radioactivity and the discovery of a new pleochroic halo, *Nature, 213*, 487–489, 1967.

Gentry, R. V., Fossil alpha-recoil analysis of certain variant radioactive haloes, *Science, 160*, 1228–1230, 1968.

Gentry, R. V., Giant radioactive halos: indicators of unknown radioactivity, *Science, 169*, 670–673, 1970.

Gentry, R. V., Radiohalos: some unique lead isotopic ratios and unknown alpha activity, *Science, 173*, 727–731, 1971.

Gentry, R. V., Radioactive halos, *Annual Review of Nuclear Science, 23*, 347–362, 1973.

Gentry, R. V., Radiohalos in a radiochronological and cosmological perspective, *Science, 184*, 62–66, 1974.

Gentry, R. V., Spectacle haloes, *Nature, 258*, 269–270, 1975.

Gentry, R. V., Time: measured responses, *EOS, Transactions of the American Geophysical Union, 60*,(22), 474, 1979.

Gentry, R. V., Polonium halos, *EOS, Transactions of the American Geophysical Union, 61*(27), 514, 1980.

Gentry, R. V., Creationism again, *Physics Today, 35*(10), 13, 1982.

Gentry, R. V., Creationism still again, *Physics Today, 36*(14), 13–15, 1983.

Gentry, R. V., Radioactive haloes in a radiochronological and cosmological perspective, in *Proceedings of the 63rd Annual Meeting, Pacific Division, American Association for the Advancement of Science, 1*(3), 38–65, 1984.

Gentry, R. V., Radioactive haloes: Implications for creation, in *Proceedings of the First International Conference on Creationism*, edited by R. E. Walsh, C. L. Brooks, and R. S. Crowell, vol. 2, pp. 89–100, Creation Science Fellowship, Pittsburgh, Pennsylvania, 1986.

Gentry, R. V., *Creation's Tiny Mystery*, Earth Science Associates, Knoxville, Tennessee, 1988.

Gentry, R. V., Response to Wise, *Creation Research Society Quarterly, 25*, 176–180, 1989.

Gentry, R. V., Radiohalos in diamonds, *Creation Ex Nihilo Technical Journal, 12*, 287–290, 1998.

Gentry, R. V., Personal correspondence, email dated July 27, 1999.

Gentry, R. V., Personal communication, open email letter dated July 31, 2003.

Gentry, R. V., T. A. Cahill, N. R. Fletcher, H. C. Kaufmann, L. R. Medsker, J. W. Nelson, and R. G. Flocchini, Evidence for primordial superheavy elements, *Physical Review Letters, 37*(1), 11–15, 1976a.

Gentry, R. V., W. H. Christie, D. H. Smith, J. F. Emery, S. A. Reynolds, R. Walker, S. S. Christy, and P. A. Gentry, Radiohalos in coalified wood: new evidence relating to the time of uranium introduction and infiltration, *Science, 194*, 315–318, 1976b.

Gentry, R. V., W. H. Christie, D. H. Smith, J. W. Boyle, S. S. Christy, and J. F. McLaughlin, Implications on unknown radioactivity of giant and dwarf haloes in Scandinavian rocks, *Nature, 274*, 457–459, 1978.

Gentry, R. V., S. S. Christy, J. F. McLaughlin, and J. A. McHugh, Ion microprobe confirmation of Pb isotope ratios and search for isomer precursors in polonium radiohalos, *Nature, 244*, 282–283, 1973.

Gentry, R. V., L. D. Hulett, S. S. Christy, J. F. McLaughlin, J. A. McHugh, and M. Bayard, "Spectacle" array of [210]Po halo radiocentres in biotite: a nuclear geophysical enigma, *Nature, 252*, 564–566, 1974.

Giggenbach, W. F., The origin and evolution of fluids in magmatic-hydrothermal systems, in *Geochemistry of Hydrothermal Ore Deposits*, third edition, edited by H. L. Barnes, pp. 737–796, John Wiley & Sons, New York, 1997.

Gleeson, S. A., J. J. Wilkinson, H. F. Shaw, and R. J. Herrington, Post-magmatic hydrothermal circulation and the origin of base metal mineralization, Cornwall, UK, *Journal of the Geological Society, London, 157*, 589–600, 2000.

Gleeson, S. A., J. J. Wilkinson, F. M. Stuart, and D. A. Banks, The origin and evolution of base metal mineralising brines and hydrothermal fluids, south Cornwall, UK, *Geochimica et Cosmochimica Acta, 65* (13), 2067–2079, 2001.

Hall, A., *Igneous Petrology*, second edition, Addison Wesley Longman, Harlow, England, 1996.

Harada, K., W. C. Burnett, P. A. LaRock, and J. B. Cowart, Polonium in Florida groundwater and its possible relationship to the sulfur cycle and bacteria, *Geochimica et Cosmochimica Acta, 53*, 143–150, 1989.

Harris, N., D. Vance, and M. Ayres, From sediment to granite: timescales of anatexis in the upper crust, *Chemical Geology, 162*, 155–167, 2000.

Harrison, T.M., and I. McDougall, The thermal significance of potassium feldspar K-Ar ages inferred from $^{40}Ar/^{39}Ar$ age spectrum results, *Geochimica et Cosmochimica Acta, 46*, 1811–1820, 1982.

Harrison, T.M., R.L. Armstrong, C.W. Naeser, and J.E. Harakal, Geochronology and thermal history of the Coast Plutonic Complex, near Prince Rupert, British Columbia, *Canadian Journal of Earth Sciences, 16*, 400–410, 1979.

Harrison, T.M., P. Morgan, and D.D. Blackwell, Constraints on the age of heating at the Fenton Hill site, Valles Caldera, New Mexico, *Journal of Geophysical Research, 91*(B2), 1899–1908, 1986.

Hawkins, D.P., S.A. Bowring, B.R. Ilg, K.E. Karlstrom, and M.L. Williams, U-Pb geochronologic constraints on the Paleoproterozoic crustal evolution of the Upper Granite Gorge, Grand Canyon, Arizona, *Geological Society of America Bulletin, 108*(9), 1167–1181, 1996.

Hayba, D.O., and S.E. Ingebritsen, Multiphase groundwater flow near cooling plutons, *Journal of Geophysical Research, 102*, 12,235–12,252, 1997.

Henderson, G.H., A quantitative study of pleochroic haloes—V. The genesis of haloes, *Proceedings of the Royal Society of London, Series A, 173*, 250–264, 1939.

Henderson, G.H., and S. Bateson, A quantitative study of pleochroic haloes—I, *Proceedings of the Royal Society of London, Series A, 145*, 563–581, 1934.

Henderson, G.H., and F.W. Sparks, A quantitative study of pleochroic haloes—IV. New types of haloes, *Proceedings of the Royal Society of London, Series A, 173*, 238–249, 1939.

Henderson, G.H., and L.G. Turnbull, A quantitative study of pleochroic haloes—II, *Proceedings of the Royal Society of London, Series A, 145*, 582–598, 1934.

Henderson, G.H., G.M. Mushkat, and D.P. Crawford, A quantitative study of pleochroic haloes—III. Thorium, *Proceedings of the Royal Society of London, Series A, 158*, 199–211, 1934.

Hendricks, J.D., and G.M. Stevenson, Grand Canyon Supergroup: Unkar Group, in *Grand Canyon Geology*, second edition, edited by S.S. Beus and

M. Morales, pp. 39–52, Oxford University Press, New York, 2003.

Holmes, A., Radioactivity and geological time, *Bulletin of the National Research Council, 80*, 124–460, 1931.

Holtz, F., H. Behrens, D.B. Dingwell, and W. Johannes, Water solubility in haplogranitic melts: compositional, pressure and temperature dependence, *American Mineralogist, 80*, 94–108, 1995.

Hopwood, T.P., Stratigraphy and structural summary of the Cooma Metamorphic Complex, *Journal of the Geological Society of Australia, 23*, 345–360, 1976.

Huang, W.L., and P.J. Wyllie, Melting reactions in the system $NaAlSi_3O_8$-$KAlSi_3O_8$-SiO_2 to 35 kilobars, dry with excess water, *Journal of Geology, 83*, 737–748, 1975.

Humphreys, D.R., Accelerated nuclear decay: a viable hypothesis?, in *Radioisotopes and the Age of the Earth: A Young-Earth Creationist Research Initiative*, edited by L. Vardiman, A.A. Snelling, and E.F. Chaffin, pp. 333–379, Institute for Creation Research, El Cajon, California, and Creation Research Society, St. Joseph, Missouri, 2000.

Humphreys, D.R., Young helium diffusion age of zircons supports accelerated nuclear decay, in *Radioisotopes and the Age of the Earth: Results of a Young-Earth Creationist Research Initiative*, edited by L. Vardiman, A.A. Snelling, and E.F. Chaffin, pp. 25–100, Institute for Creation Research, El Cajon, California, and Creation Research Society, Chino Valley, Arizona, 2005.

Humphreys, D.R., S.A. Austin, J.R. Baumgardner, and A.A. Snelling, Helium diffusion rates supports accelerated nuclear decay, in *Proceedings of the Fifth International Conference on Creationism*, edited by R.L. Ivey, Jr., pp. 175–195, Creation Science Fellowship, Pittsburgh, Pennsylvania, 2003. See *http://www.icr.org/research/icc03/pdf/Helium_ICC_7-22-03.pdf.*

Humphreys, D.R., S.A. Austin, J.R. Baumgardner, and A.A. Snelling, Helium diffusion age of 6,000 years supports accelerated nuclear decay, *Creation Research Society Quarterly, 41*, 1–16, 2004. See *http://www. creationresearch.org/crsq/articles/41/41_1/Helium_lo_res.pdf.*

Hurford, A.J., On the closure temperature for fission tracks in zircon, *Nuclear Tracks, 10*, 415, 1985.

Hussain, N., T.M. Church, G.W. Luther III, and W.S. Moore, [210]Po and ^{210}Pb disequilibrium in the hydrothermal vent fluids in chimney deposits from Juan de Fuca Ridge, *Geophysical Research Letters, 22*, 3175–3178, 1995.

Iimori, S., and J. Yoshimura, Pleochroic halos in biotite: probable existence of the independent origin of the actinium series, *Scientific Papers of the Institute of Physical and Chemical Research, 5*(66), 11–24, 1926.

Ilton, E. S., and D. R. Veblen, Copper inclusions in sheet silicates from porphyry Cu deposits, *Nature, 334*, 516–518, 1988.

Ingebritsen, S. E., and D. O. Hayba, Fluid flow and heat transport near the critical point of H_2O, *Geophysical Research Letters, 21*, 2199–2202, 1994.

Jackson, N. J., J. Willis-Richards, B. A. C. Manning, and M. S. Sams, Evolution of the Cornubian ore field, southwest England: Part II. Mineral deposits and ore-forming processes, *Economic Geology, 84*, 1101–1133, 1989.

Jahns, R. H., Internal evolution of pegmatite bodies, in *Granitic Pegmatites in Science and Industry,* edited by P. Cerny, pp. 293–327, Mineralogical Association of Canada, Short Course Handbook 8, 1982.

Jahns, R. H., and C. W. Burnham, Experimental studies of pegmatite genesis: melting and crystallization of granite and pegmatite, *U.S. Geological Survey Bulletin, 69*, 1592–1593, 1958.

Jahns, R. H., and C. W. Burnham, Experimental studies of pegmatite genesis: I. A model for the derivation and crystallization of granitic pegmatites, *Economic Geology, 64*, 843–864, 1969.

Johannes, W., and S. Holtz, *Petrogenesis and Experimental Petrology of Granitic Rocks*, Springer-Verlag, Berlin, 1996.

Johnson, S. E., R. H. Vernon, and B. E. Hobbs, *Deformation and Metamorphism of the Cooma Complex, Southeastern Australia*, Specialist Group in Tectonics and Structural Geology, Field Guide No. 4, Geological Society of Australia, Sydney, 1994.

Joly, J., Pleochroic halos, *Philosophical Magazine, 13*, 381–383, 1907.

Joly, J., Radio-active halos, *Philosophical Transactions of the Royal Society of London, Series A, 217*, 51–79, 1917a.

Joly, J., Radio-active halos, *Nature, 99*, 456–458, 476–478, 1917b.

Joly, J., Radio-active halos, *Proceedings of the Royal Society of London, Series A, 102*, 682–705, 1923.

Joly, J., The radioactivity of the rocks, *Nature, 114*, 160–164, 1924.

Joplin, G.A., Petrological studies in the Ordovician of New South Wales. I.

The Cooma Complex, *Proceedings of the Linnean Society of New South Wales, 67,* 156–196, 1942.

Karlstrom, K. E., B. R Ilg, M. L. Williams, D. P. Hawkins, S. A. Bowring, and S. J. Seaman, Paleoproterozoic rocks of the Granite Gorges, in *Grand Canyon Geology,* second edition, edited by S. S. Beus and M. Morales, pp. 9–38, Oxford University Press, New York, 2003.

Kerr-Lawson, D. E., Pleochroic haloes in biotite from near Murray Bay, *University of Toronto Studies in Geology Series, 24,* 54–71, 1927.

Kerr-Lawson, D. E., Pleochroic haloes in biotite, *University of Toronto Studies in Geology Series, 27,* 15–27, 1928.

Knapp, R. B., and D. Norton, Preliminary numerical analysis of processes related to magma crystallization and stress evolution in cooling pluton environments, *American Journal of Science, 281,* 35–68, 1981.

Kwak, T. A. P., The conditions of formation of the King Island scheelite contact skarn, King Island, Tasmania, Australia, *American Journal of Science, 278,* 969–999, 1978a.

Kwak, T. A. P., Mass balance relationship and skarn forming processes at the King Island scheelite deposit, King Island, Tasmania, Australia, *American Journal of Science, 278,* 943–968, 1978b.

Laney, R., and A. W. Laughlin, Natural annealing of the pleochroic haloes in biotite samples from deep drill holes, Fenton Hill, New Mexico, *Geophysical Research Letters, 8*(5), 501–504, 1981.

LaRock, P. A., J.-H. Hyun, S. Boutelle, W. C. Burnett, and C. D. Hull, Bacterial mobilization of polonium, *Geochimica et Cosmochimica Acta, 60,* 4321–4328, 1996.

Larson, E. E., P. E. Patterson, and F. E. Mutschler, Lithology, chemistry, age, and origin of the Proterozoic Cardenas Basalt, Grand Canyon, Arizona, *Precambrian Research, 65,* 255–276, 1994.

LeCloarec, M. F., M. Pennisi, E. Corazza, and G. Lambert, Origin of fumerolic fluids emitted from a nonerupting volcano: radionuclide constraints at Vulcano (Aeolian Islands, Italy), *Geochimica et Cosmochimica Acta, 58,* 4401–4410, 1994.

Lingen, J. S., van der, Ueber pleochroitische höfe, *Zentralel. Mineralogie und Geologie, Abteilung A.,* 177–183, 1926.

Lofgren, G., Experimental studies on the dynamic crystallization of silicate melts, in *Physics of Magmatic Processes*, edited by R.B. Hargreaves, pp. 487–551, Princeton University Press, New Jersey, 1980.

London, D., The application of experimental petrology to the genesis and crystallization of granitic pegmatites, *Canadian Mineralogist, 30*, 499–540, 1992.

London, D., Granitic pegmatites, *Transactions of the Royal Society of Edinburgh: Earth Sciences, 87*, 305–319, 1996.

Luth, W.C., Granitic rocks, in *The Evolution of the Crystalline Rocks*, edited by D.K. Bailey and R. MacDonald, pp. 333–417, Academic Press, London, 1976.

Mahadevan, C., Pleochroic haloes in cordierite, *Indian Journal of Physics, 1*, 445–455, 1927.

Meier, H., and W. Hecker, Radioactive halos as possible indicators for geochemical processes in magmatites, *Geochemical Journal, 10*, 185–195, 1976.

Mügge, O., Radioaktivität als ursuche der pleochroitischen höfe des cordierit, *Zentralel. Mineralogie und Geologie, 1907*, 397–399, 1907.

Müller, S.A., A new model of the continental crust, in *The Earth's Crust: Its Nature and Physical Properties*, edited by J.G. Heacock, pp. 289–317, Geophysical Monograph Series 20, American Geophysical Union, Washington, DC, 1977.

Mustart, D.A., Hydrothermal synthesis of large single crystals of albite and potassium feldspar, *EOS, Transactions of the American Geophysical Union, 50*, 675, 1969.

Naeser, C.W., The fading of fission tracks in the geologic environment: data from deep drill holes, *Nuclear Tracks, 5*, 248–250, 1981.

Naeser, C.W., and R.B. Forbes, Variation of fission-track ages with depth in two deep drill holes, *EOS, Transactions of the American Geophysical Union, 57*, 353, 1976.

Naeser, C.W., I.R. Duddy, D.P. Elston, T.A. Dumitru, and P.F. Green, Fission-track dating: ages from Cambrian strata and Laramide and post-middle Eocene cooling events from the Grand Canyon, Colorado, in *Geology of Grand Canyon, Northern Arizona (with Colorado River Guides)*, edited by D.P. Elston, G.H. Billingsley, and R.A. Young, pp. 139–144, American Geophysical Union, Washington, DC, 1989.

Nasdala, L., M. Wenzel, M. Andrut, R. Wirth, and P. Blaum, The nature of radiohaloes in biotite: experimental studies and modeling, *American Mineralogist, 86*, 498–512, 2001.

Nielson, R. L., Mineralization and alteration in calcareous rocks near the Santa Rita stock, New Mexico, *New Mexico Geological Society, Guidebook, 21st Field Conference*, 133–139, 1970.

Norton, D. L., and L. M. Cathles, Thermal aspects of ore deposition, in *Geochemistry of Hydrothermal Ore Deposits*, second edition, edited by H. L. Barnes, pp. 611–631, John Wiley & Sons, New York, 1979.

Petford, N., Segregation of tonalitic-trondhjemitic melts in the continental crust: the mantle connection, *Journal of Geophysical Research, 100*, 15735–15742, 1995.

Petford, N., R. C. Kerr, and J. R. Lister, Dike transport of granitoid magmas, *Geology, 21*, 845–848, 1993.

Petford, N., A. R. Cruden, K. J. W. McCaffrey, and J.-L. Vigneresse, Granite magma formation, transport and emplacement in the Earth's crust, *Nature, 408*, 669–673, 2000.

Pitcher, W. S., *The Nature and Origin of Granite*, Blackie Academic, Glasgow, 1993.

Poole, J. H. J., The action of heat on pleochroic halos, *Philosophical Magazine, Seventh Series, 5*, 132–141, 1928a.

Poole, J. H. J., Note on the formation of pleochroic halos in biotite, *Philosophical Magazine, Seventh Series, 5*, 444, 1928b.

Ramdohr, P., *Neues Jahrbuch für Mineralogie Beilageband Abteilung A, 67*, 53–65, 1933.

Ramdohr, P., *Abh. Deut. Akad. Wiss. Berlin Kl. Chem. Geol. Biol., 2*, 1–17, 1957.

Ramdohr, P., Neue beobachtungen an Radioacktiven Höfen in verschiedenen Mineralien mit kritischen bemerkungen zur auswertung der Höfe zur Altersbestimmung, *Geologische Rundschau, 49*, 253–263, 1960.

Reed, M. H., Hydrothermal alteration and its relationship to ore fluid composition, in *Geochemistry of Hydrothermal Ore Deposits*, third edition, edited by H. L. Barnes, pp. 303–365, John Wiley & Sons, New York, 1997.

Rimsaite, J. H. Y., *Studies of Rock-Forming Micas*, Geological Survey of Canada, Bulletin 149, 1967.

Robertson, H. P., and T. W. Noonan, *Relativity and Cosmology*, W. B. Saunders Company, Philadelphia, 1968.

Rubin, K., Degassing of metals and metalloids from erupting seamount and mid-ocean ridge volcanoes: observations and predictions, *Geochimica et Cosmochimica Acta, 61*, 3525–3542, 1997.

Rumbold, R., Radioactive minerals in Cornwall and Devon, *Mining Magazine, 91*, 16–27, 1954.

Sasada, M., Fluid inclusion evidence for recent temperature increases at Fenton Hill Hot Dry Rock test site west of the Valles Caldera, New Mexico, U.S.A., *Journal of Volcanology and Geothermal Research, 36*, 257–266, 1989.

Schilling, A., Die radioacktiven höfe im flusspat von Wölsendorf, *Neues Jahrbuch für Mineralogie, Geologie und Palaeontology, Abteilung A, 53*, 241–265, 1926.

Scott, S. D., Submarine hydrothermal systems and deposits, in *Geochemistry of Hydrothermal Ore Deposits*, third edition, edited by H. L. Barnes, pp. 797–875, John Wiley & Sons, New York, 1997.

Seward, T. M., and H. L. Barnes, Metal transport by hydrothermal ore fluids, in *Geochemistry of Hydrothermal Ore Deposits*, third edition, edited by H. L. Barnes, pp. 435–486, John Wiley & Sons, New York, 1997.

Sheppard, S. M. F., The Cornubian Batholith, SW England: D/H and $^{18}O/^{16}O$ studies of kaolinite and other alteration minerals, *Journal of the Geological Society, London, 133*, 573–591, 1977.

Smith, R. L., R. A. Bailey, and C. S. Ross, *Geologic Map of the Jemez Mountains, New Mexico*, U. S. Geological Survey, Miscellaneous Geological Investigation Map I-571, 1970.

Snelling, A. A., *The Geology of the Margins of the Bathurst Granite between Sodwalls and Tarana*, Unpublished, B.Sc. Honours Thesis, The University of New South Wales, Sydney, 1974.

Snelling, A. A., Towards a creationist explanation of regional metamorphism, *Creation Ex Nihilo Technical Journal, 8*(1), 51–77, 1994a.

Snelling, A. A., Regional metamorphism within a creationist framework: what garnet compositions reveal, in *Proceedings of the Third International Conference on Creationism*, edited by R. E. Walsh, pp. 485–496, Creation Science Fellowship, Pittsburgh, Pennsylvania, 1994b.

Snelling, A. A., Radiohalos, in *Radioisotopes and the Age of the Earth: A Young-Earth Creationist Research Initiative*, edited by L. Vardiman, A. A. Snelling, and E. F. Chaffin, pp. 381–468, Institute for Creation Research, El Cajon, California, and Creation Research Society, St. Joseph, Missouri, 2000.

Snelling, A. A., Isochron discordances and the role of inheritance and mixing of radioisotopes in the mantle and crust, in *Radioisotopes and the Age of the Earth: Results of a Young-Earth Creationist Research Initiative*, edited by L. Vardiman, A. A. Snelling, and E. F. Chaffin, pp. 393–524, Institute for Creation Research, El Cajon, California, and Creation Research Society, Chino Valley, Arizona, 2005.

Snelling, A. A., and M. H. Armitage, Radiohalos—a tale of three granitic plutons, in *Proceedings of the Fifth International Conference on Creationism*, edited by R. L. Ivey, Jr., pp. 243–267, Creation Science Fellowship, Pittsburgh, Pennsylvania, 2003. See *http://www.icr.org/research/icc03/pdf/ICRRADIOHALOS-AASandMA.pdf.*

Snelling, A. A., and J. Woodmorappe, The cooling of thick igneous bodies on a young earth, in *Proceedings of the Fourth International Conference on Creationism*, edited by R. E. Walsh, pp. 527–545, Creation Science Fellowship, Pittsburgh, Pennsylvania, 1998.

Snelling, A. A., J. R. Baumgardner, and L. Vardiman, Abundant Po radiohalos in Phanerozoic granites and timescale implications for their formation, *EOS, Transactions of the American Geophysical Union, 84*(46), Fall Meeting Supplement, Abstract V32C-1046, 2003. Poster at *http://www.icr.org.research/AGURadiohaloPoster_Snelling.pdf.*

Spear, F. S., *Metamorphic Phase Equilibria and Pressure-Temperature-Time Paths*, Mineralogical Society of America, Washington, DC, 1993.

Spera, F. J., Thermal evolution of plutons: a parameterized approach, *Science, 207*, 299–301, 1982.

Stacey, F. D., *Physics of the Earth*, third edition, Brookfield Press, Brisbane, 1992.

Stark, M., Pleochroitische (Radioacktive) Höfe, ihre Verbreitung in den Gesteinen und Veränderlickheit, *Chemie der Erde, 10*, 566–630, 1936.

Strunz, H., and Seeliger, E., Erzpetrographie der primärien Uranmineralien von Wölsendorf. Erste Feststellung von Coffinit auf einer uranalgerstätte mitteleuropas, *Neues Jahrbuch für Mineralogie Abteilung, 94*, 681–719, 1960.

Swanson, S. E., J. A. Whitney, and W. C. Luth, Growth of large quartz and feldspar crystals from synthetic granitic liquids, *EOS, Transactions of the American Geophysical Union, 53*, 1172, 1972.

Taylor, H. P., Jr., Oxygen and hydrogen isotope relationships in hydrothermal mineral deposits, in *Geochemistry of Hydrothermal Ore Deposits*, third edition, edited by H. L. Barnes, pp. 229–302, John Wiley & Sons, New York, 1997.

Tsuchiyama, A., Crystallization kinetics in the system $CaMgSi_2O_6$-$CaAl_2Si_2O_8$: the delay in nucleation of diopside and anorthite, *American Mineralogist, 68*, 687–698, 1983.

Tuttle, O. F., and N. L. Bowen, *Origin of Granite in the Light of Experimental Studies in the System $NaAlSi_3O_8$-$KAlSi_3O_8$-SiO_2-H_2O*, Geological Society of America, Memoir 74, 1958.

Vardiman, L., A. A. Snelling, and E. F. Chaffin (editors), Appendix, July 2000: research proposals for RATE, in *Radioisotopes and the Age of the Earth: A Young-Earth Creationist Research Initiative*, pp. 561–627, Institute for Creation Research, El Cajon, California, and Creation Research Society, St. Joseph, Missouri, 2000.

Wakefield, J. R., Gentry's tiny mystery—unsupported by geology, *Creation/Evolution, XXII*, 13–33, 1988a.

Wakefield, J. R., The geology of Gentry's "tiny mystery," *Journal of Geological Education, 36*, 161–175, 1988b.

Wampler, J. M., and P. Wallace, Misconceptions of crystal growth and cooling rates in the formation of igneous rocks: the case of pegmatites and aplites, *Journal of Geological Education, 46*, 497–499, 1998.

Wedepohl, K. H., Chemical composition and fractionation of the continental crust, *Geologische Rundschau, 80*, 207–223, 1991.

Wedepohl, K. H., The composition of the continental crust, *Geochimica et Cosmochimica Acta, 59*, 1217–1232, 1995.

Wesoloski, D., *Geochemistry of Tungsten in Scheelite Deposits: The Skarn Ores at King Island, Tasmania*, Unpublished Ph. D. Thesis, Pennsylvania State University, 1984.

Wilkerson, G., Polonium radio-halos do not prove fiat creation, *Origins*

Research, 12, 1989.

Williams, I.S., Response of detrital zircon and monazite, and their U-Pb isotopic systems, in regional metamorphism and host-rock partial melting, Cooma Complex, south-eastern Australia, *Australian Journal of Earth Sciences, 48*, 557–580, 2001.

Willis-Richards, J., and N.J. Jackson, Evolution of the Cornubian ore field, southwest England: Part I. Batholith modeling and ore distribution, *Economic Geology, 84*, 1078–1100, 1989.

Wiman, E., Studies of some Archaean rocks in the neighbourhood of Uppsala, Sweden, and of their geological position, *Bulletin of the Geological Institute, University of Uppsala, 23*, 1–170, 1930.

Winkler, H. G. F., and H. von Platen, Experimentelle Gesteinsmetamorphose— II. Bildung von anatektischen granitischen Schmelzen bei der Metamorphose von NaCl—führenden kalkfreien Tonen, *Geochimica et Cosmochimica Acta 15*, 91–112, 1958.

Wise, K.P., Radioactive halos: geological concerns, *Creation Research Society Quarterly, 25*, 171–176, 1989.

Zeitler, P.K., Closure temperature implications of concordant [40]Ar/[39]Ar potassium feldspar and zircon fission-track ages from high-grade terranes, *Nuclear Tracks, 10*, 441–442, 1985.

Ziehr, H., Uranparagenese in den Fluoritgängen von Nabburg-Wölsendorf/ Ostbayern, *Aufschluß, 31*, 62–82, 1980.

208

Chapter 4

Fission Tracks in Zircons: Evidence for Abundant Nuclear Decay

Andrew A. Snelling, Ph.D.*

Abstract. Fission tracks are a physical record of *in situ* nuclear decay, their density being directly proportional to the amount of nuclear decay that has occurred. The aim of this study was to investigate whether the amounts of fission tracks in zircon grains in targeted rock units (that is, their fission track "ages") matched the radioisotope "ages" of those rocks. Stratigraphically well-constrained volcanic ash or tuff beds located in the Grand Canyon-Colorado Plateau "type section" of the Flood strata record were chosen—the Cambrian Muav and Tapeats tuffs from the western Grand Canyon (early Flood), Jurassic Morrison Formation tuff beds, southeastern Utah (middle Flood), and the Miocene Peach Springs Tuff, southeastern California and western Arizona (late Flood or post-Flood). The fission track "ages" of zircon grains separated from samples of these tuff units were determined by a specialized professional laboratory using the external detector method and a zeta (ζ) calibration factor. The observed fission track densities measured in all the zircons (and thus the fission track "ages") from the samples of the Jurassic and Miocene tuffs, and in some of the zircons from the Muav and Tapeats tuffs, were found to exactly equate to the quantities of nuclear decay measured by radioisotope determinations of the same rock units. Though thermal annealing of fission tracks had occurred in some zircon grains in the two Cambrian Grand Canyon tuffs, the U-Pb radioisotope system had also been thermally reset, the resulting reset ages in both instances coinciding

* *Geology Department, Institute for Creation Research, Santee, California*

with the onset of the Laramide uplift of the Colorado Plateau. The fact that the thermal annealing of the fission tracks and the thermal resetting of the U-Pb radioisotope system in those zircon grains were exactly parallel is unequivocal confirmation that the radioisotope ratios are a product of radioactive decay, in just the same way as the fission tracks are physical evidence of nuclear decay. Furthermore, because the resetting of the U-Pb radioisotope system in zircons will only occur at elevated temperatures, the fact that it has been reset in these zircons could therefore be due to them having been heated by accelerated nuclear decay. Even so, in spite of this thermal annealing and resetting, there remains sufficient strong evidence to conclude that both the fission tracks and radioisotope ratios in the zircons in the Cambrian Grand Canyon tuff beds record more than 500 million years worth (at today's rates) of nuclear and radioisotope decay during deposition of the Phanerozoic strata sequence of the Grand Canyon-Colorado Plateau region. Given the independent evidence that most of this strata sequence was deposited catastrophically during the year-long global Flood about 4500 years ago, then 500 million or more years worth (at today's rates) of nuclear and radioisotope decay had to have occurred during the Flood year about 4500 years ago. Thus, the fission tracks in the zircons in these tuffs are physical evidence of accelerated nuclear decay.

1. Introduction

The radioisotope dating of minerals and rocks is based on analyses of radioactive parent and radiogenic daughter isotope pairs, often ratioed against related stable isotopes because of the convenient measurement of isotope ratios using mass spectrometers. The interpretation that calculates ages from these radioisotope ratio analyses depends on crucial assumptions, in particular that the daughter isotopes have been derived by radioactive decay of the parent isotopes, and that radioisotope decay has occurred at a constant rate, as measured experimentally today. On the other hand, if either or both were shown to be false, then it could be argued that either the measured isotope ratios are merely an artifact of the mineral compositions and the geochemistry of the rocks and the sources from which they were derived, or radioactive decay had been accelerated. If either or both of these possibilities were demonstrated to be true, then the interpreted radioisotope ages that are an integral part of the modern geological synthesis of the earth's history would be falsified. Indeed, the parent/daughter assumption is often not fulfilled, so those particular rocks cannot be radioisotope dated. And in many cases, the concentrations of the daughter isotope are independent of the parent isotope, which has led to alternative explanations for the daughter isotope concentrations apart from radioisotope decay, such as inheritance and mixing [*Snelling*, 2000a, 2005b].

One available method to test whether radioactive decay has really occurred *in situ* in rocks after they have formed is fission track dating. Fission tracks are a physical record in minerals of the nuclear decay of their trace U contents. The number and density of fission tracks that can be observed in certain minerals is directly proportional to the amount of nuclear decay that has occurred. If this method is valid, then it is possible to investigate whether the amount of radioactive decay implied by chemical analyses of the radioisotope ratios is matched by the required observable amounts of fission tracks. Such verification of the equivalent observable physical evidence of radioactive decay with the amount measured by radioisotope ratios would seem to rule out any claim that the interpreted radioisotope ages are merely artifacts of the chemical analyses and the assumptions implicit in these methods. Furthermore, demonstration that there is observable physical evidence that hundreds of millions of years of nuclear decay has occurred *in situ* in minerals within rocks since they formed implies that within the Biblical timescale of only 6000–7000 years for earth history those huge amounts of nuclear decay had to have occurred at accelerated rates. This then is the focus of the research being reported in this chapter.

Because fission track dating is a different nuclear decay dating method that is not as well known and understood as the radioisotope methods, some background information on how fission track dating is performed seems warranted. This is provided in an Appendix, drawn from *Faure* [1986], *Dickin* [1995], and *Faure and Mensing* [2005].

2. Previous Creationist Research on Fission Track Dating

There has been very little creationist research into fission track dating. In a review article concerning radioactive dating, *Chaffin* [1987] discussed the possibility that fission tracks might result from other isotopes with shorter half-lives than those of ^{238}U and ^{244}Pu. *Bielecki* [1994] reported his examination of fission track densities in obsidian from the Resting Spring Range near Shoshone, California. He found that the fission track densities were equivalent to the reported uniformitarian Miocene "age" of this obsidian. He had thought that if this rock was post-Flood then it might have fission track densities smaller than its claimed multi-million year age. However, the data did not support that hypothesis, the observed fission track densities being physical evidence of millions of years of nuclear decay. *Bielecki* [1998] reported on his literature investigation of the fission track densities in man-made and natural glasses of known historical age, as well as in natural glasses and volcanic debris of comparatively recent geologic age. He concluded that the spontaneous fission tracks in man-made and natural glasses are a reliable nuclear decay dosimeter for the recent past, and that the spontaneous fission track densities in glasses within volcanic strata throughout western North America of Pleistocene and Miocene geologic age indicate an over-abundance of nuclear decay has occurred since formation of those glasses. Because he was seeking to use spontaneous fission track densities as a means of distinguishing between Flood and post-Flood rocks he had to conclude his attempt to do that had failed.

Chaffin [2000] posed the question as to whether it is possible to determine what type of nuclide could produce the observed fission tracks within the time frame of a young earth, and assuming that fission decay constants had truly been the same throughout earth history. He found that when α-decay half-lives are compared with spontaneous fission half-lives there theoretically are some radionuclides that might have produced the observed spontaneous fission track densities within a young-earth time frame without recourse to postulating accelerated nuclear decay. The prime candidates would be three isotopes of the trans-uranium element Cf which undergo both rapid α-decay and rapid spontaneous fission. However, it was admitted that it is impossible to distinguish the spontaneous fission of ^{252}Cf from that of ^{238}U by the lengths of the fission tracks, and it is impossible to confirm the presence of spontaneous fission of ^{252}Cf by analyzing for any infinitesimally small quantities of its decay product ^{250}Cm. On the other hand, because of the radiohalo evidence that millions of years of α-decay of ^{238}U has occurred [*Snelling*, 2000b; 2005a], the smaller quantities of spontaneous fission of ^{238}U that would have to have occurred contemporaneously would explain, and be commensurate with, the observed spontaneous fission track densities. Thus, because the physical evidence of millions of years of α-decay of ^{238}U would need to be explained by accelerated nuclear decay within a young-earth time frame, other nuclides with much shorter half-lives such as ^{252}Cf would also have experienced accelerated decay, rendering it unnecessary to attribute to ^{252}Cf the observed spontaneous fission track densities.

It can thus be concluded from these few studies that the physical evidence of millions of years of spontaneous fission of ^{238}U cannot be easily accounted for in a young-earth time frame without recourse to postulating accelerated nuclear decay. And even if there are fission tracks produced by isotopes with much shorter half-lives, they are virtually irrelevant in dealing with the observed spontaneous fission track densities that appear to match the physical evidence in radiohalos of millions of years worth of α-decay from ^{238}U [*Chaffin*, 2000]. Furthermore, the presence of spontaneous fission track densities in geologically recent natural glasses and volcanic strata commensurate with the presumed geologic ages of such strata and their ages measured by radioisotope decay cannot be ignored, particularly when such volcanic strata are deemed, in most creationist models of earth history, to have formed after the Flood during which the postulated accelerated nuclear decay would have occurred.

3. Rationale of the Present Study

The focus of the present research effort is not only to verify that the fission tracks provide physical evidence of millions of years of nuclear decay, but to determine whether the observed fission track densities do or do not equate to millions of years of contemporaneous α-decay in the same rocks as determined from radioisotope dating analyses. For example, if the fossil content of a rock unit according to evolutionary criteria has been labeled as Cambrian and the radioisotope determinations have dated that rock unit as 540 million years old, then do the observed fission track densities yield fission track "dates" that are commensurate with both the biostratigraphic Cambrian designation and the radioisotope "age" determinations? If the answer is yes, then the physical evidence of nuclear decay in the form of the observed fission tracks confirms that the radioisotope determinations are indeed a record of radioisotope decay, rather than simply being just chemical analyses open to other interpretations. Furthermore, the fact that so many millions of years of nuclear decay has occurred implies that within the young-earth time frame such large quantities of nuclear decay have to be explained by an accelerated rate of nuclear decay. However, an additional outcome would potentially be the quantification of just how much accelerated nuclear decay had to have occurred, for example, during the Flood. Thus if the fission tracks observed in a Cambrian (early Flood) rock unit yield a fission track "age" of 540 million years equivalent to the rock unit's radioisotope "age," then it is possible to conclude that over 500 million years worth of accelerated nuclear decay must have occurred during the Flood year.

4. Sample Selection

To fulfill the objective of this study it was concluded that suitable samples needed to be obtained from stratigraphically well-constrained volcanic ash or tuff beds from which zircons would be extracted for fission track dating. Zircon would be the preferred mineral to be fission track dated because of its durability and high closing temperature, plus the fact that it can also be readily radioisotope dated using the U-Th-Pb system, or such data would already be available in the literature. Tuff beds would also be ideal because they represent time-specific event horizons that are therefore specific time markers that can be geologically and radioisotope dated.

It was also decided that ideally the required volcanic ash or tuff beds should be located in the Grand Canyon-Colorado Plateau region because of that area already being well-studied by creationist geologists as a "type section" of the Flood [*Austin*, 1994]. Not only is there a very thick stratigraphic section, but most of the systems of the standard geological column are represented, spanning from the Precambrian crystalline basement (granites and metamorphic rocks that have been interpreted as Creation week rocks), up through Paleozoic and Mesozoic sedimentary strata deposited over an enormous geographical extent, to the uppermost Tertiary sedimentary strata (most or all of which would be interpreted as post-Flood) [*Austin*, 1994]. Sampling and fission track dating the zircons in the volcanic ash or tuff beds in this area would thus allow the results to be added to other studies in the region, and to be correlated with other data from the voluminous literature on this region.

Finally, it was decided that ideally it would be best to sample at least one Paleozoic tuff unit, one Mesozoic tuff unit and one Tertiary tuff unit, if such could be found in this Grand Canyon-Colorado Plateau "type section." Such tuff units would thus be representative of the early Flood, middle Flood and late Flood/early post-Flood periods that would potentially allow assessment of the behavior of nuclear decay through the Flood event and possibly into the post-Flood era, perhaps even constraining when the postulated accelerated nuclear decay occurred, and as also indicated previously, just how much accelerated nuclear decay might have occurred during the Flood. Fortunately, tuff units meeting these criteria were able to be found and sampled in the Grand Canyon-Colorado Plateau "type section."

4.1 Cambrian Tuff Units, Western Grand Canyon, Arizona

Naeser et al. [1989a] located, sampled and zircon fission track dated two thin bentonitic volcanic ash (tuff) units in the Tonto Group section in the western Grand Canyon. The outcrops sampled are to be found at River Mile 179.8 (179.8 miles or 289.3 km downstream from Lees Ferry), a bench on the left below Lower Lava Rapid where a thin tuff bed sits on top of the Peach Springs Member of the Muav Limestone marking its contact with the overlying Kanab Canyon Member, and at River Mile 205.7 (205.7 miles or 331.0 km downstream of Lees Ferry), a prominent thin, green tuff bed near the base of a red-brown sandstone unit at the top of the Tapeats Sandstone where it transitions into the Bright Angel Shale above, as described by *Billingsley and Elston* [1989]. These two tuff units were not reported by *McKee and Resser* [1945] in their classic study of the Cambrian Tonto Group of the Grand Canyon, in which numerous stratigraphic sections were carefully measured and described in detail. Nor have they been referred to by *Middleton and Elliott* [1990, 2003] in their contribution to the present comprehensive textbook on Grand Canyon geology.

However, *Elston* [1989] provides a description of these two tuff units that accurately places their positions in the stratigraphy of the Tonto Group in the western Grand Canyon (Figure 1). The first of these tuff units is described as a 2–3 cm thick bentonite layer in a thin, thin-bedded interval of limestone that separates the single relatively uniform depositional unit of the Peach Springs Member from the overlying Kanab Canyon Member of the Middle Cambrian Muav Limestone. This thin ash-fall tuff bed evidently marks this contact in many places, and fifteen zircon grains from it have yielded a fission track age of 535±48 Ma [*Elston*, 1989; *Naeser et al.*, 1989a]. The second and stratigraphically lower of these tuffs is described as an ash-fall tuff near the base of the red-brown sandstone at the top of an interval of shale and subordinate sandstone of Tapeats Sandstone lithology that overlies the early Cambrian *Olenellus* horizon, which in turn closely overlies the lower cliff-forming massive sandstone units of the Tapeats Sandstone, that can be traced to the Grand Wash Cliffs to the west. This 8–10 cm thick bentonitic tuff unit beneath the uppermost red-brown sandstone of the Tapeats Sandstone thus appears to approximately correlate with the *Zacanthoides* cf *walpai* horizon of the Toroweap stratigraphic section (Figure 1), considered by *McKee and Resser* [1945] to be of early Middle Cambrian age [*Elston*, 1989]. Twelve zircon grains from this

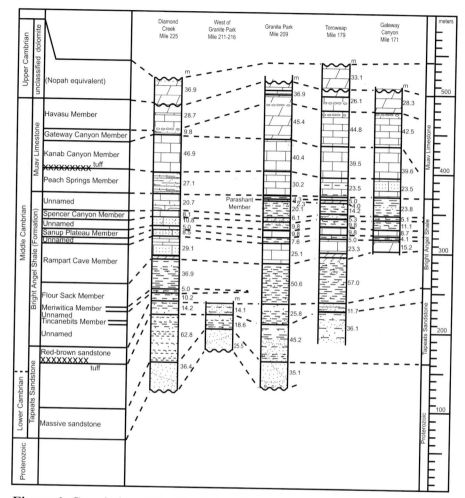

Figure 1. Correlation of the Cambrian Tonto Group showing facies changes in the western Grand Canyon (after *McKee and Resser* [1945]; *Elston* [1989]). The stratigraphic position of the thin Muav and Tapeats tuff units are indicated by xxxxxx.

tuff yielded a fission track age of 563±49 Ma [*Naeser et al.*, 1989a].

Both of these tuff units were sampled for this study from these outcrops, two samples of the Muav tuff and a single sample of the Tapeats tuff. The details of these samples and the published ages of these two tuff units are shown in Table 1.

RATE Sample No.	Sample Source (Unit, Member, Formation)	Location	Latitude Longitude	Geological Age	Published Age (Ma) (±2σ)	Method	References
MT-3 MT-2	Tuff in middle of Muav Limestone	RM 179.8, Grand Canyon, Arizona	N 36°11.684' W 113°05.364'	Middle Cambrian	535±48	zircon FT (15 grains)	Elston [1989], Naeser et al. [1989a]
TT-1	Tuff in top of Tapeats Sandstone	RM 205.7, Grand Canyon, Arizona	N 36°00.201' W 113°20.487'	Middle Cambrian	563±49	zircon FT (12 grains)	Elston [1989], Naeser et al. [1989a]
NMF-64	Unit 64, top of Brushy Basin Member, Morrison Formation		N 38°15.279' W 111°05.733'		106±6 (Unit 64)	zircon FT (6 grains)	Petersen and Roylance [1982], Kowallis and Heaton [1987]
NMF-49	Unit 49, middle of Brushy Basin Member, Morrison Formation	Type Section A, Notom, Utah	N 38°15.117' W 111°06.168'	Late Jurassic	141±6 (Unit 54) 145±13 (Unit 54) 142±6 (Unit 49)	zircon FT (8 grains) apatite FT (11 grains) zircon FT (6 grains)	
BMF-28	Unit 28, top of Brushy Basin Member, Morrison Formation	Brushy Basin, near Blanding, Utah	N 37°38.338' W 109°34.188'	Late Jurassic	—	—	Gregory [1938]
BMF-14	Unit 14, bottom of Brushy Basin Member, Morrison Formation		N 37°38.297' W 109°34.906'		—	—	
MMF-1	Near top, Brushy Basin Member, Morrison Formation	Montezuma Creek, Utah	N 37°19.503' W 109°19.511'	Late Jurassic	147.6±0.8 (plag.) 149.2±0.4 (Kspar)	^{40}Ar/^{39}Ar (single crystal laser-fusion)	Turner and Fishman [1991], Kowallis et al. [1991]
MMF-4	Near bottom, Brushy Basin Member, Morrison Formation	Utah	N 37°19.454' W 109°19.473'		149.4±0.7 (plag.) 149.8±0.3 (Kspar)		
PST-1	Peach Springs Tuff	Snaggletooth area, California	N 34°35.983' W 114°39.199'		18.7±1.5*	sphene FT	Young and Brennan [1974], Beusch and Valentine [1986],
PST-2	Peach Springs Tuff	I-40 road cut, Kingman, Arizona	N 35°10.729' W 114°04.435'	Early Miocene	17.3±0.4 (?)	sanidine K-Ar	Gusa [1986], Glazner et al.
PST-3	Peach Springs Tuff	Rte-66 road cut, Kingman, Arizona	N 35°11.316' W 114°02.233'		18.5±0.2	sanidine ^{40}Ar/^{39}Ar laser fusion	[1986], Gusa et al. [1987], Nielson et al. [1990]

*from Bristol Mountains, California, Gusa [1986] sample 15, collected by Miller, dated by Green [Nielsen et al., 1990]

Table 1 (left). Details of the samples obtained for this study, including locations, geological age designations, and previously published age determinations. The latitude and longitude for each sample was determined by a hand-held Garmin G. P. S. II unit with an accuracy of between 3 and 10 m.

4.2 Jurassic Morrison Formation Tuffs, Southeastern Utah

The Morrison Formation (Middle? and Upper Jurassic) is one of the most colorful and widely recognized stratigraphic units in the western interior of the United States, primarily because in it are found some of the best preserved and most scientifically significant deposits of fossil dinosaur bones in the world [*Bilbey et al.*, 1974; *Peterson and Turner-Peterson*, 1987; *Anderson and Lucas*, 1996; *Turner and Peterson*, 2004]. It has also received much attention because of the rich U deposits contained in its sandstones that in 1980 represented fully 50% of the U.S.'s U reserves. Characteristically 50–150 m thick but in places exceeding 250 m in thickness, the Morrison Formation has been recognized over an area of more than 600,000 square miles (more than 1.5 million km²), stretching from southern Canada to central Arizona and New Mexico, and from southern Idaho and central Utah to Kansas. Although the internal stratigraphy of the Morrison Formation is locally complex, it is not so on a regional scale. The lower part is dominated by fine to coarse grained, cross-bedded, conglomeratic sandstone, intercalated with redbed mudstone and siltstone, known as the Salt Wash Member. It interfingers with the overlying claystone-dominated Brushy Basin Member. Many of the claystone units in this member are bentonitic and have been derived from volcanic ash, both primary ash-fall tuff and water reworked ash. Other distinctive units within the Morrison Formation have also been assigned member status where they have developed in local depositional basins [*Peterson and Turner-Peterson*, 1987; *Turner and Peterson*, 2004].

For the purposes of this study, the bentonitic mudstone units of the Brushy Basin Member of the Morrison Formation were targeted in southeastern Utah. Three stratigraphic sections that have been measured and well-documented in the literature were chosen for sampling, their locations being shown in Figure 2. At Notom, the

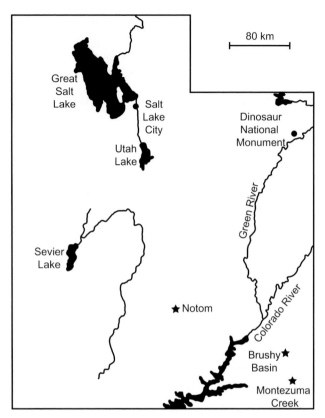

Figure 2. Map of Utah showing the location of the three Brushy Basin Member stratigraphic sections sampled in this study at Notom, Brushy Basin and Montezuma Creek.

Morrison Formation is unusually well exposed along the Waterpocket Fold beyond the eastern boundary of Capitol Reef National Park, which enabled *Petersen and Roylance* [1982] to measure and describe five stratigraphic sections. Their stratigraphic section A, shown in Figure 3, was sampled for this study, primarily because bentonites and bentonitic mudstones in this section have already been zircon fission track dated [*Kowallis and Heaton*, 1987]. Two samples were collected for this study from Peterson and Roylance's units 49 and 64, their stratigraphic position being shown in Figure 3. The second stratigraphic section of the Brushy Basin Member chosen for sampling was in the Brushy

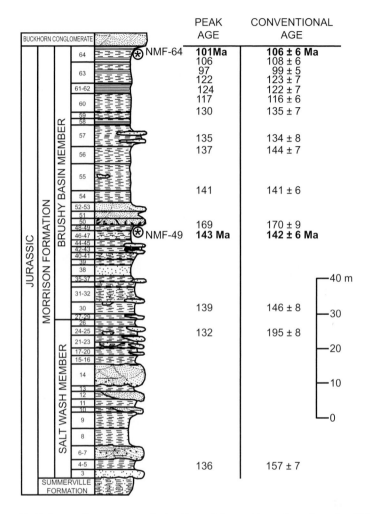

Figure 3. Schematic measured stratigraphic section showing the lithologies and unit numbers (3–64) in the Morrison Formation, and the location of some previously fission track dated samples from Notom, Utah (after *Petersen and Roylance* [1982]; *Kowallis and Heaton* [1987]). The stratigraphic positions of the samples obtained for this study (NMF-49 and NMF-64) are indicated. The peak age represents the age of the youngest peak in the age spectrum plotted for all grains in a sample, whereas the conventional age was obtained by combining all the count data from all grains in a sample [*Kowallis and Heaton*, 1987]. Fission track ages less than 142 Ma are Cretaceous, contrary to the accepted Jurassic stratigraphic age for the Morrison Formation.

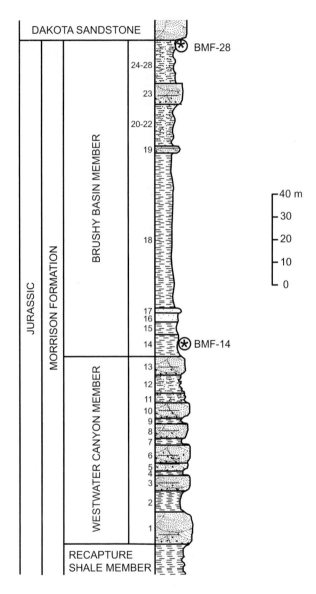

Figure 4. Schematic measured stratigraphic section showing the lithologies and unit numbers (1–28) in the Morrison Formation in the Brushy Basin, west of Blanding, Utah (after *Gregory* [1938]). The stratigraphic positions of the samples obtained for this study (BMF-14 and BMF-28) are indicated.

Basin just to the west of Blanding, section 25 of *Gregory* [1938], which is shown in Figure 4. Units 14 and 28 were sampled (as marked on Figure 4) because of the ease of identifying those bentonitic mudstone units which are adjacent to prominent sandstone units. Whereas the Brushy Basin Member in the Notom type section A is 79.5 m thick, here in the Brushy Basin section 25 due west of Blanding the Brushy Basin Member is 137 m thick, and comparison of these two sections in Figures 3 and 4 illustrate how difficult it is to correlate units within the member from section to section. Because *Kowallis et al.* [1991] have suggested that the unit at the top of the Notom section may not be the top unit of the Brushy Basin Member elsewhere, this could imply that it is not possible to correlate unit 64 at the top of the Notom section A with unit 28 at the top of the Brushy Basin section 25. It is also difficult to correlate the units in both these measured stratigraphic sections with the Montezuma Creek stratigraphic section measured by *Turner and Fishman* [1991] (Figure 5). The samples collected from this section were again chosen because of the ease of locating their positions within the stratigraphic section, being adjacent to prominent sandstone units, and because these same tuffaceous mudstone units had previously been ^{40}Ar-^{39}Ar dated by *Kowallis et al.* [1991]. All the location details and previous dating results for all the samples collected are summarized in Table 1.

4.3 Miocene Peach Springs Tuff, Southeastern California and Western Arizona

The Peach Springs Tuff is a Lower Miocene welded pyroclastic ash flow or ignimbrite that formerly blanketed a minimum area of 2000 square miles (more than 5000 km^2) on both sides of the western edge of the Colorado Plateau in northwestern Arizona, and filled northeast-trending, pre-Colorado River canyons cut through the Paleozoic rocks [*Young and Brennan*, 1974]. The tuff is characterized by abundant large (up to 5 mm) and clear sanidine phenocrysts, with subordinate subequal amounts of plagioclase, biotite, hornblende, sphene, apatite, and zircon in a groundmass that constitutes 80–90 volume percent

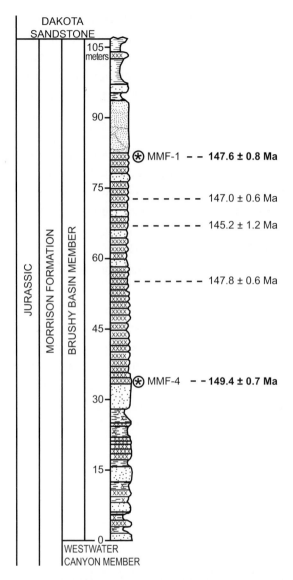

Figure 5. Schematic measured stratigraphic section showing the lithologies in the Brushy Basin Member of the Morrison Formation at Montezuma Creek, Utah (after *Turner and Fishman* [1991]). Tuff beds or tuffaceous intervals are marked with **xxxx**. The stratigraphic positions of the samples obtained for this study are indicated, as are the positions of previously obtained plagioclase ^{40}Ar-^{39}Ar dates (*Kowallis et al.* [1991]).

of the total rock [*Glazner et al.*, 1986]. Rock fragments (often basalt) as large as 10 cm or more are sometimes present and are generally locally derived. This tuff was first recognized and described in the Peach Springs and Kingman areas of Arizona because of the extensive prominent outcrops, but it was subsequently proposed that the tuff may correlate with ash-flow tuff outcrops occurring to the west across the Mojave Desert in southeastern California as far as Barstow [*Glazner et al.*, 1986] (Figure 6). However, because ash-flow tuffs are commonly difficult to correlate due to lateral and vertical variations in welding, mineralogy and chemistry, complex depositional mechanisms, and other complicating factors [*Hildreth and Mahood*, 1985], correlation of the Peach Springs Tuff over this expansive area has been based primarily

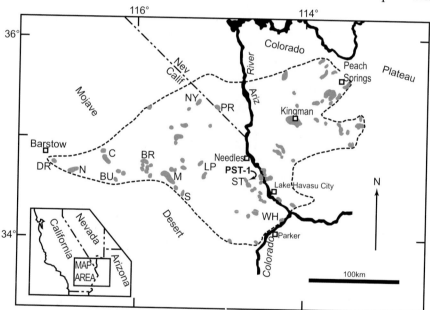

Figure 6. Map showing the distribution of the Peach Springs Tuff (after *Nielson et al.* [1990]). Abbreviations of ranges in California: BR, Bristol Mountains; BU, Bullion Mountains; C, Cady Mountains; DR, Daggett Ridge; LP, Little Piute Mountains; M, Marble Mountains; NY, New York Mountains; PR, Piute Range; S, Ship Mountains; ST, Snaggletooth area; WH, Whipple Mountains. The location of the outcrop from which sample PST-1 was obtained for this study is indicated.

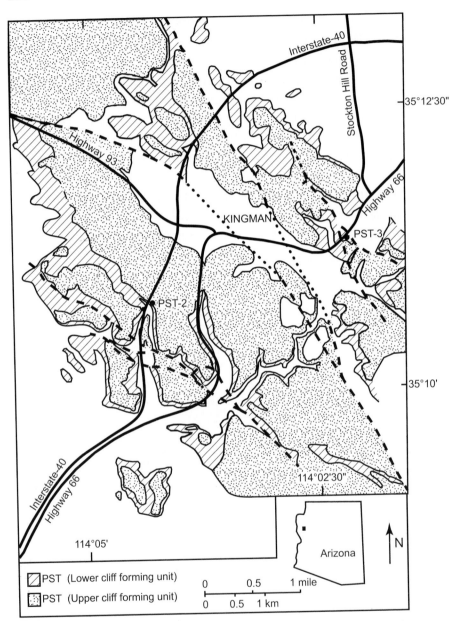

Figure 7. Map of the Kingman area, Arizona, showing the local extent of the Peach Springs Tuff (after *Buesch and Valentine* [1986]). The locations from which samples PST-2 and PST-3 were obtained for this study are indicated.

on field relations, such as its Lower Miocene stratigraphic position, and the phenocryst assemblage, particularly the presence of sphene, which has been confirmed by studies of the heavy mineral suites in the tuff by *Gusa* [1986] and *Gusa et al.* [1987]. Subsequent K-Ar and ^{40}Ar-^{39}Ar radioisotope dating of sanidine phenocrysts from seventeen locations [*Nielson et al.*, 1990] has confirmed that the Peach Springs Tuff probably originally covered an area of approximately 35,000 km^2 over a lateral distance of 350 km (Figure 6), representing an erupted volume of volcanic ash of at least several hundred cubic kilometers [*Glazner et al.*, 1986].

The Peach Springs Tuff (ignimbrite) exposed near Kingman, Arizona, probably forms a single, simple cooling unit, even though it is exposed as two cliffs [*Buesch and Valentine*, 1986; *Glazner et al.*, 1986] (Figure 7). Two types of local facies have been described: (1) an "open valley facies" which occurs where the pyroclastic flow moved through relatively unobstructed valleys; and (2) an "edge facies" which occurs where the pyroclastic flow was affected by valley edges and paleo-topographic highs [*Buesch and Valentine*, 1986]. The open valley facies of the Peach Springs Tuff commonly has two cliff-forming zones, the lowest due to dense welding and the uppermost due to vapor phase crystallization and lithification. The areal extent of these two cliff-forming units in the Kingman area is shown in Figure 7, and the prominent stratigraphic section through the Peach Springs Tuff as exposed in road cuts along U.S. Interstate-40 near Kingman is reproduced in Figure 8. The internal stratigraphy of the Peach Springs Tuff is comparable to the "typical" ignimbrite sequence of *Sparks et al.* [1973], with a basal ground surge layer 1 m or less thick that is thinly laminated, overlain by the massive and very poorly sorted ignimbrite that in places is 70 m or more thick (Figure 8).

Three samples of the Peach Springs Tuff were collected for this study, based on prior knowledge of the presence of zircon in the tuff at those outcrops, on ease of access to, and identification of, well-documented outcrops, and on locations where the tuff has previously been sampled for dating. Details of these three samples are summarized in Table 1. The first sample was collected from the Snaggletooth area

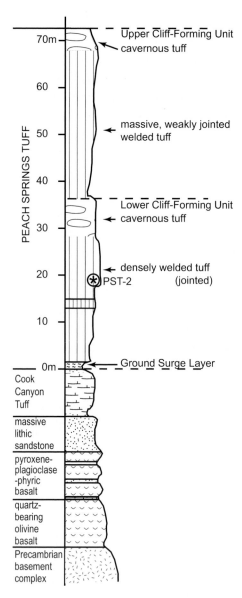

Figure 8. Schematic measured section through the Peach Springs Tuff (ope
valley facies) along Interstate-40 west of Kingman, Arizona (Figure 7
section 1 of *Beusch and Valentine* [1986], with underlying strata indicated
The stratigraphic position from which PST-2 was obtained for this study i
shown.

in southeastern California (see Figure 6), the same outcrop as sample 10 of *Gusa* [1986] and *Gusa et al.* [1987]. The second sample was obtained in the U.S. Interstate-40 road cut near Kingman (Figure 7) that was the location of *Buesch and Valentine's* [1986] Peach Springs Tuff stratigraphic section 1 (Figure 8). The sample was obtained from a densely welded and jointed prominent layer in about the middle of the lower cliff-forming unit of the tuff (Figure 8). This also appears to be the approximate location of sample 1 of *Gusa* [1986] and *Gusa et al.* [1987], and possibly the sample from which sanidine phenocrysts were extracted and yielded a K-Ar date of 17.3 ± 0.4 Ma, as reported by *Young and Brennan* [1974], *Glazner et al.* [1986], and *Nielson et al.* [1990]. Finally, the third sample was obtained from the same position in the same road cut on U.S. Highway 66 just east of downtown Kingman that was sampled for sanidine ^{40}Ar-^{39}Ar dating by *Nielson et al.* [1990], Stop 2 of *Buesch and Valentine* [1986] (Figure 7). Samples 2 and 3 are definitely from the lower cliff-forming unit of the Peach Springs Tuff (Figures 7 and 8), and sample 1 is probably also, given the relative stratigraphic position from which it was obtained from the outcrop of the tuff in the Snaggletooth area. In any case, given that the Peach Springs Tuff was erupted and deposited as a single cooling unit over an area of at least $35,000\,km^2$ in a period of days to weeks [*Glazner et al.*, 1986; *Nielson et al.*, 1990], sampling anywhere in the tuff at any stratigraphic level should yield the same age.

5. Analytical Procedures

The 3–5 kg tuff samples from each of these locations were sent to the Geotrack International laboratory in Melbourne, Australia. That laboratory was chosen because it specializes in fission track dating, its principal scientific staff having decades of experience in performing fission track analyses and in fission track research. At this laboratory the samples were reduced to chips of a few mm in size in a jaw crusher, and this material was then ground to sand grade in a rotary disc mill. The ground material was then washed to remove dust, dried, and processed by conventional heavy liquid and magnetic separation techniques to recover the heavy minerals as separate fractions of zircon, sphene (titanite), and apatite.

The zircon grains from each sample were embedded in FEP teflon between heated microscope slides on a hot plate at ~350°C. The short time needed for this process, during which the zircon grains were subjected to this temperature, would not have allowed any annealing of fission tracks in the grains. The mounted grains were then ground and polished on diamond laps, and then etched in molten KOH:NaOH eutectic at 220°C [*Gleadow et al.*, 1976]. Satisfactory etching of the spontaneous fission tracks in the zircons from each of the samples was achieved after etching for different lengths of time—15 hours for samples MT-2, TT-1, NMF-49 and NMF-64, 17.5 hours for sample MT-3, 43 hours for sample BMF-14, 47 hours for samples PST-1 and PST-3, 67 hours for samples BMF-28, MMF-1 and MMF-4, and 91 hours for sample PST-2. The longer time periods required on some samples potentially reflected their younger ages (and consequently lower degrees of radiation damage). Subsequent examination of the grain mounts showed that extremely high quality etched grains suitable for age determinations were present in all samples.

After etching, grain mounts were cut down to 1.5×1 cm, and cleaned in detergent, alcohol, and distilled water. The mounts were then sealed in intimate contact with low-U muscovite detectors within heat shrink plastic film, and then stacked between two pieces of U standard glass which had been prepared in similar fashion. The stack was then inserted into an aluminum can for irradiation.

Neutron irradiations were carried out in a well-thermalized flux (X-7 facility; Cd ratio for Au ~98) in the Australian Nuclear Science and Technology Organisation's HIFAR research reactor at Lucas Heights near Sydney. The total neutron fluence was monitored by counting the induced fission tracks in the mica external detectors attached to the two pieces of corning standard glass U3 included in the irradiation canisters at each end of the sample stack. A small flux gradient has often been present in the irradiation facility over the length of the sample package, this having developed only in late 1991 after extended refurbishment of the reactor. As a detectable gradient was found to be present, the track count in the external detector adjacent to each standard glass was converted to a track density ρ_D and a value for each mount in the stack was calculated by linear interpolation. (If no detectable gradient had been present, the track counts in the two external detectors would have been pooled to give a single value ρ_D which would then have been used to calculate the fission track ages for each of the samples.)

After irradiation, the mica detectors were removed from the grain mounts and standard glasses and etched in hydrofluoric acid to reveal the fission tracks produced by the induced fission of ^{235}U within the zircon grains and the standard glass. In determining the induced track densities in the external mica detectors irradiated adjacent to the U standard glasses, twenty-five fields were normally counted in each detector, and the total track count N_D was divided by the total area counted to obtain the track density ρ_D. The positions of the counted fields are arranged in a 5×5 grid covering the whole area of the detector. For typical track densities of between $\sim 5 \times 10^5$ and 5×10^6 this is a convenient arrangement to sample across the detector while gathering sufficient counts to achieve a precision of approximately $\pm 2\%$ in a reasonable time.

The fission track ages were calculated using the standard fission track age equation and the ζ calibration method (equation 5 of *Hurford and Green* [1983]):

$$Fission\ track\ age = \frac{1}{\lambda_D} \ln\left[1 + \left(\frac{\zeta \lambda_D \rho_S g \rho_D}{\rho_i} \right) \right] \qquad (1)$$

where: λ_D = total decay constant of ^{238}U (1.55125×10^{-10})
 ζ = zeta calibration factor
 ρ_s = spontaneous track density
 ρ_i = induced track density
 ρ_D = track density for U standard glass
 g = a geometry factor (0.5)

Fission track ages were thus determined by the external detector method [*Gleadow*, 1981] (see the Appendix, Section A2). This method has the advantage of allowing fission track ages to be determined on single grains. For the analyses of the zircon grains in the samples in this study, twenty zircon grains for each sample were normally analyzed. In those samples where the desired number of grains was not present, all available grains were counted, the actual number depending on the availability of suitably etched and oriented grains. Only zircon grains oriented with surfaces parallel to the crystallographic c-axis were analyzed. Such grains could be identified on the basis of their etching characteristics, as well as from morphological evidence in euhedral grains. The grain mounts were scanned sequentially, and the first twenty suitably oriented grains identified were analyzed.

All track counting was carried out by Dr. Paul Green using Zeiss® axioplan microscopes, with an overall linear magnification of 1068× using dry objectives. All tracks were counted with an eyepiece graticule divided into one hundred grid squares. In each grain, the number of spontaneous tracks, N_s, within a certain number of grid squares, N_a, was recorded. The number of induced tracks, N_i, in the corresponding location within the mica external detector was then counted. Spontaneous and induced track densities, ρ_s and ρ_i respectively, were calculated by dividing the track counts by the total area counted, given by the product of N_a and the area of each grid square (determined by calibration against a ruled stage graticule or diffraction grating). The fission track age of each zircon grain could then be calculated by substituting the track counts N_s and N_i for track densities ρ_s and ρ_i in equation (1), since the areas (N_a) cancel in the ratio.

Translation between zircon grains in each grain mount and the external detector locations corresponding to each grain was carried out using Autoscan™ microcomputer-controlled automatic stages [*Smith and Leigh-Jones*, 1985]. This system allowed repeated movement between each grain and detector, and all grain locations were stored for later reference if required.

The zeta calibration factor, ζ, had previously been determined empirically for zircon by analyzing a set of carefully chosen age standards with independently determined K-Ar radioisotope ages, following the methods outlined by *Hurford and Green* [1983] and *Green* [1985] (see the Appendix, Section A4). The zeta calibration factor used by Dr. Paul Green to calculate the fission track ages of the zircons in the samples in this study was 87.7±0.8 for the U3 glass standard used. Further details and background information on the practical aspects of fission track age determinations can be found in *Fleischer et al.* [1975] and *Naeser* [1979].

6. Zircon Fission Track Dating Results

All samples yielded sufficient zircon grains for fission track age determinations to be obtained. Whereas around twenty grains from each sample were analyzed, sample NMF-49 only yielded nine suitable grains, but these were still deemed sufficient to provide a good fission track age estimate. Representative zircon grains from some of the samples are shown in Figure 9. *Green* [2001, 2002, 2003] reported that all analyzed grains were characterized by very high quality, well-etched surfaces suitable for analysis. In two other samples, BMF-28 and MMF-4, slightly fewer grains were analyzed due to the abundance in those samples of grains with highly zoned, non-uniform track densities and inclusions or other defects which rendered reliable track counting impossible. Otherwise, spontaneous track densities were typically in the range 2×10^6 to 3×10^7 tracks/cm^2, allowing reliable track counting. Typical fission tracks in the polished and etched surfaces of some of the zircon grains are shown in the photomicrographs of Figure 10.

Nevertheless, the etching process was highly selective, and so a large number of grains with higher and lower track densities were also present which couldn't be analyzed. At track densities higher than $\sim 3 \times 10^7$ tracks/cm^2, individual tracks cannot be resolved, while at track densities lower than $\sim 5 \times 10^5$ tracks/cm^2, etching becomes anisotropic and full track revelation is not possible. This would have the potential to severely bias the distribution of measured ages, so such grains were not used for the age determinations. However, the zircon grains in these samples are typical of zircon suites that show a sufficiently large range of U contents so that the zircons of whatever ages provide enough grains with spontaneous track densities suitable for track counting. Because of these factors, all the reported fission track age determinations on these samples were regarded as extremely reliable.

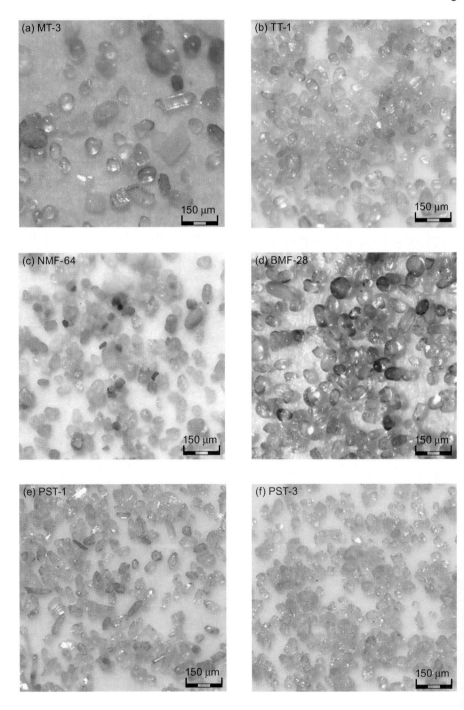

Figure 9 (left). Some of the zircon grains from six of the tuff samples in this study: (a) MT-3, (b) TT-1, (c) NMF-64, (d) BMF-28, (e) PST-1, and (f) PST-3. For details of these samples see Table 1. The photographs were obtained under a binocular microscope, courtesy of Pat Kelly, Operations Manager, Geotrack International.

All twelve samples listed in Table 1, with details of outcrop locations and previous dating results, were processed at the Geotrack International laboratory and the zircon fission track ages determined were reported by *Green* [2001, 2002, 2003]. All results are summarized in Table 2, while the data and age determinations for all individual zircon grains analyzed in each sample are tabulated in *Green* [2001, 2002, 2003].

All the individual zircon grain fission track ages were calculated, as indicated previously, using the standard fission track age equation of *Hurford and Green* [1983], equation (1) above. The zeta (ζ) calibration factor used was 87.7±0.8 for the U3 standard glass as determined empirically by *Green* [1985] by direct comparison with K-Ar radioisotope ages for a set of carefully chosen age standards, following the methods outlined by *Hurford and Green* [1982, 1983]. Individual grain fission track ages were calculated from the ratio of the number of spontaneous fission tracks (N_s) to the number of induced fission tracks (N_i) counted for each grain, and the errors in the single grain ages were calculated using Poissonian statistics, as explained in more detail by *Galbraith* [1981] and *Green* [1981]. All errors are quoted as ±1σ. The pooled or maximum probability age for each sample was determined from the ratio of the total spontaneous and induced track counts (N_s/N_i) in all analyzed grains within each sample (Table 2). Errors for each pooled age were calculated using the "conventional" technique outlined by *Green* [1981], based on the total number of tracks counted for each track density measurement of all the analyzed grains for each sample.

The variability of fission track ages between individual zircon grains within each sample was assessed using a chi-square (χ^2) statistic [*Galbraith*, 1981], the results of which are summarized for each sample in Table 2. If all the grains counted in each sample belong to a single age population, then the probability of obtaining the observed χ^2 value,

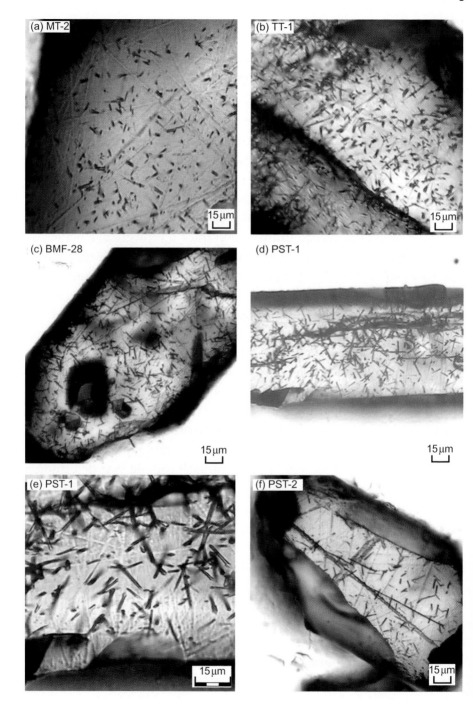

(a) MT-2

(b) TT-1

(c) BMF-28

(d) PST-1

(e) PST-1

(f) PST-2

Figure 10 (left). The spontaneous fission tracks in the polished and etched surfaces of some of the mounted zircon grains in five of the tuff samples in this study: (a) MT-2, (b) TT-1, (c) BMF-28, (d) PST-1, (e) PST-1 (high magnification), and (f) PST-2. Sample details are in Table 1. These photomicrographs were obtained courtesy of Pat Kelly, Operations Manager, Geotrack International.

for v degrees of freedom (where v = number of crystals − 1) is listed in Table 2, and in the data sheets for all the grains analyzed in each sample supplied by *Green* [2001, 2002, 2003], as $P(\chi^2)$.

A probability of greater than 5% can be taken as evidence that all grains are consistent with a single population of fission track ages for that sample. In that case, the best estimate of the fission track age of the sample is given by the "pooled age," calculated from the ratio of the total spontaneous and induced track counts (N_s/N_i) in all the grains analyzed in the sample. Errors for the pooled age are calculated using the "conventional" technique outlined by *Green* [1981], based on the total number of tracks counted for each track density measurement (see also *Galbraith* [1981]).

A $P(\chi^2)$ value of less than 5% denotes a significant spread of single grain ages in the sample, and suggests that real differences exist between the fission track ages of the individual zircon grains. A significant spread in grain ages can result either from inheritance of detrital grains from mixed source areas, or from differential annealing in zircon grains of different composition, within a certain range of temperature.

Calculation of the pooled age inherently assumes that only a single population of ages is present, and is thus not appropriate for samples containing a significant spread of individual grain fission track ages. In such cases, *Galbraith* [1981, 1984] has devised a means of estimating the modal age of a distribution of single grain fission track ages in a sample which is referred to as the "central age" of the sample. Calculation of the central age assumes that all single grain ages belong to a normal distribution of ages with a standard deviation, σ, known as the "age dispersion." An iterative algorithm, as yet unpublished [*Green*, 2001, 2002, 2003], is used to provide estimates of the central age with its

RATE Sample No.	Number of Grains	ρ_D (N_D) × 10^6 per cm^2	ρ_S (N_S) × 10^6 per cm^2	ρ_i (N_i) × 10^6 per cm^2	U content (ppm)	P(χ^2) (%)	Age Dispersion (%)	Fission Track Ages (Ma) (±1σ)			Age Spread (Ma) (±1σ)	
								Pooled Age	Central Age	Youngest Group (Pooled) Age	From	To
MT-3	23	1.208 (3684)	11.575 (4050)	4.053 (1418)	179	<1	57	149.6±5.4	165.8±20.7	**74.6±3.9**	68.4±8.3	473.5±150.5
MT-2	20	0.585 (1866)	10.156 (3643)	1.650 (592)	150	<1	75	155.9±7.9	139.0±24.5	**62±4**	34.9±7.2	611.2±254.9
TT-1	20	0.586 (1866)	10.307 (4547)	2.079 (917)	189	<1	105	126.3±5.5	127.4±30.5	**75±7**	48.0±14.9 (12.3±1.2)	914.3±414.8
NMF-64	20	0.590 (1866)	10.329 (3029)	1.419 (416)	128	<1	42	185.6±10.7	178.6±19.8	**132±10**	93.1±18.7	651.3±210.4
NMF-49	9	0.588 (1866)	11.590 (671)	1.606 (93)	146	15	19	**183.4±20.8**	178.7±23.4	—	113.6±42.0	343.1±145.4
BMF-28	19	1.717 (2763)	6.301 (3101)	2.625 (1292)	81	<1	39	178.2±7.0	173.7±17.1	**136±6**	104.2±22.3	592.3±137.4
BMF-14	20	1.706 (2763)	7.611 (2069)	2.954 (803)	92	<1	40	189.9±8.9	188.3±19.2	**144±10***	98.2±16.7	689.9±187.6
MMF-1	20	1.728 (2763)	9.688 (2841)	3.318 (973)	102	<1	45	217.6±9.3	205.1±22.4	**137±9**	87.6±15.4	1036.2±309.8
MMF-4	18	1.739 (2763)	7.697 (1671)	3.901 (847)	120	7	12	**148.8±7.0**	148.2±8.3	—	114.6±18.6	233.5±46.3
PST-1	20	0.591 (1866)	1.779 (1172)	1.871 (1233)	169	14	10	**24.6±1.2**	24.5±1.3	—	17.0±4.6	34.5±15.2
PST-2	20	0.580 (1803)	2.183 (1470)	2.658 (1790)	244	33	4	**20.9±0.9**	20.9±0.9	—	16.4±3.7	27.3±5.2
PST-3	20	0.593 (1866)	2.885 (1921)	3.591 (2291)	323	70	1	**20.9±0.8**	20.9±0.8	—	17.3±2.2	29.3±4.9

Notes: *12 euhedral grains yield a pooled age of 147.8±8.2 Ma.

ρ_S = spontaneous track density; ρ_i = induced track density; ρ_D = track density in external detector.

Brackets show number (N) of tracks counted – ρ_D and ρ_i measured in external detector; ρ_S measured in internal sample surfaces.

The "fission track" ages in **bold** were interpreted as the best estimates (statistically defendable) of the ages of the samples.

Ages were calculated using dosimeter glass U3, with a zeta (ζ) of 87.7±0.8 for all samples.

All samples were analyzed by Dr. Paul F. Green of Geotrack International, Melbourne.

Table 2 (left). Results of the zircon fission track dating of twelve tuff samples from the Grand Canyon-Colorado Plateau region. Counting data, statistics and calculated ages are shown. Full details discussed in the text.

associated error, and the age dispersion, which are all quoted for each sample in Table 2, and for all the single grain data in the laboratory reports. This treatment replaces use of the "mean age," which has often been used in the past for those samples in which $P(\chi^2) < 5\%$. For samples in which $P(\chi^2) > 5\%$, the central age and the pooled age should be equal, and the age dispersion should be less than ~10%, as is the case for the relevant samples listed in Table 2.

However, single grain fission track age data for each sample are best represented in the form of radial plot diagrams [*Galbraith*, 1988, 1990]. As illustrated in Figure 11, these plots display the variation of individual grain ages in a plot of y against x, where:

$$y = (z_j - z_o)/\sigma_j \tag{2}$$

$$x = 1/\sigma_j \tag{3}$$

and z_j = the fission track age of grain j
z_o = a reference fission track age
σ_j = the standard error in age for grain j
y_j = the standardized estimates
x_j = the precision

In this plot, all points on a radial straight line emanating from the origin (since each such line has a slope $z_j - z_o$) define a single fixed value of fission track age (z_j), and at any point along the line the value of x is a measure of the precision of each individual grain fission track age. Therefore, precise individual grain fission track ages fall to the right on the plot (small error, high x or precision) (Figure 12a), which is useful, for example, in enabling precise, young grains to be identified. Error bars on all points plotted on the diagram are the same size. The age scale is shown radially around the perimeter of the plot (in Ma). If all

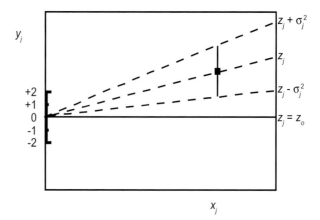

Figure 11. Basic construction of a normal radial plot (after *Galbraith* [1988, 1990]). Radial lines emanating from the origin with positive slopes correspond to fission track ages (z_j) greater than the reference age (z_o), while lines with negative slopes correspond to fission track ages less than the reference age. x_j is the precision and y_j the standardized estimate of the fission track age of grain j.

grains plotted on the diagram belong to a single age population, all data should scatter between $y=+2$ and $y=-2$, equivalent to a scatter within $\pm2\sigma$. Scatter outside these boundaries would show a significant spread of individual grain ages, as also would be reflected in the values of $P(\chi^2)$ and age dispersion.

In detail, rather than using the fission track age for each grain as in equations (2) and (3), it is preferable to use the measured counts of the spontaneous and induced fission tracks in each grain so that:

$$z_j = \frac{N_{sj}}{N_{ij}} \tag{4}$$

and

$$\sigma_j = \left(\frac{1}{N_{sj}}\right) + \left(\frac{1}{N_{ij}}\right) \tag{5}$$

as the objective is to display the scatter **within** the individual grain fission track data from each sample in comparison with that allowed by the Poissonian uncertainty in the track counts, within the additional

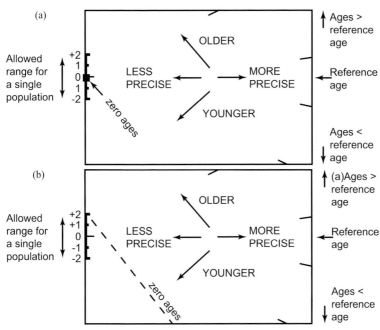

Figure 12. (a). Simplified structure of a normal radial plot (after *Galbraith* [1988]). Zero ages plot at the origin. The allowed range in *y* is in units of σ. (b). Simplified structure of an arc sin radial plot (after *Galbraith* [1990]). Zero ages plot along the dashed sloping line. The allowed range in *y* is in units of σ.

terms which are involved in determination of the fission track ages (ρ_D, ζ, etc.).

Zero ages cannot be displayed in such a plot (Figure 12a). This can be achieved using a modified plot [*Galbraith*, 1990], in which:

$$z_j = \arc \sin \sqrt{\left(\frac{N_{sj} + \frac{3}{8}}{N_{sj} + N_{ij} + \frac{3}{4}} \right)} \tag{6}$$

and

$$\sigma_j = \frac{1}{2} \sqrt{\left(\frac{1}{N_{sj} + N_{ij}} \right)} \tag{7}$$

Note that the numerical terms in equation (6) for z_j are standard terms, introduced for statistical reasons. Using this arc-sin transformation, zero ages plot on a diagonal line which slopes from upper left to lower right (Figure 12b). Note that this zero ages line does not go through the origin. Figure 12 illustrates the difference between the conventional and arc-sin radial plots, and also provides a simple guide to the structure of these radial plots.

Use of arc-sin radial plots is particularly useful in assessing the relative importance of zero ages. For instance, grains with $N_s=0$, $N_i=1$ are compatible with ages up to ~900 Ma (at the 95% confidence level), whereas grains with $N_s=0$, $N_i=50$ are only compatible with ages up to ~14 Ma. These two data would readily be distinguishable on the radial plot, as the 0, 50 datum would plot well to the right (high x) compared to the 0, 1 datum.

Note that the x-axis of the radial plot is normally not labeled, as this would obscure the age scale around the plot. In general labeling is not considered necessary, as the focus is only on the relative variation within the data, rather than the absolute values of precision.

In this study the value of z corresponding to the pooled $(P(\chi^2)>5\%)$ or central $(P(\chi^2)<5\%)$ fission track age of each sample was adopted as the reference age, z_o. In Figures 13, 14 and 15 are the radial plots of the single grain fission track age data for the zircon grains analyzed in each sample, and alongside are conventional histogram plots of the number of grains which fall within a given fission track age range, another way of showing the spread and distribution of the individual zircon grain fission track ages within each sample. In Figure 13 are radial plots and histograms for the Cambrian Muav and Tapeats tuffs samples from the western Grand Canyon, in Figure 14 are the radial plots and histograms for the Jurassic Morrison Formation tuffs from Notom, the Brushy Basin and Montezuma Creek, Utah, and Figure 15 shows the radial plots and histograms for the three Miocene Peach Springs Tuff samples.

7. Discussion of Results

The results obtained in this study were discussed in detail by *Green*

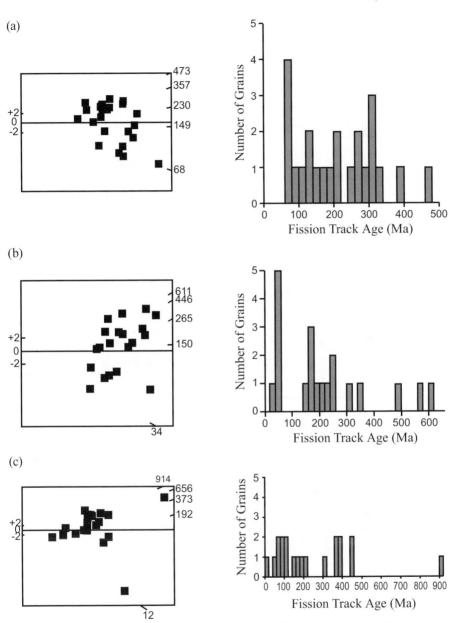

Figure 13. Radial plots (left) and histograms (right) of the individual zircon grain fission track ages in the early Middle Cambrian tuff samples from the western Grand Canyon: (a) Muav tuff MT-3, (b) Muav tuff MT-2, and (c) Tapeats tuff TT-1.

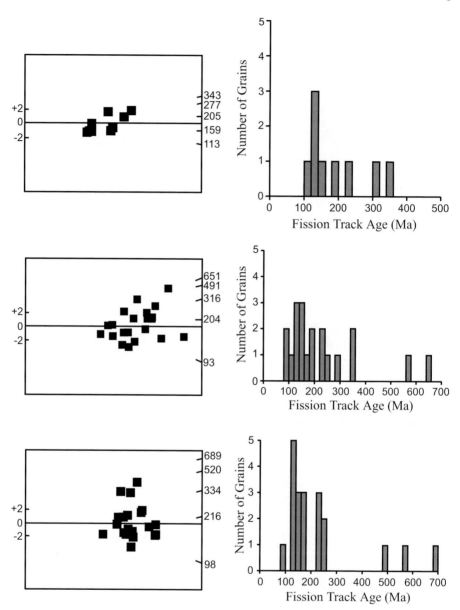

Figure 14. Radial plots (left) and histograms (right) of the individual zircon fission track ages in the Upper Jurassic Morrison Formation tuff samples from southeastern Utah: Notom tuffs (a) NMF-49, (b) NMF-64; Brushy Basin tuff (c) BMF-14.

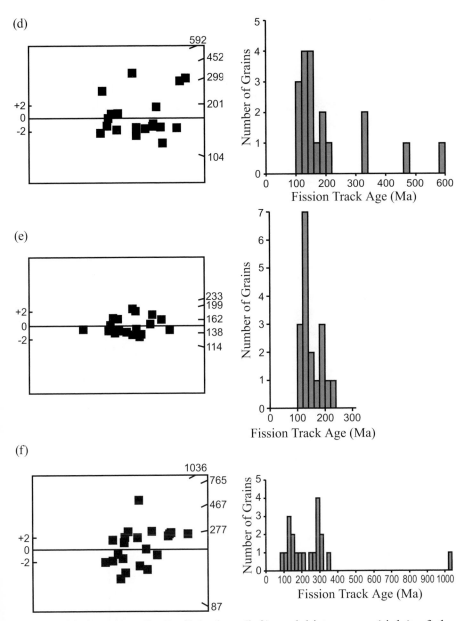

Figure 14 (continued). Radial plots (left) and histograms (right) of the individual zircon fission track ages in the Upper Jurassic Morrison Formation tuff samples from southeastern Utah: Brushy Basin tuff (d) BMF-28; and Montezuma Creek tuffs (e) MMF-4, (f) MMF-1.

A.A. Snelling

(a)

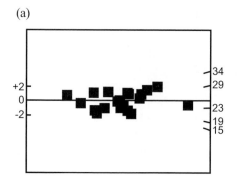

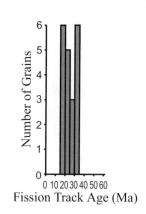

(b)

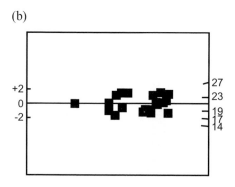

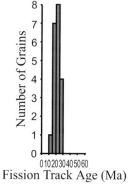

(c)

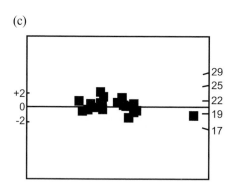

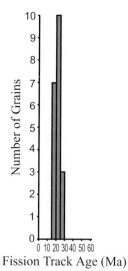

Figure 15 (left). Radial plots (left) and histograms (right) of the individual zircon grain fission track ages in the Miocene Peach Springs Tuff samples from southeastern California and western Arizona: (a) PST-1, (b) PST-2, and (c) PST-3.

[2001, 2002, 2003]. It should be noted that when the samples were submitted to the Geotrack International laboratory no specific location data for the samples were supplied, although some indication was given of the expected age of each sample. This procedure was adopted so that on the one hand the laboratory could optimize its analytical procedures, and yet on the other hand no bias would be introduced by the laboratory to obtain the ages required by prior knowledge of other age dating results on those sampled rock units. The discussion here is based on the information and results in Tables 1 and 2 respectively, and on the radial plots and histograms in Figures 13–15.

7.1 Cambrian Tuff Units, Western Grand Canyon, Arizona

It is immediately evident that the zircon fission track ages obtained in this study for the Muav and Tapeats tuffs from the western Grand Canyon did not match the early Middle Cambrian biostratigraphic ages [*McKee and Resser*, 1945] or reproduce the previously obtained zircon fission track ages of 535±48 Ma and 563±49 Ma respectively [*Naeser et al.*, 1989a]. Only three of the sixty-three individual zircon grain fission track ages were close to the target early Middle Cambrian ages for these two tuff units, and even then the 1σ errors are exceedingly large (Table 2 and Figure 13).

The individual zircon grains in Muav tuff sample MT-3 show a statistically significant spread in fission track ages $(P(\chi^2)<5\%)$, from a youngest limit of 68.4±8.3 Ma to an oldest limit of 473.5±150.5 Ma (all errors are quoted at the $\pm1\sigma$ level). A variety of grain morphologies were reported by *Green* [2001] to be present within the sample, from euhedral to rounded as well as intermediate forms. As the minerals in a cooling lava form they crystallize as euhedral grains. If the lava is then shattered by the volcanic eruption to produce ash, some of the grains will be abraded during their transport before deposition in the resultant tuff bed. The degree of rounding of the grains will usually be an indication of how much abrasion and transport they have suffered. Another possibility is that rounded grains might represent grains that were eroded from other rocks (and thus inherited) as the volcanic ash was transported over them before deposition. The youngest group of ages within this sample were measured consistently only in euhedral grains (five in number), and these collectively define a pooled fission track age of 74.6±3.9 Ma (Table 2). The older ages were measured in grains having a variety of forms, including both euhedral and rounded grains as well as intermediate forms. No other distinct groupings are discernible within these older ages, as reflected by the radial plot of the single grain ages (Figure 13a), except that perhaps the histogram could indicate a grouping around 300 Ma.

The second sample of the Muav tuff (MT-2) is characterized by a central age of 139.0±24.5 Ma (Table 2). However, the individual zircon grains show a spread in fission track ages ($P(\chi^2)$<5%) from 34.9±7.2 Ma to 611.2±254.9 Ma. Thus the numerical value of the central age has no significance other than characterizing the spread of ages within the sample. On the other hand, statistical analysis of the single grain ages [*Green*, 2002] suggests the presence of three dominant populations characterized by ages of 62±4 Ma, 200±15 Ma, and 432±66 Ma. However, the relevant histogram in Figure 13b, while justifying the existence of the two younger age groupings, does not support the oldest age grouping due to the large spread in the ages of the five grains represented. *Green* [2002] reported a variety of grain morphologies were present within this sample, from euhedral to rounded as well as intermediate forms, similar to sample MT-3 from the same outcrop (as would be expected). The youngest group of fission track ages were measured consistently only in euhedral grains (six in number), and these yielded the pooled age of 62±4 Ma. However, some grains belonging to the intermediate age group were also euhedral in form (three grains), while other grains in this group and all grains in the older age group showed rounded to sub-rounded forms.

The sample of the Tapeats tuff (TT-1) is characterized by a central age of 127.4±30.5 Ma. However, the individual zircon grains have fission track ages from 12.3 ± 1.2 Ma to 914.3 ± 414.8 Ma, so the numerical value of the central age again has no significance. The youngest single grain fission track age measured in this sample (12.3 ± 1.2 Ma) is distinctly younger than all other grains, and stands out prominently in the radial plot of single grain data in Figure 13c. Disregarding this grain, a statistical analysis of the remaining single grain fission track ages [*Green*, 2002] suggests the presence of three prominent populations characterized by ages of 75 ± 7 Ma, 158 ± 15 Ma, and 408 ± 35 Ma. The existence of these three age groupings is justified from the relevant histogram in Figure 13c. *Green* [2002] reported a variety of grain morphologies were present within this sample, from euhedral to rounded as well as intermediate forms (which is similar to the samples from the Muav tuff). Four of the five grains comprising the youngest group of fission track ages were euhedral in form, while the fifth was sub-euhedral. Four grains belonging to the intermediate age group were also euhedral in form, and one of the older group was also euhedral. Other grains in the intermediate and oldest groups showed rounded to sub-rounded forms.

In summary, these three samples from the early Middle Cambrian Muav and Tapeats tuffs contain identical groups of euhedral grains within the youngest fission track pooled ages in the range 62–75 Ma, with all but two of the remaining forty-seven single grain fission track ages spread out up to the published 535–563 Ma zircon fission track ages for these tuffs [*Naeser et al.*, 1989a]. This raises the obvious question as to why these samples from the same outcrops did not yield identical zircon fission track ages?

It is abundantly clear from the pattern of spread of the single grain fission track ages that an event at 62–75 Ma, recorded by the pooled single zircon grain fission track ages in the youngest age group in each of the samples, resulted in annealing of many of the zircon grains in these tuff units. Indeed, *Naeser et al.* [1989a] had found that apatite grains in Precambrian granitic rocks in the central and western Grand Canyon had been totally annealed by the onset of the Laramide uplift of the Colorado Plateau. The average fission track age for four apatite concentrates of the Proterozoic basement at Phantom Ranch was

62.4±5.2 Ma (±2σ). The identities of these samples in this study were thus revealed to Dr. Paul Green at Geotrack International, because his zircon fission track age determinations on the Grand Canyon tuff samples in this study were so different from the earlier results of fission track dating of samples from the same outcrops by *Naeser et al.* [1989a]. He responded with the comment:

> I can only understand these results in terms of the zircon fission track ages having been similarly reset as a result either of burial prior to the onset of Laramide uplift of the Colorado Plateau, or of igneous intrusions in the area, or a combination of both ... this timing fits very well indeed with the youngest zircon ages in the three samples analyzed. I am surprised that those samples have been sufficiently hot to cause resetting of the zircon ages, which I would normally expect to require around 250 to 300°C. But we do have evidence to suggest that some zircons are more easily reset than others, so it's not totally unexpected [*Green*, personal communication, 27 March, 2003].

However, this interpretation of the zircon fission track ages obtained for the three tuff samples in this study appears to be at variance with the conclusion reached by *Naeser et al.* [1989a]. They concluded that fission track ages of ~1000 Ma obtained from zircons from Proterozoic rocks now exposed at river level indicate that those rocks have been at temperatures of 200°C or less for the last 1000 million years. A critical issue is the temperature at which fission tracks in zircons are annealed, which is not well known, the limited data available suggesting a temperature in the range 200±40°C [*Harrison et al.*, 1979; *Hurford*, 1985; *Zeitler*, 1985; *Naeser et al.*, 1989b]. Other estimates suggest a temperature of between 250°C and 300°C depending on the cooling rate [*Sharma et al.*, 1980; *Bal et al.*, 1983].

So why were the *Naeser et al.* [1989a] zircon fission track ages for these tuffs so much older? Those grains were analyzed by Dr. Charles Naeser at the U.S. Geological Survey, and perhaps he was only measuring the oldest population of zircons in those samples [*Green*, personal communication, 27 March, 2003] because he already knew the early Middle Cambrian biostratigraphic age for those samples. Certainly, in the samples in this study there is an older population of individual zircon grain fission track ages which approaches the results of Naeser's analyses of his samples, but it is only represented by a few grains. However, all the grains that Naeser analyzed in his samples had very high spontaneous fission track densities and relatively low induced fission track densities, consistent with their older ages [*Naeser*, personal communication, 4 June, 2003]. Nevertheless, contrary to the *Naeser et al.* [1989a] paper, a total of twenty-three zircon grains were analyzed in their Muav tuff sample, and these included five younger grains with fission track ages of 249±50 Ma, 353±67 Ma, 297±128 Ma, 308±96 Ma and 183±34 Ma. In their Tapeats tuff sample there was also a younger grain with a fission track age of 387±74 Ma (all the errors in these ages being ±2σ). It should also be noted that in each sample there were two grains older than the published ages [*Naeser*, personal communication, 4 June, 2003]. Thus there was evidence of thermal resetting of some grains in the *Naeser et al.* [1989a] samples, but not complete resetting to coincide with the time of the Laramide uplift, as is so clearly evident in the pooled age for the youngest group of zircons in each of the samples in this study.

Another possible explanation of this discrepancy could be differences in the etching conditions used in the two laboratories. Naeser re-examined the mounts of zircon grains from his two samples and found a few under-etched grains in them [*Naeser*, personal communication, 5 June, 2003]. He thus suggested that it is quite probable that he and Green may have looked at different populations of grains in the respective samples. Because the time required to properly etch a zircon grain is a function of the total radiation damage the zircon has suffered, grains with high fission track densities will etch more rapidly than grains with low fission track densities. Thus Precambrian age zircons would be expected to etch in a few hours, while a Pleistocene zircon grain would probably take a week or more. As admitted by Naeser:

When I etch a zircon mount I periodically check the progress of the etch. When I see a reasonable number of countable grains I will stop, even though there could be additional grains that could be counted if I doubled the etch time. It is a judgment call. Will I get more or fewer grains by continuing the etch? When I am dating Paleozoic or Precambrian samples I choose to stop earlier rather than later [*Naeser*, personal communication, 4 June, 2003].

However, the Geotrack laboratory did not use a long etching time on the three Grand Canyon tuff samples in this study (refer back to Section 5 above). If anything, the short etching times used would have favored the exposing of older grains with higher spontaneous fission track densities than younger grains. Rather, because the Geotrack laboratory had no bias in knowing the supposed ages of the samples when working on them, they would have been more careful to look for a range of ages in the samples and count grains with a variety of fission track densities, morphologies, etc., compared to Naeser's approach, which would have been to count the grains with the highest fission track densities because of already knowing the "target age" [*Green*, personal communication, 4 June, 2003]. So by admission of both laboratories there is a possibility of bias being introduced in the etching times of the grains and in the grains chosen for analysis. Nevertheless, there is no "concrete" evidence to suggest that such would have had any more than a minimal effect on the resultant fission track age determinations on the respective samples in the *Naeser et al.* [1989a] study and in this study. Naeser may have missed zircon grains with younger fission track ages when he did his analyses, but it may have been more to do with the zircon grains that ended up in the sample mounts from the larger quantity of zircon grains separated from the samples (that is, bias unwittingly introduced in the sub-population of grains selected for mounting).

So are there any other clues, or means of finding out, about the thermal history of the Paleozoic strata in the Grand Canyon area that might confirm that conditions were in fact conducive to annealing of the fission tracks in the zircon grains in the Muav and Tapeats tuffs? The single zircon grain fission-track ages obtained from the samples in this study seem to clearly indicate that most of the zircons were reset during the Laramide uplift, so this means that if these tuff units were only subjected to temperatures <200°C since their formation, these zircon grains with young ages must have been anomalously sensitive to resetting. As indicated earlier, fission track ages of ~1000 Ma obtained from zircons from Proterozoic rocks now exposed at river level in the

Grand Canyon suggest that these rocks have only been exposed to temperatures of <200°C for the last 1000 million years. Furthermore, apatite fission track ages of Precambrian granitic rocks in the central Grand Canyon record the effects of the Laramide uplift at around 62.4 Ma, the original fission tracks in the apatite being totally annealed at temperatures between 105°C and 150°C [*Naeser*, 1981; *Naeser et al.*, 1989a, b]. *Dumitru et al.* [1994] have shown from numerous apatite fission track data that between 2.7 and 4.5 km thickness of Mesozoic strata were eroded from the Grand Canyon area as a result of the erosion subsequent to the Laramide uplift. Thus the original late Cretaceous paleodepth of these Cambrian tuffs, combined with an assumed normal geothermal gradient, would have resulted in these tuffs being subjected to temperatures of 110–130°C. Furthermore, because the apatite fission track ages of the Grand Canyon Precambrian basement samples were totally reset at around 63 Ma, and the mean lengths of the fission tracks are slightly shorter than normal, *Dumitru et al.* [1994] concluded that the cooling as a result of the erosion of the overlying Mesozoic strata caused by the Laramide uplift was protracted (over millions of years in conventional terms). This conclusion was derived from comparison with the normal mean fission track lengths in rapidly cooled rocks and laboratory annealing studies [*Gleadow et al.*, 1986; *Green et al.*, 1989]. Such shortening of the fission tracks also reduces the fission track ages [*Green*, 1988], so it is necessary to correct for this to determine the time of this Laramide cooling. The corrected ages would be ~75 Ma. Significantly, that is the pooled age of the youngest group of zircon grains in two of the three tuff samples in this study, further confirming that the youngest groups of zircon grains in these samples do record the time of the Laramide uplift.

However, because all these claims concerning the thermal history since burial of these Cambrian tuff units in the western Grand Canyon are all based on fission track data, including the estimates of the temperatures at which fission tracks are totally annealed in apatite and zircon, it would be helpful to have confirmation of this claimed thermal history from other independent geological indicators. *Naeser* [personal communication, 21 June, 2003] referred to the work of *Wardlaw and*

Harris [1984] who used the color of alteration of conodont fossils in the Paleozoic rocks across Arizona, due to the heating resulting from burial and diagenesis of the sediments, as an indication of the thermal history of those Paleozoic strata. This method of using a Color Alteration Index (CAI) of conodonts (microfossils composed of apatite) to determine the temperatures of diagenesis and burial metamorphism of sediments was developed and calibrated by *Epstein et al.* [1977] and *Harris* [1979, 1981], and has been successfully applied and widely used since [*Harris*, 1979; *Rejebian et al.*, 1987]. Thus Wardlaw [*Naeser*, personal communication, 21 June, 2003] has concluded that the maximum temperature achieved in the Paleozoic strata of the Grand Canyon would have been <150°C, consistent with the conclusion reached by *Dumitru et al.* [1994] based on the apatite fission track data.

A further suggestion made by *Naeser* [personal communication, 4 June, 2003] was to have x-ray diffraction (XRD) analyses undertaken on the tuff samples to determine their illite/smectite ratios and their illite crystallinities, both of which could potentially indicate the maximum temperature to which the tuff units had been subjected. Experimental studies of the conversion of smectite to illite have demonstrated its potential use as a geothermometer [*Huang et al.*, 1993; *Essene and Peacor*, 1995], which has been confirmed by field studies [*Smart and Clayton*, 1985; *Pytte and Reynolds*, 1989; *Velde and Espitalié*, 1989; *Pollastro*, 1993; *Velde and Lanson*, 1993; *Hillier et al.*, 1995; *Renac and Meunier*, 1995]. Similarly, many studies have demonstrated the value of using illite crystallinity as an indicator to distinguish between diagenesis, very low-grade metamorphism and low-grade metamorphism [*Kubler*, 1964, 1967, 1968; *Kisch*, 1983, 1987; *Blenkinsop*, 1988; *Barrenechea et al.*, 1995; *Frey and Robinson*, 1999; *Kubler and Goy-Eggenberger*, 2001]. This advice was followed and portions of a sample from each of these tuffs were sent for XRD analyses to determine their illite/smectite ratios and illite crystallinities (see below for further details).

Another way of checking the supposed ages of the zircons in these tuff units is to apply the U-Th-Pb radioisotope dating technique to some of the individual zircon grains. Ideally the same grains on which the zircon fission track ages were obtained should be U-Th-Pb dated so as to compare the two methods of age determination and thus see if they directly equate to one another. If they did, then this would settle the argument over whether the radioisotope ratios were derived by radioactive decay or are just geochemical properties of the rocks and minerals. It would be hard to deny that the radioisotope ratios were not derived from radioactive decay when the fission tracks as physical evidence of nuclear decay are present in the same zircon grains in the right quantities to match the radioactive decay measured by the radioisotope ratios. Another potential outcome is to thereby confirm just how much radioactive and nuclear decay has occurred in these Cambrian tuffs since they were deposited early in the Flood year, which thereby potentially indicates just how much acceleration of nuclear decay has to have occurred during the Flood year. And finally, if deep burial of these tuff units and the Laramide uplift have also effected the U-Th-Pb radioisotope system, then the U-Th-Pb dates of the zircon grains might match the pooled fission track ages for the youngest groups of zircon grains in these samples. If not, then even those grains (with the young fission track ages) should still yield Cambrian U-Th-Pb ages comparable with the *Naeser et al.* [1989a] zircon fission track ages. Unfortunately, because the zircon grains that had been fission track dated were still mounted and etched, it was not possible to U-Th-Pb radioisotope date those same grains, though attempts were made to organize this with a laboratory using an ion microprobe. Instead, some unmounted zircon grains from one of the Muav tuff samples and from the Tapeats tuff sample were submitted to a laboratory for TIMS (thermal ionization mass spectrometry) U-Th-Pb radioisotope analyses (see below for the results).

7.2 Jurassic Morrison Formation Tuffs, Southeastern Utah

It is immediately evident upon comparing the results on these six samples, two each from three different stratigraphic sections through the Morrison Formation in southeastern Utah, that the zircon fission track ages obtained in this study (Table 2) are directly comparable to previously published dating results (Table 1). Indeed, five of the six samples yielded almost identical ages, the only somewhat different and older result being obtained on the Notom sample NMF-49 from which only nine zircon grains were recovered. Furthermore, in each of the three stratigraphic sections the two samples yielded zircon fission track ages commensurate with their stratigraphic order. The upper and therefore younger sample yielded a younger zircon fission track age for that tuff unit, and the lower or older tuff unit yielded an older zircon fission track age.

The nine individual zircon grains analyzed from sample NMF-49, the stratigraphically lower sample from the section at Notom (Figure 3), are consistent with a single population ($P(\chi^2)>5\%$), characterized by a pooled fission track age of 183.4 ± 20.8 Ma ($\pm1\sigma$ error) (Table 2). *Green* [2002] reported that a variety of grain morphologies were present within the sample, from euhedral to rounded as well as intermediate forms. The ages from euhedral grains (two in number) were consistent with the ages measured from obviously rounded grains (three in number). The ages from the other grains, with intermediate forms, were also consistent with the entire data set. Thus the individual zircon grain fission track data are consistent with a common origin for all these grains, the clustering of the data in both the radial plot and histogram of Figure 14a being consistent with a satisfactory pooled age using all nine grains. However, if the two oldest grains were eliminated from the analysis, because of potentially being outliers as evident in the histogram, the remaining seven grains would likely yield a pooled age almost identical with the published zircon fission track age on six grains for this same tuff unit [*Kowallis and Heaton*, 1987] (Table 1 here).

The sample NMF-64 from the uppermost tuff unit in the Brushy Basin Member of the Morrison Formation in the Notom section (Figure 3) is characterized by a central age of 178.6 ± 19.8 Ma (Table 2). However, the individual zircon grains show a statistically significant spread in fission track ages ($P(\chi^2)<5\%$), from a youngest limit of 93.1 ± 7 Ma to an oldest limit of 651.3 ± 210.4 Ma (all errors $\pm1\sigma$). Thus the numerical value of the central age has no significance other than characterizing the spread of ages within the sample. On the other hand, statistical analysis of the individual grain fission track ages [*Green*, 2002] suggests the presence of two dominant populations characterized by ages of 132±10 Ma and 321±35 Ma. However, the relevant histogram in Figure 14b does not really support the existence of the suggested population of older grains, but the youngest group with a pooled age of 132±10 Ma is dominant and therefore can be justified as being the fission track age assigned to this sample and the tuff unit it represents. A variety of grain morphologies were reported by *Green* [2002] to be present within this sample, from euhedral to rounded as well as intermediate forms. All of the clearly euhedral grains analyzed (six grains) give ages which fall within the youngest group of ages. However, in addition, three grains falling within this youngest group are clearly rounded, while the older ages were measured only in rounded to sub-rounded grains. The presence of these rounded grains in addition to euhedral grains within the youngest age grain population, just as there are both rounded and euhedral grains within the single age population of sample NMF-49, perhaps suggests some degree of transport may have taken place prior to ultimate deposition of these tuff units. Note also that the older ages in this sample (see the histogram in Figure 14b) indicate that there may be a significant component of older non-volcanic material also present within this tuff unit.

Sample BMF-14 from the lowermost tuffaceous mudstone unit of the Brushy Basin Member in the Brushy Basin type section (Figure 4) is characterized by a central age of 188.3±19.2 Ma (Table 2). However, the individual zircon grains show a spread of fission track ages ($P(\chi^2) < 5\%$) from 98.2±16.7 Ma to 689.9±187.6 Ma. So the numerical value of the central age again has no significance, other than as an estimate of the modal value of the distribution of ages within this sample. *Green* [2003] reported that the zircon grains obtained from this sample showed a variety of morphologies, from euhedral to well-rounded as well as intermediate forms. Data from only the euhedral grains (twelve in number) are all consistent with a single age population characterized by a pooled age of 147.8±8.2 Ma. Furthermore, a statistical analysis of the complete single grain fission track age data set [*Green*, 2003], using the approach outlined by *Galbraith and Green* [1990], suggests the presence of three dominant populations characterized by ages of 144±10 Ma, 225±30 Ma, and 583±91 Ma. While the existence of the grain population with the highest age might seem justified in the radial plot of Figure 14c, the histogram shows a large spread for these three oldest grains. Nevertheless, the two clusterings on the histogram justifies the identification of the two younger populations, especially the strong clustering of so many samples that yields a pooled age for the youngest group of 144±10 Ma. This youngest group of single grain ages within this sample was measured consistently only in euhedral grains [*Green*, 2003], while grains giving older ages showed sub-rounded to well-rounded forms. This pooled age for the youngest group of zircon grains, comprising the majority of the grains analyzed within this sample, is consistent with the published fission track and radioisotope ages for the equivalent tuffaceous units in the other two Morrison Formation sections (Table 1). Furthermore, the dominance of euhedral grains in this age group suggests that this probably represents the timing of the volcanism contemporaneous with deposition of this tuffaceous mudstone unit.

Sample BMF-28 from the topmost unit of the Brushy Basin Member in the Brushy Basin section (Figure 4) is characterized by a central age of 173.7±7.1 Ma (Table 2). However, the individual zircon grains have fission track ages from 104.2±22.3 Ma to 592.3±137.4 Ma, so the numerical value of the central age again has no significance. However, a statistical analysis by *Green* [2003] of the complete single grain age data set, using the approach outlined by *Galbraith and Green* [1990], suggests the presence of three dominant populations characterized by ages of 136±6 Ma, 201±26 Ma, and 372±30 Ma. Examination of the radial plot in Figure 14d might suggest some evidence of structure in the older group, with populations of two grains each at 339±32 Ma and 564±119 Ma. However, with so few grains this further division is unwarranted by the available data. Furthermore, the histogram shows such a large spread of ages for these four grains that this oldest grouping doesn't appear to be justified. On the other hand, the histogram shows a strong clustering of younger ages with a distribution that would seem to justify a division into two populations of grains. Quite clearly the youngest group with a pooled age of 136±6 Ma is dominant, because eleven of the nineteen grains analyzed fall into that youngest group. *Green* [2003] reported only a very small number of euhedral grains were present in this sample (four grains in number). These four grains show a similar spread of ages to the group as a whole (two fall into the youngest group and two into the oldest group), so therefore no significance can be attached to the grain morphologies. However, it is very significant that the pooled age of 136±6 Ma of the dominant youngest age group in this sample (from the topmost unit of the Brushy Basin Member in the Brushy Basin type section) is identical to the pooled age of 132±10 Ma of the youngest group of zircon grains in the sample from the topmost unit of the Brushy Basin Member in the Notom stratigraphic section (Table 2).

All individual zircon grains analyzed from sample MMF-4, from near the bottom of the Brushy Basin Member in the Montezuma Creek stratigraphic section (Figure 5), are consistent with a single population ($P(\chi^2)$ >5%) characterized by a pooled age of 148.8±7.0 Ma (±1σ error). The tight grouping of all eighteen analyzed grains consistent with a single fission track age population is clearly evident in both the radial plot and histogram of Figure 14e. *Green* [2003] reported that all eighteen zircon grains analyzed from this sample were euhedral in form, consistent with the rock unit being volcanic ash-rich. Thus these dated zircon grains most likely represent the primary volcanic component of this tuff unit. Note also that the central age for this sample is 148.2±8.3 Ma, identical to the pooled age (Table 2). What is even more noteworthy is that these fission track ages for this unit are also identical to the ^{40}Ar-^{39}Ar single plagioclase and K-feldspar crystal laser-fusion radioisotope ages obtained for this same unit (Table 1) by *Kowallis et al.* [1991]. This is unequivocal confirmation that the measured fission track physical evidence of nuclear decay is equivalent to the amount of radioisotope decay in the mineral grains that compose this tuff unit as determined by those radioisotope analyses. The zircon fission track age of this sample in this study is also almost identical to the zircon fission track age obtained for the sample (BMF-14) from the lowermost tuffaceous mudstone unit in the Brushy Basin Member in the Brushy Basin type section (Table 2), consistent with a late Jurassic age for the deposition of the earliest units of the Brushy Basin Member of the Morrison Formation.

Sample MMF-1, from a tuff unit near the top of the Brushy Basin Member in the Montezuma Creek stratigraphic section (Figure 5), is characterized by a central age of 205.1±22.4 Ma (Table 2). However, the twenty individual zircon grains show a statistically significant spread in their fission track ages (P(χ^2)<5%), from 87.6±15.4 Ma to 1036.2±309.8 Ma (all errors ±1σ). Thus the numerical value of the central age has no significance other than characterizing the spread of ages within this sample. However, a statistical analysis by *Green* [2003] of the complete single grain age data set, using the approach outlined by *Galbraith and Green* [1990], suggests the presence of three dominant populations characterized by ages of 137±9 Ma, 277±17 Ma, and 1036±309 Ma. The oldest of these three groups can be seen on both the radial plot and histogram in Figure 14f to be represented by one grain that is an extreme outlier, which can therefore be discounted on the basis that it represents contamination of this tuff unit by older material. Otherwise, the two younger populations of zircon grains are clearly evident in both the radial plot and histogram of Figure 14f. *Green* [2003] reported that a variety of grain morphologies were present within this sample, from euhedral to rounded as well as intermediate forms. However, all the grains comprising the youngest group of ages (eight grains) are euhedral in form, while the only other euhedral grain gives an age that falls in the intermediate age group. All other grains belonging to the intermediate and oldest age groups are rounded in form, consistent with these representing older material that has contaminated the tuff. On the other hand, the complete dominance of euhedral grains in the youngest group of zircons with a pooled age of 137±9 Ma clearly suggests that this age represents the timing of the volcanism contemporaneous with the deposition of this tuff unit. Furthermore, even though this zircon fission track age is not quite identical to the [40]Ar-[39]Ar single plagioclase and K-feldspar crystal laser-fusion radioisotope ages obtained on a sample from this same tuff unit by *Kowallis et al.* [1991] (Table 1 here), it is identical to the zircon fission track ages obtained in this study on samples in a similar stratigraphic position from the Notom and Brushy Basin sections (Table 2). These results confirm the possibility, first suggested by *Kowallis and Heaton* [1987], that the uppermost units of the Brushy Basin Member of the Morrison Formation may in fact be of earliest Cretaceous age.

7.3 Miocene Peach Springs Tuff, Southeastern California and Western Arizona

The three samples of this tuff all yielded excellent results (Table 2), consistent with previously published dating results (Table 1). All twenty individual zircon grains analyzed from each of the samples PST-1, PST-2, and PST-3 are consistent with single populations $(P(\chi^2)>5\%)$ characterized by pooled ages of 24.6±1.2 Ma, 20.9±0.9 Ma, and 20.9±0.8 Ma (±1σ errors) respectively, with identical central ages due to the narrow spreads in the data. This can be seen in the radial plots and histograms of Figure 15a, b and c respectively. *Green* [2002, 2003] reported that only euhedral grains were obtained from each of these samples, consistent with the nature of this welded crystal-rich tuff.

The two samples, PST-2 and PST-3, from the Kingman area (Figure 7) yielded identical ages which are only marginally older than the published sanidine K-Ar and ^{40}Ar-^{39}Ar laser-fusion radioisotope dates for these same outcrops (Table 2; *Nielson et al.*, 1990). This outcome, given that the two samples in this study were analyzed in separate analytical runs, is reassuring that the laboratory's analytical procedures are identical from run to run. Furthermore, it demonstrates that the samples from different outcrops of the same rock unit are nonetheless representative of what is a homogeneous tuff unit. On the other hand, PST-1 from an outcrop about 100 km away to the southwest (Figure 6) has yielded a slightly older zircon fission track age. *Green* [2002] noted that the difference between the zircon fission track age of this sample compared with the identical zircon fission track ages for samples PST-2 and PST-3 is not statistically significant at 95% confidence limits. However, the high degree of internal consistency within the single grain fission track age data from each sample suggests the difference between these ages could be real. Thus the outcrop from which sample PST-1 was taken could be slightly older than those outcrops from which samples PST-2 and PST-3 were taken. However, a sphene fission track age obtained for a sample from an outcrop even further to the west in the Bristol Mountains (Figure 6) is virtually identical to the zircon fission track ages obtained in this study for the two samples from the Kingman area (Table 2; *Nielsen et al.* [1990]). This supports the claim of *Gusa* [1986], *Glazner et al.* [1986], and *Gusa et al.* [1987], that all these outcrops belong to the Peach Springs Tuff. The only other possibility is that there is some contamination of the tuff with older material in the outcrop from which sample PST-1 was taken. There may be a hint of this possibility in the histogram in Figure 15a, where there appears to be a possible second, older population of grains close to the right of the main population of grains. That main population on its own would yield a pooled zircon fission track age identical to that for the outcrops in the Kingman area.

Nevertheless, for the stated purpose of this study it is clearly evident that these samples from this Miocene tuff unit have yielded a quantity of fission tracks in their zircon grains consistent with ages obtained by radioisotope dating of sanidine grains in samples from the same outcrops of this same tuff unit. This confirms that the radioisotope ratios have resulted from an amount of radioactive decay that has occurred equivalent to the physical evidence for nuclear decay provided by the fission tracks.

8. Additional Analytical Work on the Cambrian Tuffs, Western Grand Canyon, Arizona

8.1 X-Ray Diffraction (XRD) Determinations of their Mineralogy

Portions of Muav tuff sample MT-3 and the Tapeats tuff sample TT-1 were sent to Dr. Sam Iyengar, the technical director of the Technology of Materials laboratory in Wildomar, California, to be analyzed by x-ray powder diffraction (XRD) to determine their mineralogical constituents in the fine (<2–4 μm) fraction. At the laboratory the samples were analyzed according to Laboratory Standard Operating Procedure-100 for clay mineral analyses. The samples were gently ground to break up the aggregates and then air-dried. They were then suspended and shaken in distilled water to promote dispersion. The time required to separate the <2–4 μm fractions was calculated from Stokes' law and the suspensions were allowed to stand for the appropriate time. The supernatant (with colloids) solutions were decanted into separate beakers. The process of adding water and allowing settling was continued until the supernatants became clear.

Portions of the clay suspensions in the beakers were used to make oriented clay mounts on Millipore filters. The suspensions were filtered through 45 μm filter papers on a Millipore filter set-up using a vacuum. They were then washed thoroughly with distilled water to remove excess salts. The clay cakes on the filter papers were transferred, while still wet, onto glass slides and kept in an ethylene glycol chamber for twenty-four hours. A drop of glycol was placed on the edge of each slide before the slides were placed in the chamber.

The oriented and glycolated clay mounts were then scanned from 3 to 30° 2θ using a Phillips' x-ray diffractometer running with Cu-K$_\alpha$ radiation at 35 kV and 20 ma.

8.2 U-Th-Pb Radioisotope Determinations on Zircons

The zircon grains separated from Muav tuff sample MT-3 and Tapeats tuff sample TT-1 by the Geotrack International laboratory that were not used for the zircon fission track analyses were sent to Dr. Yakov Kapusta in the geochronology and isotope geochemistry laboratory at Activation Laboratories in Ancaster, Ontario, Canada. There the grains were examined under a microscope and six grains from each sample were selected for U-Th-Pb radioisotope analyses. The six grains from the Muav tuff were abraded with air in order to clean their surfaces and to remove any secondary overgrowths and/or portions of any other mineral grains that might be still clinging to them. On the other hand, the six grains from the Tapeats tuff were chemically abraded in order to totally eliminate any discordance caused by Pb loss. Thus the grains were first annealed at 900°C for sixty hours and then leached in concentrated HF at 170°C for twelve hours. They were then fluxed in warm 5N HNO_3 and rinsed with MQ water several times. These leached grains were then spiked with mixed Pb-U tracer and dissolved completely in concentrated HF at 210°C for forty-eight hours. All twelve abraded zircon crystals were then dissolved using the standard dissolution techniques (conversion to HCl and column chemistry) so that the relevant elements could be separated in solution for depositing on filaments for insertion in the mass spectrometer. Once prepared, the filament for each zircon grain was run in a thermal ionization mass spectrometer (TIMS) to determine the relevant radioisotope ratios and thus calculate the U-Pb ages for these zircon grains.

9. Results and Discussion of the Additional Analytical Work

9.1 The X-Ray Diffraction (XRD) Determinations

The XRD patterns for the oriented and glycolated clay fractions for both samples are shown in Figure 16. The appropriate peak positions for the various clay and other minerals present are marked on the oriented pattern. Both samples contain illite interstratified with smaller amounts of smectite. Discrete smectite, as estimated by expansion to ~17.8 Å upon glycolation, is also present, but in small amounts. The proportions of the various minerals in the clay (<2–4 μm) fractions of the two samples are listed in Table 3, along with the Kubler Index for illite crystallinity determined from the peak at 10.2 Å, in accordance with the internationally-recognized standard procedures [*Kisch*, 1991; *Warr and Rice*, 1994].

As already noted, the rationale for these XRD analyses of the clay minerals in these two tuff units is that the amount of smectite interstratified in illite has been used as a geothermometer. Its primary application has been to estimate the temperatures to which sediments containing organic matter have been subjected to by burial in sedimentary basins so as to determine whether maturation has

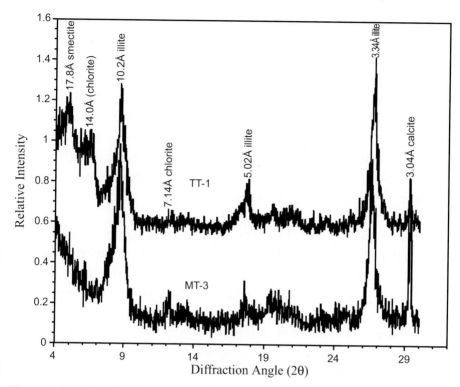

Figure 16. The XRD (x-ray diffraction) patterns for the oriented and glycolated <2–4 μm clay fractions of Muav tuff sample MT-3 and Tapeats tuff sample TT-1, showing the peak positions for the various clay and other minerals present (as marked).

Table 3. The mineral composition of the <2–4 μm fraction of Muav and Tapeats tuff samples MT-3 and TT-1 respectively determined by XRD analyses (Analyst: Dr. Sam Iyengar, Technology of Materials, Wildomar, California). The illite is interstratified with smectite. The smectite/illite ratio and the Kubler (illite crystallinity) Index for each sample has also been calculated.

Sample	Smectite (%)	Illite (%)	Smectite/Illite ratio	Illite/Smectite ratio	Kubler Index	Other Minerals (%)
MT-3	~20	~65	~0.3	~3.25	0.45	Chlorite (~10) Calcite (~5)
TT-1	~5	~80	~0.06	~16.0	0.65	Chlorite (<5) Calcite (~10)

occurred and hydrocarbons generated and released. The application of this geothermometer to these two tuff units seemed feasible, because a petrographic examination indicated they primarily consisted of a clay matrix in which the clay minerals appear to have accumulated at the time of deposition, rather than having formed *in situ* after deposition. In volcanic eruptions ash is produced by pulverization of the congealing lavas, so that the ultra-fine mineral fragments are then well mixed with super-hot steam as they are rapidly transported and deposited. It would have been the steam acting on the ultra-fine mineral fragments that would have reduced them to clay minerals by the time these tuff units were deposited.

However, the smectite/illite ratio relationship to temperature appears to be neither simple nor unequivocal, because of various factors such as the ion content and concentrations in interstitial waters and the geothermal gradient, not just at the present time but also during the history of the sediment pile. Nevertheless, *Hower* [1981] found clear relationships between depth, temperature and the percent illite in illite interstratified with smectite in the sediments intersected by oil wells in the Gulf of Mexico coast region (Figure 17) [*Pollastro*, 1993], one of which is directly comparable to the sedimentary strata sequence in the Grand Canyon-Colorado Plateau region. There *Dumitru et al.* [1994] estimated that the Cambrian strata of the Tonto Group would have been, prior to the erosion of the Mesozoic section from off the top of the Grand Canyon sequence, at a depth of burial of between 4.5 and 6 km, with the apatite fission track data suggesting temperatures of between 110° and 130°C. In Figure 17 the percent illite in the illite interstratified with smectite in the two samples from these Grand Canyon tuff units, as recorded in Table 3, have been plotted on the curve from oil well (B), and projected onto the depth and temperature axes. This suggests that with that geothermal gradient, these tuff beds would have been, prior to the erosion of the Mesozoic strata above, at depths of 4800–5600 m and subjected to temperatures of between 110° and 130°C, consistent with the estimates by *Dumitru et al.* [1994]. Confirmation that the interpretation of these results is entirely reasonable is the fact that these two tuff units plot on the depth axis in the correct stratigraphic order, the Muav tuff

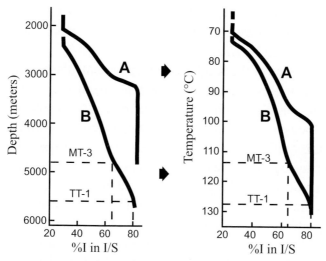

Figure 17. Proportion of illite (I) layers in mixed-layer illite/smectite (I/S) versus depth (left) and temperature (right) for samples from (A) an Oligocene well, and (B) a Miocene well, in the Gulf of Mexico coast region (modified from *Hower* [1981]). The %I in I/S data for the Muav tuff MT-3 and Tapeats tuff TT-1 samples are plotted on curve B and the interpreted depths and temperatures are projected from that curve.

being higher up the stratigraphic sequence above the Tapeats tuff by 200 m or more (Figure 1). *Dumitru et al.* [1994] based their estimation on a pre-Cretaceous geothermal gradient of 20–30°C/km, and the geothermal gradient in the Miocene oil well (B) (Figure 17) is of the order of 20°C/km. Such a geothermal gradient is not unreasonable in the time frame of the Flood event, given the catastrophic deposition of the thick Paleozoic and Mesozoic strata sequence [*Austin*, 1994] and the elevated temperatures of the waters depositing those sediments [*Austin et al.*, 1994]. Thus the estimates of depth and temperature based on the percent illite in the illite interstratified with smectite for these two tuff samples, though very approximate due to the likely large errors in the XRD determinations, are not unreasonable. Therefore, because of the consistency of these estimates with the apatite fission track data of *Naeser et al.* [1989a] and *Dumitru et al.* [1994], it seems reasonable to conclude that these two tuff units have since their burial only been subjected to maximum temperatures of 110–130°C, well below the 200±40°C temperature for total annealing of fission tracks in zircon [*Harrison et al.*, 1979; *Hurford*, 1985; *Zeitler*, 1985].

The significance of the Kubler Index values calculated from the XRD clay mineral analyses of the two samples from these two tuff units (Table 3) are harder to interpret from the available literature, which primarily focuses on low-grade metamorphism of sedimentary strata sequences. Estimating the temperatures to which these two tuff units were subjected based on these approximate Kubler Index values depends on the value of the Kubler Index used to define the boundary between diagenesis and the lowest grade metamorphism, which is otherwise defined by mineralogical changes in the clay minerals [*Kubler*, 1967; *Kisch*, 1987]. As indicated by *Blenkinsop* [1988], early studies using the Kubler Index for illite crystallinity all adopted different values of the index to define this crucial boundary, so standardization was warranted. Using the standardized definition of *Kisch* [1991] and *Brime* [1999] with a Kubler Index of 0.42 for the boundary between diagenesis and the lowest grade metamorphism, as successfully applied by *Brime et al.* [2003], the estimated Kubler Index values for the Muav and Tapeats tuffs (Table 3) indicate that they are on the lower temperature side of this boundary, as they only suffered diagenesis. Temperature estimates for that boundary place it at 150±50°C [*Frey and Kisch*, 1987; *Robinson and Merriman*, 1999; *Bucher and Frey*, 2002]. Thus the Kubler Index values for these two tuff units are consistent with the estimate of 110–130°C for the temperatures to which these tuff units have been subjected from both the apatite fission track data of *Naeser et al.* [1989a] and *Dumitru et al.* [1994], and their smectite/illite ratios.

9.2 Zircon U-Th-Pb Age Determinations

Some of the zircon grains in Muav tuff sample MT-3, and the six zircon grains selected from them when ready for analysis after being air abraded, are shown photographed in Figure 18. The six chemically abraded zircon grains from Tapeats tuff sample TT-1 are shown in Figure 19. There do not appear to have been any secondary overgrowths

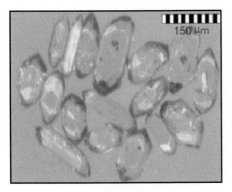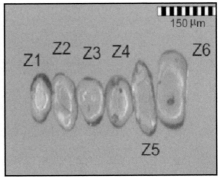

Figure 18. Zircon grains from Muav tuff sample MT-3. (a) Raw grains separated from the tuff. (b) The six selected grains after being air abraded to remove any overgrowths, metamict zones, or portions of other minerals still clinging to their outer surfaces. Photomicrographs courtesy of Dr. Yakov Kapusta at Activation Laboratories, Ancaster, Ontario, Canada.

on these selected and abraded grains, and the photographs don't show any obvious internal primary growth zones in them. The results of the U-Th-Pb radioisotope analyses of the twelve abraded zircon grains and the resultant calculated ages are shown in Table 4.

In the Muav tuff sample MT-3, only two of the zircons, z4 and z6, yielded concordant ages of 74.8±3.2 Ma and 169.0±0.5 Ma (2σ errors) respectively, and these results are plotted on the concordia diagrams in Figure 20. Otherwise, the individual ages derived for the zircon grains from the U-Pb radioisotope analyses range from a $^{206}Pb/^{238}U$ age of 68.2 Ma for grain z5 through to a $^{207}Pb/^{206}Pb$ age of 1621.2 Ma for grain z3 (Table 4). When the $^{206}Pb/^{204}Pb$ and $^{207}Pb/^{204}Pb$ ratios are plotted on a $^{206}Pb/^{207}Pb$ diagram the scatter in the data precludes the fitting of an isochron to them. However, when the data point for grain z6 is not included in the isochron plotting routine used, *Isoplot/Ex* [*Ludwig*, 2001], an isochron line fits the five remaining data points, with an MSWD (mean square of weighted deviates) value of 16 and corresponding to an age of 1609±204 Ma (Figure 21). This MSWD value is too high for this to be an acceptable isochron for an age determination (the ideal is a value of 1; *Dickin* [1995]), and the data point ignored is for grain z6 which yielded the best concordant U-Pb age (Table 4 and

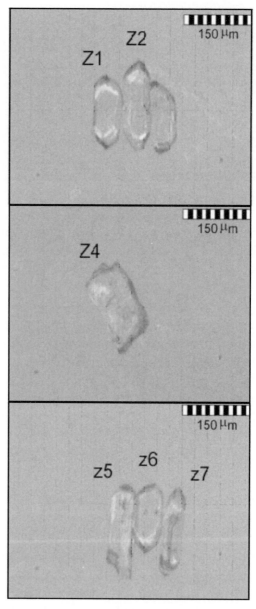

Figure 19. Zircon grains from Tapeats tuff sample TT-1. The six selected grains are labeled z1-z2, z4-z7 and are shown after being chemically abraded. Photomicrographs courtesy of Dr. Yakov Kapusta at Activation Laboratories, Ancaster, Ontario, Canada.

Table 4. The U-Th-Pb radioisotope analyses and ages of six abraded zircon grains (z1-z6) from Muav tuff sample MT-3, and of six abraded zircon grains (z1-z2, z4-z7) from Tapeats tuff sample TT-1, as analyzed by Dr. Yakov Kapusta, Activation Laboratories, Ancaster, Ontario, Canada.

Sample	Sample Fractions	Concentrations							Ratios						Ages (Ma)			correlation coefficient
		Weight (µg) (a)	U (ppm)	Pb (ppm)	Pb(c) (pg) (b)	$^{206}Pb/^{204}Pb$ (c)	$^{208}Pb/^{206}Pb$ (d)	$^{207}Pb/^{204}Pb$	$^{206}Pb/^{238}U$ (e)	error (2σ%)	$^{207}Pb/^{235}U$ (e)	error (2σ%)	$^{207}Pb/^{206}Pb$ (e)	error (2σ%)	$^{206}Pb/^{238}U$	$^{207}Pb/^{235}U$	$^{207}Pb/^{206}Pb$	
MT-3	z1	1.3	924	38.9	1.9	1568.5	0.096	146.39	0.040422	(.16)	0.52014	(.18)	0.09333	(.07)	255.4	425.2	1494.5	0.921
	z2	1.9	194	8.3	3.8	219.5	0.147	11.26	0.034146	(.58)	0.24153	(.85)	0.05130	(.57)	216.4	219.7	254.5	0.743
	z3	1.3	247	45.8	3.8	855.5	0.177	85.42	0.160868	(.16)	2.21465	(.20)	0.09985	(.12)	961.6	1185.7	1621.2	0.821
	z4	1.4	140	0.9	1.3	131.4	0.300	6.24	0.011645	(4.23)	0.07630	(4.96)	0.04752	(2.36)	74.6	74.7	75.3	0.880
	z5	2.2	76	0.9	1.8	82.9	0.206	4.25	0.010639	(3.03)	0.07514	(4.65)	0.05122	(3.31)	68.2	73.6	250.7	0.706
	z6	3.9	360	10.1	1.4	1686.5	0.161	83.38	0.026561	(.20)	0.18105	(.26)	0.04944	(.16)	169.0	169.0	168.6	0.799
TT-1	z1	2.6	353	5.1	0.4	2026.2	0.198	96.79	0.013431	(.11)	0.08847	(.29)	0.04777	(.26)	86.0	86.1	88.1	0.460
	z2	2.7	214	10.5	0.2	7953.9	0.092	434.20	0.049947	(.06)	0.37598	(.10)	0.05459	(.08)	314.2	324.1	395.7	0.595
	z4	5.8	267	85.7	3.2	9266.6	0.147	964.57	0.298127	(.15)	4.23308	(.16)	0.10298	(.05)	1682.0	1680.5	1678.5	0.958
	z5	2.1	135	44.0	0.4	129050.6	0.187	1319.41	0.294489	(.07)	4.13683	(.09)	0.10188	(.06)	1663.9	1661.6	1658.7	0.734
	z6	2.5	57	0.9	0.3	450.8	0.184	21.40	0.015362	(.48)	0.10055	(1.64)	0.4747	(1.49)	98.3	97.3	73.2	0.448
	z7	1.7	301	4.7	0.3	1378.8	0.241	65.92	0.014073	(.15)	0.09277	(.28)	0.04781	(.23)	90.1	90.1	89.9	0.583

Notes:

(a) Sample weights are estimated by using a video monitor and are known to within 40%.

(b) Total common-Pb in analyses.

(c) Measured ratio corrected for spike and fractionation only.

(d) Radiogenic Pb.

(e) Corrected for fractionation, spike, blank, and initial common Pb.

Mass fractionation correction of 0.15%/amu±0.04%/amu (atomic mass unit) was applied to single-collector Daly analyses and 0.12%/amu±0.04% for dynamic Faraday-Daly analyses. Total procedural blank less than 0.6 pg (MT-3) and 0.2 pg (TT-1) for Pb and less than 0.1 pg for U.
Blank isotopic composition: $^{206}Pb/^{204}Pb = 19.10\pm0.1$, $^{207}Pb/^{204}Pb = 15.71\pm0.1$, $^{208}Pb/^{204}Pb = 38.65\pm0.1$.
Age calculations are based on the decay constants of Steiger and Jäger [1977].
Common-Pb corrections were calculated by using the model of Stacey and Kramers [1975] and the interpreted age of the sample.

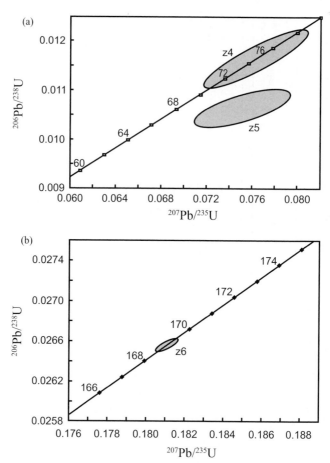

Figure 20. Concordia plots of the U-Pb radioisotope data obtained from zircon grains from Muav tuff sample MT-3. Only two grains yield concordant U-Pb ages: (a) z4 (74.6 Ma), and (b) z6 (169.0 Ma).

Figure 20). Therefore, if grain z6 is included in the isochron analysis, then the data points for grains z1 and z3 have to be rejected in order to fit an isochron to the remaining data. However, the resulting isochron justifies this procedure, because the four data points yield an isochron with an excellent fit measured by an MSWD value of 0.61 and a probability of 0.54 (Figure 21). The age for the isochron is 166±30 Ma (2σ errors), which not surprisingly is the same as the concordant U-Pb age of 169.0±0.5 Ma for grain z6 (Table 4 and Figure 20).

In the Tapeats tuff sample TT-1, all six zircon grains yielded essentially concordant ages. Grains z1, z6, and z7 yielded concordant ages of 86.2±0.3 Ma, 98.2±1.3 Ma, and 90.1±0.2 Ma (2σ errors) respectively, and these are plotted on the concordia diagram in Figure 22. Grains z2, z4, and z5 yielded older essentially concordant ages of approximately 319 Ma, 1681 Ma, and 1662 Ma respectively (Table 4). Otherwise, the individual grain ages derived from the U-Th-Pb radioisotope analyses range from a $^{207}Pb/^{206}Pb$ age of 73.2 Ma for grain z6 to a $^{206}Pb/^{238}U$ age of 1682.0 Ma for grain z4 (Table 4). When the $^{206}Pb/^{204}Pb$ and $^{207}Pb/^{204}Pb$ ratios are plotted on a $^{206}Pb/^{207}Pb$ diagram the scatter in the data precludes the fitting of an isochron to them. However, when the data points for grains z4 and z5 are not included in the isochron plotting routine used, *Isoplot/Ex* [*Ludwig*, 2001], an isochron line fits excellently

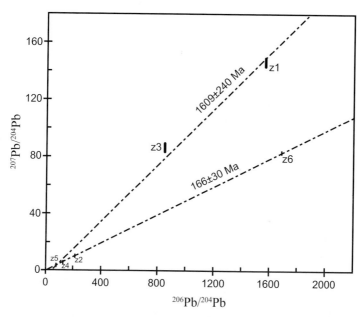

Figure 21. $^{206}Pb/^{204}Pb$ versus $^{207}Pb/^{204}Pb$ isochrons fitted to the Pb radioisotope data obtained from the six zircon grains from Muav tuff sample MT-3. Five grains (z1, z2, z3, z4, z5) yield an apparent isochron age of 1609±240 Ma, but with an MSWD of 16 the fit is poor. However, four grains (z2, z4, z5, z6) yield an isochron age of 166±30 Ma, with a good MSWD of 0.61 and a probability of 0.54.

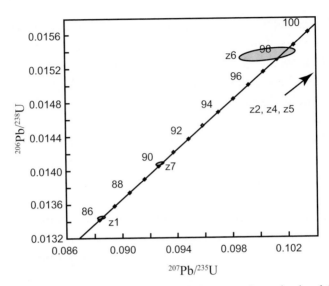

Figure 22. Concordia plot of the U-Pb radioisotope data obtained from three zircon grains (z1, z6, z7) from Tapeats tuff sample TT-1. The three concordant U-Pb ages are 86.2 Ma, 98.2 Ma, and 90.1 Ma respectively.

to the four remaining data points, with an MSWD value of 0.69 and a probability of 0.50 (Figure 23). This isochron corresponds to an age of 437±100 Ma (2σ errors). On the other hand, if the data point for grain z2 is excluded from the isochron plotting routine, the other five data points lie close to an isochron line with an MSWD value of 6.0, and corresponding to an age of 1774±200 Ma (Figure 23).

From all of these various U-Th-Pb radioisotope age determinations on the twelve zircon grains, the following observations can be made. First, none of the resultant ages matches either the biostratigraphic age of early Middle Cambrian for these Muav and Tapeats tuff units, or the zircon fission track ages of 535±48 Ma and 563±49 Ma respectively determined by *Naeser et al.* [1989a]. The only result that comes close is the Pb-Pb isochron age of 437±100 Ma for four grains from the Tapeats tuff sample. Second, the really old ages, for grains z1 and z3 from the Muav tuff and grains z2 and z4 from the Tapeats tuff (Table 4), suggest that the tuffs have a very small component of contamination by older sedimentary or igneous material. This is also hinted at in the histogram for the Tapeats tuff sample TT-1 in Figure 13c and in the Pb-Pb isochron ages of 1609±204 Ma and 1774±200 Ma in Figures 21 and 23. Indeed, the zircon U-Pb ages of the granitic basement rocks in the western Grand Canyon [*Karlstrom et al.*, 2003] fall within the ranges of these Pb-Pb isochron ages. If some older zircon grains have been inherited by these tuffs, most of the fission tracks in those grains have been inherited with them, having then survived the subsequent thermal annealing. Third, the concordant age of 74.8±3.1 Ma for grain z4 and the ^{206}Pb/^{238}U and ^{207}Pb/^{235}U ages for grain z5 from the Muav tuff (Table 4) coincide with the age of the Laramide uplift of the Colorado Plateau and the subsequent cooling due to the erosion of the Mesozoic strata sequence covering the Paleozoic strata in which these tuff units are found. These results are thus consistent with the pooled fission track age of 74.6±3.9 Ma for the youngest group of zircons in this same Muav tuff sample MT-3

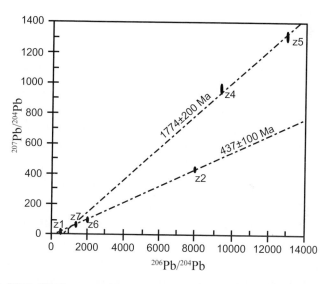

Figure 23. ^{206}Pb/^{204}Pb versus ^{207}Pb/^{204}Pb isochrons fitted to the Pb radioisotope data obtained from the six zircon grains from Tapeats tuff sample TT-1. Four grains (z1, z2, z6, z7) yield an isochron age of 437±100 Ma with a good MSWD of 0.69 and a probability of 0.50. Five of the grains (z1, z4, z5, z6, z7) yield an isochron age of 1774±200 Ma, and with an MSWD of 6 the fit is reasonable.

(Table 2), which is also matched in the youngest group of zircons from Tapeats tuff sample TT-1. And finally, fourth, the in-between spread of ages (even concordant U-Pb ages) is consistent with some thermal resetting of the U-Pb radioisotope system, due to the temperatures of 110–130°C of burial of these tuffs. This is also reflected in the spread of the zircon fission track ages obtained for the three samples of these tuffs in this study (Figure 13). Thus if the U-Pb radioisotope system has been thermally reset, it is not surprising that this is reflected in the thermal annealing of the fission tracks in the zircons in these tuffs, even though the estimated maximum temperatures of burial of 110–130°C are well below the temperature of 200±40°C for total thermal annealing of fission tracks in zircons. Thus, the suggestion by *Green* [personal communication, 25 August, 2003] that most of these zircons must have been particularly susceptible to thermal resetting seems to be consistent with all the evidence.

However, zircon is known to be stable up to 1690°C [*Finch and Hanchar*, 2003], and the closure temperature of the U-Th-Pb radioisotope system in unaltered zircon is very high at >900°C [*Ireland and Williams*, 2003]. Even though the crystallization of new zircon during metamorphism has been recorded for a wide range of temperatures and pressures, at pressure-temperature conditions lower than upper-amphibolite and granulite grades new zircon is rare [*Hoskin and Schaltegger*, 2003]. Thus, the U-Th-Pb radioisotope system in zircons has been routinely used to "date" what are claimed to be the earth's oldest rocks [*Parrish and Noble*, 2003], such as gneisses in Greenland [*Nutman et al.*, 2000] and in Canada [*Bowring et al.*, 1989] at 3800–4000 Ma. The U-Th-Pb radioisotope system in such zircons is reset at the temperatures of 600–750°C at which metamorphic gneisses and granites form, but is thermally stable below those temperatures, even though Pb loss due to diffusion can occur [*Baadsgaard*, 1973; *Cherniak and Watson*, 2003].

Therefore, thermal resetting of the U-Pb radioisotope system within most of the zircon grains in the Middle Cambrian Muav and Tapeats tuffs in Grand Canyon, as indicated by these U and Pb isotope measurements (Table 4), would seem to have been impossible at the 110–130°C burial temperatures experienced by the tuff. However, there is a possible explanation. If this tuff bed and its contained zircons were buried at the outset of the Flood year, and during that year radioisotope decay was accelerated, then the heat generated locally within the zircon grains by this accelerated decay may possibly have raised the temperatures within the zircons sufficiently to reset the U-Pb radioisotope system in them by diffusion of Pb. The fission tracks in the zircons would also have thus been annealed. For such a scenario to work, the wet clay matrix surrounding the zircon grains within the tuff would need to have acted as an insulator that confined this heat to the zircon grains without the tuff matrix's temperature being raised beyond 110–130°C. However, there would then be the problem of dissipating this heat, so this scenario is somewhat speculative.

Nevertheless, assuming this scenario, what temperature might be required within a 50 μm long zircon grain for it to lose about 90% of its contained radiogenic Pb by 550 million years worth (at today's rate) of accelerated radioisotope decay within the Flood year? Using the same equation and data as *Magomedov* [1970] and *Gentry et al.* [1982] for Pb diffusion in zircon, it can be calculated that a temperature of about 725°C would be required. If the diffusion data of *Cherniak and Watson* [2001] were instead used in the calculation, then the required temperature would be much higher at about 1485°C. Both these temperatures are within the range in which zircon is stable and the U-Pb radioisotope system in it is thermally reset. However, in their determination of Pb diffusion in zircon, *Cherniak and Watson* [2001] did not take into account the effect of radiation damage on Pb diffusion, whereas the zircons on which *Magomedov* [1970] measured the Pb diffusion were metamict from radiation damage. If accelerated nuclear decay did occur in these zircon grains in the Muav tuff, then the intense blast of radiation would have undoubtedly caused much damage to their crystal structure, thus facilitating faster Pb diffusion from them and the resetting of the U-Pb radioisotope system. So it is unlikely these zircon grains had to reach a temperature of more than 725°C for the measured resetting of the U-Pb radioisotope system in them from 550 Ma to 70 Ma. The heat required for this resetting is potentially therefore evidence of accelerated nuclear decay.

10. Discussion of the Overall Study

As stated in the introduction to this chapter and in the section explaining the rationale of this present research study, this study was designed to test whether or not the radioisotope ratios measured in minerals and rocks are the product of the quantity of radioactive decay equivalent to the respective radioisotope ages inferred from them. Fission tracks were chosen for study because they provide physical evidence of nuclear decay. Samples were thus chosen from early Middle Cambrian, uppermost Jurassic, and Miocene tuff units in the strata sequence of the Grand Canyon-Colorado Plateau region for zircon fission track dating. The results have confirmed that the physical evidence of millions of years of nuclear decay provided by the observed fission track densities does equate to the millions of years of contemporaneous radioactive decay in the same rocks as determined by radioisotope dating methods. Thus the physical evidence of nuclear decay in the form of the observed fission tracks does confirm that the radioisotope determinations on these minerals and rocks are a record of radioisotope decay, rather than simply being just chemical analyses open to other interpretations. This confirmation that the fission track ages correspond directly to the radioisotope ages is clearly seen in the Jurassic Morrison Formation tuffs and the Miocene Peach Springs Tuff. Furthermore, even though there is clear evidence of thermal resetting of both fission tracks and the U-Pb radioisotope system in the zircons in the early Middle Cambrian Muav and Tapeats tuffs, there is still a direct correspondence between the observed quantities of fission tracks and the measured amounts of α-decay of U in the zircons in these tuffs, which corresponds to identical age determinations by both dating methods and identical evidence of thermal resetting. There is even identical evidence of minor contamination of these tuffs by older material. Thus, the claim that the radioisotope ratios measured in minerals and rocks have nothing to do with radioisotope decay, but are merely artifacts of the compositions of minerals and the geochemistry of rocks and the sources from which they were derived, cannot be sustained.

However, in response to this assertion it might be argued by some that this direct correspondence between fission track and radioisotope ages is to be expected because the ζ calibration used in fission track dating is derived by using the fission track densities of standard minerals whose ages have been independently determined by radioisotope methods. In other words, the fission track dating method has been calibrated by radioisotope dating, and therefore one would automatically expect there to be a consistency between the two methods. However, in this present study all zircon fission track age determinations were performed in the same laboratory by the same investigator using the same value for the ζ calibration regardless of the resultant calculated fission track ages for the individual zircon grains from all twelve samples spanning from the Cambrian to the Miocene. In other words, the ζ calibration was a constant, and thus it was the fission track densities that varied according to the calculated fission track ages for the zircons in the samples. Thus the younger the age of the zircon the lower was the fission track density, and the older the age of the zircon, the greater the density of the fission tracks. Thus the quantities of fission tracks are directly proportional to the ages of the zircon grains, regardless of the value chosen for the ζ calibration, and thus regardless of that value being obtained using the fission track densities in samples whose ages had been determined by radioisotope determinations. Therefore, the accusation that the fission track ages may be an artifact of calibration against radioisotope ages simply cannot be sustained.

Furthermore, the presence of the fission tracks in the zircons shows that *in situ* U decay has indeed occurred, which implies that *in situ* generation of daughter products has also occurred. This is independent of any pre-existing daughter isotopes that may have been in the rocks. Thus it can be legitimately argued that the radioisotope ratios measured in the rocks are likely the result of *in situ* radioisotope decay, the amount corresponding to the fission track densities.

The remaining question is just how much nuclear decay has occurred during accumulation of the Phanerozoic strata sequence of the Grand Canyon-Colorado Plateau region? Because the zircon fission track ages are equivalent to the radioisotope ages of the Jurassic Morrison Formation tuffs and Miocene Peach Springs Tuff, then 145 or so million years worth of radioisotope and nuclear decay has occurred during and since deposition of the Brushy Basin Member of the Morrison Formation. The initial zircon fission track age results from the Cambrian Muav and Tapeats tuffs were somewhat equivocal, because the only benchmark for them to be measured against were previous fission track age determinations that yielded nuclear decay ages more or less equivalent to the early Middle Cambrian biostratigraphic ages for these tuffs. The zircon fission track ages obtained in this study simply did not replicate the previously published zircon fission track dating results. However, the subsequent additional analytical work to determine the temperatures to which these tuff units were subjected by burial, and the U-Pb radioisotope age determinations of some of the zircons in two samples, have confirmed that this discrepancy between the two sets of zircon fission track age determinations has been caused by thermal resetting of both fission tracks and the U-Pb radioisotope system in many of the zircons in these tuffs. The fact that both the fission tracks and the U-Pb radioisotope system have been reset by equivalent amounts is reflected in both methods giving identical results for the onset of the Laramide uplift of the Colorado Plateau. This provides confidence to assert that **if** there had been **no thermal annealing** of the fission tracks **and no thermal resetting** of the U-Pb radioisotope system, then the previously published zircon fission track ages for these tuffs equivalent to their biostratigraphic ages would have been confirmed by both zircon fission track and U-Pb radioisotope age determinations in this study. This assertion is further confirmed by the fact that in both the previous and present zircon fission track dating analyses of samples from the same outcrops of these Cambrian tuffs, ages older than their biostratigraphic Cambrian age were found ([*Naeser*, personal communication, 4 June 2003]; and Table 2 and Figure 13). Such older ages were also found by the U-Pb radioisotope age determinations on zircon grains in this present study. In other words, one-to-one correspondence is routinely maintained between the spontaneous fission track densities in the zircons and their contained U-Pb radioisotope systems. Thus, it is concluded that **if** there had been **no thermal annealing** of the fission tracks in the zircons in these Cambrian tuffs, the fission track densities would have recorded the physical evidence of more than 500 million years worth of nuclear and radioisotope decay (at today's decay rates).

Thus, if more than 500 million years worth of nuclear and radioisotope decay has occurred in the zircon grains within the Cambrian tuff units during and since their deposition, then this is consistent with more than 500 million years of elapsed time **only if** the nuclear and radioisotope decay rates have remained constant at today's measured rates throughout that elapsed time during which the Phanerozoic strata sequence of the Grand Canyon-Colorado Plateau region was accumulating. However, *Austin* [1994] maintains that most of that sedimentary strata sequence was deposited during the year of the catastrophic global Flood only about 4500 years ago, as recorded in the Scriptures (Genesis 7–9). *Austin* [1994] provides ample documentation of the evidence in the sedimentary strata sequence of the Grand Canyon-Colorado Plateau region that the sedimentary strata, whether sandstones, shales, or limestones, were deposited catastrophically over this vast area, consistent with a catastrophic global Flood of a year's duration. Similarly, these thin tuff units in the Muav Limestone and Tapeats Sandstone, sampled in this study, represent catastrophic event horizons, as do the tuffs in the Morrison Formation and the Peach Springs Tuff. Indeed, there is no present-day analog for the scale of the eruption responsible for the Peach Springs Tuff, when at least several hundred cubic kilometers of volcanic ash was deposited over a lateral distance of 350 km and an area of at least 35,000 km^2 [*Glazner et al.*, 1986]. So, if the geologic evidence for catastrophic deposition of the strata sequence in the Grand Canyon-Colorado Plateau region is consistent with the Biblical record of a year-long global catastrophic Flood only 4500 or so years ago, then by implication 500 or more million years worth (at today's rates) of nuclear and radioisotope decay, that has occurred during deposition of much of this strata sequence during that year-long global Flood, must therefore have been occurring at accelerated rates. Furthermore, the occurrence of ^{238}U and Po radiohalos together in the same biotite grains in granites is consistent with accelerated radioisotope decay and rapid granite formation during the Flood [*Snelling and Armitage*, 2003; *Snelling et al.*, 2003b; *Snelling*, 2005a]. Thus the fission tracks in the zircons in these Cambrian tuff units in the western Grand Canyon provide physical evidence of at least 500 million years worth (at today's rates) of nuclear and radioisotope decay during the Flood.

Of course, such a conclusion presupposes the correctness of interpreting the evidence for catastrophic deposition of the strata sequence in the Grand Canyon-Colorado Plateau region in terms of a year-long global Flood only 4500 or so years ago. The question arises as to whether there is independent evidence that quantifies the timescale for the Flood and since, and for the age of the earth, for that matter? Yes, the diffusion of He, a by-product of U and Th decay, from where it has been generated in zircons within granites indicates a diffusion age of only thousands of years, even though the U-Th-Pb radioisotope dating of the same zircon grains records many millions of years of radioisotope decay [*Humphreys et al.*, 2003a,b, 2004; *Humphreys*, 2005]. Also, the presence of primordial ^{14}C in organic matter such as coal and fossil wood, and in diamonds, that are supposedly hundreds of millions of years old and therefore ^{14}C "dead," is only consistent with a young earth and a recent, year-long, global catastrophic Flood [*Baumgardner et al.*, 2003a,b; *Baumgardner*, 2005]. Furthermore, the occurrence of ^{238}U and Po radiohalos together in the same biotite grains in granites is consistent with accelerated radioisotope decay and rapid granite formation during the Flood [*Snelling and* Armitage, 2003; *Snelling et al.*, 2003b; Snelling, 2005a]. Thus on this basis, the quantities of fission tracks found in the zircons from the tuff units examined in this study are evidence for hundreds of millions of years of accelerated nuclear decay during a global, catastrophic Flood in the recent past.

This conclusion of course raises many questions. How would the enormous amount of heat generated by accelerated decay be removed? And the radiation involved would surely have killed off living organisms? Would the decay of all radioisotopes have been similarly accelerated by the same factor? And by what mechanism was the decay accelerated? These issues are too complex to be dealt with here, but are discussed by *Chaffin* [2000, 2005], *Humphreys* [2000, 2005], *Austin* [2005], and *Snelling* [2005a, b].

There is one final consideration. *Bielecki* [1994, 1998] had hoped that if accelerated nuclear decay had occurred during the Flood year and fission tracks are a physical measure of the amount of accelerated nuclear decay that has occurred in Flood rocks, then perhaps there should be a lack of spontaneous fission tracks in post-Flood rocks, because they would have been deposited after accelerated nuclear decay had presumably ceased only 4500 years ago. He therefore focused on Tertiary and Quaternary tuffs and volcanic glasses, as well as man-made and natural glasses of known historical age. This was because most geologists who are studying the rocks within the framework of a young earth and global catastrophic Flood would place the boundary between Flood and post-Flood rocks either at the beginning or near the end of the Tertiary. However, as in this present study of the Miocene Peach Springs Tuff, Bielecki found that the spontaneous fission track densities in the tuffs and natural glasses he studied from the Tertiary and Quaternary of western North America still indicated that millions of years of nuclear decay had occurred in them. He thus concluded that his attempt to distinguish between Flood and post-Flood rocks had failed.

If the Miocene Peach Springs Tuff, for example, were a post-Flood rock that should therefore only be thousands of years old, then in the zircons there should only be fission tracks representing just a few thousand years of nuclear decay. This is of course assuming accelerated nuclear decay was confined to the Flood event only. This present study has therefore cast no further light on this dilemma. However, it is unwarranted to conclude that, for example, the Miocene Peach Springs Tuff must therefore be a Flood rock, because *Bielecki* [1998] found that even Pleistocene natural glasses (contemporaneous with the post-Flood Ice Age) still contained an over-abundance of spontaneous fission tracks commensurate with their million year plus radioisotope age. Because there is much other geologic evidence that is relevant to placement of the Flood/post-Flood boundary with which this fission track evidence clearly appears to be in conflict, it can only be concluded that there is much more to learn yet with respect to fission tracks, nuclear decay, and radioisotopes in the rock strata through earth history. It may well be that at the end of the Flood there was a gradual deceleration of decay rates that continued on well into the post-Flood period, rather than an abrupt termination of accelerated decay. Thus it is premature to use the fission tracks as a criterion for deciding where to put the Flood/post-Flood boundary in the geologic record.

11. Conclusions

The observed fission track densities measured in zircons from samples of Cambrian, Jurassic, and Miocene tuffs in the Grand Canyon-Colorado Plateau region were found to exactly equate to the quantities of nuclear decay measured by radioisotope age determinations of these same rocks. Though thermal annealing has occurred in some zircon grains in the two Cambrian tuffs from the western Grand Canyon, the U-Pb radioisotope system has also been thermally reset, the resulting reset ages in both instances coinciding with the onset of the Laramide uplift of the Colorado Plateau. The fact that the thermal annealing of the fission tracks and the thermal resetting of the U-Pb radioisotope system in those zircons are exactly parallel is confirmation that the radioisotope ratios are a product of radioactive decay in just the same way as the fission tracks are physical evidence of nuclear decay. Furthermore, because the resetting of the U-Pb radioisotope system in zircons will only occur at elevated temperatures, the fact that it has been reset in these zircons could therefore be due to them having been heated by accelerated nuclear decay.

There has clearly been thermal annealing of the fission tracks and thermal resetting of the U-Pb radioisotope system in the zircons from the Cambrian tuff units in the western Grand Canyon. However, there remains sufficient strong evidence to conclude that both the fission tracks and radioisotope ratios in the zircons in these tuff units record more than 500 million years worth (at today's rates) of nuclear and radioisotope decay during deposition of the Phanerozoic strata sequence in the Grand Canyon-Colorado Plateau region. Given the evidence in that strata sequence of catastrophic deposition and independent evidence that most of this strata sequence was deposited during the year-long global catastrophic Biblical Flood only 4500 years ago, then 500 million or more years worth (at today's rates) of nuclear and radioisotope decay had to have occurred during the Flood year only 4500 or so years ago. Thus, this nuclear and radioisotope decay had to have occurred at accelerated rates, and the fission tracks in the zircons in the tuffs within that strata sequence are physical evidence of that accelerated nuclear decay.

12. Further Work

For completeness sake, it is recommended that further work be undertaken on the Cambrian Muav and Tapeats tuffs in the western Grand Canyon to further resolve the discrepancy between the zircon fission track dates obtained in this study and those obtained in the previously published study. There is a brief mention in *Elston* [1989] of other outcrops of the Muav tuff (in particular) in the western Grand Canyon and beyond in Nevada, so these should be located and sampled for zircon fission track dating, because of the possibility that those zircons may not all have had their fission tracks thermally annealed. Then second, zircon grains from the outcrops sampled in this study, as well as those from outcrops sampled in future work, should be submitted for SHRIMP (sensitive high resolution ion microprobe) U-Pb radioisotope analyses and age determinations. Given that the SHRIMP can obtain U-Pb radioisotope analyses of microscopic spots in the zircon grains, this is a far more effective way of controlling the results obtained, particularly if zircon grains have growth zones. Furthermore, many more zircon grains can be cost effectively analyzed using the SHRIMP, compared with the twelve grains analyzed by TIMS in this study, which was a statistically small sample set. As a side benefit to this further work, the extent of these tuff beds may thus be better delineated because they could represent a catastrophic event horizon of considerable areal extent.

The phenomenon of annealing is a separate process from radioisotope and nuclear decay that most likely is also time dependent. This could thus provide the basis for tests of the hypothesis that decay rates have changed in the past, or may help discriminate the limits of when decay rates were different. For example, tests of annealing of minerals in contact metamorphic zones versus the host rock and intrusive body could be constructive lines of research that may identify annealing independent of internal heating due to accelerated decay.

Otherwise, there is a lot still to learn about the history of nuclear and radioisotope decay during accumulation of the geologic record. In particular, the dilemma of whether fission tracks do or do not help to define the Flood/post-Flood boundary in the geologic record needs further investigation and resolution. For example, did accelerated decay terminate abruptly at the end of the Flood, or did gradual deceleration extend well into the post-Flood period? It is suggested that further work might focus on an extensive literature search to compile all fission track dating results obtained right through the Phanerozoic strata record, particularly where such dating results are cross-linked with radioisotope age determinations. It may be that some pattern emerges that enables the history of nuclear decay recorded in the strata to be deciphered and the Flood/post-Flood boundary placement in the geologic record be resolved. Also, evidence may emerge consistent with variations in decay rates during historic events.

Acknowledgments

While they would not agree with all interpretations and conclusions, the following people need to be acknowledged for the tremendous help they gave during the course of this study—Dr. Paul Green of the Geotrack International laboratory, Melbourne, for his skills in zircon fission track dating and for his patience and helpfulness through many discussions; Dr. Charles Naeser of the U.S. Geological Survey, Reston, Virginia, for his helpfulness in rechecking his past work and for his suggestions; Dr. Sam Iyengar of the Technology of Materials laboratory, Wildomar, California, for his analytical work and advice; Dr. Dennis Eberl and Dr. Richard Pollastro of the U.S. Geological Survey in Boulder and Denver, Colorado, respectively for helpful advice; Professor Warren Huff of the Geology Department at the University of Cincinnati for the information he so willingly provided; and Dr. Yakov Kapusta, the geochronology laboratory manager at Activation Laboratories, Ancaster, Ontario, for his helpful analytical work. The assistance given to me with fieldwork and sampling of the Morrison Formation tuffs and Peach Springs Tuff by William (Bill) Hoesch of the Geology Department at the Institute for Creation Research, and of the Muav and Tapeats tuffs in the western Grand Canyon by Tom Vail of Canyon Ministries, was greatly appreciated and is duly acknowledged. The advice and encouragement of the other members of the RATE group is also acknowledged. Finally, this study was only made possible by donations to the RATE project from many supporters, and they are thanked for those donations.

Appendix: Fission Tracks and Fission Track Dating

A1. Fission Track Formation

When charged particles travel through a solid medium, they leave a trail of damage resulting from the transfer of energy from the particles to the atoms of the medium. The spontaneous fission of ^{238}U releases about 200 MeV of energy, much of which is transferred to the two product nuclides as kinetic energy. They travel about 7 μm in opposite directions, leaving a single trail of damage through the medium which is about 15 μm long. Such fission fragment tracks were first observed by *Silk and Barnes* [1959] during examination of irradiated solids under very high magnification with an electron microscope.

Fleischer et al. [1964] discovered that fission tracks are only found in insulating materials. In what is known as the ion-explosion spike model of fission track formation, *Fleischer et al.* [1965a] proposed that the passage of the highly charged, massive fission fragments causes ionization of atoms by violently repelling electrons away from a cylindrical tube surrounding their path (Figure 24). The positively charged ions at the crystal lattice sites along this path then mutually repel each other so that they are forced into the surrounding lattice away from the path of the fission particle, creating a cylindrical zone of damaged, disordered structure. This, in turn, causes relaxation stress in the surrounding matrix, resulting in a 100 Å (10 nm)-wide zone of strain

A.A. Snelling

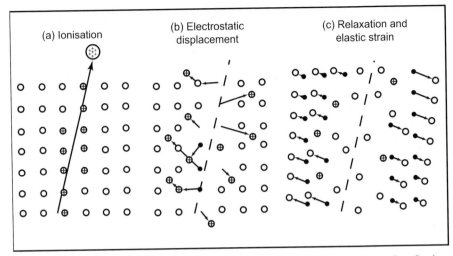

Figure 24. Schematic illustration of the process of formation of a fission track in a crystalline insulating solid (after *Fleischer et al.* [1975]).

which can actually be seen under an electron microscope. Conductors do not display fission tracks because the free movement of electrons in their lattice structures neutralizes the charged damage zones. However, if the solid in which the tracks form is an insulator at low temperatures, then the tracks may be preserved for times comparable to the claimed age of the universe.

The ability to generate fission tracks depends on the mass of the ionizing particle and the density of the material. In muscovite (white mica), the lowest mass particle which can generate tracks by irradiation is about 30 atomic mass units (amu). Fragments generated by fission of ^{238}U, with masses of about 90 and 135 amu respectively, are well above this threshold, so that they always generate tracks. On the other hand, α-particles, the major product of radioactive decay of ^{238}U, are so far below the critical mass that they cannot create tracks. Neither can they cause fission track erasure [*Fleischer et al*, 1965b].

Price and Walker [1962a] demonstrated that when irradiated materials were abraded to expose fission tracks at their surfaces, the damage zones could be preferentially dissolved by mineral acids, leading initially to very fine channels only 25 Å wide. However, these could be enlarged by further chemical etching to yield wide pits which are observable under an optical microscope. *Price and Walker* [1962b] were the first to discover "fossil" fission tracks in minerals, generated by the spontaneous fission of the dispersed ^{238}U atoms in them. Indeed, they verified that fission tracks in natural minerals are due primarily to spontaneous fission of ^{238}U [*Price and Walker*, 1963] and proposed that the density of such fission tracks could be used as a dating tool for geological materials (such as micas) up to a billion years old in which they found track densities of up to 5×10^4 per cm^2. They found that induced fission of ^{238}U by natural thermal neutrons can be ignored, as can cosmic ray-induced fission of U and cosmic ray-induced spallation tracks. Consequently, *Fleischer et al.* [1965a] verified that the density of fission tracks in various geological materials and minerals could be used to obtain dates. They found that fission track dating of artificial and natural glasses and minerals produces results in agreement with those from radioisotope dating methods (Figure 25).

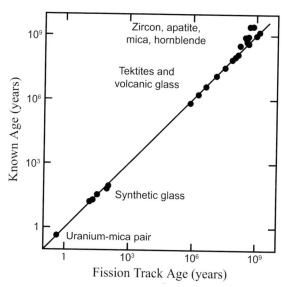

Figure 25. A comparison of specimen ages determined by fission track analysis with those from historical or other radiometric sources (after *Fleischer et al.* [1965a]).

A2. The Methodology of Fission Track Dating

The fission track method is now widely used for dating a wide variety of minerals, and therefore, the rocks containing them. It is regarded as being especially applicable to relatively young samples that have not been reheated since the time of their formation [*Fleischer and Price*, 1964b]. However, the method is also regarded as providing useful information about the thermal histories of older rocks, because the preservation of fission tracks is subject to annealing, with different minerals losing their tracks at different temperatures [*Fleischer et al*, 1969].

In order to date a mineral specimen by the fission track method, an interior surface is exposed by grinding and is then polished and etched with a suitable solvent under appropriate conditions [*Naeser*, 1967]. After etching the polished surface is examined with a petrographic microscope (magnification of 800 to 1800×) equipped with a flat-field eyepiece with a graticule to permit the counting of tracks in a known area. Fission tracks are readily distinguished by their characteristic tubular shape from other etched pits that result from imperfections or other causes. The track density due to spontaneous fission of ^{238}U is determined by counting a statistically significant number of tracks in a known area. Counting becomes difficult when the track density is less than 10 tracks per cm^2, but many minerals and glasses have much higher track densities so that from several hundred to several thousand tracks can be counted. The observed track density is related to the length of time during which tracks have accumulated and to the U concentration in the mineral or glass. *Fleischer and Price* [1964b] have estimated the dating range of fission track analyses with different types of minerals or glasses. Using the criterion that dates of reasonable precision can only be determined when the track density is at least 100 per cm^2, the lower end of the dating range can be estimated for the different minerals and glasses according to their U content (Figure 26) [*Wagner*, 1978].

The U concentration can be measured by a procedure that involves counting fission tracks produced by induced fission of ^{235}U due to irradiation of the sample with thermal neutrons in a nuclear reactor.

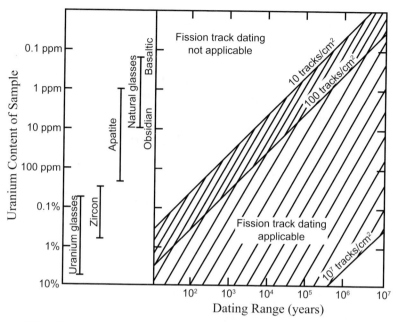

Figure 26. Diagram to show the dating range for fission track analysis of different kinds of geological material according to U content (after *Wagner* [1978]).

This can be accomplished in several ways described by *Gleadow* [1981] and *Hurford and Green* [1982]. The ideal is for the induced track count to be performed on the identical material to the spontaneous track count. Several different experimental methods are available which attempt to reach this ideal.

The method adopted by the earliest workers, such as *Price and Walker* [1963], was the population method, an expression coined by *Naeser* [1979]. This designation refers to the fact that the spontaneous and induced tracks are counted in different splits or sub-populations of the material being dated, which are nevertheless assumed to sample the same population. The success of the method depends on the material having a homogeneous distribution of U between the two splits. The method has proved particularly successful for dating glass and apatite, but unsuccessful for sphene and zircon, where U distribution is very

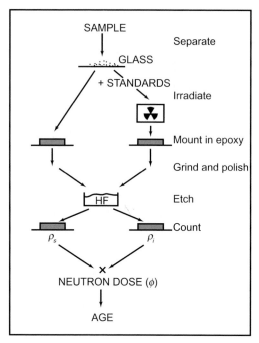

Figure 27. Schematic illustration of the population method of fission track analysis (after *Naeser and Naeser* [1984]).

variable both within and between grains. The sample is separated into two splits, one being irradiated with thermal neutrons along with the standard (flux monitor) (Figure 27). After irradiation of the induced track split, both splits are mounted in epoxy, ground, polished, and etched under identical conditions. This reveals an internal surface of the material and also removes any extraneous superficial tracks generated by U-bearing dust particles. Track densities are counted in both splits. The induced track density is calculated by subtracting the spontaneous track density (un-irradiated sample) from the total track density (irradiated sample). The population method can be statistically tested by counting track densities in numerous grains in each split.

An alternative procedure is after polishing, etching, and counting of the spontaneous tracks, they are destroyed by heating the specimen to cause annealing. The specimen in then exposed to thermal neutrons in a nuclear reactor in order to produce new tracks by induced fission of ^{235}U. After the irradiation, a new surface is polished and etched, and the density of the induced tracks is determined. The U concentration of the sample is indicated by the observed density of the induced fission tracks, provided the effective thermal neutron flux and the duration of the irradiation are known. A variation of this method involves irradiating the sample after polishing, etching, and counting of the spontaneous tracks. However, the sample itself is then re-etched and re-counted to determine the induced track density by subtraction. Some disadvantages of this re-etching method are that the induced tracks are formed with only 50% efficiency due to the 2π geometry (Figure 28), and the spontaneous track pits may be unduly enlarged after the second etch so as to obscure some of the induced tracks.

The re-polishing method [*Naeser et al.*, 1989b] is an improvement on the re-etching method. The sample is polished, etched, and counted for spontaneous track density. After irradiation it is re-polished to depths of at least 20 μm to reveal a new internal face with what is known as 4π track geometry yielding 100% efficiency (Figure 28). This new polished surface is then etched and counted to determine the induced track density by subtraction. This method has the advantage that both spontaneous and induced tracks are recorded under identical geometry, and spontaneous tracks are not over-enlarged by double etching. Also, surface contamination during irradiation is not a problem. The spontaneous and induced tracks are not generated by exactly the same sample material, but the two etched surfaces are so close together U inhomogeneity in the grain as a whole is unlikely to significantly bias the data. A disadvantage compared with the normal population method is that the two etching steps are performed separately, and may therefore vary slightly in efficiency.

The most popular method in use is the external detector method [*Fleischer et al.*, 1965a] in which the U content of the material to be dated is determined by registration of the induced fission tracks in an external detector held against the same surface in which the spontaneous tracks are to be counted, rather than in the sample material itself. The sample is ground, polished, etched, and counted, after which a sheet

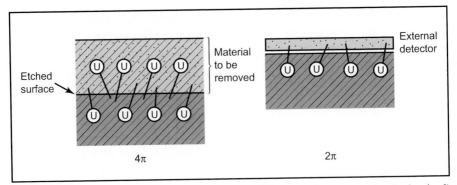

Figure 28. Schematic illustration of the difference between 4π (spherical) and 2π (hemi-spherical) geometry in track formation (after *Dickin* [1995]).

of detector material, often a sheet of low-U muscovite (white mica) or a plastic material like lexan, is placed in intimate contact with the etched surface. This must be done with absolute cleanliness to exclude U-bearing dust grains. After the neutron irradiation, the external detector is removed from the sample, etched, and the tracks caused by induced fission of ^{235}U in the specimen are counted (Figure 29). The advantage of this method is that both spontaneous and induced tracks are generated by the same sample material. It also eliminates problems caused by irregular distribution of U, and hence it is suited to the analysis of material with a very heterogeneous distribution of U, such as grains of zircon and sphene. On the other hand, the main disadvantage of this method is that the spontaneous and induced tracks are recorded under different spatial geometry conditions (see Figure 28 again). The spontaneous tracks are generated in the interior of the rock, and can therefore be formed by U atoms both above and below the polished and etched surface (spherical or 4π geometry). In contrast, the tracks induced in the external detector originate only from the U atoms in the surface of the analyzed material and are therefore generated with approximately one-half the frequency (hemi-spherical or 2π geometry). Therefore, a correction factor must be used to either reduce the observed density of spontaneous tracks by one-half, or increase the U concentration by a factor of 2. However, *Reimer et al.* [1970] question whether the efficiency of induced track formation is exactly 50%, or whether small biases are introduced by the use of external detectors. Nevertheless, the use of external detectors was supported by *Gleadow and Lovering* [1977] and *Green and Durrani* [1978], and subsequent experiments showed that in most cases the ideal efficiency of 50% is achieved [*Hurford and Green*, 1982]. Thus external detectors are now widely used to measure the U concentrations of minerals dated by the fission track method.

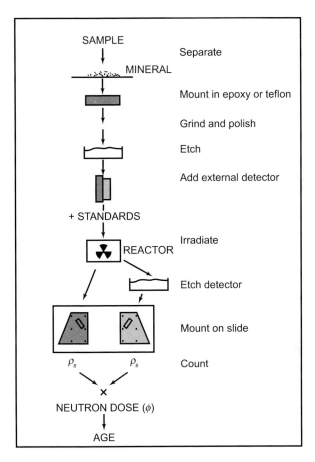

Figure 29. Schematic illustration of the external detector method of fission track analysis, as described by *Naeser* [1979]. In this version the counting of spontaneous tracks is performed after irradiation, unlike the sequence described in the text (after *Naeser and Naeser* [1984]).

The observed density of the fission tracks induced by the irradiation procedure is indicative of the U concentration of the specimen, provided the effective thermal neutron flux and the duration of the irradiation are known. The neutron "dose" (flux density × irradiation time) is determined by means of various flux monitors. One method is to include pieces of foil of Au, Cu, or Co of known weight with the mineral specimens being irradiated with thermal neutrons. After the irradiation, the induced γ-ray activity of these flux monitors can be used to determine the neutron dose, provided the neutron capture cross-section and the efficiency of the counting system are known. Alternately, one can irradiate glass of known U concentration (NBS series SRM 610 to 617 or Corning glasses U1 to U7 described by *Schreurs et al.* [1971]) and count the tracks resulting from induced fission of ^{235}U in an external detector. However, the relationship between the neutron dose and the resulting track density in U-bearing glass recorded in an external detector must be established by independent calibrations. *Hurford and Green* [1982] reported considerable scatter in that relationship over a six-year period and concluded that measurements of a neutron dose are very difficult and may be uncertain by up to ±10% of their absolute value.

The principle cause of systematic errors in fission track dates of natural samples is the fading of tracks due to annealing of the sample at elevated temperatures. For this reason, it is usually insisted that fission track dates of natural samples must be interpreted as "cooling ages" and do not necessarily coincide with the times at which the minerals crystallized in an igneous or metamorphic rock.

Another source of uncertainty inherent in fission track dating is the effectiveness of the etching process. The precise process of etching depends on the composition of the matrix and the nature, concentration, and temperature of the acid or alkali leaching solutions. This can give rise to a very large variation in the appearance of etched tracks in different materials and may thus affect the accuracy of track counting. These problems have been discussed by *Fleischer and Price* [1964a]. The three-dimensional profile or outline of an etched track depends on the rate of etching down the axis of the track (from its intersection with the surface), relative to the general rate of attack of the polished surface. One problem in accurate track counting is to distinguish etched tracks from other features. Another source of uncertainty is caused by tracks which barely register in the etched surface. For example, tracks which are almost tangential to the surface may be completely erased by etching. Other tracks may not have intersected the original polished surface, but are exposed by the general attack of the surface during etching. These discrepancies will average out statistically if large numbers of tracks are counted with identical spatial geometry, but may cause large errors when spatial geometry varies. A more detailed discussion of track formation and track etching is given by *Fleischer et al.* [1975].

Other sources of error in fission track dating are statistical errors in counting tracks, and the possible uneven distribution of U in the specimen.

In conclusion, the prerequisite conditions for dating minerals by the fission track method are:-

- the concentration of U must be sufficient to produce a track density of >10 tracks per cm^2 in the time elapsed since cooling of the sample;
- the tracks must be stable at ordinary temperatures for time intervals comparable to the age being measured;
- the material must be sufficiently free of inclusions, defects, and lattice dislocations to permit identification and counting of etched fission tracks; and
- depending on the counting method used, the U distribution in the specimen must be uniform to permit the concentration of ^{238}U to be determined from the density of induced fission tracks in a different portion of the sample.

Because it is well known that chemical weathering adversely affects dates determined by radioisotope methods, *Gleadow and Lovering* [1974] made a study of the effect of weathering on the retention of fission tracks in apatite, sphene and zircon. They concluded that chemical weathering has no affect on fission track dates of sphene and zircon, but did result in a modest reduction of the date of apatite. The latter was attributed to the difficulty in identifying tracks in badly corroded crystals and to partial fading of tracks caused by the action of groundwater. However, the apparent loss of tracks was partly offset by a lowering of the U concentration.

A3. Derivation of the Fission Track "Age" Equation

Several naturally occurring isotopes of high atomic number are known to decay by spontaneous fission and therefore produce fission tracks in minerals and glass. However, *Price and Walker* [1963] showed that in most cases such tracks are due primarily to spontaneous fission of ^{238}U. Track densities caused by spontaneous fission of ^{235}U and ^{232}Th are negligible. They also concluded that induced fission of ^{235}U due to absorption of natural thermal neutrons produced by spontaneous fission of ^{238}U is not important and can be ignored (because U concentrations in almost all rocks and minerals are too low for this process to occur), as can cosmic ray-induced fission of U and cosmic ray-induced spallation tracks. For these reasons, fission tracks in natural materials can be attributed to spontaneous fission of ^{238}U alone.

The decay constant for spontaneous fission of ^{238}U (λ_f) is approximately 7×10^{-17} yr^{-1}, which equates to a half-life ($t_{1/2}$) of 9.9×10^{15} yr [*Naeser et al.*, 1989b]. There is some disagreement as to its exact value, but this uncertainty is not relevant to geological age determinations. Because the fission decay constant of ^{238}U is over a million times lower than the α-decay constant of ^{238}U, the decay of ^{238}U can be attributed entirely to α-emission, so its fission decay can be ignored in determining the isotope abundance of U through time.

Therefore, in a mineral grain containing ^{238}U atoms distributed evenly throughout its volume, the total number of decays of ^{238}U in a given volume of sample during time t is:

$$D = {}^{238}U(e^{\lambda_\alpha t} - 1) \tag{8}$$

where D is the number of decay events per cm^3 of the sample, ^{238}U is the number of ^{238}U atoms per cm^3 of the sample at the present time, and λ_α is the decay constant of ^{238}U for α-emission, which is 1.55125×10^{-10} yr^{-1}.

The fraction of ^{238}U decays that are due to spontaneous fission and leave a track is thus:

$$F_s = \left(\frac{\lambda_f}{\lambda_a}\right)^{238}U(e^{\lambda_a t} - 1) \tag{9}$$

Only a certain fraction q of these tracks will cross the polished surface of the mineral grain and will be visible after etching to be counted. The area density of spontaneous fission tracks in that surface is therefore given by:

$$\rho_s = F_s q = \left(\frac{\lambda_f}{\lambda_\alpha}\right)^{238}U\left(e^{\lambda_a t} - 1\right)q \tag{10}$$

The number of fissions of ^{235}U induced by the thermal neutron irradiation per cm^3 of sample is:

$$F_i = {}^{235}U\varphi\sigma \tag{11}$$

where ^{235}U is the number of ^{235}U atoms per cm^3 of sample at the present time, φ is the thermal neutron dose in units of neutrons per cm^2, and σ is the cross-section for induced fission of ^{235}U by thermal neutrons, which is equal to 580.2×10^{-24} cm^2.

The fraction of induced tracks that cross an interior surface and that will be counted after etching is also equal to q, provided the U atoms are evenly distributed throughout the volume of the specimen, and provided the etching is performed exactly as before. Thus the density of induced tracks is equal to:

$$\rho_i = F_i q = {}^{235}U\varphi\sigma q \tag{12}$$

Combining equations (10) and (12) yields:

$$\frac{\rho_s}{\rho_i} = \left(\frac{\lambda_f}{\lambda_\alpha}\right)\left(\frac{e^{\lambda_a t} - 1}{\varphi\sigma I}\right) \tag{13}$$

where I is the atomic ratio of ^{235}U/^{238}U. Equation (13) can now be solved for t and thus yield the "age" equation, first formulated by *Price and Walker* [1963]:

$$t = \frac{1}{\lambda_\alpha} \ln\left[1 + \left(\frac{\rho_s}{\rho_i} \right)\left(\frac{\lambda_\alpha}{\lambda_f} \right)\varphi\sigma I \right] \qquad (14)$$

It is important to equalize the densities of the spontaneous and induced tracks in order to reduce the error of measurement of ρ_s/ρ_i.

A4. The Zeta Calibration

Fission track dates determined by the methods outlined above are subject to systematic errors arising from the uncertainty of the decay constant for spontaneous fission of ^{238}U (λ_f) [*Bigazzi*, 1981], and from difficulties with measurements of the neutron dose (φ). Of course, it is possible to determine φ and σ directly by using flux monitors, such as iron wire or copper foil, but these types of flux monitors may not respond to reactor conditions in exactly the same way as geological materials. Therefore, an alternative procedure is to do a fission track analysis of a standard material with known U concentration. *Fleischer et al.* [1965a] used fragments of glass microscope slides to calibrate a reactor in this way, but this does not avoid the uncertainty of the ^{238}U fission decay constant. Furthermore, the problem is compounded by the fact that experimental determinations of λ_f by counting fission tracks in U-bearing glasses of known age of manufacture require knowledge of the neutron dose used to determine the U contents of the glasses. Therefore, any method used affects the value of λ_f that is obtained.

Thus, to eliminate both the flux term and the decay constant term, many workers started to use minerals dated by K-Ar as internal standards for the irradiation. *Fleischer and Hart* [1972] formalized this system into the "zeta calibration." Likewise, *Hurford and Green* [1982] proposed to calibrate the fission track method of dating against minerals of known age that had been dated by other radioisotope methods. Accordingly, the parameters in equation (13) whose magnitudes are in doubt are combined into one calibration factor termed "zeta" and symbolized by

ζ:

$$\zeta = \frac{\varphi \sigma I}{\lambda_f} \tag{15}$$

The age equation for a sample of unknown age (t_{unk}) now becomes:

$$t_{unk} = \frac{1}{\lambda_\alpha} \ln\left[1 + \left(\frac{\rho_s}{\rho_i}\right)_{unk} \zeta\lambda_\alpha\right] \tag{16}$$

The value of ζ is determined by irradiating a mineral standard of known age (determined by radioisotope dating) with each batch of unknowns. Consequently, ζ is calculated from the measured ratio of the spontaneous and induced track densities of the standard. From equation (13):

$$\zeta = \frac{\left(e^{\lambda_\alpha t_{std}} - 1\right)}{\lambda_\alpha (\rho_s / \rho_i)_{std}} \tag{17}$$

The value of ζ is then used to calculate dates for the unknown samples that were irradiated with the standard. The resulting fission track dates depend on the assumptions that:

• the age of the standard is known accurately;
• the fission track densities of the standard and unknowns were determined by the same procedure; and
• that the unknowns and the standard were irradiated together.

When the age of the standard is significantly less than the half-life of ^{238}U, equation (17) can be simplified by letting $e^{\lambda_\alpha t_{std}} - 1 = \lambda_\alpha t_{std}$. In this case:

$$\zeta = \frac{t_{std}}{(\rho_s / \rho_i)_{std}} \tag{18}$$

The fission track date of unknowns then becomes:

$$t_{unk} = \frac{1}{\lambda_\alpha} \ln\left[1 + \frac{(\rho_s / \rho_i)_{unk}}{(\rho_s / \rho_i)_{std}} \lambda_\alpha t_{std}\right] \tag{19}$$

The failure to resolve the fission decay constant problem can perhaps be attributed to the use of this calibration method, which transfers the uncertainty into the age determination of the geological reference material. Use of such material was recommended for all fission track dating studies by a working group of the International Union of Geological Sciences (I.U.G.S.) Subcommission on Geochronology [*Hurford*, 1990]. Minerals to be used as calibration standards for fission track dating must have cooled rapidly and must yield concordant dates by different appropriate radioisotope methods. Moreover, they must be readily obtainable in pure form and adequate quantity. These criteria are best met by volcanic rocks that cooled rapidly and remained unaltered after crystallization. *Hurford and Green* [1983] selected zircons from three volcanic deposits and from kimberlite pipes in South Africa as standards, the most well-known of these being the zircon from the Fish Canyon Tuff in the San Juan Mountains of Colorado, U.S.A., described by *Naeser et al.* [1981] with an age of 27.9±0.7 Ma.

An alternative to the procedure outlined above is to use the standard minerals to calibrate U-bearing dosimeter glasses. The neutron dose (φ) is related to the density of induced fission tracks in the dosimeter glass (ρ_d) by the relationship:

$$\varphi = B\rho_d \qquad (20)$$

where B is a calibration constant and ρ_d is measured by an external mica track-detector. Substituting equation (20) into equation (14) yields:

$$t_{unk} = \frac{1}{\lambda_\alpha} \ln\left[1 + \left(\frac{\rho_s}{\rho_i}\right)_{unk} \left(\frac{\lambda_\alpha}{\lambda_f}\right) B\rho_d \sigma I \right] \qquad (21)$$

Next, ζ is redefined as:

$$\zeta = \frac{B\sigma I}{\lambda_f} \qquad (22)$$

Thus, the "age" equation now becomes:

$$t_{unk} = \frac{1}{\lambda_\alpha} \ln\left[1 + \left(\frac{\rho_s}{\rho_i}\right)_{unk} \lambda_\alpha \rho_\alpha \zeta \right] \qquad (23)$$

The new ζ is determined by irradiating dosimeter glasses with mineral standards of known age. After irradiation, the induced track density in the dosimeter (ρ_d) and in the standard mineral (ρ_i) are determined by counting tracks in the external detectors used with both. The value of ζ for a given glass dosimeter is then calculated by means of equation (13), in which φ is replaced by $B\rho_d$ as per equation (20) to yield:

$$\left(\frac{\rho_s}{\rho_i}\right)_{std} = \left(\frac{\lambda_t}{\lambda_\alpha}\right)\frac{\left(e^{\lambda_\alpha t_{std}} - 1\right)}{B\rho_d\sigma I} \tag{24}$$

Next, ζ as defined by equation (22) is inserted to yield:

$$\left(\frac{\rho_s}{\rho_i}\right)_{std} = \left(\frac{e^{\lambda_\alpha t_{std}} - 1}{\lambda_\alpha \zeta \rho_d}\right) \tag{25}$$

from which it follows that:

$$\zeta = \frac{\left(e^{\lambda_\alpha t_{std}} - 1\right)}{\lambda_\alpha \left(\rho_s / \rho_i\right)_{std} \rho_d} \tag{26}$$

Therefore, the modified ζ parameter for a glass dosimeter can be used to determine the age of an unknown mineral from equation (23), provided the dosimeter is irradiated with the unknown mineral and ρ_d is determined by counting the resultant tracks in an external detector. In essence, the ζ parameter enables the neutron dose to be determined directly from the density of induced tracks in the dosimeter glass. *Hurford and Green* [1983] determined values of ζ for three glass dosimeters which they irradiated numerous times with each of the zircon standards they had selected. Of course, equation (26) depends on the age of the standard (t_{std}) having been accurately determined by the radioisotope "dating" methods. However, because there is evidence that radioisotope decay was accelerated at some time or times in the past [*Humphreys et al.*, 2003a, b, 2004; *Snelling et al.*, 2003a; *Austin*, 2005; *Humphreys*, 2005; *Snelling*, 2005a, b], such past accelerated radioisotope decay would render the radioisotope "dating" of the standard suspect, which in turn makes the value of ζ suspect. Thus at best fission track dating, like radioisotope dating, would only yield relative "ages." Nevertheless, the quantity of fission tracks is physical evidence of how much nuclear decay has occurred in the past during accumulation of the geologic record.

A5. Annealing and the Closing Temperature

In most materials, fission tracks are stable for long periods of time at room temperature. However, at elevated temperatures the tracks fade as the damage done by the charged particles is healed. During this process the displaced ions within the damaged track lose their charge and return to their normal lattice positions, after which the track is no longer susceptible to preferential acid attack. The rate at which tracks fade (or are annealed) at a given temperature varies among different minerals and glasses. Consequently, two different minerals in the same rock that have been exposed to the same elevated temperature for the same length of time may have differing fission track dates. Such discordance of dates of cogenetic minerals may thus provide information about the temperature history of the rock.

In experiments on track annealing in mica, *Fleischer et al.* [1964] claimed that track annealing progressed by the accumulated "healing up" of short segments at random points along the length of tracks. However, subsequent work on other materials (for example, on glass by *Storzer and Wagner* [1969]) has shown that the healing process occurs principally at the ends of each track, causing irregular and progressive shortening. As the length of the tracks is diminished by healing they have a smaller probability of intersecting the free surface during the etching treatment. Hence, fewer tracks become etched and the apparent track density decreases. This correlation between track length and track density is termed the "random line segment model" [*Fleischer et al.*, 1975].

Early studies showed that different materials have different degrees of resistance to fission track annealing [*Fleischer and Price*, 1964b]. In addition, however, a temperature-time relationship is found for the annealing process. The higher the temperature, the shorter the time required for complete annealing of tracks in any given material. To examine this behavior, *Fleischer and Price* [1964a] performed laboratory annealing experiments in which the reduction in track density in a chosen mineral was measured as a function of increasing temperature and duration of heating. It was found that annealing obeyed a Boltzmann's law relationship:

$$t = Ae^{E/kT} \qquad (27)$$

where t is the annealing time for a specific reduction in track density, A is a constant, E is the activation energy in units of kcal/mol or electron volts (eV), k is Boltzmann's constant, which equals 8.6171×10^{-5} eV/K, and T is the absolute temperature in K. Much work has subsequently been devoted to determining accurate Boltzmann relationship annealing curves for different minerals and materials, both by laboratory and apparently well-constrained geological studies.

By taking natural logarithms of both sides a linear equation is obtained:

$$\ln t = \ln A + \frac{E}{kT} \qquad (28)$$

This is the equation of a straight line in co-ordinates of $\ln t$ and $1/T$ having a positive slope equal to E/k and an intercept on the y-axis equal to $\ln A$. The linear relationship between $\ln t$ and $1/T$ permits the extrapolation of laboratory measurements obtained at elevated temperatures and short time periods to lower temperatures and the claimed geological time periods.

Detailed laboratory experiments were performed on apatite and sphene by *Naeser and Faul* [1969]. These showed that annealing is a progressive process, with different degrees of track annealing in these two minerals each defining their own Boltzmann's relationship lines when the experimental results were plotted on what is known as an Arrhenius diagram of time against reciprocal temperature (Figure 30). The fan of annealing lines in Figure 30 is evidence for the existence of a range of activation energies for track annealing within each mineral. This implies that as annealing progresses (as measured by the fraction of tracks lost) it also becomes progressively more difficult [*Storzer and Wagner*, 1969]. Hence, when comparing the annealing properties of different minerals it is necessary to compare equal fractions of track loss, such as 50%.

Thus the data of *Naeser and Faul* [1969], shown in Figure 30, indicate that the tracks in apatite and sphene, which are common accessories in igneous and metamorphic rocks, fade at very different rates. This diagram can then be ostensibly used to predict track fading in these minerals in response to an increase in temperature for a given rate of heating. For a heating period of one million years, apatite would

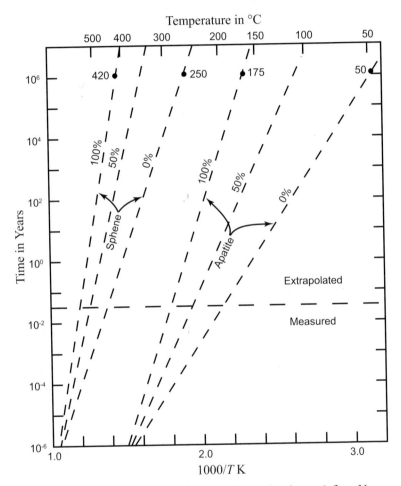

Figure 30. Fading of fission tracks in apatite and sphene (after *Naeser and Faul* [1969]). The lines marked 0% indicate temperatures and time periods at which no tracks are lost. The lines labeled 100% indicate conditions when all tracks are lost. The effective temperature recorded by the fission track age of a mineral is the value at which about 50% of the tracks are preserved. *T* is temperature in Kelvin (K).

appear to begin losing tracks at about 50°C and would be completely annealed at about 175°C, while tracks in sphene would not fade unless the temperature is raised to 250°C and the mineral would be annealed completely only at 420°C. Therefore, fission track dates of apatite can be completely reset by episodic heating under conditions implied by its track-fading curve for 100% track loss. Under the same conditions, sphene loses no tracks at all, and its fission track date remains unaffected. Therefore, when fission track dates of these two minerals extracted from the same rock are concordant, the rock presumably cooled rapidly and was not reheated at a later time. On the other hand, when the dates are discordant, that is, the sphene date is greater than the apatite date, the rock presumably either cooled slowly or was reheated to a temperature at which track fading occurred in apatite but not in sphene.

Apatite is regarded as a particularly good indicator of the cooling history of a rock, because apparently it retains fission tracks only at temperatures that are significantly less than the so-called "blocking temperatures" for the Rb-Sr or K-Ar radioisotope geochronometers in coexisting micas. The exact temperature at which apatite retains all tracks (0% loss curve in Figure 30) depends on the cooling rate. When the rate of cooling is high, the cooling time is short, and complete track retention occurs at a higher temperature than when the cooling rate is slow. At any given cooling rate, track retention increases from 0 to 100% as the temperature drops so that the observed track density represents approximately the time elapsed since the temperature passed through the value at which 50% of the tracks are retained. Consequently, fission track dates can be interpreted as the time elapsed since they cooled through their 50% retention temperatures. This temperature is also known as the "closing temperature" by analogy with the "blocking temperature" defined with respect to retention of radiogenic ^{40}Ar and ^{87}Sr.

The closing temperatures of different minerals at different cooling rates are shown in Figure 31, based primarily on a review of the literature by *Sharma et al.* [1980]. The diagram demonstrates that minerals have widely differing closing temperatures and that these temperatures increase with faster cooling rates. The closing temperatures, at a cooling

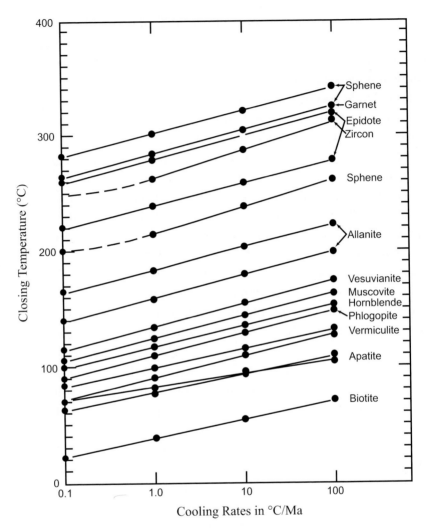

Figure 31. Closing temperatures for retention of fission tracks for minerals cooling at different rates. The closing temperature is defined as the temperature below which all fission tracks are retained in the mineral corresponding to the 50% track retention temperature. The closing temperature of chlorite is similar to that of apatite. (After *Haack* [1977]; *Sharma et al.* [1980]; *Bal et al.* [1983]; *Faure* [1986]; *Faure and Mensing* [2005].)

rate of 1°C/Ma, range from about 300°C for sphene to about 40°C for biotite. Therefore, the minerals of plutonic igneous or high-grade metamorphic rocks, that are claimed to have cooled slowly, potentially record a sequence of dates at which the temperature passed through their respective closing temperatures. Differences between fission track dates of two coexisting minerals, such as sphene and apatite, therefore would seem to indicate how long it took for the temperature to decrease from the closing temperature of sphene to that of apatite. For this reason, the fission track dates of different minerals and their closing temperatures have been used to reconstruct the apparent cooling histories of igneous and metamorphic rocks.

The closing temperatures of some minerals in Figure 31 are highly discrepant. For example, the closing temperature of sphene at a cooling rate of 1°C/Ma is 302°C according to *Nagpaul et al.* [1974], 284°C according to *Naeser and Dodge* [1969], and only 215°C according to *Bal et al.* [1983]. Similarly, discrepant closing temperatures have been reported for epidote, allanite, and vermiculite, according to the tabulation of *Sharma et al.* [1980]. These differences are caused primarily by the different etching conditions that were used to reveal the tracks during the annealing experiments from which the closing temperatures were determined. The different etchants used were not equally effective in retrieving fission tracks that had begun to fade as a result of annealing. Therefore, the experimentally determined closing temperatures depend on the etching solution used, its temperature, and the duration of the exposure. In addition, variations in the chemical compositions of the minerals being etched may affect their responses to a particular etchant. For these reasons, fission track dates of minerals should be determined by the same etching procedure as that used to determine their closing temperatures in order to avoid errors in cooling rates claimed to be derived from such data.

Fortunately, the differences in the closing temperatures of minerals do not depend on the cooling rates, as shown by the fact that the lines in Figure 31 are approximately parallel. After the presumed cooling rate has been determined as described above, the actual temperatures corresponding to the fission track dates of the minerals can apparently be determined from the relationship between cooling rates and closing temperatures [*Haack*, 1977; *Faure*, 1986; *Faure and Mensing*, 2005]. Nevertheless, it has been found that the fading of fission tracks causes fission track dates of minerals and natural glasses to be lower than their geologic ages. In some cases, it is believed that the discrepancy can be reduced by employing longer etching times or by using etchants that are more effective in retrieving partially annealed tracks. To some extent, the effect of track fading is taken into consideration when fission track dates are interpreted as the time elapsed since the temperature dropped below the 50% track retention value. However, it needs to be noted that fission tracks are still sometimes used to determine the "ages" of rocks and minerals that may not be datable by other radioisotope methods. For this reason, several procedures have been developed to ostensibly correct fission track dates for the effects of track fading, such as "plateau dating" [*Storzer and Poupeau*, 1973; *Poupeau et al.*, 1978, 1979; *Poupeau*, 1981; *Storzer and Wagner*, 1982].

References

Anderson, O.J., and S.G. Lucas, Synopsis of the Morrison Formation, in *Guidebook for the Geological Excursion of the Continental Jurassic Symposium*, edited by M. Morales, pp. 79–86, Museum of Northern Arizona, Flagstaff, 1996.

Austin, S.A. (editor), *Grand Canyon: Monument to Catastrophe*, Institute for Creation Research, Santee, California, 1994.

Austin, S.A., Do radioisotope clocks need repair? Testing the assumptions of isochron dating using K-Ar, Rb-Sr, Sm-Nd, and Pb-Pb isotopes, in *Radioisotopes and the Age of the Earth: Results of a Young-Earth Creationist Research Initiative*, edited by L. Vardiman, A.A. Snelling, and E.F. Chaffin, pp. 325–392, Institute for Creation Research, El Cajon, California, and Creation Research Society, Chino Valley, Arizona, 2005.

Austin, S.A., J.R. Baumgardner, D.R. Humphreys, A.A. Snelling, L.Vardiman, and K.P. Wise, Catastrophic plate tectonics: a global Flood model of earth history, in *Proceedings of the Third International Conference on Creationism*, edited by R.E. Walsh, pp. 609–621, Creation

Science Fellowship, Pittsburgh, Pennsylvania, 1994.

Baadsgaard, H., U-Th-Pb dates on zircons from the early Precambrian Amîtsoq Gneisses, Godthaab District, West Greenland, *Earth and Planetary Science Letters, 19*, 22–28, 1973.

Bal, K.D., N. Lal, and K.K. Nagpaul, Zircon and sphene as fission-track geochronometer and geothermometer: a reappraisal, *Contributions to Mineralogy and Petrology, 83*, 199–203, 1983.

Barrenechea, J.F., M. Rodas, and J.R. Mas, Clay mineral variations associated with diagenesis and low-grade metamorphism of early Cretaceous sediments in the Cameros Basin, Spain, *Clay Minerals, 30*, 119–133, 1995.

Baumgardner, J.R., ^{14}C evidence for a recent global Flood and a young earth, in *Radioisotopes and the Age of the Earth: Results of a Young-Earth Creationist Research Initiative*, edited by L. Vardiman, A.A. Snelling, and E.F. Chaffin, pp. 587–630, Institute for Creation Research, El Cajon, California, and Creation Research Society, Chino Valley, Arizona, 2005.

Baumgardner, J.R., A.A. Snelling, D.R. Humphreys, and S.A. Austin, Measurable ^{14}C in fossilized organic materials: confirming the young earth Creation-Flood model, in *Proceedings of the Fifth International Conference on Creationism*, edited by R.L. Ivey, Jr., pp. 127–142, Creation Science Fellowship, Pittsburgh, Pennsylvania, 2003a.

Baumgardner, J.R., A.A. Snelling, D.R. Humphreys, and S.A. Austin, The enigma of the ubiquity of ^{14}C in organic samples older than 100 ka, *EOS, Transactions of the American Geophysical Union, 84*(46), Fall Meeting Supplement, Abstract V32C-1045, 2003b.

Bielecki, J.W., *A Study in Spontaneous Fission Track Density in Resting Spring Range Obsidian (Miocene) near Shoshone, California*, Unpublished M.S. dissertation, Graduate School, Institute for Creation Research, Santee, California, 1994.

Bielecki, J.W., Search for accelerated nuclear decay with spontaneous fission of [238]U, in *Proceedings of the Fourth International Conference on Creationism*, edited by R.E. Walsh, pp. 79–88, Creation Science Fellowship, Pittsburgh, Pennsylvania, 1998.

Bigazzi, G., The problem of the decay constant λ_f of [238]U, *Nuclear Tracks, 5*, 35–44, 1981.

Bilbey, S.A., R.L. Kerns, Jr., and J.T. Bowman, Petrology of the Morrison

Formation, Dinosaur Quarry Quadrangle, Utah, *Utah Geological and Mineral Survey Special Studies 48*, 1974.

Billingsley, G. H., and D. P. Elston, Geologic log of the Colorado River from Lees Ferry to Temple Bar, Lake Mead, Arizona, in *Geology of Grand Canyon, Northern Arizona (with Colorado River Guides)*, edited by D. P. Elston, G. H. Billingsley, and R. A. Young, pp. 1–36, American Geophysical Union, Washington, DC, 1989.

Blenkinsop, T. G., Definition of low-grade metamorphic zones using illite crystallinity, *Journal of Metamorphic Geology, 6*, 623–636, 1988.

Brime, C., Metamorfismo de bajo grado: Diferencias en escala o diferencias en grado metamórfico?, *Trabajos de Geologia, 21*, 61–66, 1999.

Brime, C., J. A. Talent, and R. Mawson, Low-grade metamorphism in the Palaeozoic sequence of the Townsville hinterland, northeastern Australia, *Australian Journal of Earth Sciences, 50*, 751–767, 2003.

Bowring, S. A., I. S. Williams, and W. Compston, 3.96 Ga gneisses from the Slave Province, Northwest Territories, Canada, *Geology, 17*, 971–975, 1989.

Bucher, K., and M. Frey, *Petrogenesis of Metamorphic Rocks*, seventh edition, Springer-Verlag, Berlin, 2002.

Buesch, D. C., and G. A. Valentine, Peach Springs Tuff and volcanic stratigraphy of the southern Cerbat Mountains, Kingman, Arizona, in *Cenozoic Stratigraphy, Structure and Mineralization in the Mojave Desert, Guidebook and Volume, Field Trip Nos. 5 and 6*, compiled by P. E. Ehlig, pp. 7–14, 82nd Annual Meeting, Cordilleran Section, Geological Society of America, Los Angeles, California, 1986.

Chaffin, E. F., A young earth?—a survey of dating methods, *Creation Research Society Quarterly, 24*, 109–117, 1987.

Chaffin, E. F., Theoretical mechanisms of accelerated radioactive decay, in *Radioisotopes and the Age of the Earth: A Young-Earth Creationist Research Initiative*, edited by L. Vardiman, A. A. Snelling, and E. F. Chaffin, pp. 305–331, Institute for Creation Research, El Cajon, California, and Creation Research Society, St. Joseph, Missouri, 2000.

Chaffin, E. F., Accelerated decay: theoretical considerations, in *Radioisotopes and the Age of the Earth: Results of a Young-Earth Creationist Research Initiative*, edited by L. Vardiman, A. A. Snelling, and E. F. Chaffin, pp. 525–585, Institute for Creation Research, El Cajon, California, and Creation Research Society, Chino Valley, Arizona, 2005.

Cherniak, D. J., and E. B. Watson, Pb diffusion in zircon, *Chemical Geology, 172*, 5–24, 2000.

Cherniak, D. J., and E. B. Watson, Diffusion in zircon, in *Zircon*, edited by J. M. Hanchar and P. W. O. Hoskin, pp. 113–143, Mineralogical Society of America, Washington, DC, Reviews in Mineralogy and Geochemistry, vol. 53, 2003.

Dickin, A. P., *Radiogenic Isotope Geology*, Cambridge University Press, New York, 1995.

Dumitru, T. A., I. R. Duddy, and P. F. Green, Mesozoic-Cenozoic burial, uplift, and erosion history of the west-central Colorado Plateau, *Geology, 22*(6), 499–502, 1994.

Elston, D. P., Correlations and facies changes in the Lower and Middle Cambrian Tonto Group, Grand Canyon, Arizona, in *Geology of Grand Canyon, Northern Arizona (with Colorado River Guides)*, edited by D. P. Elston, G. H. Billingsley, and R. A. Young, pp. 131–136, American Geophysical Union, Washington, DC, 1989.

Epstein, A. G., J. B. Epstein, and L. D. Harris, Conodont color alteration—an index to organic metamorphism, *U. S. Geological Survey, Professional Paper 995*, 1977.

Essene, E. J., and P. R. Peacor, Clay mineral thermometry—a critical perspective, *Clays and Clay Minerals, 43*(5), 540–553, 1995.

Faure, G., *Principles of Isotope Geology*, second edition, pp. 341–353, John Wiley & Sons, New York, 1986.

Faure, G., and T. S. Mensing, *Isotopes: Principles and Applications*, third edition, John Wiley & Sons, Hoboken, New Jersey, 2005.

Finch, R. J., and J. M. Hanchar, Structure and chemistry of zircon and zircon-group minerals, in *Zircon*, edited by J. M. Hanchar and P. W. O. Hoskin, pp. 1–25, Mineralogical Society of America, Washington, DC, Reviews in Mineralogy and Geochemistry, vol. 53, 2003.

Fleischer, R. L., and H. R. Hart, Fission track dating: techniques and problems, in *Calibration of Hominoid Evolution*, edited by W. Bishop, J. Miller, and S. Cole, pp. 135–170, Scottish Academic Press, 1972.

Fleischer, R. L., and P. B. Price, Glass dating by fission fragment tracks,

Journal of Geophysical Research, 69, 331–339, 1964a.

Fleischer, R. L., and P. B. Price, Techniques for geological dating of minerals by chemical etching of fission fragment tracks, *Geochimica et Cosmochimica Acta, 28*, 1705–1714, 1964b.

Fleischer, R. L., P. B. Price, E. M. Symes, and D. S. Miller, Fission track ages and track-annealing behavior of some micas, *Science, 143*, 349–351, 1964.

Fleischer, R. L., P. B. Price, and R. M. Walker, Tracks of charged particles in solids, *Science, 149*, 383–393, 1965a.

Fleischer, R. L., P. B. Price, and R. M. Walker, Effects of temperature, pressure, and ionization on the formation and stability of fission tracks in minerals and glasses, *Journal of Geophysical Research, 70*, 1497–1502, 1965b.

Fleischer, R. L., P. B. Price, and R. M. Walker, Nuclear tracks in solids, *Scientific American, 220*, 30–39, 1969.

Fleischer, R. L., P. B. Price, and R. M. Walker, *Nuclear Tracks in Solids: Principles and Applications*, University of California Press, Berkeley, 1975.

Frey, M., and H. J. Kisch, Scope of subject, in *Low Temperature Metamorphism*, edited by M. Frey, pp. 1–8, Blackie, Glasgow, 1987.

Frey, M., and D. Robinson (editors), *Low-Grade Metamorphism*, Blackwell Science, London, 1999.

Galbraith, R. F., On statistical models for fission track counts, *Mathematical Geology, 13*, 471–488, 1981.

Galbraith, R. F., On statistical estimation in fission track dating, *Mathematical Geology, 16*, 653–669, 1984.

Galbraith, R. F., Graphical display of estimates having differing standard errors, *Technometrics, 30*(3), 271–281, 1988.

Galbraith, R. F., Radial plot: graphical assessment of spread in ages, *Nuclear Tracks and Radiation Measurements, 17*(3), 207–214, 1990.

Galbraith, R. F., and P. F. Green, Estimating the component ages in a finite mixture, *Nuclear Tracks and Radiation Measurements, 17*(3), 197–206, 1990.

Gentry, R. V., T. K. Sworski, H. S. McKown, D. H. Smith, R. E. Eby, and W. H. Christie, Differential lead retention in zircons: implications for nuclear waste management, *Science, 216*, 296–298, 1982.

Glazner, A. F., J. E. Nielson, K. A. Howard, and D. M. Miller, Correlation of the Peach Springs Tuff, a large-volume Miocene ignimbrite sheet in California and Arizona, *Geology, 14*(10), 840–843, 1986.

Gleadow, A. J. W., Fission-track dating: what are the real alternatives?, *Nuclear Tracks, 5*, 3–14, 1981.

Gleadow, A. J. W., and J. F. Lovering, The effect of weathering on fission track dating, *Earth and Planetary Science Letters, 22*, 163–168, 1974.

Gleadow, A. J. W., and J. F. Lovering, Geometry factor for external track detectors in fission-track dating, *Nuclear Tracks, 1*, 99–106, 1977.

Gleadow, A. J. W., I. R. Duddy, P. F. Green, and J. F. Lovering, Confined fission track lengths in apatite: a diagnostic tool for thermal history analysis, *Contributions to Mineralogy and Petrology, 94*, 405–415, 1986.

Gleadow, A. J. W., A. J. Hurford, and R. D. Quaife, Fission track dating of zircon: improved etching techniques, *Earth and Planetary Science Letters, 33*, 273–276, 1976.

Green, P. F., A new look at statistics in fission-track dating, *Nuclear Tracks, 5*(1/2), 77–86, 1981.

Green, P. F., Comparison of zeta calibration baselines for fission-track dating of apatite, zircon and sphene, *Chemical Geology, 58*, 1–22, 1985.

Green, P. F., The relationship between track shortening and fission track age reduction in apatite: combined influences of inherent instability, annealing and anisotropy, length bias, and system calibration, *Earth and Planetary Science Letters, 89*, 335–352, 1988.

Green, P. F., Fission track dating of zircon from a sample of tuff, *Geotrack Report #823*, unpublished, Geotrack International Pty Ltd, Melbourne, 2001.

Green, P. F., Fission track dating of zircon from five volcanic rock samples, *Geotrack Report #841*, unpublished, Geotrack International Pty Ltd, Melbourne, 2002.

Green, P. F., Fission track dating of zircon from six volcanic rock samples, *Geotrack Report #860*, unpublished, Geotrack International Pty Ltd, Melbourne, 2003.

Green, P. F., and S. A. Durrani, A quantitative assessment of geometry factors for use in fission-track studies, *Nuclear Track Detectors, 2*, 207–213, 1978.

Green, P. F., I. R. Duddy, G. M. Laslett, K. A. Hegarty, A. J. W. Gleadow, and J. F. Lovering, Thermal annealing of fission tracks in apatite. 4, Qualitative modelling techniques and extension to geological timescales, *Chemical Geology*, *79*, 155–182, 1989.

Gregory, H. E., The San Juan country: a geographic and geologic reconnaissance of southeastern Utah, *U. S. Geological Survey, Professional Paper 188*, 1938.

Gusa, S., Recognition of the Peach Springs Tuff, California and Arizona, using heavy mineral suites, *U. S. Geological Survey, Open-File Report 86-522*, 1986.

Gusa, S., J. E. Nielson, and K. A. Howard, Heavy-mineral suites confirm the wide extent of the Peach Springs Tuff in California and Arizona, U. S. A., *Journal of Volcanology and Geothermal Research, 33*, 343–347, 1987.

Haack, U., The closing temperature for fission track retention in minerals, *American Journal of Science, 277*, 459–464, 1977.

Harris, A. G., Conodont color alteration, an organo-mineral metamorphic index, and its application to Appalachian Basin geology, in *Aspects of Diagenesis*, edited by A. Scholle and P. R. Schluger, pp. 3–16, Society of Economic Paleontologists and Mineralogists, Special Publication 26, Tulsa, Oklahoma, 1979.

Harris, A. G., Color and alteration: an index to organic metamorphism in conodont elements, *Treatise on Invertebrate Paleontology, Part W, Miscellanea Supplement 2, Conodonta*, edited by R. A. Robison, pp. W56–W60, Geological Society of America, Boulder, Colorado, 1981.

Harrison, T. M., R. L. Armstrong, C. W. Naeser, and J. E. Harakal, Geochronology and thermal history of the Coast Plutonic Complex, near Prince Rupert, British Columbia, *Canadian Journal of Earth Sciences, 16*, 400–410, 1979.

Hildreth, W., and G. Mahood, Correlation of ash-flow tuffs, *Geological Society of America Bulletin, 96*, 968–974, 1985.

Hillier, S., J. Mátyás, A. Matter, and G. Vasseur, Illite/smectite diagenesis and its variable correlation with vitrinite reflectants in the Pannonian Basin, *Clays and Clay Minerals, 43*(2), 174–183, 1995.

Hoskin, P. O. W., and U. Schaltegger, The composition of zircon and igneous and metamorphic petrogenesis, in *Zircon*, edited by J. M. Hanchar and P. O. W. Hoskin, pp. 27–62, Mineralogical Society of America, Washington, DC, Reviews in Mineralogy and Geochemistry, vol. 53, 2003.

Hower, J., Shale diagenesis, in *Clays and the Resource Geologist*, edited by F. J. Longstaffe, pp. 60–80, Mineralogical Association of Canada, Short Course Handbook 7, 1981.

Huang, W.-L., J. M. Longo, and D. R. Pevear, An experimentally derived kinetic model for smectite-to-illite conversion and its use as a geothermometer, *Clays and Clay Minerals, 41*(2), 162–177, 1993.

Humphreys, D. R., Accelerated nuclear decay: a viable hypothesis?, in *Radioisotopes and the Age of the Earth: A Young-Earth Creationist Research Initiative*, edited by L. Vardiman, A. A. Snelling, and E. F. Chaffin, pp. 333–379, Institute for Creation Research, El Cajon, California, and Creation Research Society, St. Joseph, Missouri, 2000.

Humphreys, D. R., Young helium diffusion age of zircons supports accelerated nuclear decay, in *Radioisotopes and the Age of the Earth: Results of a Young-Earth Creationist Research Initiative*, edited by L. Vardiman, A. A. Snelling, and E. F. Chaffin, pp. 25–100, Institute for Creation Research, El Cajon, California, and Creation Research Society, Chino Valley, Arizona, 2005.

Humphreys, D. R., S. A. Austin, J. R. Baumgardner, and A. A. Snelling, Helium diffusion rates support accelerated nuclear decay, in *Proceedings of the Fifth International Conference on Creationism*, edited by R. L. Ivey, Jr., pp. 175–195, Creation Science Fellowship, Pittsburgh, Pennsylvania, 2003a.

Humphreys, D. R., S. A. Austin, J. R. Baumgardner, and A. A. Snelling, Recently measured helium diffusion rate for zircon suggests inconsistency with U-Pb age for Fenton Hill granodiorite, *EOS, Transactions of the American Geophysical Union, 84*(46), Fall Meeting Supplement, Abstract V32C-1047, 2003b.

Humphreys, D. R., S. A. Austin, J. R. Baumgardner, and A. A. Snelling, Helium diffusion age of 6000 years supports accelerated nuclear decay, *Creation Research Society Quarterly, 41*, 1–16, 2004.

Hurford, A. J., On the closure temperature for fission tracks in zircon, *Nuclear Tracks, 10*, 415, 1985.

Hurford, A. J., Standardization of fission track calibration: recommendations by the Fission Track Working Group of the I.U.G.S. Subcommision on Geochronology, *Chemical Geology, 80*, 171–178, 1990.

Hurford, A. J., and P. F. Green, A user's guide to fission track dating calibration, *Earth and Planetary Science Letters, 59*, 343–354, 1982.

Hurford, A. J., and P. F. Green, The zeta age calibration of fission-track dating, *Chemical Geology (Isotope Geoscience), 1*, 285–317, 1983.

Ireland, T. R., and I. S. Williams, Considerations in zircon geochronology by SIMS, in *Zircon*, edited by J. M. Hanchar and P. O. W. Hoskin, pp. 215–241, Mineralogical Society of America, Washington, DC, Reviews in Mineralogy and Geochemistry, vol. 53, 2003.

Karlstrom, K. E., B. R. Ilg, M. L. Williams, D. P. Hawkins, S. A. Bowring, and S. J. Seaman, Paleoproterozoic rocks of the Granite Gorges, in *Grand Canyon Geology*, edited by S. S. Beus and M. Morales, second edition, pp. 9–38, Oxford University Press, New York, 2003.

Kisch, H. J., Mineralogy and petrology of burial diagenesis (burial metamorphism) and incipient metamorphism in clastic rocks, in *Diagenesis in Sediments and Sedimentary Rocks, 2*, edited by G. Larsen and G. Chilingar, pp. 289–493, Elsevier, Amsterdam, 1983.

Kisch, H. J., Correlation between indicators of very low-grade metamorphism, in *Low Temperature Metamorphism*, edited by M. Frey, pp. 227–304, Chapman and Hall, New York, 1987.

Kisch, H. J., Illite crystallinity: recommendations on sample preparation, x-ray diffraction settings, and interlaboratory samples, *Journal of Metamorphic Geology, 9*, 665–670, 1991.

Kowallis, B. J., and J. S. Heaton, Fission-track dating of bentonites and bentonitic mudstones from the Morrison Formation in central Utah, *Geology, 15*, 1135–1142, 1987.

Kowallis, B. J., E. H. Christiansen, and A. L. Deino, Age of the Brushy Basin Member of the Morrison Formation, Colorado Plateau, western USA, *Cretaceous Research, 12*, 483–493, 1991.

Kubler, B., Les argiles, indicateurs de métamorphisme, *Revue de L'Institut Française de Pétrole, 19*, 1093–1112, 1964.

Kubler, B., La cristallinité d'illite et les zones tout à fait supérieures du métamorphisme, in *Etages Tectoniques, Colloque de Neûchatel*, pp. 105–122, Institute de Géologie, Université de Neûchatel, Neûchatel, Switzerland, 1967.

Kubler, B., Evaluation quantitative de métamorphisme par la cristallinité de l'illite, *Centre de Recherches de Pau Société Nationale de Pétroles d'Aquitaine Bulletin, 2*, 385–397, 1968.

Kubler, B., and D. Goy-Eggenberger, La cristallinité de l'illite revisitée, un bilan des connaissances acquises ces trente derniéres années, *Clay Minerals, 36*, 143–157, 2001.

Ludwig, K. R., *Isoplot/Ex (Version 2.49): The Geochronological Toolkit for Microsoft Excel*, University of California, Berkeley, Berkeley Geochronology Center, Special Publication No. 1a, 2001.

Magomedov, Sh. A., Migration of radiogenic products in zircon, *Geokhimiya, 2*, 263–267, 1970.

McKee, E. D., and C. E. Resser, *Cambrian History of the Grand Canyon Region*, Carnegie Institution of Washington Publication 563, Washington, DC, 1945.

Middleton, L. T., and D. K. Elliott, Tonto Group, in *Grand Canyon Geology*, edited by S. S. Beus and M. Morales, first edition, pp. 83–106, Oxford University Press, New York, and Museum of Northern Arizona Press, Flagstaff, Arizona, 1990.

Middleton, L. T., and D. K. Elliott, Tonto Group, in *Grand Canyon Geology*, edited by S. S. Beus and M. Morales, second edition, pp. 90–106, Oxford University Press, New York, 2003.

Naeser, C. W., The use of apatite and sphene for fission track age determinations, *Geological Society of America Bulletin, 78*, 1523–1526, 1967.

Naeser, C. W., Fission-track dating and geological annealing of fission tracks, in *Lectures in Isotope Geology*, edited by E. Jäger and J. C. Hunziker, pp. 154–169, Springer-Verlag, Berlin, 1979.

Naeser, C. W., The fading of fission tracks in the geologic environment: data from deep drill holes, *Nuclear Tracks, 5*, 248–250, 1981.

Naeser, C. W., and F. C. W. Dodge, Fission-track ages of accessory minerals from granitic rocks of the central Sierra Nevada Batholith, California, *Geological Society of America Bulletin, 80*, 2201–2212, 1969.

Naeser, C. W., and H. Faul, Fission track annealing in apatite and sphene, *Journal of Geophysical Research, 74*, 705–710, 1969.

Naeser, N. D., and C. W. Naeser, Fission-track dating, in *Quaternary Dating Methods*, edited by W. C. Mahaney, pp. 87–100, Developments in Palaeontology and Stratigraphy 7, Elsevier, Amsterdam, 1984.

Naeser, C. W., I. R. Duddy, D. P. Elston, T. A. Dumitru, and P. F. Green, Fission-track dating: ages for Cambrian strata and Laramide and post-Middle Eocene cooling events from the Grand Canyon, Arizona, in *Geology of Grand Canyon, Northern Arizona (with Colorado River Guides)*, edited by D. P. Elston, G. H. Billingsley, and R. A. Young, pp. 139–144, American Geophysical Union, Washington, DC, 1989a.

Naeser, N. D., C. W. Naeser, and P. H. McCulloh, The application of fission-track dating to the depositional and thermal history of rocks in sedimentary basins, in *Thermal History of Sedimentary Basins*, edited by N. D. Naeser and T. H. McCulloh, pp. 157–180, Springer-Verlag, Berlin, 1989b.

Naeser, C. W., R. A. Zimmermann, and G. T. Cebula, Fission-track dating of apatite and zircon: an interlaboratory comparison, *Nuclear Tracks, 5*, 65–72, 1981.

Nagpaul, K. K., P. K. Mehta, and M. L. Gupta, Correction of fission-track dates due to thermal annealing in apatite, biotite and sphene, *Pure and Applied Geophysics, 112*, 131–139, 1974.

Nielson, J. E., D. R. Lux, G. B. Dalrymple, and A. F. Glazner, Age of the Peach Springs Tuff, southeastern California and western Arizona, *Journal of Geophysical Research, 95*(B1), 571–580, 1990.

Nutman, A. P., V. C. Bennett, C. R. L. Friend, and V. R. McGregor, The early Archaean Itsaq Gneiss Complex of southern West Greenland: the importance of field observations in interpreting age and isotopic constraints for early terrestrial evolution, *Geochimica et Cosmochimica Acta, 64*, 3035–3060, 2000.

Parrish, R. R., and S. R. Noble, Zircon U-Th-Pb geochronology by isotope dilution-thermal ionization mass spectrometry (ID-TIMS), in *Zircon*, edited by J. M. Hanchar and P. O. W. Hoskin, pp. 183–213, Mineralogical Society of America, Washington, DC, Reviews in Mineralogy and Geochemistry, vol. 53, 2003.

Petersen, L. M., and M. M. Roylance, Stratigraphy and depositional environments of the upper Jurassic Morrison Formation near Capitol Reef National Park, Utah, *Brigham Young University Geology Studies, 29* (2), 1–12, 1982.

Peterson, F., and C. E. Turner-Peterson, The Morrison Formation of the Colorado Plateau: recent advances in sedimentology, stratigraphy and paleotectonics, *Hunteria, 2* (1), 1–18, 1987.

Pollastro, R. M., Considerations and applications of the illite/smectite geothermometer in hydrocarbon-bearing rocks of Miocene to Mississippian age, *Clays and Clay Minerals, 41*(2), 119–133, 1993.

Poupeau, G., Precision, accuracy and meaning of fission-track ages, *Proceedings of the Indian Academy of Sciences, Earth and Planetary Science, 90,* 403–436, 1981.

Poupeau, G., J. Carpena, A. Chambaudiet, and Ph. Romary, Fission-track plateau-age dating, in *Solid State Nuclear Track Detectors,* edited by H. Francois, J. P. Massue, R. Schmitt, N. Kurtz, M. Monnin, and S. A. Durrani, pp. 965–971, Pergamon, Lyon, France, 1979.

Poupeau, G., Ph. Romary, and P. Toulhoat, On the fission-track plateau ages of minerals, *U.S. Geological Survey, Open File Report 78-701,* 339–340, 1978.

Price, P. B., and R. M. Walker, Chemical etching of charged particle tracks in solids, *Journal of Applied Physics, 33,* 3407, 1962a.

Price, P. B., and R. M. Walker, Observation of fossil particle tracks in natural micas, *Nature, 196,* 732, 1962b.

Price, P. B., and R. M. Walker, Fossil tracks of charged particles in mica and the age of minerals, *Journal of Geophysical Research, 68,* 4847–4862, 1963.

Pytte, A. M., and R. C. Reynolds, The thermal transformation of smectite to illite, in *Thermal History of Sedimentary Basins,* edited by N. D. Naeser and T. H. McCulloh, pp. 133–140, Springer-Verlag, Berlin, 1989.

Reimer, G. M., D. Storzer, and G. A. Wagner, Geometry factor in fission track counting, *Earth and Planetary Science Letters, 9,* 401–404, 1970.

Rejebian, V. A., A. G. Harris, and J. S. Huebner, Conodont color and textural alteration: an index to regional metamorphism, contact metamorphism and hydrothermal metamorphism, *Geological Society of America Bulletin, 99,* 471–479, 1987.

Renac, C., and A. Meunier, Reconstruction of palaeothermal conditions in the passive margin using illite-smectite mixed-layer series (BA1 scientific deep drill-hole, Ardeche, France), *Clay Minerals, 30,* 107–118, 1995.

Robinson, D., and R. J. Merriman, Low-temperature metamorphism: an overview, in *Low-Grade Metamorphism,* edited by M. Frey and D.

Robinson, pp. 1–9, Blackwell, Oxford, 1999.

Schreurs, J. W. H., A. M. Friedman, D. J. Rockop, M. W. Hair, and R. M. Walker, Calibrated U-Th glasses for neutron dosimetry and determination of uranium and thorium concentrations by the fission-track method, *Radiation Effects, 7*, 231–233, 1971.

Sharma, Y. P., N. Lal, K. D. Bal, R. Parshad, and K. K. Nagpaul, Closing temperatures of different fission-track clocks, *Contributions to Mineralogy and Petrology, 72*, 335–336, 1980.

Silk, E. C. H., and R. S. Barnes, Examination of fission fragment tracks with an electron microscope, *Philosophical Magazine, 4*, 970, 1959.

Smart, G., and T. Clayton, The progressive illitization of interstratified illite-smectite from Carboniferous sediments of northern England and its relationship to organic maturity indicators, *Clay Minerals, 30*, 455–466, 1985.

Smith, M. J., and P. Leigh-Jones, An automated microscope scanning stage for fission track dating, *Nuclear Tracks, 10*, 395–400, 1985.

Snelling, A. A., Geochemical processes in the mantle and crust, in *Radioisotopes and the Age of the Earth: A Young-Earth Creationist Research Initiative*, edited by L. Vardiman, A. A. Snelling, and E. F. Chaffin, pp. 123–304, Institute for Creation Research, El Cajon, California, and Creation Research Society, St. Joseph, Missouri, 2000a.

Snelling, A. A., Radiohalos, in *Radioisotopes and the Age of the Earth: A Young-Earth Creationist Research Initiative*, edited by L. Vardiman, A. A. Snelling, and E. F. Chaffin, pp. 381–468, Institute for Creation Research, El Cajon, California, and Creation Research Society, St. Joseph, Missouri, 2000b.

Snelling, A. A., Radiohalos in granites: evidence for accelerated nuclear decay, in *Radioisotopes and the Age of the Earth: Results of a Young-Earth Creationist Research Initiative*, edited by L. Vardiman, A. A. Snelling, and E. F. Chaffin, pp. 101–207, Institute for Creation Research, El Cajon, California, and Creation Research Society, Chino Valley, Arizona, 2005a.

Snelling, A. A., Isochron discordances and the role of inheritance and mixing of radioisotopes in the mantle and crust, in *Radioisotopes and the Age of the Earth: Results of a Young-Earth Creationist Research Initiative*, edited by L. Vardiman, A. A. Snelling, and E. F. Chaffin, pp. 393–518, Institute for

Creation Research, El Cajon, California, and Creation Research Society, Chino Valley, Arizona, 2005b.

Snelling, A. A., and M. H. Armitage, Radiohalos—a tale of three granitic plutons, in *Proceedings of the Fifth International Conference on Creationism*, edited by R. L. Ivey, Jr., pp. 243–267, Creation Science Fellowship, Pittsburgh, Pennsylvania, 2003.

Snelling, A. A., S. A. Austin, and W. A. Hoesch, Radioisotopes in the diabase sill (Upper Precambrian) at Bass Rapids, Grand Canyon, Arizona: an application and test of the isochron dating method, in *Proceedings of the Fifth International Conference on Creationism*, edited by R. L. Ivey, Jr., pp. 269–284, Creation Science Fellowship, Pittsburgh, Pennsylvania, 2003a.

Snelling, A. A., J. R. Baumgardner, and L. Vardiman, Abundant Po radiohalos in Phanerozoic granites and timescale implications for their formation, *EOS, Transactions of the American Geophysical Union, 84*(46), Fall Meeting Supplement, Abstract V32C-1046, 2003b.

Sparks, R. S. J., S. Self, and G. P. L. Walker, Products of ignimbrite eruptions, *Geology, 1*, 115–118, 1973.

Stacey, J. S., and J. D. Kramers, Approximation of terrestrial lead isotope evolution by a two-stage model, *Earth and Planetary Science Letters, 26*, 207–221, 1975.

Steiger, R. H., and B. Jäger, Subcommission on geochronology: convention on the use of the decay constants in geo- and cosmochronology, *Earth and Planetary Science Letters, 36*, 359–362, 1977.

Storzer, D., and G. Poupeau, Age-plateaux de verres et mineraux par la methode des traces de fission, *Comptes Rendu Academie Sciences Paris, 276D*, 137–139, 1973.

Storzer, D., and G. A. Wagner, Correction of thermally lowered fission track ages of tektites, *Earth and Planetary Science Letters, 5*, 463–468, 1969.

Storzer, D., and G. A. Wagner, The application of fission track dating in stratigraphy: a critical review, in *Numerical Dating in Stratigraphy*, edited by G. S. Oldin, pp. 199–221, John Wiley & Sons, New York, 1982.

Turner, C. E., and N. S. Fishman, Jurassic Late T'oo'dichi': a large alkaline, saline lake, Morrison Formation, eastern Colorado Plateau, *Geological Society of America Bulletin, 103*(4), 538–558, 1991.

Turner, C. E., and F. Peterson, Reconstruction of the Upper Jurassic Morrison Formation extinct ecosystem—a synthesis, *Sedimentary Geology, 167,* 309–355, 2004.

Velde, B., and J. Espitalié, Comparison of kerogen maturation and illite/smectite composition in diagenesis, *Journal of Petroleum Geology, 12*(1), 103–110, 1989.

Velde, B., and B. Lanson, Comparison of I/S transformation and maturity of organic matter at elevated temperatures, *Clays and Clay Minerals, 41*(2), 178–183, 1993.

Wagner, G. A., Archaeological applications of fission-track dating, *Nuclear Track Detectors, 2,* 51–63, 1978.

Wardlaw, B. R., and A. G. Harris, Conodont-based thermal maturation of Paleozoic rocks in Arizona, *American Association of Petroleum Geologists Bulletin, 68*(9), 1101–1106, 1984.

Warr, L. N., and A. H. N. Rice, Interlaboratory standardization and calibration of clay mineral crystallinity and crystallite size data, *Journal of Metamorphic Geology, 12,* 141–152, 1994.

Young, R. A., and W. J. Brennan, Peach Springs Tuff: its bearing on structural evolution of the Colorado Plateau and development of Cenozoic drainage in Mojave County, Arizona, *Geological Society of America Bulletin, 85*(1), 83–90, 1974.

Zeitler, P. K., Closure temperature implications of concordant $^{40}Ar/^{39}Ar$ potassium feldspar and zircon fission-track ages from high-grade terranes, *Nuclear Tracks, 10,* 441–442, 1985.

Chapter 5

Do Radioisotope Clocks Need Repair?
Testing the Assumptions of Isochron Dating
Using K-Ar, Rb-Sr, Sm-Nd, and Pb-Pb Isotopes

Steven A. Austin, Ph.D.*

Abstract. The assumptions of conventional whole-rock and mineral isochron radioisotope dating were tested using a suite of radioisotopes from two Precambrian rocks. Amphibolite from the Beartooth Mountains of Wyoming shows evidence of thorough metamorphism by isochemical processes from andesite by an early Precambrian magma-intrusion event. A diabase sill, exposed within the wall of Grand Canyon at Bass Rapids, formed by a rapid intrusion event. The event segregated minerals gravitationally, apparently starting from an isotopically homogeneous magma. Although K-Ar, Rb-Sr, Sm-Nd, and Pb-Pb methods ought to yield concordant isochron dates for each of these magmatic events, these four radioisotope pairs gave significantly discordant ages. Special allowance was made for larger-than-conventional uncertainties expressed as 2σ errors associated with the calculated "ages." Within a single Beartooth amphibolite sample, three discordant mineral isochron "ages" range from 2515±110 Ma (Rb-Sr mineral isochron) to 2886±190 Ma (Sm-Nd mineral isochron). The diabase sill in Grand Canyon displays discordant isochron "ages" ranging from 841.5±164 Ma (K-Ar whole-rock isochron) to 1379±140 Ma (Sm-Nd mineral isochron). Although significant discordance exists between the K-Ar, Rb-Sr, Sm-Nd, and Pb-Pb radioisotope methods, each radioisotope pair appears to yield concordant "ages" internally between whole-rocks and minerals. Internal concordance is best illustrated from the Bass Rapids diabase sill by the tightly constrained Rb-Sr whole-rock and mineral

---

* *Chairman, Geology Department, Institute for Creation Research, Santee, California*

isochron "ages" of 1055±46 Ma and 1060±24 Ma, respectively. The most problematic discordance is the Sm-Nd and Pb-Pb whole-rock and mineral isochron "ages" that significantly exceed the robust Rb-Sr whole-rock and mineral isochron "ages." It could be argued that the robust Rb-Sr whole-rock and mineral isochron "ages" are in error, but an adequate explanation for the error has not been offered. The geological context of these Precambrian rocks places severe limitations on possible explanations for isochron discordance. Inheritance of minerals, slow cooling, and post-magmatic loss of daughter radioisotopes are not supported as processes causing isochron discordance in Beartooth amphibolite or Bass Rapids diabase. Recently, geochronologists researching the Great Dyke, a Precambrian layered mafic and ultramafic intrusion of Zimbabwe in southeast Africa, have documented a similar pattern of radioisotope discordance. Alpha-emitting radioisotopes (^{147}Sm, ^{235}U, and ^{238}U) give older "ages" than β-emitting radioisotopes (^{87}Rb and ^{40}K) when applied to the same rocks. Therefore, it can be argued that a change in radioisotope decay rates in the past could account for these discordant isochron "ages" for the same geologic event. Conventional radioisotope clocks need repair.

1. Introduction

Do conventional radioisotope dating methods when applied to a single rock or rock unit give concordant ages? Specifically, do the K-Ar, Rb-Sr, Sm-Nd, and Pb-Pb radioisotope pairs each give the same age, within the uncertainties allowed using radioisotope dating, for a single rock or rock unit? If *concordant* ages were obtained for a single rock or cogenetic suite of rocks using different radioisotope pairs, these would be impressive evidence for the consistency of radioisotope dating and be an affirmation of the assumptions underlying these dating methods. However, if *discordant* ages were obtained, then some qualifications would need to be applied to the assumptions undergirding these dating methods.

We sought to apply the whole-rock and mineral isochron dating methods to answer our question concerning concordant/discordant ages using K-Ar, Rb-Sr, Sm-Nd, and Pb-Pb radioisotope pairs. Specifically, we sought to date ancient rocks that have been in existence through a major portion of earth history, whose parent isotopes (^{40}K, ^{87}Rb, ^{147}Sm, ^{238}U, ^{235}U, and ^{232}Th) should have been altered by significant amounts of decay to produce significant quantities of daughter isotopes (^{40}Ar, ^{87}Sr, ^{143}Nd, ^{206}Pb, ^{207}Pb, and ^{208}Pb respectively). We sought to date rocks whose geological context is already well understood so that possible geological reasons for isochron discordance could be recognized.

The rationale for the proposed research [*Austin*, 2000] was to address the kind of discordance obtained from the whole-rock and mineral isochron methods applied to the same rock or cogenetic rock unit. *Austin* [2000] described the scientific literature concerning multiple dating methods applied to the same rocks. As noted by *Austin* [2000], discordance of isochron ages is often obtained. Because isochron discordance has not been thoroughly described and explained, *Austin* [2000] proposed a fourfold classification of isochron discordance:

Category one discordance—a cogenetic suite of rocks with two or more discordant whole-rock isochron ages,

Category two discordance—a cogenetic suite of rocks that generates a whole-rock isochron age older than the associated mineral isochron ages from specific rocks,

Category three discordance—two or more discordant mineral isochron ages from the same rock, and,

Category four discordance—a cogenetic suite of rocks that generates a whole-rock isochron age younger than the associated mineral isochron ages.

Literature review indicates that geochronologists have offered various, sometimes contradictory, and extremely controversial explanations when isochron discordance is obtained for different radioisotope pairs [*Austin*, 2000]. Category four discordance, where one radioisotope pair gives a whole-rock "age" significantly younger than a mineral isochron "age" of a different radioisotope pair, has been the hardest to explain.

Before we can compare isochron "ages" obtained from different radioisotope pairs, we need a working definition of "concordance" and "discordance." The age interpretation of an isochron is usually stated in statistical terms derived from the analytical precision of the points defining the line on an isochron plot. As *Ludwig* [2001] noted in a hypothetical example of a particular formation being dated, if we find eight points whose regression gives an isochron age of 320 ± 8 Ma (2σ), then this result is equivalent to the statement:

> If one were to repeat the sampling and regression procedure an infinite number of times, the probability that the grand mean of the resulting isochron ages would fall between 312 and 328 Ma is 95%.

Ludwig, [2001] noted,

> ... this statement does not say that the *true* age of the samples has a 95% probability of falling between 312–328 Ma, only that the mean of the infinitely-replicated regressions would yield an isochron age within this interval.

As affirmed by Ludwig, three other factors also affect the real age uncertainty (not the conventional "analytical-error-only" uncertainty) associated with isochrons:

(1) errors concerning the assumption of a closed system,

(2) errors concerning the invariant beginning isotope ratio, and

(3) errors concerning the parent radioisotope decay constant.

Renne et al. [1998] affirmed in the title of their paper, "Absolute ages aren't exactly" because these age determinations usually fail to incorporate uncertainties associated with the modern measurements of decay constants. Thus, at least *four* uncertainties must be incorporated into our understanding of the overall error associated with any isochron. The real uncertainty may be significantly larger than the commonly stated "analytical-error-only" uncertainty.

A special case involving the massive volcanism in the Siberian Traps at the Permian-Triassic boundary illustrates our need for a rigorous definition of isochron concordance and discordance. *Renne et al.* [1998] reported for Siberian volcanism a high-precision ^{238}U-^{206}Pb date of 251.3 ± 0.2 Ma and a high-precision $^{40}Ar/^{39}Ar$ date of 250.0 ± 0.3 Ma. These two dates assume 2σ errors derived only from uncertainties in the analytical methods. The two dates appear to be *discordant.* However, as recognized by *Renne et al.* [1998], significant error exists in both our estimate of the ^{40}K decay constant and in the isotope ratio of standards used to calibrate the $^{40}Ar/^{39}Ar$ method. Thus, a better expression of the $^{40}Ar/^{39}Ar$ date, according to *Renee et al.* [1998], is 250.0 ± 4.4 Ma, clearly not statistically resolvable from the ^{238}U-^{206}Pb date of 251.3±0.2 Ma. Therefore, these two ages by the two radioisotope pairs can be regarded as *concordant*.

Recently, the geochronologic community has recommended a new method for evaluating uncertainties associated with isochron ages [*Ludwig*, 2001]. A statistic called the "mean square of weighted deviates" (MSWD) is a ratio characterizing the observed scatter of the points (from the best-fit regression line of an isochron) to the expected scatter (from the various assigned errors, including but not limited to, analysis equipment). If the assigned errors have been correctly characterized, the observed scatter should approximate the expected scatter, so the value of MSWD should be near unity. Thus, two isochrons having errors assigned to points both giving MSWD values near unity will express two uncertainties associated with the two calculated "ages" that will be better suited to evaluate "concordance" than the older method of using "analytical-error-only" uncertainties. Therefore, "concordance" between two isochron ages must incorporate this expanded understanding of isochron uncertainties.

For data contained in this paper we attempt to incorporate broader estimates of isochron errors. When we quote isochron determinations of other scientists, we use care to define which uncertainties these scientists are using.

Two Precambrian rock units were selected for detailed radioisotope analysis in this study. The purpose was to recognize, classify, and evaluate isochron concordance/discordance within specific rocks and within cogenetic units of rocks by the K-Ar, Rb-Sr, Sm-Nd, and Pb-Pb radioisotope pairs. The first rock unit selected is a lower Precambrian (Archean) metamorphic rock from the southeastern Beartooth Mountains of Wyoming (Figure 1). The second rock unit is the upper Precambrian (Proterozoic) diabase sill at Bass Rapids in the central Grand Canyon, Arizona (Figure 2).

2. Geologic Setting of the Beartooth Amphibolite

Ancient metamorphosed basement rocks comprise the deeper

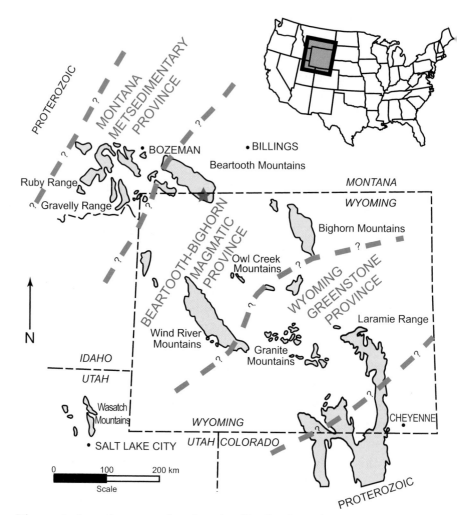

Figure 1. Location map showing the distribution of Precambrian rocks in the northern Rocky Mountain region. The map shows the location of the Beartooth Mountains and the collection site of Beartooth andesitic amphibolite sample BT-1 (indicated by ★ in northwestern Wyoming). Three provinces of Archean rocks in Montana and Wyoming are positioned between two regions of younger Proterozoic rocks (after *Mueller et al.* [1998]).

continental crust in the northern Rocky Mountain region of the United States. Tectonic and erosion processes have exposed these basement rocks within numerous mountain ranges (Figure 1). According to *Mueller et al.* [1998], the Archean rocks of this region can be divided into three southwest-to-northeast-trending belts or provinces: the Montana metasedimentary province (Idaho and western Montana), the Beartooth-Bighorn magmatic province (northwestern Wyoming and eastern Montana), and the Wyoming greenstone province (southeastern Wyoming). These three Archean metamorphic provinces are sandwiched between younger Proterozoic rocks on the northwest and southeast (Figure 1).

Gneissic rocks within the core of the Beartooth Mountains of northwestern Wyoming and south-central Montana lie within the Beartooth-Bighorn magmatic province (Figure 1). Archean rocks of the Beartooth Mountains are widely claimed to be among the oldest rocks within the United States dating to about 3000 Ma [*Mueller et al.*, 1987, 1998]. Granitic rocks within the mountains have enveloped a wide variety of older rock types; the most common of these is fine- to coarse-grained amphibolite of andesitic composition [*Mueller et al.*, 1983]. Metamorphic rocks of the Beartooth complex also include lesser amounts of mafic amphibolites, quartzite, tonalitic gneiss, granitic gneiss, ironstone and impure quartz-rich rocks [*Mueller et al.*, 1987].

The most carefully studied andesitic amphibolite comes from the Long Lake magmatic complex on the Beartooth Highway in Wyoming [*Mueller et al.*, 1988]. According to *Warner et al.* [1982], this complex includes andesitic amphibolite intruded by Long Lake granodiorite (foliated granitic to tonalitic rocks) and Long Lake granite (more massive leucocratic granite to tonalite). Metasedimentary inclusions of orthoquartzite include detrital zircons dated up to 3960 Ma [*Mueller et al.*, 1998]. Using major and trace elements, particularly the light rare earth elements, *Mueller et al.* [1983] argued that the elemental abundance pattern of the andesitic amphibolite is the result of an isochemical metamorphic process with final crystallization reactions associated with the intrusion of Long Lake granodiorite and granite. According to *Mueller et al.* [1983], granitic intrusions did not significantly alter the original chemistry of the andesitic amphibolite. Mineral assemblages within the amphibolite indicate that original igneous rocks were

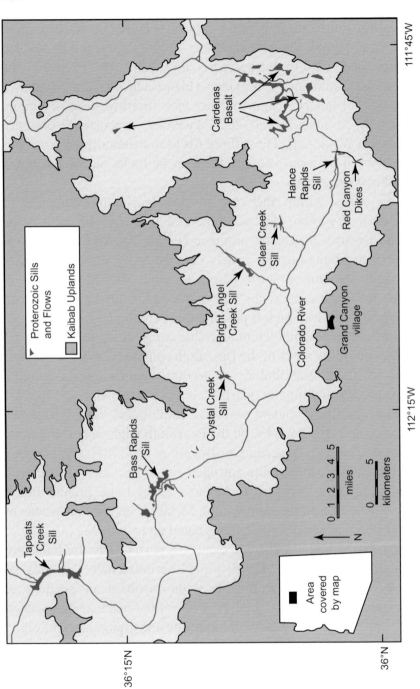

Figure 2. Location of the Bass Rapids diabase sill in Grand Canyon, northern Arizona.

metamorphosed to the epidote-amphibolite facies at a final equilibration temperature of about 400°C [*Warner et al.*, 1982]. Geochemistry and mineralogy do not support hydrothermal metasomatism. According to *Mueller et al.* [1983], the amphibolites were derived from andesite, specifically an andesite enriched in rare earth elements and other incompatible trace elements. Beartooth amphibolites are dominated by plagioclase, quartz, hornblende, and biotite, with lesser amounts of magnetite, ilmenite and titanite. Biotite strongly fractionates Rb at the expense of Sr, and titanite strongly fractionates rare earth elements (for example, Sm), as well as U and Th. Thus, because significant variation in parent radioisotope abundance is required for isochron dating, whole-rock and mineral isochron methods should be able to discern the age of the amphibolite.

Significant effort has been expended to date Beartooth rocks. A 2790 Ma model date was obtained by U-Pb in a zircon from the andesitic amphibolite [*Mueller et al.*, 1987]. This age was confirmed by an impressive, 28-point Rb-Sr whole-rock isochron age of 2790±35 Ma (initial $^{87}Sr/^{86}Sr = 0.7022\pm0.0002$ and uncertainties from analytical errors being 2σ). Figure 3 shows this whole-rock isochron replotted from the data of *Wooden et al.* [1982], including thirteen samples of Long Lake granite (plotting mostly in the more-radiogenic area in the upper right), five samples of Long Lake granodiorite (plotting mostly near the middle), and ten samples of amphibolite (plotting in the lower left). The 2790 Ma isochron is supposed to date the thermal event that recrystallized and homogenized the Sr isotopes of these metamorphic rocks [*Wooden et al.*, 1982]. The granitoid rocks of the southeastern Beartooth Mountains gave a Rb-Sr whole-rock isochron age of 2810±40 Ma with initial $^{87}Sr/^{86}Sr = 0.7018\pm0.0002$, an age and initial Sr ratio essentially indistinguishable from the amphibolite [*Mueller et al.*, 1983]. The protolith from which the andesitic amphibolite recrystallized is suggested to be 2950 Ma [*Mueller et al.*, 1983].

3. Geologic Setting of the Bass Rapids Diabase Sill

Mafic igneous rocks occur as sills, dikes and flows in the thick

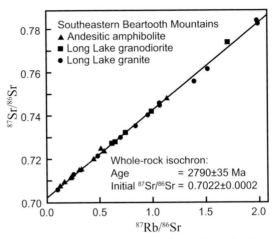

Figure 3. Composite Rb-Sr whole-rock isochron from the Long Lake granitic complex in the southeastern Beartooth Mountains of northwestern Wyoming. Plot includes Long Lake granite (thirteen samples), Long Lake granodiorite (five samples), and Beartooth andesitic amphibolite (ten samples). Data replotted from *Wooden et al.* [1982].

succession of strata making up the middle Proterozoic Unkar Group of the Grand Canyon, Arizona (Figure 2). The Unkar Group sedimentary sequence is comprised of four formations (in ascending order, the Bass Limestone, Hakatai Shale, Shinumo Quartzite and the Dox Sandstone) which are overlain by the 300 m plus thick flow sequence of lava flows of the Cardenas Basalt [*Hendricks and Stevenson, 1990, 2003*]. The younger Precambrian sediments of the Nankoweap Formation and the Chuar Group overlie this Unkar Group succession, which unconformably rests on the early Proterozoic metamorphic and igneous crystalline basement [*Babcock, 1990; Ilg et al., 1996; Karlstrom et al., 2003*].

The diabase sills and dikes are believed to be the intrusive equivalents of the Cardenas lava flows, but they are not found in direct association with the Cardenas Basalt [*Hendricks, 1972, 1989; Hendricks and Lucchitta, 1974*]. Thus the relationship between them is obscure because the direct feeders to the flows have never been recognized among the available diabase outcrops. The diabase sills are, in fact, confined to the lower part of the Unkar Group, particularly intruding near the boundary between the Bass Limestone and Hakatai Shale, whereas the related dikes are intruded into all the formations above the sills along faults that predate, or are contemporaneous with, the sills. These mafic sills crop out in seven locations along a 70–80 km length of the Grand Canyon (Figure 2), whereas the Cardenas Basalt flows are restricted to the area around Basalt Canyon in the eastern Grand Canyon. The sills range in thickness from 20 m (about 65 feet) near Hance Rapids in the east to more than 200 m (655 feet) near Tapeats Creek in the west. They are composed chiefly of medium-grained ophitic olivine-rich diabase that is uniform in texture and mineralogy from sill to sill in the Canyon. The dikes have a similar composition but are finer grained, as are the chilled margins of the sills. Early in-place differentiation and crystal settling in the sills is evidenced by granophyre layers up to 6 m thick and felsite dikes, and by layers that are richer in olivine.

Noble was the first to describe the diabase sills in the Bass Canyon-Shinumo Creek area [*Noble* 1910, 1914]. *Maxson* [1967, 1968] mapped the intrusive rocks of the Grand Canyon but did not describe the diabase sills and dikes. Detailed mapping and sampling of the sills and dikes, and the Cardenas Basalt flows, followed by petrographic examination and chemical analysis of the samples collected, were reported by *Hendricks* [1972, 1989] and *Hendricks and Lucchitta* [1974]. They found that chemical variation diagrams indicated a potential common parentage for the diabase in the sills and the lower third of the basalt flows. However, the flows in the upper two-thirds of the Cardenas Basalt sequence were found to be much more silicic than the diabase sills, and, therefore, it was concluded that they probably were not emplaced during the same phase of igneous activity. Nevertheless, the mineral composition of the unaltered basalt flows in the bottom third of the sequence is similar to that of the diabase sills, which suggested that those lavas and the diabase sills were co-magmatic and probably coeval. Thus, they concluded that the basalt lavas in the top two-thirds of the sequence were extruded after differentiation of the parent magma.

The 1.1 Ga Rb-Sr isochron date for the Cardenas Basalt is widely regarded as perhaps the best "age" obtained for Grand Canyon strata

[*McKee and Noble*, 1974; *Larson et al*, 1994]. This date was derived from two whole-rock Rb-Sr data sets combined to form a ten-point isochron plot. According to *Larson et al.* [1994], the Rb-Sr whole-rock isochron age of the Cardenas Basalt based on two data sets (ten points) is 1103±66 Ma (uncertainty assumes 2σ analytical errors) with initial $^{87}Sr/^{86}Sr$ of 0.7062±0.0024 (again, uncertainty assumes 2σ analytical errors). This age and the initial Sr ratio are statistically indistinguishable from 1070±70 Ma and $^{87}Sr/^{86}Sr$ of 0.7065±0.0015 (2σ analytical errors with age recalculated using new ^{87}Rb decay constant) originally obtained from the five-point isochron by *McKee and Noble* [1974] and restated by *McKee and Noble* [1976]. According to *Elston and McKee* [1982], the Bass Rapids diabase sill yields a five-point Rb-Sr whole-rock isochron age of 1070±30 Ma and initial $^{87}Sr/^{86}Sr$ of 0.7042±0.0007 (2σ analytic errors). This age for the Bass Rapids diabase sill provided apparent confirmation of the relationship between the diabase sills and the Cardenas Basalt flows, and this age appears to have less uncertainty than the age of the associated Cardenas Basalt. Figure 4 shows the Bass Rapids diabase sill Rb-Sr whole-rock isochron originally published by *Elston and McKee* [1982; their Figure 7]. The higher precision of age and initial Sr of the Bass Rapids diabase sill [*Elston and McKee*, 1982] comes from the wider spread in the Rb-Sr data on the isochron plot because two of the data points are from high-Rb granophyre occurring at the top of the sill. As shown by *Elston and McKee* [1982], the Bass Rapids diabase sill provides every indication that it was well mixed isotopically when it was intruded, even though during cooling the sill segregated mineralogically and chemically by crystal settling to produce a granophyre on top of the diabase. Such a condition of initial thorough isotopic mixing of the original magma body followed by rapid chemical segregation is suited to the assumptions of whole-rock and mineral isochron dating.

Hendricks and Stevenson [1990, 2003] have summarized most of the details of the Unkar Group, including the diabase sills and dikes, and the Cardenas Basalt flows. Subsequently, while focusing on the Cardenas Basalt, *Larson et al.* [1994] found that, whereas the major-element chemistry of the diabase sills exhibit similarities and dissimilarities

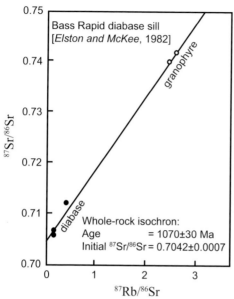

Figure 4. The original Rb-Sr whole-rock isochron plot for the Bass Rapids diabase sill published by *Elston and McKee* [1982]. Isochron age obtained was 1070±30 Ma.

with the lower-member flows of the Cardenas Basalt [*Hendricks and Lucchitta,* 1974], the trace and rare earth element data from a sample of the sill at Hance Rapids show very similar variation patterns to those in the lower-member flows of the Cardenas Basalt. Only Ti and P contents are markedly higher in the sill, and the negative Eu anomaly for the sill is smaller than that for the lower-member Cardenas Basalt flows. Thus, *Larson et al.* [1994] suggested a common origin for the diabase of the sills and the basalt of the lower-member flows similar to continental flood basalts, except that the higher Ti and P contents of the diabase may indicate that the magma that fed the intrusions did not also directly feed the flows of the lower member. Alternately, they suggested that the higher silica, Ti and P contents of the basalt flows are due either to greater crustal contamination of the basalt magma on its passage to the earth's surface, or heterogeneity in the mantle source. Paleomagnetic determinations by *Elston and Grommé* [1974], *Elston and McKee* [1982], and *Elston* [1989] suggested that the diabase sills have a different paleomagnetic pole position than the Cardenas Basalt flows. *Elston and McKee* [1982], recognizing the analytical uncertainties of the Rb-Sr measurements, suggested that the sills date 40–50 Ma older than the Cardenas Basalt. However, *Weil et al.* [2003] argued that the sills and associated Cardenas Basalt have the same paleomagnetic pole position, and could, therefore, be the same age. Although the Rb-Sr whole-rock isochron ages are identical for the Cardenas Basalt and the Bass Rapids diabase sill, the flows and sill were found to have slightly different initial $^{87}Sr/^{86}Sr$ ratios (see above, 0.70650±0.0015 and 0.70420±0.0007, analytical errors 2σ respectively). This small initial Sr difference is probably due to bias in sampling the Cardenas Basalt. Bias was introduced because *Elston and McKee* [1982] did not sample the lower flows of the Cardenas Basalt that are lower in radiogenic Sr.

Potassium-Ar analysis of Precambrian diabase and Cardenas Basalt of Grand Canyon has not presented ages concordant with Rb-Sr. A K-Ar model age of 944 Ma was obtained on pyroxene extracted from a sample of the diabase sill, presumably at Hance Rapids, by *Ford et al.* [1972], whereas *Elston and McKee* [1982] obtained two K-Ar model ages of 913±40 Ma for pyroxene in the diabase sill at Hance Rapids, and 954±30 Ma for plagioclase from the diabase sill at Tapeats Creek (K-Ar model ages are reported here, as is customary in the literature, with 1σ analytical errors). Additionally, *Elston and McKee* [1982] reported a total fusion $^{40}Ar/^{39}Ar$ age of 907±35 Ma for pyroxene from the diabase sill near Shinumo Creek and a $^{40}Ar/^{39}Ar$ isochron age of 904±100 Ma from seven-step incremental heating of a whole-rock sample from the diabase sill at Tapeats Creek. *Austin and Snelling* [1998] reported K-Ar data on five further samples of these Grand Canyon intrusive rocks, one from the diabase dike in Red Canyon adjacent to Hance Rapids, one from the diabase sill near Hance Rapids, and three from the sill near Bass Rapids (one diabase and two granophyre). The K-Ar model ages range from 703±15 Ma to 895±20 Ma. When combined with the two samples analyzed by *Elston and McKee* [1982], the K-Ar data yield a K-Ar seven-point isochron. According to *Austin and Snelling* [1998] the

K-Ar whole-rock isochron age of the Grand Canyon diabase intrusives is 837±52 Ma, significantly discordant with *Elston and McKee's* [1982] Rb-Sr five-point isochron age of 1070±30 Ma for Bass Rapids diabase sill (both isochron ages with 2σ analytical uncertainties). *Larson et al.* [1994] argued that the post-emplacement cooling temperatures of the Cardenas Basalt and diabase intrusives never exceeded 250°C and a pressure of 1.5 kbar. They supposed that Ar leakage might explain the anomalously young K-Ar ages. *Timmons et al.* [2001] reported $^{40}Ar/^{39}Ar$ spectra ages for three diabase intrusives that are consistent with the K-Ar model ages. *Timmons et al.* [2001] supposed that a hydrothermal event at about 800 Ma caused pervasive Ar leakage. *Austin and Snelling* [1998] noted the systematic ^{40}Ar variation in Cardenas Basalt and diabase sills is not matched by a systematic loss pattern for non-radiogenic ^{36}Ar. They concluded that the Rb-Sr and K-Ar discordance could not be explained by Ar loss due to either resetting or leakage. *Austin and Snelling* [1998] offered three alternative explanations—

(1) argon inheritance,

(2) argon mixing, or

(3) change in the radioisotopic decay rates that affected ^{87}Rb and ^{40}K decay by different factors.

The sill at Bass Rapids appears to be the best candidate for detailed radioisotopic study. How then are the radioisotope daughters distributed through the granophyre and diabase, and through the mineral phases of the latter? The various radioisotope pairs would be expected to give concordant whole-rock isochron and mineral isochron "ages." However, published K-Ar model "ages" for the diabase sills (and the Cardenas Basalt) are significantly younger than their associated Rb-Sr isochron "ages" [*Elston and McKee,* 1982; *Austin and Snelling,* 1998].

For this study the thick sill near Bass Rapids was chosen because of its excellent outcrop exposures and because of its well-defined 6 m thick granophyre layer on top of the 85 m thick diabase [*Snelling et al.,* 2003]. Furthermore, more geochemical and radioisotopic analyses have been undertaken previously on this sill than any of the other sills in Grand Canyon.

4. Sample Collection, Preparation and Analysis

4.1 Beartooth Andesitic Amphibolite

A single, multi-kilogram sample of the Beartooth andesitic amphibolite was collected from the southeastern Beartooth Mountains of northwestern Wyoming to see if concordant mineral isochrons could be obtained by K-Ar, Rb-Sr, Sm-Nd, and Pb-Pb. The sample was collected from a road cut on U. S. Highway 212, west of Beartooth Pass, 1.3 km east-northeast of Long Lake (Deep Lake, Wyoming 7.5 minute Quadrangle, U. S. G. S., 1991). The outcrop sampled is on the east side of Highway 212 at North 44° 52.187' latitude and West 109° 28.937' longitude (North American Datum of 1927) with a position error estimate by G. P. S. and topographic control of about 10 m. The sample location is an exposure in the deep excavation engineered for the highway at an elevation of 3110 m. The rock possesses excellent coarse-grained crystalline texture with very little evidence of weathering or low-temperature alteration. The outcrop was specifically selected because it was apparently one of the sample locations of *Wooden et al.* [1982] for their Rb-Sr whole-rock isochron. Thus, this andesitic amphibolite was used by *Wooden et al.* [1982] to define the Rb-Sr isochron's slope (and, therefore, the age of the cogenetic suite), as well as to define the assumed initial homogeneous Sr from which the cogenetic suite of rocks is supposed to have evolved. This rock is, therefore, considered representative of the andesitic amphibolite in the southeastern Beartooth Mountains.

The Beartooth andesitic amphibolite sample comes from a tabular amphibolite body that is tens of meters wide. It is in contact association with the Long Lake granodiorite, an intrusive igneous body that is supposed to have metamorphosed the amphibolite [*Wooden et al.,* 1982]. The amphibolite sample possesses coarse-grained, equigranular texture with slight foliation due to the biotite. Grain size is approximately 1 mm. Major mineral composition in order of abundance by weight is plagioclase, quartz, biotite, hornblende, magnetite, and titanite. The amphibolite appears ideal for mineral isochron analysis because biotite, titanite and hornblende fractionate radiogenic parent isotopes.

The Beartooth andesitic amphibolite sample was crushed in an iron mortar to produce 1.01 kg of sieved powder consisting of −140 to +270 mesh grains representative of the whole rock. The powder passed through the 140-mesh sieve (140 squares per inch) but was collected on top of a 270-mesh sieve (270 squares per inch). Five mineral separates from the powders were progressively concentrated by centrifugation in three heavy liquids diluted to produce liquids of precisely calibrated densities. Centrifugation was performed on up to 1 liter bottles of heavy liquids with high-strength armatures delivering g-forces more than 50 times normal gravity. The three heavy liquids used were tribromomethane ($CHBr_3$) with specific gravity of 2.85 at room temperature, diiodomethane (CH_2I_2) with specific gravity of 3.32 at room temperature, and a solution of thallium malonate-formate [$HCO_2Tl\,CH_2(COOTl)_2$] in water with a specific gravity at full saturation of about 4.05 at room temperature. Dilutents used to adjust densities of heavy liquids included acetone, distilled water and ethyl alcohol. Cleaning and concentration using a strong magnet followed heavy-liquid separations. Microscopic examination and x-ray diffraction analyses insured excellent recovery of the desired mineral phases. The five mineral phases separated from the Beartooth amphibolite whole-rock were

(1) quartz-plagioclase,
(2) biotite,
(3) hornblende,
(4) magnetite, and
(5) titanite.

Because of the density similarity of quartz and plagioclase, we were unable to separate quartz from andesine. The six samples (whole-rock plus five mineral separates) had abundant grains for K-Ar, Rb-Sr, Sm-Nd and Pb-Pb analyses plus elemental and x-ray diffraction analyses.

4.2 Bass Rapids Diabase Sill

The Bass Rapids diabase sill was sampled as eleven rocks from a composite section through the sill at Bass Rapids (north bank of the Colorado River at mile 107.6 to 108.0), the same section sampled from outcrop by *Hendricks and Lucchitta* [1974] some 800 m east of Shinumo Creek [*Snelling et al.*, 2003]. The eleven samples were chosen to represent the overall petrographic variability within the complete thickness of the sill (Figure 5). Eight of the samples are diabase from the lower approximately 85 m of the sill. Three of the samples are from the 6 m thick granophyre at the top of the sill. These eleven whole-rock samples were prepared by clean laboratory techniques as –200-mesh powders for chemical and isotopic analyses. Thin-sawed slices of the whole rocks were prepared as thin sections for petrographic analysis. Two of the eight diabase samples representative of the sill were each crushed to produce more than 1 kg of –140 to +270 mesh grains, and the various minerals within the powders were progressively concentrated by centrifugation in the three different heavy liquids, followed by further cleaning using a strong magnet. Six mineral phases were thus separated from whole-rock diabase sample DI-13 (normal plagioclase, high-density plagioclase, biotite, clinopyroxene, olivine and magnetite). Using the experience gained from sample DI-13, a very thorough search was made for smaller quantities of additional mineral phases in whole-rock sample DI-15. Eleven mineral phases were separated from sample DI-15 (plagioclase, high-density plagioclase, biotite, normal clinopyroxene, high-density clinopyroxene, orthopyroxene, normal hornblende, high-density hornblende, olivine, ilmenite, and magnetite). The Fe-Ti oxide (opaque "titanomagnetite" in thin section) of the diabase contains mostly magnetite, but the less-abundant mineral ilmenite occurs as well. In sample DI-15 a small quantity of ilmenite was recovered. Because "titanomagnetite" was so easily separated from these rocks, magnetite (with a small fraction of ilmenite) was separated from samples (DI-7, DI-10, DI-11, DI-16, and DI-17). X-ray diffraction analysis (XRD) and/or optical microscopy were used to confirm the identity and purity of the minerals concentrated.

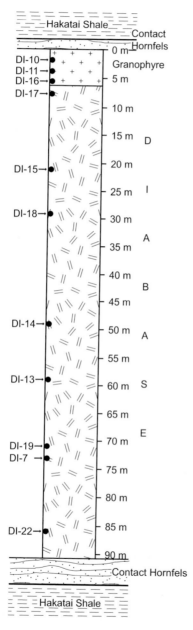

Figure 5. Diagrammatic section through the Bass Rapids sill showing the 6 m thick granophyre capping above the 85 m thick diabase body of the sill. The location of samples within the sill is indicated (after *Snelling et al.* [2003]).

4.3 Analysis Procedures

X-ray diffraction analyses of mineral separates were performed on a Scintag x-ray diffractometer scanning from 5 to 50° 2θ using a Cu K-α radiation, with the resulting patterns matched to more than 60,000 reference standards in the Joint Committee for Powder Diffraction Standards database. Sam Iyengar was the XRD analyst.

All Beartooth andesitic amphibolite and Bass Rapids diabase sill samples were analyzed for major and trace elements. XRAL Laboratories of Don Mills, Ontario, using XRF (x-ray fluorescence), ICP (inductively coupled plasma), and ICP-MS (inductively coupled plasma mass spectrometer) methods, performed chemical analyses of the whole-rock powders for 67 elements.

Whole rocks were subjected to standard K-Ar analysis by Geochron Laboratories, Cambridge, Massachusetts (R. Reesman, analyst) and Activation Laboratories, Ancaster, Canada (Y. Kapusta, analyst). The abundance of K was measured in whole rocks by flame photometry. Additionally, the five mineral separates from the Beartooth amphibolite, because of their abundance, were submitted as 5 g separates for K-Ar analysis, but technical problems occurred in the acid digestion process of magnetite and titanite. Potassium-Ar data on Beartooth andesitic amphibolite include only four parts, the whole-rock, quartz-andesine, hornblende and biotite.

Rubidium-Sr, Sm-Nd, and Pb-Pb analyses were performed on whole-rocks and mineral separates using a Finnigan-MAT 6-collector solid source mass spectrometer at the University of Colorado. *Farmer et al.* [1991] described the analytic technique, and G. L. Farmer supervised the analysis process. Rubidium, Sr, Sm, Nd, and Pb were separated by conventional cation-exchange chromatography; isotopic concentrations were measured by isotope dilution analysis. The U. S. G. S. andesite AGV-1 standard yielded Rb and Sr concentrations within 1.0% of the accepted value. The CIT mixed Sm/Nd standard yielded Sm and Nd concentrations within 0.7% of the accepted values. The NIST Sr isotopic standard yielded $^{87}Sr/^{86}Sr$ of 0.71028 ± 0.0002 (2σ) during the time period of most of the measurements. The La Jolla Nd isotopic standard yielded $^{143}Nd/^{144}Nd$ of 0.511838±0.00005 (2σ) during the time period of most of the measurements. Lead isotope ratios were calibrated relative to NBS-981 with standard deviations (2σ) for $^{206}Pb/^{204}Pb$ of 0.19%, $^{207}Pb/^{204}Pb$ of 0.2%, and $^{208}Pb/^{204}Pb$ of 0.28% during the time of most of the measurements.

Technical problems were encountered in isotope dilution analysis of the abundance of Sm and Nd in the mineral titanite from the Beartooth amphibolite. The extremely high abundance of Sm and Nd in titanite required several attempts to achieve reproducibility of the measurements at the University of Colorado. Two separate splits of titanite were supplied for Sm-Nd analysis with close agreement obtained.

Radiogenic isotope data were interpreted by the popular software package called *Isoplot* written by Kenneth R. Ludwig of the Berkeley Geochronology Center [*Ludwig*, 2001]. *Isoplot* does basic plotting and calculation functions including the Rb-Sr, Sm-Nd, and Pb-Pb isochrons. The slope of the linear-array plot is interpreted to be an isochron by *Isoplot* using the two-error regression method of *York* [1969]. *Isoplot* calculates the "mean square of weighted deviates" (MSWD), a ratio of the observed scatter of the points from the best-fit line to the expected scatter from the assigned errors. *Isoplot* also calculates a probability that helps evaluate the degree of confidence one might attach to an isochron.

5. Petrography and Chemistry

5.1 Beartooth Andesitic Amphibolite

The coarse-grained, equigranular, Beartooth andesitic amphibolite displays excellent crystallinity in thin section. Major mineral composition in order of abundance by weight is plagioclase (44%), quartz (27%), biotite (16%), hornblende (7%), magnetite (3%), and titanite (2%). Table 1 displays the major element oxides and abundances of selected trace elements. Biotite, and to a lesser degree hornblende, form the foliated texture of the metamorphic rock. Plagioclase is strongly twinned andesine (An≈30 composition) dominating the prominent,

Table 1. Major-element oxide and selected trace element analyses of the Beartooth andesitic amphibolite from the southeastern Beartooth Mountains, northwest Wyoming. Analysis includes the whole-rock BT-1 and five mineral separates. (Analyst: XRAL Laboratories of S.G.S. Canada, Don Mills, Ontario, October 1999.)

Oxide/Element	BT-1WR Whole Rock	BT-1QA Quartz-Andesine	BT-1B Biotite	BT-1H Hornblende	BT-1M Magnetite	BT-1T Titanite
SiO_2 (%)	56.9	69.9	38.0	40.4	3.03	28.9
TiO_2 (%)	1.50	0.34	1.85	1.35	0.45	29.1
Al_2O_3 (%)	13.9	15.4	14.3	11.0	0.71	1.69
Fe_2O_3 (%)	11.1	0.77	19.2	20.6	95.3	5.97
MgO (%)	2.65	0.33	10.5	8.14	0.25	0.00
MnO (%)	0.14	0.02	0.41	0.53	0.05	0.08
CaO (%)	5.84	4.06	2.22	11.8	0.80	26.4
Na_2O (%)	3.08	4.24	0.66	1.18	0.12	0.26
K_2O (%)	2.36	2.12	6.92	1.39	0.14	0.05
P_2O_5 (%)	0.62	0.35	0.23	0.11	0.08	2.31
S (%)	0.21	0.04	0.10	0.04	1.07	3.95
LOI (%)	0.45	0.50	1.60	0.39	0.00	3.23
TOTAL	98.75	98.07	95.99	96.93	102.00	101.94
Cr (ppm)	71	5	100	130	827	40
V (ppm)	187	25	336	382	1470	661
Ni (ppm)	28	4	99	44	72	38
Co (ppm)	20	3	28	32	55	>6000
Cu (ppm)	25.4	15.7	30.8	22.6	59.7	16.3
Zn (ppm)	98.6	17.0	366	240	75.4	13.4
Rb (ppm)	54.2	31.9	202	7.2	2.5	2.0
Sr (ppm)	855	1132	197	336	56.9	112
Zr (ppm)	159	121	43	45	9	22730
Nb (ppm)	15	9	4	6	5	237
Ba (ppm)	1770	2350	2430	156	89	37
Pb (ppm)	14.2	14.8	8.53	11.9	78.8	19.4
Th (ppm)	20.0	1.8	19.0	61.8	3.5	21.0
U (ppm)	<0.05	<0.05	<0.05	<0.05	<0.05	33.0
La (ppm)	152	36.3	202	715	66.0	386
Ce (ppm)	305	77.2	352	1300	133	1890
Nd (ppm)	143	27.0	68.4	258	45.9	1852
Sm (ppm)	20.2	4.30	5.57	24.5	4.59	401
Cl (ppm)	708	169	2060	2910	60	127

coarse, granular fabric of the rock. Biotite is dark brown, pleochroic, Fe-rich, high density, well formed, with good indication of hexagonal outline. Hornblende is greenish, pleochroic with high Mg and high rare earth element (REE) content. Magnetite is Fe-rich with only a small quantity of associated ilmenite. Titanite occurs as translucent yellowish crystals some of which possess brown and black metamict regions, evidently lattice disruptions caused by significant radioactive decay of U or Th. Titanite, like hornblende, is strongly enriched in REEs. Other incompatible elements, like the REEs, appear to be enriched within hornblende and titanite. The most obvious exception is Rb that is enriched in the biotite, not hornblende and titanite.

The whole-rock elemental composition of this single sample of the Beartooth amphibolite resembles overall the "incompatible-element-rich andesitic amphibolite" generalized from the Beartooth Mountains of Wyoming and Montana [*Mueller et al.*, 1983]. The rare earth element (REE) pattern closely follows the generalized Beartooth amphibolites of *Mueller et al.* [1983], even in the enrichment of light REE over heavy REE. Titanium and Zr, elements that *Mueller et al.* [1983] argue are conserved during metamorphism, appear in the normal Beartooth abundance within our new rock sample. Because our new sample has significantly higher incompatible element concentration than the surrounding Long Lake granodiorite, the source of the incompatible elements cannot be the granodiorite at the time of the metamorphic event [*Mueller et al.*, 1983]. Strontium is also more abundant in the amphibolite than the surrounding granodiorite. Therefore, a case can be made that metamorphism was isochemical. Amphibolite retains its incompatible elements, including REEs and Sr, which were distinguishing characteristics of the rock before the metamorphic event. Hydrothermal alteration of the original andesite is not a viable explanation.

5.2 Bass Rapids Diabase Sill

The sill at Bass Rapids just east of Shinumo Creek is similar to other sills within the Unkar Group being composed of olivine diabase, but it is capped by granophyre (Figure 5), making this sill a classic example of in-place differentiation of a basaltic magma. The 6 m thick granophyre consists predominantly of K-feldspar (55–60%) and quartz (12–25%), with biotite, plagioclase, some clinopyroxene, and titanomagnetite making up the remaining 20–28% [Snelling et al., 2003]. The rock is holocrystalline, coarse-grained, and has a well-developed granophyric texture in which quartz, plagioclase, biotite, clinopyroxene and titanomagnetite fill interstices between the orthoclase crystals. The transition between the granophyre and diabase below occurs over a vertical distance of less than 1 m and is a zone rich in biotite and accessory minerals [Hendricks, 1989]. Apatite makes up as much as 5–10% of the rock. Ilmenite and titanite occur, and zircon with reaction halos is present within the biotite grains.

The olivine diabase interior of the sill is medium- to coarse-grained, containing plagioclase (30–45%), olivine (20–35%), clinopyroxene (15–30%), titanomagnetite and ilmenite (5%), and biotite (1%), with accessory apatite [Snelling et al., 2003]. The texture is diabasic to subophitic, although a crude alignment of feldspar laths can be seen in many places. The plagioclase laths (composition An_{45-60} [45–60% anorthite]) average 1.5 mm in length and are partially to completely altered to sericite. Both normal and reverse zoning of crystals are common. Anhedral to subhedral olivine crystals up to 1 mm in diameter are often partially altered along borders and fractures to chlorite, talc, magnetite, iddingsite, and serpentine. Fresh grain interiors have compositions of approximately Fo_{80} (80% forsterite) and interference colors that suggest normal zoning. Plagioclase laths and olivine grains are often enclosed by large, optically continuous, poikilitic clinopyroxene grains, giving the rock its subophitic texture. The clinopyroxene is brownish-pink, non-pleochroic augite that is usually fresh. Large irregular grains of titanomagnetite partly altered to hematite and biotite, as well as primary pleochroic brown biotite partially altered to chlorite, occupy interstices between the plagioclase and olivine grains.

The olivine concentration tends to increase towards the center of the sill, whereas the clinopyroxene decreases. Immediately below the granophyre the diabase contains about 5% modal olivine, which increases rapidly to 20–30% through the central part of the sill [Hendricks and Lucchitta, 1974]. About 15 m above the base of the sill is an olivine-rich layer that contains about 50% modal olivine, and then the olivine content of the diabase decreases to about 10% near the base. *Hendricks* [1989] and *Hendricks and Lucchitta* [1974] suggested that this distribution of the olivine in the sill can be explained by the process of flow differentiation, that involves the movement of early-formed olivine grains away from the margins of the sill during flow of the intruding magma [*Bhattacharji and Smith*, 1964; *Bhattacharji*, 1967; *Simkin*, 1967]. It is envisaged that, as the magma intrudes up through the conduit and then outward to form the sill, fluid-dynamic forces concentrate toward the center of the moving mass the already-formed olivine crystals, with crystal concentration occurring even before the emplacement of the sill. As the magma also moves laterally, gravity acting on the olivine crystals could have produced a gradational change in the olivine content from the lower contact upward, while causing an abrupt change in olivine from the upper contact downward. Once emplaced, crystallization of the remaining liquid magma within the sill would then have yielded the remaining minerals in relatively constant proportions [*Simkin*, 1967].

Although there is a general uniformity of the diabase throughout the sill, there are two types of textural variations described by *Noble* [1914]. First, there are "lumps" or "balls" similar in mineralogy to the surrounding diabase, that is, olivine and plagioclase with augite filling interstices. The plagioclase laths in the lumps are up to 7.5 mm in length, filling embayments in large olivine crystals. The augite occurs as ophitic intergrowths with the plagioclase. Second, pegmatite veins consisting of plagioclase and augite with a very similar texture are found in the upper part of the sill. These textural variations undoubtedly represent segregation features produced during crystallization of the sill.

The lower chilled margin and contact of the sill with the underlying Hakatai Shale is covered, but is probably similar to the fine-grained chilled margins found in most of the other sills intruding the Unkar Group in Grand Canyon. The upper contact of the sill is marked by the 6 m thick capping of granophyre, the contact with the overlying Hakatai Shale is sharp (Figure 5), and no xenoliths of Hakatai Shale are found in the granophyre, suggesting that it was not produced by assimilation of the shale. Instead, the transition zone between the granophyre and the diabase beneath it in the sill suggests that the granophyre was a residual magma that "floated" to the top of the sill as the diabase crystallized, so that there was little late-stage mixing of it with the diabase part of the sill [*Hendricks and Lucchitta,* 1974].

Contact metamorphism of the Hakatai Shale has occurred above and below the sill, the shale being altered to a knotted hornfels (Figure 5). This contact metamorphism is greater below the sill than above it. The hornfels below the sill extends for 5 m below the contact and forms a prominent outcrop. Biotite porphyroblasts as much as 0.25 mm in size occur within 5 cm of the contact with the sill, and at 10 cm the shale is a knotted hornfels containing porphyroblasts of probable andalusite and cordierite that have been replaced pseudomorphically by muscovite and green chlorite respectively. These porphyroblasts become larger and less numerous away from the sill, reflecting a slower rate and lower density of nucleation. No recrystallization of the shale has occurred beyond 5 m below the sill contact, while the mineralogy of the metamorphism suggests that it was of low–medium grade.

The whole-rock, major element oxide and selected trace element data (Table 2) come from the full thickness of the sill (Figure 5). The major element oxide percentages are very similar to those reported by *Hendricks* [1989]. The granophyre as expected has a much higher SiO_2 content than the diabase making up the main portion of the sill, because the granophyre contains free quartz. Similarly, the diabase has a higher Fe_2O_3 and MgO content than the granophyre because of its olivine and augite content, the MgO concentration increasing towards the central part of the sill due to the higher olivine content there. Similarly, the higher Al_2O_3 and CaO values in the center of the sill would result from the concentration there of more calcic plagioclase. The high P_2O_5 content of sample DI-17 at the top of the diabase in close proximity to the granophyre is consistent with the apatite that is abundant in the transition zone. On a total alkalis-silica (TAS) diagram the diabase plots in the alkali olivine basalt field [*Hendricks,* 1989]. *Larson et al.* [1994], using their own data and that of *Hendricks and Lucchitta* [1974], suggested that chemically the diabase sills in the Unkar Group

Table 2. Whole-rock, major-element oxide and selected trace element analyses of eleven samples from the Bass Rapids sill, Grand Canyon, northern Arizona. Sample locations are shown in Figure 5. (Analyst: XRAL Laboratories of S.G.S. Canada, Don Mills, Ontario; January 1997 and February 2002.)

Oxide/ Element	Granophyre			Diabase							
	DI-10	DI-11	DI-16	DI-17	DI-15	DI-18	DI-14	DI-13	DI-19	DI-7	DI-22
	2 m below top	3.8 m below top	5.5 m below top	7.5 m below top	21 m below top	29 m below top	49 m below top	59 m below top	71 m below top	73 m below top	86 m below top
SiO_2 (%)	60.4	60.9	57.8	46.5	45.4	46.0	45.2	44.7	44.5	45.2	46.2
TiO_2 (%)	0.903	1.18	0.03	0.16	0.25	0.16	0.17	0.18	0.17	0.16	0.21
Al_2O_3 (%)	14.8	15.4	14.2	11.6	13.8	15.8	14.0	14.6	12.8	15.7	14.9
Fe_2O_3 (%)	5.96	4.79	8.24	16.2	14.1	12.5	13.3	12.4	12.6	10.3	13.5
MgO (%)	5.87	5.57	6.25	8.40	10.9	11.4	13.5	15.3	16.5	13.2	9.06
MnO (%)	<0.01	0.01	0.03	0.16	0.25	0.16	0.17	0.18	0.17	0.16	0.21
CaO (%)	0.27	0.09	0.65	4.16	6.89	8.13	7.68	7.80	4.16	8.48	7.15
Na_2O (%)	0.57	1.47	1.63	3.15	2.06	2.18	1.86	1.87	1.71	1.93	2.23
K_2O (%)	8.05	7.75	6.64	1.32	1.82	0.97	0.81	0.68	0.64	0.62	1.90
P_2O_5 (%)	0.03	0.02	0.32	1.23	0.51	0.26	0.28	0.09	0.27	0.19	0.43
S (%)	0.007	0.004	0.02	0.03	0.12	0.15	0.12	0.03	0.09	0.052	0.10
LOI (%)	2.85	2.90	2.95	3.15	2.2	1.75	1.85	1.2	2.7	2.4	2.45
TOTAL	99.8	100.2	100.0	99.0	99.9	100.4	100.3	100.1	100.4	99.4	100.30
Cr (ppm)	55	14	69	52	237	326	317	395	460	400	165
V (ppm)	108	116	72	200	195	142	140	88	131	110	231
Ni (ppm)	31	11	30	25	214	244	317	455	558	478	191
Co (ppm)	15	12	21	38	62	68	64	67	83	69	56
Cu (ppm)	3.4	7.9	15.6	51.4	98.3	129	63.9	30.3	55.0	31.0	101
Zn (ppm)	23.1	33.8	48.4	79.0	203	88.3	78.6	81.3	116	82.5	125
Rb (ppm)	104	106	87	23	39	23	18	16	23	14	51
Sr (ppm)	36	34	113	168	342	470	363	441	379	441	395
Zr (ppm)	228	313	349	342	160	92	116	82	116	68	161
Nb (ppm)	16	18	10	11	8	4	6	3	5	21	7
Ba (ppm)	567	633	613	327	322	184	134	167	161	239	352
Pb (ppm)	<2	<2	<2	7	7	<2	<2	<2	3	<2	5
Th (ppm)	9.4	12.0	12.2	6.4	<0.5	2.3	2.3	0.7	2.4	0.6	1.2
U (ppm)	1.9	2.5	4.0	4.8	1.7	<0.5	1.3	0.9	1.9	<0.5	0.9
La (ppm)	36.6	31.9	29.4	39.5	15.5	7.1	8.2	3.6	7.5	7.3	11.9
Ce (ppm)	80.8	68.9	65.5	94.0	38.2	17.8	20.5	8.2	18.8	16.9	29.7
Nd (ppm)	38.0	31.6	34.4	59.4	24.2	11.7	13.1	6.0	11.9	10.6	19.4
Sm (ppm)	8.1	6.2	7.9	13.3	6.3	3.1	3.3	1.5	2.9	3.2	4.6
Cl (ppm)	430	600	1050	580	1620	835	1070	363	842	954	2690

exhibit similarities and dissimilarities with the lower-member flows of the Cardenas Basalt, which are commonly regarded as the extrusive equivalents of these intrusive diabase sills.

Based on selected trace element data for one sample of the Hance Rapids sill, *Larson et al.* [1994] concluded that the variation in those data was very similar to trace element patterns for the lower-member flows of the Cardenas Basalt. The selected trace element data in Table 2 for the Bass Rapid diabase sill are also similar. Furthermore, the differences in trace element contents of the granophyre compared to the diabase are very obvious, and reflect the mineralogical differences. For example, Cr, Ni, Co, Cu, and Zn are much higher in the diabase than the granophyre, because of the olivine and trace sulfides found in the diabase that are not in the granophyre. In contrast, Ba, Rb, La, Ce, and Nd are much higher in the granophyre than in the diabase, reflecting differences in the feldspar contents of the two rock types, orthoclase being dominant in the granophyre, whereas plagioclase is dominant in the diabase and contains higher Sr. The higher content of Cl in the diabase parallels the higher content of P_2O_5 due to the presence of trace apatite. Zirconium is, as expected, higher in the granophyre where zircon is more likely to be in trace amounts.

6. Radioisotope Results for the Beartooth Amphibolite

The K-Ar analytical data and K-Ar model "ages" for Beartooth amphibolite are shown in Table 3. Potassium-Ar data were obtained for the whole rock and three mineral separates (quartz-plagioclase, biotite and hornblende). Although sufficient quantities of magnetite and titanite were obtained for the procedure, technical problems in acid digestion prevented K-Ar analysis of these two minerals. Potassium-Ar model ages within the three mineral phases from the single rock differ from 1520±31 Ma (quartz-plagioclase) to 2620±53 Ma (hornblende), with the whole rock giving a "model age" averaged from the minerals of 2011±45 Ma (K-Ar model ages with assigned 1σ uncertainties). The model age method assumes no radiogenic [40]Ar was retained when the andesite cooled during the metamorphic event to form the amphibolite. Because it is extremely unlikely that the minerals of the amphibolite within a few centimeters of each other record a billion year cooling

Table 3. K-Ar data for the whole rock and selected minerals from the Beartooth andesitic amphibolite, sample BT-1, northwestern Wyoming. (Analyst: Dr. R. Reesman, Geochron Laboratories, Cambridge, Massachusetts.)

Sample	Sample Type	K_2O (wt%)	^{40}K (ppm)	^{40}K (mol/g) $\times 10^{-8}$	$^{40}Ar^*$ (ppm)	$^{40}Ar^*$ (mol/g) $\times 10^{-9}$	$^{40}Ar^*$ (%)	total ^{40}Ar (mol/g) $\times 10^{-9}$	^{36}Ar (mol/g) $\times 10^{-13}$	Model Age (Ma)	Uncertainty (1σ error in Ma)
BT-1WR	whole rock	2.437	2.412	6.036	0.5180	12.96	96.6	13.42	15.57	2011	±45
BT-1QA	plagioclase/quartz	1.951	1.931	4.832	0.2677	6.699	95.0	7.052	11.95	1520	±31
BT-1B	biotite	6.285	6.223	15.57	1.819	45.52	98.4	46.26	25.04	2403	±53
BT-1H	hornblende	1.305	1.292	3.233	0.4434	11.10	96.7	11.48	12.86	2620	±53

history, differential Ar loss can be supposed. The quartz-plagioclase fraction, that has lost the largest proportion of its ^{40}Ar, also has the lowest concentration of ^{36}Ar, consistent with an Ar loss model. Biotite and hornblende give the oldest "ages." Biotite has significant ^{40}K and significant ^{40}Ar, differing from the other minerals. Although the biotite data could allow a K-Ar isochron plot, we assign little statistical significance to it and do not show it as a figure by Isoplot.

Rubidium-Sr, Sm-Nd, and Pb-Pb data for the Beartooth amphibolite are shown in Table 4. Figures 6, 7, and 8 are the three discordant mineral isochrons constructed by *Isoplot*. The Rb-Sr mineral isochron age (Figure 6) is 2515±110 Ma (2σ with expanded MSWD estimated errors) with initial $^{87}Sr/^{86}Sr$ for the rock of 0.7044. This initial

Table 4. Whole-rock and mineral Rb-Sr, Sm-Nd, and Pb-Pb radioisotopic data for the Beartooth andesitic amphibolite, sample BT-1, northwestern Wyoming. (Analyst: Assoc. Prof. G. L. Farmer, University of Colorado at Boulder.)

Sample	Sample Type	Rb (ppm)	Sr (ppm)	$^{87}Rb/^{86}Sr$	$^{87}Sr/^{86}Sr$	Sm (ppm)	Nd (ppm)	$^{147}Sm/^{144}Nd$	$^{143}Nd/^{144}Nd$	$^{206}Pb/^{204}Pb$	$^{207}Pb/^{204}Pb$	$^{208}Pb/^{204}Pb$
BT-1WR	Whole rock	54.2	855	0.183	0.70988	20.2	143	0.0856	0.510492	16.305	15.333	46.064
BT-1QA	Quartz and albite	31.9	1132	0.0816	0.70602	4.3	27.0	0.0963	0.510790	14.455	15.007	35.618
BT-1B	Biotite	202	197	3.00	0.81352	5.57	68.4	0.0492	0.509852	16.342	15.333	63.045
BT-1H	Hornblende	7.2	336	0.0620	0.70892	24.5	258	0.0574	0.509981	16.610	15.412	90.22
BT-1M	Magnetite	2.5	56.9	0.127	0.71025	4.59	45.9	0.0605	0.510703	17.108	15.485	37.546
BT-1T	Titanite	2.0	112	0.0517	0.70525	401	1852	0.131	0.511381	165.587	42.666	97.878
BT-1T2	Titanite	1.0	75	0.0380	0.70427	487	2152	0.1369	0.511412	173.759	44.466	93.366

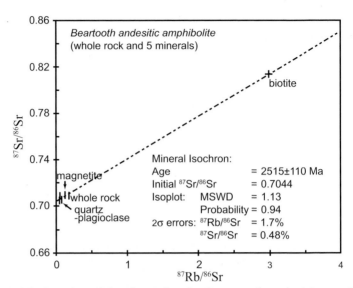

Figure 6. Rb-Sr mineral isochron for the Beartooth andesitic amphibolite. Error bars in this and following plots are 2σ.

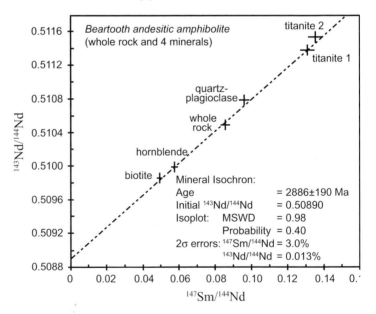

Figure 7. Sm-Nd mineral isochron for the Beartooth andesitic amphibolite. The mineral separate called "titanite 2" was not used in the regression analysis.

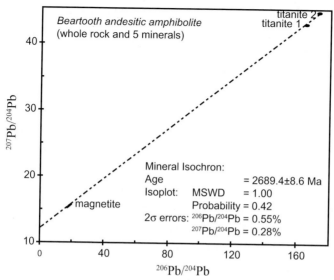

Figure 8. Pb-Pb mineral isochron for the Beartooth andesitic amphibolite. Both "titanite 1" and "titanite 2" were included in the regression analysis. Error ellipses (2σ) are very small at the scale of the plot.

$^{87}Sr/^{86}Sr$ is slightly higher than the value of 0.7022 obtained regionally by the whole-rock isochron of *Wooden et al.* [1982]. The Rb-Sr mineral isochron age is discordant with the 28-point Rb-Sr whole-rock isochron of *Wooden et al.* [1982]. This 6-point mineral isochron in Figure 6, although largely determined by the biotite and including magnetite, has an MSWD near unity and high probability. Figure 7 is the 5-point Sm-Nd mineral isochron of 2886±190 Ma, discordant from Rb-Sr. The mineral magnetite (without significant ilmenite included) appears to lie off the line described by the other five points, suggesting that the magnetite did not remelt completely in the metamorphic process, but retained its initial $^{143}Nd/^{144}Nd$ from the protolith, not from the homogenization of the subsequent metamorphic event. The 5-point Sm-Nd mineral isochron in Figure 7 has an MSWD near unity (indicating assigned errors are properly stated) and acceptable probability. The spread of the data in Figure 7 is very good, with titanite being strongly enriched in light REEs thus producing a higher $^{147}Sm/^{144}Nd$ beneficial to the isochron. Because of the technical difficulty of measuring very high abundances of Sm and Nd in titanite, two separate splits of titanite were submitted for Sm-Nd analysis. Although the second sample was reprocessed to produce a higher purity sample (BT-1T2), general agreement between these measurements indicates accuracy. Only one titanite sample (BT-1T) was used for the regression analysis. Figure 8 is the Pb-Pb mineral isochron of 2689±9 Ma, including magnetite and two separate splits and measurements of the extremely radiogenic Pb of titanite. The MSWD is unity (indicating assigned errors are properly stated) and *Isoplot* calculates acceptable probability. The Pb-Pb mineral isochron has very low error associated with the estimated age because of the extreme difference in radiogenic Pb's between the minerals, and because the isochron interpretation supposes the radiogenic Pb's to have been homogenized during the essentially instantaneous metamorphic event. The Pb-Pb mineral isochron for Beartooth amphibolite is discordant with the Rb-Sr mineral isochron and the whole-rock Rb-Sr isochron of *Wooden et al.* [1982]. Also, the Sm-Nd mineral isochron is discordant with the Rb-Sr mineral isochron.

7. Radioisotope Results for the Bass Rapids Diabase Sill

7.1 K-Ar Data

The K-Ar analytical data and K-Ar model "ages" for all eleven samples are listed in Table 5. These model ages are calculated by the standard equation of *Dalrymple and Lanphere* [1969] using the ratio of the abundances of $^{40}Ar^*$ (the radiogenic ^{40}Ar) to ^{40}K listed in Table 5. The model age method assumes no radiogenic ^{40}Ar was present when the basaltic magma cooled to form the diabase sill. The model "ages" range from 656±15 Ma to 1053±24 Ma (1σ age errors derived from analytical errors only), with the mean age being 816 Ma (n = 11). Model ages with such wide variation are difficult to explain, because they are not easily predicted by any possible sequence in the formation of the sill, such as the bottom and top of the sill cooling before the center of the sill, or the granophyre cooling before the diabase below. Indeed, there is no recognizable pattern, except that the model "ages" are discordant

Table 5. K-Ar data for whole rocks from the Bass Rapids diabase sill, Grand Canyon, northern Arizona. (Analysts: Dr. R. Reesman, Geochron Laboratories, Cambridge, Massachusetts, and Dr. Y. Kapusta, Activation Laboratories, Ancaster, Canada.)

Sample	Rock Type	Position (from top)	K_2O (wt%)	^{40}K (ppm)	^{40}K (mol/g) $\times 10^{-8}$	$^{40}Ar^*$ (ppm)	$^{40}Ar^*$ (mol/g) $\times 10^{-9}$	$^{40}Ar^*$ (%)	total ^{40}Ar (mol/g) $\times 10^{-9}$	^{36}Ar (mol/g) $\times 10^{-13}$	Model Age (Ma)	Uncertainty (1σ error in Ma)
DI-10	Granophyre	2m	8.61	8.527	21.34	0.5737	14.36	96.4	14.90	18.27	895	±20
DI-11		3.8m	8.245	8.166	20.43	0.4206	10.52	94.3	11.16	21.66	721	±14
DI-16		5.5m	5.764	5.706	14.28	0.4281	10.71	92.85	11.53	27.75	974	±20
DI-17	Diabase	7.5m	1.413	1.399	3.501	0.1162	2.908	86.4	3.366	15.50	1053	±24
DI-15		21m	2.661	2.634	6.591	0.1211	3.030	86.15	3.517	16.48	656	±15
DI-18		29m	1.356	1.342	3.358	0.06572	1.645	76.45	2.152	17.16	692	±14
DI-14		49m	0.959	0.950	2.377	0.06567	1.643	76.1	2.159	17.46	914	±22
DI-13		59m	0.958	0.948	2.372	0.05014	1.255	83.45	1.504	8.426	737	±18
DI-19		71m	0.778	0.770	1.926	0.04973	1.244	75.8	1.641	13.44	866	±24
DI-7		73m	0.754	0.747	1.869	0.03893	0.9742	80.0	1.218	8.250	728	±20
DI-22		86m	2.157	2.135	5.343	0.11107	2.779	91.21	3.047	9.069	740	±22

from one another. The mean model "age" for the granophyre is 863 Ma (n = 3), whereas the mean model "age" for the diabase is 798 Ma (n = 8), but the model "age" for sample DI-14 in the center of the diabase sill is much older at 914±22 Ma. Furthermore, pairs of samples very close to one another give highly discordant model "ages," such as granophyre samples DI-10 and DI-11 which are only 1.8 m apart and yet yield model "ages" of 895±20 Ma and 721±14 Ma respectively, and diabase samples DI-19 and DI-7 which are only 2 m apart and, yet, yield model "ages" of 866±24 Ma and 728±20 Ma respectively.

Figure 9 is the ^{40}K versus $^{40}Ar^*$ diagram for the Bass Rapids diabase sill. The error bars plotted with the data are the estimated 2σ uncertainties, and the strong linear trend that is apparent is plotted as an isochron using the *Isoplot* program of *Ludwig* [2001] that utilizes the least-squares linear regression method of *York* [1969]. All eleven samples were included in the regression calculation, although the assigned 2σ errors were large. The isochron "age" calculated from the slope of the line is 841.5±164 Ma (2σ error). The initial ^{40}Ar is zero, so this is consistent with the assumption of zero $^{40}Ar^*$ in the model age technique. This K-Ar isochron "age" is discordant with the published

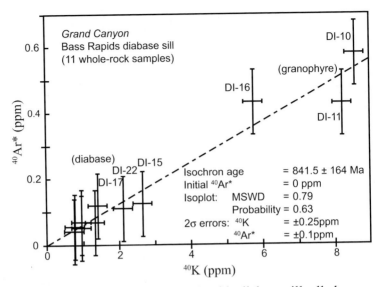

Figure 9. ^{40}K versus $^{40}Ar^*$ in the Bass Rapids diabase sill, all eleven samples being used in the isochron and age calculation. The bars represent 2σ uncertainties.

five-point Rb-Sr whole-rock isochron "age" for the sill of 1070 ± 30 Ma [*Elston and McKee, 1982*]. Note also that the slope of the line is heavily influenced by the three granophyre data points with their high K contents due to their contained orthoclase. Because all the samples are cogenetic it was important that all be included in the calculation, even though it leads to a large 2σ uncertainty in the isochron age. This large uncertainty must be due to more than analytical errors, and is thus indicative of the minor hydrothermal alteration present (plagioclase altered to sericite) and perhaps some contamination of the granophyre from the hornfels wall-rock during contact metamorphism.

Figure 10 shows $^{40}K/^{36}Ar$ plotted against $^{40}Ar/^{36}Ar$ for the sill, based on the data in Table 5. The error bars again represent the 2σ uncertainties in the data points, which again are large, with all eleven samples included in the regression analysis. The calculated isochron "age" is therefore 840.4 ± 179 Ma with an initial $^{40}Ar/^{36}Ar$ value of 214. This is much less than the present atmospheric $^{40}Ar/^{36}Ar$ value of 295.5, and suggests the possibility of a small Ar loss or that the regression line needs to be appropriately adjusted. This would reduce the isochron age, and make it even more discordant with the published Rb-Sr whole-rock isochron age, even though it would still be concordant with the K-Ar isochron age determined here and shown in Figure 9. Alternately, the low $^{40}Ar/^{36}Ar$ value could indicate incorporation into the basaltic magma of "primitive argon" thus inherited from its mantle source [*Dalrymple, 1969*].

7.2 Rb-Sr Data

The whole-rock Rb-Sr, Sm-Nd and Pb-Pb radioisotope data for all eleven samples from the sill are listed in Table 6. As anticipated, the radioisotope ratios in the three granophyre samples are distinctly

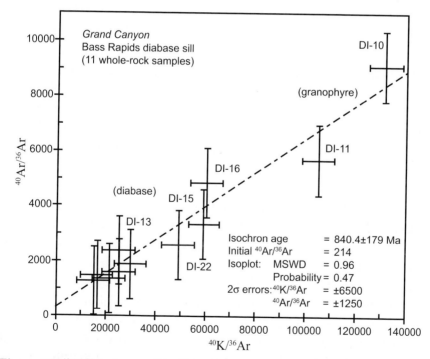

Figure 10. $^{40}K/^{36}Ar$ versus $^{40}Ar/^{36}Ar$ in the Bass Rapids diabase sill, all eleven samples being used in the isochron and age calculation. The bars represent 2σ uncertainties.

Table 6. Whole-rock Rb-Sr, Sm-Nd, and Pb-Pb radioisotopic data for the Bass Rapids diabase sill, Grand Canyon, northern Arizona. (Analyst: Assoc. Prof. G.L. Farmer, University of Colorado at Boulder.)

Sample	Rock Type	Position (from top)	Rb (ppm)	Sr (ppm)	^{87}Rb/^{86}Sr	^{87}Sr/^{86}Sr	Sm (ppm)	Nd (ppm)	^{147}Sm/^{144}Nd	^{143}Nd/^{144}Nd	^{206}Pb/^{204}Pb	^{207}Pb/^{204}Pb	^{208}Pb/^{204}Pb
DI-10	Granophyre	2m	101.5	35	8.4302	0.83703	8.25	37.8	0.132	0.512070	22.948	15.933	42.233
DI-11		3.8m	95.8	33	8.439	0.82481	8.11	32.59	0.150	0.511992	25.432	16.135	45.201
DI-16		5.5m	82.8	106	2.2643	0.741297	7.98	36.3	0.1329	0.512084	21.923	15.878	41.482
DI-17	Diabase	7.5m	24.2	154	0.4539	0.713329	14.55	62.4	0.1411	0.512391	19.368	15.702	38.574
DI-15		21m	38.5	312	0.3568	0.709139	6.0	25.0	0.1456	0.512441	17.255	15.475	36.981
DI-18		29m	21.8	422	0.1492	0.706359	3.08	12.5	0.1495	0.512458	17.358	15.494	37.003
DI-14		49m	11.7	328	0.1026	0.705461	3.37	13.8	0.1473	0.512443	18.355	15.561	38.154
DI-13		59m	15.4	383	0.1165	0.704818	2.65	10.8	0.1480	0.512438	17.699	15.510	37.353
DI-19		71m	16.9	329	0.1487	0.705019	3.60	15.0	0.1452	0.512466	17.260	15.452	36.854
DI-7		73m	11.5	347	0.0959	0.704502	1.64	6.04	0.164	0.512554	17.407	15.480	37.005
DI-22		86m	51.3	371	0.4005	0.711306	5.13	21.1	0.1471	0.512446	19.429	15.687	38.711

different from those obtained in the eight diabase samples. This reflects the major and trace element differences between these two rock types and their different mineralogies, the granophyre having a much higher K_2O content than the diabase because of the abundant orthoclase in it (Table 5). Thus, the Rb content of the granophyre is higher than that of the diabase, whereas the Sr content is higher in the diabase because it partitions with the Ca in plagioclase (Table 6). The generally higher REE and Pb contents of the granophyre likewise cause significantly different radioisotope ratios in the granophyre compared to the diabase. These differences are ideal for plotting of isochrons because of the larger spreads in the radioisotope ratios.

Figure 11 shows ^{87}Rb/^{86}Sr plotted against ^{87}Sr/^{86}Sr for the whole-rocks of the sill, based on the data in Table 6. The error bars again represent the 2σ uncertainties in the data points, which were small. The regression analysis using the *Isoplot* program of *Ludwig* [2001] yielded an excellent-fitting isochron with a high probability and MSWD near unity. The resultant isochron "age" of 1055±46 Ma is only marginally less than the five-point Rb-Sr isochron "age" of 1070±30 Ma obtained by *Elston and McKee* [1982]. At 0.7043, the initial ^{87}Sr/^{86}Sr for this isochron is virtually identical to the value of 0.70420±0.0007 obtained by *Elston and McKee* [1982]. Significantly, when we added the

Rb-Sr data for the five Elston and McKee samples to that of our eleven samples the resulting regression analysis yielded an even better sixteen-point isochron with a higher probability (0.86) from the same 2σ uncertainties for each of the data points. The isochron "age" of 1055 ± 44 Ma is identical, as is the initial $^{87}Sr/^{86}Sr$. Nevertheless, the uncertainty of ±44 Ma is higher than the ±30 Ma obtained by *Elston and McKee* [1982], but a lot of this uncertainty is due to the poorer fit of the two high Rb granophyre samples DI-10 and DI-11. Our uncertainties also assume more sources of error than those assigned by Elston and McKee, and our uncertainties appear to be better justified by our larger data set.

Rubidium-Sr data for minerals separated from the whole-rock diabase samples appear in Tables 7 and 8. Six mineral phases were separated from whole rock DI-13, and eleven mineral phases were separated from whole rock DI-15. In addition to magnetite separated from diabase whole rocks DI-13 and DI-15, magnetite was also separated from two other diabases (DI-7 and DI-17) and all three granophyres (DI-10,

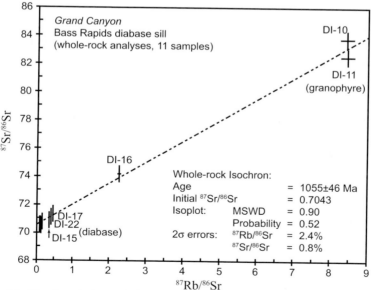

Figure 11. Rb-Sr whole-rock isochron for the Bass Rapids diabase sill. The bars represent 2σ uncertainties.

Table 7. Mineral Rb-Sr, Sm-Nd, and Pb-Pb radioisotopic data for diabase sample DI-13 from the Bass Rapids sill, Grand Canyon, northern Arizona. (Analyst: Assoc. Prof. G. L. Farmer, University of Colorado at Boulder.)

DI-13 fraction	Rb (ppm)	Sr (ppm)	^{87}Rb/^{86}Sr	^{87}Sr/^{86}Sr	Sm (ppm)	Nd (ppm)	^{147}Sm/^{144}Nd	^{143}Nd/^{144}Nd	^{206}Pb/^{204}Pb	^{207}Pb/^{204}Pb	^{208}Pb/^{204}Pb
Whole-rock	15.4	383	0.1165	0.704818	2.65	10.8	0.1480	0.512438	17.699	15.510	37.353
Biotite	92.2	187	1.4294	0.724746	2.37	11.3	0.1266	0.512225	17.457	15.486	37.150
Clinopyroxene	0.74	32.8	0.0651	0.704166	5.19	14.3	0.2190	0.512922	17.463	15.477	37.191
Plagioclase	28.5	784	0.1050	0.704769	0.63	9.4	0.0408	0.511448	17.194	15.471	36.913
High-density Plagioclase	27.3	634	0.1244	0.704967	8.96	39.1	0.1385	0.512403	17.085	15.461	36.791
Olivine	0.36	7.62	0.1348	0.704752	1.15	5.9	0.1189	0.512097	17.384	15.536	37.171
Magnetite (+ilmenite)	1.01	7.98	0.3669	0.708408	0.88	27.1	0.0196	0.511161	18.423	15.640	38.035

DI-11 and DI-16). All this magnetite data is shown in Table 9. The strong partitioning of the relevant trace elements into the different mineral phases is evident as expected. For example, Rb is high in the biotite, whereas the Sr is high in the plagioclase. This was expected to provide a good spread in the radioisotopic data, and improve the statistics of the

Table 8. Mineral Rb-Sr, Sm-Nd, and Pb-Pb radioisotopic data for diabase sample DI-15 from the Bass Rapids sill, Grand Canyon, northern Arizona. (Analyst: Assoc. Prof. G. L. Farmer, University of Colorado at Boulder.)

DI-15 fraction	Rb (ppm)	Sr (ppm)	^{87}Rb/^{86}Sr	^{87}Sr/^{86}Sr	Sm (ppm)	Nd (ppm)	^{147}Sm/^{144}Nd	^{143}Nd/^{144}Nd	^{206}Pb/^{204}Pb	^{207}Pb/^{204}Pb	^{208}Pb/^{204}Pb
Whole-rock	38.5	312	0.3568	0.709139	6.0	25.0	0.1456	0.512441	17.255	15.457	36.981
Biotite	114.01	90.7	3.651	0.760260	2.59	13.7	0.1145	0.512107	18.258	15.595	37.967
Hornblende	0.85	36.0	0.068	0.704743	6.47	18.4	0.2125	0.512924	17.478	15.531	37.185
Heavy Hornblende	3.02	53.7	0.1625	0.706273	6.62	24.8	0.1617	0.512512	17.524	15.497	37.241
Clinopyroxene	0.88	38.2	0.0663	0.704856	7.13	21.4	0.2017	0.512857	17.427	15.474	37.068
Heavy Clinopyroxene	3.2	55.7	0.1661	0.706477	6.61	22.2	0.1805	0.512664	17.457	15.500	37.267
Orthopyroxene	11.4	343.3	0.0937	0.705124	274	1188	0.1395	0.512397	17.624	15.545	37.419
Plagioclase	78.8	649	0.351	0.709055	1.41	6.7	0.1265	0.511850	17.445	15.579	37.145
High-density Plagioclase	61.1	549	0.3214	0.708425	73.4	345	0.1287	0.512401	17.742	15.506	37.445
Olivine	1.0	4.2	0.441	0.709888	1.59	6.4	0.1506	0.511808	17.398	15.600	37.311
Magnetite	2.4	124	0.0552	0.706713	0.44	2.3	0.1194	0.511910	17.613	15.515	37.425
Ilmenite	0.69	5.4	0.3712	0.709848	0.37	1.7	0.1299	No data	19.275	15.671	38.429

Table 9. Magnetite and ilmenite Rb-Sr, Sm-Nd, and Pb-Pb radioisotopic data for the Bass Rapids diabase sill, Grand Canyon, northern Arizona. (Analyst: Assoc. Prof. G. L. Farmer, University of Colorado at Boulder.)

Magnetite Sample (ilmenite status)	Host Rock	Rb (ppm)	Sr (ppm)	^{87}Rb/^{86}Sr	^{87}Sr/^{86}Sr	Sm (ppm)	Nd (ppm)	^{147}Sm/^{144}Nd	^{143}Nd/^{144}Nd	^{206}Pb/^{204}Pb	^{207}Pb/^{204}Pb	^{208}Pb/^{204}Pb
DI-10 MAG (+ILM)		8.2	4.0	6.443	0.797199	3.03	18.3	0.1004	0.511898	20.021	15.83	39.556
DI-11 MAG (+ILM)	Granophyre	3.03	4.6	1.9021	0.734262	5.32	39.6	0.0814	0.511733	22.152	16.181	41.246
DI-16 MAG (+ILM)		4.7	11	1.21	0.726166	4.32	23.5	0.1111	0.511970	22.959	15.988	40.543
DI-17 MAG (+ILM)		1.3	9.0	0.3933	0.715454	2.03	9.3	0.1325	0.512179	20.033	15.765	39.325
DI-15 MAG (-ILM)		2.4	124	0.0552	0.706713	0.44	2.3	0.1194	0.511910	17.613	15.515	37.425
DI-15 ILM (-MAG)	Diabase	0.69	5.4	0.3712	0.709848	0.37	1.7	0.1299	No data	19.275	15.671	38.429
DI-13 MAG (+ILM)		1.01	7.98	0.3669	0.708408	0.88	27.1	0.0196	0.511161	18.423	15.640	38.035
DI-7 HM (-ILM)		2.4	34	0.2893	0.70578	1.72	9.69	0.107	0.512160	18.158	15.585	37.738

isochron fits. For the specific Rb-Sr plots in Figures 12 through 14, we plotted all the Rb-Sr mineral data at the same scale as the Rb-Sr whole-rock data (Figure 11) so the extraordinary linearity of the data can be better appreciated.

Figure 12 is the ^{87}Rb/^{86}Sr versus ^{87}Sr/^{86}Sr diagram for the six mineral fractions from sample DI-13, plus the whole rock, plotted on the same scale as the whole rocks. The regression analysis produced an excellent isochron fit, with good probability and MSWD near unity. The resultant isochron "age" is 1060±24 Ma, the 2σ uncertainty being low because the 2σ error bars on the data points are also low, and the data spread, thanks to the biotite, is high. This mineral isochron age is, of course, totally concordant with the whole-rock Rb-Sr isochron "age" (1055±46 Ma, Figure 11), but at 0.70301 the initial ^{87}Sr/^{86}Sr is marginally lower than that for the whole-rock isochron.

Figure 13 is the ^{87}Rb/^{86}Sr versus ^{87}Sr/^{86}Sr diagram for the eleven mineral fractions from sample DI-15, plus the whole rock. Again, the regression analysis, when plotted on the same scale as the whole rocks, produces an excellent isochron fit, with good probability and MSWD near unity.

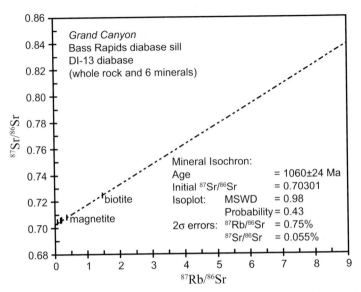

Figure 12. Rb-Sr mineral isochron for diabase sample DI-13 from the Bass Rapids diabase sill. The bars represent 2σ uncertainties. This age has the most tightly constrained error obtained from the sill.

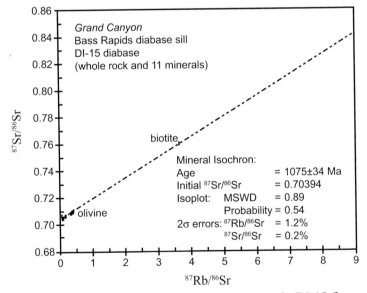

Figure 13. Rb-Sr mineral isochron for diabase sample DI-15 from the Bass Rapids diabase sill. The bars represent 2σ uncertainties.

The resultant isochron "age" is 1075±34 Ma, the 2σ uncertainty being low. This mineral isochron age is concordant with the whole-rock Rb-Sr isochron "age" (1055±46 Ma, Figure 11), but at 0.70394 the initial $^{87}Sr/^{86}Sr$ is also marginally lower than that for the whole-rock isochron. This mineral isochron age is also concordant with the Rb-Sr mineral isochron age from DI-13 (1060±24 Ma, Figure 12), with essentially the same initial Sr ratio.

Figure 14 is the Rb-Sr magnetite mineral isochron assembled from the various rocks. This plot includes all seven magnetites plus the ilmenite from DI-15. As expected, the magnetites from the granophyre (samples DI-10, DI-11, and DI-16) are more radiogenic than the magnetites and ilmenite from the diabase samples. *Isoplot* gives the magnetite mineral isochron "age" of 1007±79 Ma, marginally less but still concordant with the most robust Rb-Sr mineral isochron from sample DI-13 (1060±24 Ma, Figure 12).

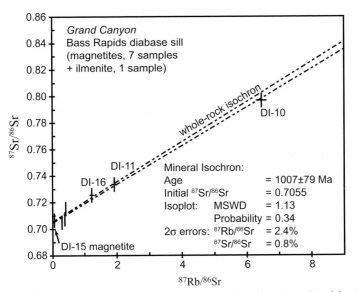

Figure 14. Rb-Sr magnetite mineral isochron for the Bass Rapids diabase sill. The bars represent 2σ uncertainites. The whole-rock Rb-Sr isochron is shown for comparison.

7.3 Sm-Nd Data

Figure 15 is the ^{147}Sm/^{144}Nd versus ^{143}Nd/^{144}Nd diagram for the Bass Rapids diabase sill using the whole-rock data in Table 6. These whole-rock samples are tightly grouped showing that little variation within the Sm-Nd system exists within the whole rocks. No Sm-Nd age information can be derived from the eleven whole-rock samples. All eight diabase samples do suggest a line in Figure 15, but *Isoplot* [*Ludwig,* 2001] attaches little age significance to it. The DI-13 Sm-Nd mineral isochron (see below) is plotted in Figure 15 and appears to pass through the eight whole-rock diabase samples. The three granophyre samples (DI-10, DI-11, and DI-16) plot on the diagram in a random

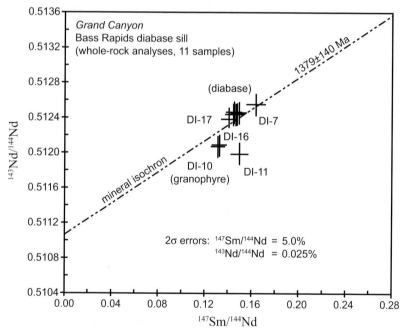

Figure 15. ^{147}Sm/^{144}Nd versus ^{143}Nd/^{144}Nd diagram for all eleven whole-rock samples of the Bass Rapids diabase sill. The bars represent the 2σ uncertainties. The Sm-Nd mineral isochron of Figure 16 is shown for comparison. The eight diabase samples plot on the mineral isochron whereas the three granophyre samples (DI-10, DI-11, and DI-16) do not, suggesting they have been contaminated from the hornfels wall rock.

scatter widely separated from any apparent relationship with the eight diabase samples, which is suggestive of contamination of the feldspar from the overlying hornfels wall rock, perhaps by some assimilation of less radiogenic Nd. Magnetite mineral data for the three granophyre samples (DI-10, DI-11, and DI-16) reported in Table 9 supports this interpretation. If we suppose that the magnetite of granophyre samples DI-10, DI-11, and DI-16 reflects the whole-rock Sm-Nd, we can plot those magnetites as a proxy for each of the altered whole-rocks. The Sm-Nd of the three magnetites of the granophyres do appear to plot on the line with the normal diabase whole-rocks.

Figure 16 shows the ^{147}Sm/^{144}Nd versus ^{143}Nd/^{144}Nd diagram for the six mineral fractions, plus the whole rock, of sample DI-13 from the Bass Rapids diabase sill. These Sm-Nd data are plotted at the same scale as the

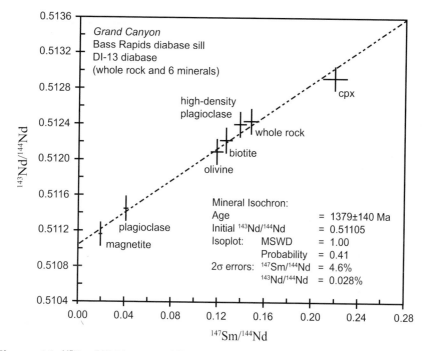

Figure 16. ^{147}Sm/^{144}Nd versus ^{143}Nd/^{144}Nd diagram for six mineral fractions from diabase sample DI-13 (plus the whole rock) from the Bass Rapids diabase sill. All seven data points were used in the isochron and age calculations, and the bars represent the 2σ uncertainties.

Sm-Nd of the whole rocks. The diagram shows an excellent large spread among the seven data points, from magnetite with the lowest $^{147}Sm/^{144}Nd$ ratio through to the highest $^{147}Sm/^{144}Nd$ ratio in the clinopyroxene. The regression analysis again produced an excellent isochron fit with a good probability and MSWD exactly unity. The resultant mineral isochron "age" for DI-13 is 1379±140 Ma that is strongly discordant with the four robust Rb-Sr isochrons. The relatively large 2σ uncertainty in the isochron age is of course due to the relatively large 2σ error bars for each of the data points, and to the scatter of some of the data points (for example, the whole rock and clinopyroxene) either side of the isochron (the line of best fit).

Figure 17 shows the $^{147}Sm/^{144}Nd$ versus $^{143}Nd/^{144}Nd$ diagram for eight of the eleven mineral fractions, plus the whole rock, of sample DI-15.

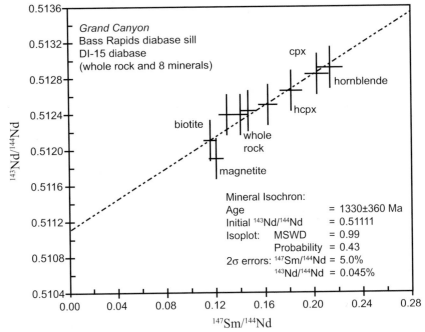

Figure 17. $^{147}Sm/^{144}Nd$ versus $^{143}Nd/^{144}Nd$ diagram for eight mineral fractions from diabase sample DI-15 (plus the whole rock) from the Bass Rapids diabase sill. Nine data points were used in the isochron and age calculations, and the bars represent the 2σ uncertainties.

These Sm-Nd data are plotted at the same scale as the Sm-Nd of the whole rocks and the minerals in DI-13. The diagram shows moderate spread among the nine data points, from biotite with the lowest ^{147}Sm/^{144}Nd ratio through to the highest ^{147}Sm/^{144}Nd ratio in the hornblende. The regression analysis produced an adequate isochron fit with a good probability and MSWD near unity. The resultant mineral isochron age for DI-15 is 1330±360 Ma. The very large uncertainty comes from the larger uncertainties associated with the points and the narrow spread of the data. This plot does not include three mineral fractions and means that this plot from DI-15 is not very good for defining the age. Evidently some open-system behavior characterizes Nd isotopes limiting the variability between the mineral phases. However, the "age" calculated and the initial ^{143}Nd/^{144}Nd is essentially identical to DI-13.

Figure 18 shows the ^{147}Sm/^{144}Nd versus ^{143}Nd/^{144}Nd diagram for the seven magnetites, three from the granophyre and four from the diabase.

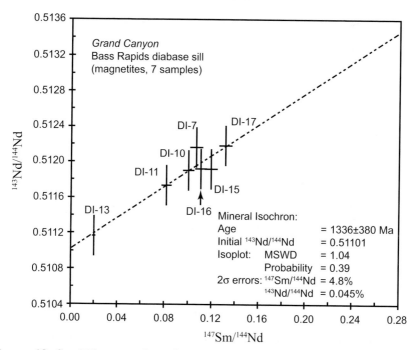

Figure 18. Sm-Nd magnetite mineral isochron for the Bass Rapids diabase sill.

The diagram shows moderate spread among the seven data points. The regression analysis produced an adequate isochron fit with lower probability and MSWD near unity. The resultant mineral isochron "age" for the magnetites is 1336±380 Ma. The plot in many ways resembles the minerals of DI-15 (Figure 17).

7.4 Pb-Pb Data

Figure 19 shows $^{206}Pb/^{204}Pb$ plotted against $^{207}Pb/^{204}Pb$ for the whole-rock samples from the Bass Rapids diabase sill, based on the data in Table 6. All eleven whole-rock samples were used in the regression analysis and yielded an isochron fit with an "age" of 1250±130 Ma, with a good probability and MSWD near unity. The relatively large 2σ uncertainty in the resultant age is primarily due to the size of the 2σ errors in the data points represented by the ellipses on the diagram.

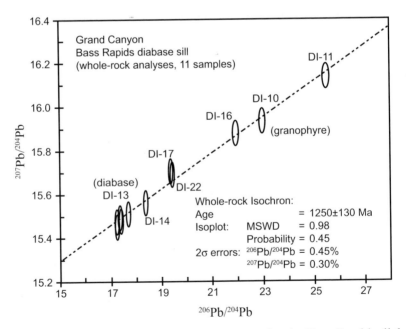

Figure 19. $^{206}Pb/^{204}Pb$ versus $^{207}Pb/^{204}Pb$ diagram for the Bass Rapids diabase sill, using all eleven whole-rock samples in the isochron and age calculations. The error ellipses represent the 2σ uncertainties.

On the other hand, the three granophyre samples (DI-10, DI-11, and DI-16) give a greater spread to the data which otherwise yields good regression statistics for the isochron.

Figures 20, 21, and 22 show $^{206}Pb/^{204}Pb$ plotted against $^{207}Pb/^{204}Pb$ for the various minerals, based on the data in Tables 7, 8, and 9 respectively. These three figures are plotted at the same scale as the Pb-Pb whole-rock data (Figure 19). Minerals of DI-13 and DI-15 are shown in Figures 20 and 21. These data are tightly grouped, showing that U is not strongly partitioned between the mineral phases within a single rock. *Isoplot* [*Ludwig,* 2001] shows no significant Pb-Pb age information can be derived from these seven and ten data points respectively. These mineral data do not define good isochrons, but these minerals do plot along the whole-rock Pb-Pb isochron that is included in both Figures 20 and 21 for reference. Five magnetites and one ilmenite appear to define an

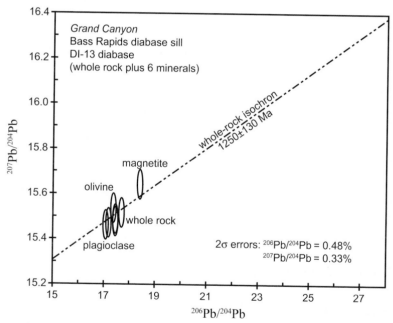

Figure 20. $^{206}Pb/^{204}Pb$ versus $^{207}Pb/^{204}Pb$ diagram for six mineral fractions from diabase sample DI-13 (plus the whole rock) from the Bass Rapids diabase sill. The error ellipses represent the 2σ uncertainites, and the Pb-Pb whole-rock isochron of Figure 19 is shown for comparison.

Steven A. Austin

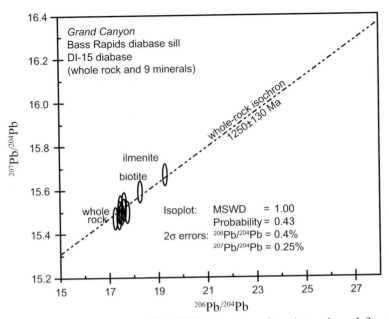

Figure 21. $^{206}Pb/^{204}Pb$ versus $^{207}Pb/^{204}Pb$ diagram for nine mineral fractions from diabase sample DI-15 (plus the whole rock) from the Bass Rapids diabase sill. The error ellipses represent the 2σ uncertainties, and the Pb-Pb whole-rock isochron of Figure 19 is shown for comparison.

adequate isochron in Figure 22. Two magnetites from the upper contact of the granophyre (DI-10 and DI-11) plot significantly above the line in Figure 22, suggesting Pb contamination from the overlying wall-rock (Figure 5). The lesson to be learned is that the Pb-Pb mineral isochron data is generally concordant with the Pb-Pb whole-rock isochron data.

8. Discussion

8.1 Nature of the Linear Isotope Plots

Isochron plots for the Beartooth amphibolite and Bass Rapids diabase sill reveal extraordinary linearity within the ^{40}K-^{40}Ar, ^{87}Rb-^{87}Sr, ^{147}Sm-^{143}Nd, and ^{207}Pb-^{206}Pb-^{204}Pb radioisotope systems. Three mineral isochrons (Rb-Sr, Sm-Nd, and Pb-Pb) are well defined within the Beartooth amphibolite. For Bass Rapids diabase sill, each of the four radioisotope pairs produced an eleven-point, whole-rock plot. The five Bass Rapids diabase sill whole-rock data plots (Figures 9, 10, 11, 15, and 19) contain 55 data points with 52 points following linear trends. Remarkably, only three of the whole-rock data points plotted significantly off the linear trends. These three data points plotting significantly off the line in Figure 15 are easily explained by the granophyre's assimilation of Nd due to contamination from the adjoining hornfels just above the sill (Figure 5). Certain hydrothermal conditions have been shown to cause REE mobility in rhyolite and granite [*Poitrasson et al.*, 1995], the Nd isotopes being perturbed during hydrothermal alteration. That such hydrothermal alteration of the granophyre in the sill has occurred during contact metamorphism with the overlying shale is evidenced by plagioclase altered to sericite and biotite altered to chlorite. If we allow the magnetite of granophyre samples DI-10,

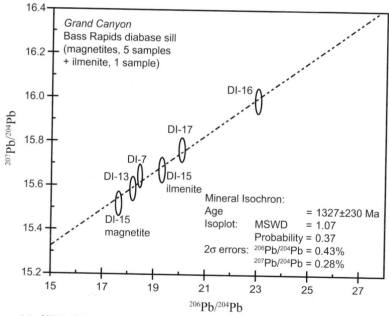

Figure 22. $^{206}Pb/^{204}Pb$ versus $^{207}Pb/^{204}Pb$ diagram for six magnetite mineral fractions from the Bass Rapids diabase sill. The error ellipses represent the 2σ uncertainties. Two magnetite samples from the granophyre (DI-10 and DI-11) plot above the line and are not shown.

DI-11 and DI-16 to be a proxy for the altered granophyre whole rock, all 55 data points representing whole rocks lie on linear trends.

Some creationists may want to consider the possibility that the remarkably linear isotope ratios within the diabase and granophyre were derived, not by radioisotope decay, but by mixing of two different magmas. Such a model has been proposed by *Giem* [1997], and discussed by *Austin and Snelling* [1998] and *Snelling et al.* [2003]. We might suppose the sill at Bass Rapids was formed from a granophyre magma (higher K, Ar, Rb, Sm, Nd, and U) combined with different proportions of a diabase magma (lower K, Ar, Rb, Sm, Nd, and U). The mixing model supposes these two magmas, and their various magma mixtures, were never in an isotopically homogeneous condition. Isotopes from these two magma types may then have formed the mixing lines in Figures 9, 10, 11, 15, and 19 without radioisotope decay within the rocks. As pointed out by *Austin* [2000], mineral isochron plots provide the data critical for testing the magma mixing model. Mineral phases within any single rock should be homogeneous, because the mixing model supposes rocks crystallized from large, locally mixed, batches of melt, and because, after crystallization, radioisotope decay is assumed to have been minor. For the Bass Rapids diabase sill, however, radioisotopes differ significantly between mineral phases within diabase samples DI-13 and DI-15. Thus, significant radioisotope decay, not mixing, is the favored explanation of the extraordinary linearity. Furthermore, the petrographic and geochemical data from the Bass Rapids sill argues that "unmixing" has occurred (chemical and gravitational segregation from an initially homogeneous, molten condition). The best explanation is exactly opposite the mixing model.

Potassium-40-^{40}Ar, ^{87}Rb-^{87}Sr, ^{147}Sm-^{143}Nd, and ^{207}Pb-^{206}Pb-^{204}Pb radioisotope data provide strong evidence that the Bass Rapids diabase sill was intruded while in an isotopically mixed, homogeneous condition. Initially, the sill was chemically and isotopically homogeneous when the basaltic magma was intruded rapidly into the Hakatai Shale. The word "homogeneous" allows for less than 1% initial variation in ^{87}Sr/^{86}Sr within the cogenetic suite of whole-rocks (Figure 11), and allows for less than 0.2% initial variation in ^{87}Sr/^{86}Sr among the minerals within a single rock (Figure 13). The subsequent mineralogical segregation within the sill was produced by flow differentiation and gravitational settling, resulting in olivine diabase overlain by granophyre. At that time of intrusion the different parts of the newly formed sill had the same Ar, Sr, Nd, and Pb isotopic ratios. The words "the same...isotopic ratios" allows for small variation in the daughter isotope ratios as specified by the isochron plots, and, especially, the MSWD analysis. This must be, and is conventionally by definition, the agreed initial condition in order for radioisotope dating of the diabase to be achievable.

8.2 Summary of Isochron Discordance

What then is the finding concerning radioisotopes within minerals of the Beartooth amphibolite sample? What then can be said about the *present* isotopic ratios within whole rocks and minerals of the Bass Rapids sill? Do parent-daughter radioisotope ratios produce a consistent picture of the "age" of the amphibolite metamorphism and intrusion of the sill respectively? A robust Rb-Sr mineral isochron plot (Figure 12) appears to constrain the "age" of the diabase sill to 1060±24 Ma (2σ error). That is the currently accepted age of this Grand Canyon diabase sill according to *Elston and McKee* [1982] and *Larson et al.* [1994] when the diabase sill was isotopically homogeneous with respect to Sr. However, the Sm-Nd mineral isochron plot from DI-13 (Figure 16) is strongly linear giving the "age" for initial homogeneous Nd as 1379±140 Ma (2σ error). Although the uncertainty associated with this Sm-Nd mineral isochron is larger, its "age" is clearly discordant with Rb-Sr. How could the suite of minerals in sample DI-13 have Nd isotopes homogenized at 1379±140 Ma (Figure 16) but not have Nd rehomogenized within the minerals by the event that thoroughly homogenized the Sr isotopes within the minerals of DI-13 at 1060±24 Ma (Figure 12)?

The Pb-Pb whole-rock isochron plot (Figure 19) gives the "age" for initial homogeneous Pb as 1250±130 Ma (2σ error), again discordant with Rb-Sr. How could the suite of whole-rocks within the sill have Pb isotopes homogenized at 1250±130 Ma (Figure 19) but not have Pb rehomogenized within the rocks by the event that thoroughly homogenized the Sr isotopes at 1060±24 Ma (Figure 12)? Both of these "ages" are discordant with the K-Ar whole-rock isochron age (Figure 9) of 841.5±164 Ma assuming no initial ^{40}Ar. Which of these is the true "age" of the initial isotopic mixing? No internally consistent "age" emerges from these data.

These discordant isochron dates for the Beartooth amphibolite and the Bass Rapids diabase sill are not unique. Indeed, *Austin* [2000] has already documented that, when the mineral isochron method is applied as a test of the assumptions of radioisotope dating, discordances inevitably result. According to *Austin* [2000] four categories of discordance are found in cogenetic suites of rocks—

(1) two or more discordant whole-rock isochron ages,
(2) a whole-rock isochron age older than the associated mineral isochron ages,
(3) two or more discordant mineral isochrons from the same rock, and
(4) a whole-rock isochron age younger than the associated mineral isochron ages.

Our radioisotope data from the Beartooth amphibolite and Bass Rapids diabase sill exhibit all four categories of isochron discordance. Thus the assumptions of radioisotope dating must be questioned.

8.3 Similarity to the Great Dyke of Zimbabwe

The Great Dyke of the Zimbabwe craton in southeast Africa is a 550 km long layered mafic and ultramafic intrusion 3 to 11 km wide. According to *Oberthür et al.* [2002], five complexes within the Great Dyke are each composed of a lower ultramafic sequence (dunites, harzburgites, olivine bronzitites and pyroxenites) overlain by an upper mafic sequence (plagioclase-rich rocks such as norites, gabbronorites and olivine gabbros). The variation in chemistry and mineralogy of the Great Dyke is particularly suitable to Rb-Sr dating, similar to the diabase to granophyre transition within the Bass Rapids sill of Grand Canyon. *Davies et al.* [1970] reported an eight-point Rb-Sr whole-rock isochron age from the Great Dyke of 2477±90 Ma with initial ^{87}Sr/^{86}Sr of 0.7024±0.0008. *Hamilton* [1977] very precisely reconfirmed this age and initial Sr ratio by plotting a nine-point Rb-Sr whole-rock and mineral isochron (five whole rocks and four mineral separates) of 2455 ± 16 Ma and initial $^{87}Sr/^{86}Sr$ of 0.70261 ± 0.00004. Both of the above ages and initial Sr ratios were again reconfirmed by *Mukasa et al.* [1998] using the core from a single drill-hole into the Great Dyke yielding an 11-point whole-rock and mineral isochron of 2467 ± 85 Ma and initial $^{87}Sr/^{86}Sr$ of 0.7026 ± 0.0004. (All three ages are calculated using λ for $^{87}Rb = 1.42\times10^{-11}$ per year, and errors being 2σ only from the analytical equipment.) The robustness of the Rb-Sr data appears to restrict the age of the Great Dyke to 2455 ± 16 Ma with an initial $^{87}Sr/^{86}Sr$ of 0.70260 ± 0.00005.

Although the 2455 ± 16 Ma Rb-Sr isochron age of the Great Dyke has been widely accepted, recent Sm-Nd, Pb-Pb, and U-Pb data indicate the intrusion is ≈120 Ma older than indicated by Rb-Sr. Recently, *Mukasa et al.* [1998] reported an age of 2586 ± 16 Ma (Sm-Nd whole-rock isochron), 2596 ± 14 Ma (Pb-Pb mineral and whole-rock isochron), and 2587 ± 8 Ma (U-Pb rutile). Also recently, numerous reported U-Pb zircon ages [summarized by *Oberthür et al.,* 2002] are concordant with the Great Dyke Sm-Nd and Pb-Pb isochrons. These new data are now widely regarded as having discredited the once generally accepted Rb-Sr isochron age of Great Dyke [*Oberthür et al.,* 2002]. The acceptable "age" of intrusion of Great Dyke is no longer 2455 ± 16 Ma (Rb-Sr whole-rock and mineral isochron), but 2586 ± 16 Ma (Sm-Nd whole-rock isochron), 2587 ± 8 Ma (U-Pb mineral concordia), or 2596 ± 14 Ma (Pb-Pb mineral and whole-rock isochrons), the latter three "ages" being concordant.

Discordant isochron ages were obtained also on the Stuart dyke swarm (Late Proterozoic of south-central Australia) and the Uruguayan dike swarm (Precambrian of Uruguay). The Stuart dyke swarm gave discordant mineral isochron ages of 1076 ± 33 Ma (Sm-Nd mineral isochron) and 897 ± 9 Ma (Rb-Sr mineral isochron with biotite), according to *Zhao and McCulloch* [1993]. The Uruguayan dike swarm yielded a discordant date of 1766 ± 124 (Rb-Sr isochron for fifteen whole rocks) and 1366 ± 18 Ma (Rb-Sr mineral isochron including biotite), according to *Teixeira et al.* [1999].

8.4 Explanations of Discordance

Five possible explanations of the discordant isotope data need to be considered. Here we seek to discover the possible explanations for isochron discordance and evaluate whether the evidence supports such explanation.

8.4.1 Mineral Inheritance with Magma Contamination

The first explanation to consider is the possibility that the Rb-Sr system is telling us the correct age, and the significantly older Pb-Pb and Sm-Nd systems are giving incorrect or spurious ages. We need an elaborate explanation giving reasons why the Sm-Nd and Pb-Pb systems were not homogeneous isotopically with respect to $^{143}Nd/^{144}Nd$ and Pb isotopes. *Mukasa et al.* [1998] and *Oberthür et al.* [2002] entertained the possibility that crustal contamination of rising magma in the Great Dyke could create an isotope mixing condition causing false Sm-Nd and Pb-Pb whole-rock isochrons. These authors noted that a high Sr (and low Nd and Pb) magma could be contaminated with smaller amounts of crustal Sr, Pb, and Nd, not significantly affecting the Rb-Sr whole-rock isochron, but causing significant mixing lines on the Pb-Pb and Sm-Nd whole-rock plots, yielding false Pb-Pb and Sm-Nd whole-rock ages. Two explanations can be offered:

(1) the contaminants were in the liquid phase of the magma, and
(2) the contaminants were within an included mineral phase or phases within the magma.

The first proposal does not offer an explanation of concordance between Sm-Nd and Pb-Pb whole-rock and mineral isochrons, because the minerals must generate the same false isochron as the suite of whole rocks by some unknown process. Therefore, researchers like *Mukasa et al.* [1998] and *Oberthür et al.* [2002] have entertained the second possibility (that is, the contaminant resided within a mineral phase within the original magma). These researchers, however, have not defended the proposal.

In order to explain the zircon U-Pb data collected by *Oberthür et al.* [2002] for the Great Dyke (and presumably the titanite Pb data for the Beartooth amphibolite), zircon crystals (and presumably titanite in

Beartooth amphibolite) were crystals within the magma at the time of intrusion. We might suppose the zircons were assimilated from the wall rocks that have a much older age. Thus, rocks and cogenetic suites of rocks would not be homogenized isotopically in the beginning. They either acquire contaminants from deep magma chambers and/or from interaction with wall rock within transport conduits. Magmas on the small scale of rocks to the larger scale of extensive formations would either retain or acquire clumps of high and low isotope abundance ratios.

After considering the explanation only briefly, *Mukasa et al.* [1998] and *Oberthür et al.* [2002] dismiss the possibility of mineral inheritance and accompanying magma contamination as an explanation for discordant isochrons in the Great Dyke. These authors report concordant U-Pb concordia and Pb-Pb isochron ages for three mineral phases within the Great Dyke (zircon, rutile, and baddeleyite). Unusually high Th/U ratios in zircon within the Great Dyke argue that zircon is the product of very late stage magmatic crystallization as would occur within a dike [*Oberthür et al.*, 2002]. Zircon chemistry is atypical of most other igneous rocks, including gabbros, disputing the notion that zircon in the Great Dyke is an inherited mineral component.

Within the Beartooth amphibolite and the Bass Rapids diabase sill, major-abundance mineral phases (not just minor-abundance mineral phases) define the Sm-Nd mineral isochrons (Figures 7, 16, and 17). Plagioclase, hornblende and biotite, the main minerals composing the metamorphic fabric of the Beartooth amphibolite, define the Sm-Nd mineral isochron (Figure 7). Plagioclase, hornblende, and biotite must reflect the metamorphic event, not imagined component minerals resistant to metamorphism retained from the protolith. Plagioclase and clinopyroxene, the main minerals composing the Bass Rapids diabase sill, define the Sm-Nd isochron (Figure 16 and 17). Plagioclase and clinopyroxene (along with several other mineral phases) must have been part of the molten magma in order for the mechanical process of sill intrusion to occur. Therefore, plagioclase and clinopyroxene were not inherited mineral phases in the diabase. Furthermore, the concordant Sm-Nd magnetite mineral isochron within the diabase (Figure 18) indicates that magnetite is not an inherited mineral phase. We can reject the mineral inheritance and magma contamination model for discordant isochron ages in Beartooth amphibolite, Bass Rapids diabase sill, and the Great Dyke.

8.4.2 Slow Cooling

A second explanation for discordant isochrons is the possibility that the different isochron ages can be explained by the minerals cooling extremely slowly to form rocks over hundreds of millions of years. In this view it is impossible to read a single age of amphibolite metamorphism supposing it to be an event. It would also be impossible to discern the age of intrusion and cooling of diabase within a sill as an event. We can think of the slow cooling model as an explanation for discordant mineral isochrons (category three discordance). Also, slow cooling could be offered as an explanation where the mineral isochron of one radioisotope pair is younger than the whole-rock isochron of another radioisotope pair (category two discordance). Proterozoic metamorphic basement rocks of southern Mexico yielded a Sm-Nd whole-rock isochron age of 1440 Ma interpreted as the time of original formation of the continental crust [*Weber and Köhler,* 1999]. Younger U-Pb zircon ages and various mineral isochrons (including a biotite plus whole-rock Rb-Sr isochron) are interpreted as documenting a cooling history extending over 500 Ma [*Weber and Köhler,* 1999].

The proposal of slow cooling does not offer an explanation for discordant whole-rock isochrons (category one discordance) or mineral isochron ages older than associated whole-rock isochron ages (category four discordance). Thus, slow cooling can be rejected as a proposal for category four discordance in the Beartooth amphibolite, and category one and four discordances in the Bass Rapids diabase sill. *Mukasa et al.* [1998] rejected slow cooling as an explanation for the discordant isochron ages in the Great Dyke.

The explanation of slow cooling also leads to a faulty explanation of the geologic context of the Bass Rapids diabase sill. The diabase sill was intruded into much cooler sedimentary rocks (the Hakatai Shale), and the physics of conductivity of heat through solids causes us to question how a 91 m thick magma sill was able to retain molten minerals within much cooler sediments for hundreds of millions of years [see discussion by *Harrison and McDougall,* 1980]. Thus, in specific details the slow cooling model lacks convincing argument and direct application, especially to the Bass Rapids diabase sill.

8.4.3 Post-Magmatic Loss of Radiogenic Sr

A third possible explanation is that discordant ages are caused by a violation of the closed system assumption of radioisotope dating. If we accept the Pb-Pb and Sm-Nd whole rock and mineral isochrons as true ages, then the Rb-Sr isochrons would be interpreted as significantly altered with a specific bias to give significantly younger but spurious ages. We need to imagine some type of Sr loss process that removed significant ^{87}Sr and/or added significant ^{87}Rb over geologic time. Less likely, but also making Rb-Sr ages much younger, would be addition of Rb, a process not considered further here. Because solid-state diffusion is unlikely through crystalline rocks, a fluid-based Sr-loss process might be imagined resembling a hydrothermal condition [*Mukasa et al.,* 1998]. This Sr-loss process must occur at low temperature because Ar closure evidence within Cardenas Basalt and associated dikes and sills of Grand Canyon indicates temperatures have not exceeded ~250 to 300°C after magma emplacement and crystallization [*Larson et al.,* 1994]. Because biotite is the significant mineral determining the Rb-Sr mineral isochrons in the Beartooth amphibolite and the Bass Rapids diabase sill, biotite's closure temperature relative to Sr loss is important. A closure temperature of ~320°C is usually assumed [*Harrison and McDougall,* 1980; *Weber and Köhler,* 1999].

Rubidium-Sr whole-rock isochrons for the Uruguayan dike swarm are significantly older than the Rb-Sr biotite mineral isochron [*Teixeira et al.,* 1999]. According to *Teixeira et al.* [1999], the Rb-Sr mineral data from the Uruguayan dike swarm show significant scatter from the line, a property thought to be diagnostic of post-magmatic Sr isotope disruption. Also diagnostic of post-magmatic Sr disruption in the Rb-Sr mineral isochron, according to *Teixeira et al.* [1999], is *higher* initial ^{87}Sr/^{86}Sr than that with the associated Rb-Sr whole-rock isochron.

The Beartooth amphibolite Rb-Sr mineral data show very good linearity (Figure 6), and do not possess scatter suggesting the Sr disruption process (low scatter indicated by the high probability value in Figure 6). Higher initial $^{87}Sr/^{86}Sr$ does occur in the Beartooth Rb-Sr mineral isochron (0.7044 in Figure 6) than the associated Rb-Sr whole-rock isochron (0.7022 in Figure 3), a possible indication of alteration. Because the mineral composition and texture of the sample of Beartooth andesitic amphibolite resembles the probable precursor andesite, post-magmatic hydrothermal alteration at ~300°C is not indicated [Mueller et al., 1983]. The geochemical evidence, especially the abundance of REEs, also, points to isochemical metamorphism of the probable andesite precursor, not significant hydrothermal alteration [Mueller et al., 1983]. Thus, it is doubtful if post-magmatic Sr loss can explain the Rb-Sr mineral isochron in the Beartooth amphibolite.

The Bass Rapids diabase sill Rb-Sr mineral isochrons (Figures 12 and 13) display excellent linearity, not suggestive of post-magmatic Sr disruption. Lower initial $^{87}Sr/^{86}Sr$ occur in the diabase sill Rb-Sr mineral isochrons (0.7030 and 0.7039 in Figures 12 and 13) than the associated Rb-Sr whole-rock isochron (0.7043 in Figure 11), another significant problem for post-magmatic Sr loss. Strontium remains in high abundance relative to geochemically similar Ca (Table 2) indicating conservation of Sr, not loss of Sr. Conservation of Sr is evident even though petrographic evidence indicates some alteration of plagioclase to sericite and some alteration of biotite to chlorite. The geochemical evidence for open-system behavior is limited to the Nd in the Sm-Nd radioisotope system in the granophyre whole-rock samples (perturbed by contamination from the overlying hornfels wall rock), and possibly to a few mineral species that lie off the trend lines established strongly by the majority of the other minerals. The general closed-system assumption for the Bass Rapids diabase sill Rb-Sr system is not unreasonable.

The post-magmatic Sr loss (and/or Rb gain) explanation for the Rb-Sr mineral isochron for the Bass Rapids diabase sill has one last extremely significant problem. Post-magmatic Sr loss (and/or Rb gain) could, possibly, explain the robust Rb-Sr mineral isochrons, but how does it explain the concordant Rb-Sr whole rock isochron? We need to explain why Figures 12 and 13 compare so well with Figure 11. As

Mukasa et al. [1998] admitted for the concordant Rb-Sr mineral and whole-rock isochrons for the Great Dyke, "...there is no good reason why both mineral and whole-rock samples would be altered to give the same erroneous age." Not only must the Rb-Sr whole rocks of the Bass Rapids diabase sill be depleted of significant ^{87}Sr, but the Cardenas Basalt and other associated dikes and sills must be depleted as well. As pointed out by *Larson et al.* [1994] a regionally extensive Rb-Sr whole-rock pattern exists indicating an "age" of 1103 ± 66 Ma. To dispose of ^{87}Sr on such a large scale would require an extraordinary hydrothermal alteration system. Thus, post-magmatic Sr loss is an extremely unlikely explanation for the Rb-Sr mineral and whole-rock isochrons in the Bass Rapids diabase sill.

8.4.4 Uncertainties in Determinations of Decay Constants

As already argued, corroborative evidence indicates that both the amphibolite and the diabase sill initially had a homogeneous mixture of Ar, Sr, Nd, and Pb isotopes. Thus the assumption about the initial conditions for the sill and these radioisotope systems must be valid. Also, a very good case can be made for the general closed-system behavior for these rocks with respect to most of the radioisotope pairs. Therefore, could the differences in the calculated "ages" above be caused by errors in determining the "constants" of radioisotope decay? According to *Steiger and Jäger* [1977], U decay constants are measured reproducibly with great precision to four significant figures. Therefore, no significant decay-constant error occurs with Pb-Pb isochrons. *Steiger and Jäger* [1977] recommended the decay constant for ^{87}Rb of 1.42×10^{-11} per year that is in wide use by the geochronologic community, but offered no uncertainty associated with the decay constant. *Begemann et al.* [2001] recommend λ ^{87}Rb $= 1.406\pm0.008 \times 10^{-11}$ per year, whereas *and Zaitsev* [2002] suggested λ for ^{87}Rb $= 1.396\pm0.006 \times 10^{-11}$ per year. However, this small change would not close the discordance between the Rb-Sr and either the Pb-Pb or Sm-Nd systems in Beartooth amphibolite or Bass Rapids diabase. According to *Begemann et al.* [2001], researchers generally agree that the decay constant for ^{147}Sm has been determined to three significant figures (6.54×10^{-12}).

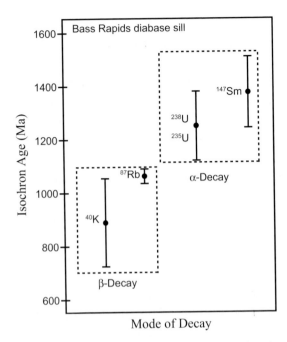

Figure 23. Isochron age versus mode of decay for the four radioisotope systems within Bass Rapids diabase sill. Alpha-emitters give older "ages" than β-emitters.

8.4.5 Have Decay Constants Always been Constant?

Our data indicate that the α-emitters (^{238}U, ^{235}U, and ^{147}Sm) have yielded older ages than the β-emitters (^{87}Rb and ^{40}K) when used to date the same geologic event, that is, the metamorphism of andesite to produce the Beartooth amphibolite or the intrusion of the Bass Rapids diabase sill. Ages for the Bass Rapids diabase sill are shown in Figure 23. A logical explanation of these data is that the radioisotope decay of the various parent isotopes has not always proceeded at the rates described by modern decay "constants," the discordances being due to the different parent radioisotopes decaying at different rates over the *same* time periods since the metamorphism of the andesite and the intrusion of the diabase sill. These data are consistent with the notion that the decay of these parent radioisotopes was accelerated by different amounts. Thus, our data indicate that α-decay was accelerated more than β-decay at some time or times in the past.

Do our data suggest a correlation between the present radioactive decay constants for these α- and β-emitters and the "ages" they have yielded for these same geologic events? Of the α-emitters, [147]Sm has the smallest decay constant (and thus the longest half-life), and it yielded the oldest "age" for the diabase sill, a Sm-Nd mineral isochron "age" of 1379±140 Ma (Figure 16), compared to the Pb-Pb whole-rock isochron "age" of 1250±130 Ma (Figure 19). Although error bars on "ages" for these two α-emitters overlap for the diabase sill, error bars for the Beartooth mineral isochrons more strongly indicate older "ages" for Sm-Nd than for Pb-Pb (compare Figures 7 and 8). Similarly, of the β-emitters, [87]Rb has the smaller decay constant (and thus the longer half-life) and it yielded the older "ages" for the diabase sill, a whole-rock isochron "age" of 1055±46 Ma (Figure 11) and a mineral isochron "age" of 1060±24 Ma (Figure 12), compared to the K-Ar whole-rock isochron "age" of 841.5±164 Ma (Figure 9). We can say our data are consistent with the possibility that the longer the half-life of the α- or β-emitter the more its decay has been accelerated, relative to the other α- or β-emitters, at some time or times in the past.

Other explanations for the same discordant isochron data can be offered. It is even possible to use the same data to argue that there is *no correlation* between the present radioactive decay constants and the "ages" they have yielded for the same geologic events. Thus, for the α-emitters, the diabase mineral isochron age of 1379±140 Ma (Figure 16) can be regarded statistically as concordant with the Pb-Pb whole-rock isochron "age" of 1250±130 Ma (Figure 19) because the assigned errors overlap (Figure 23). The notion of concordance between the α-emitters is supported by concordant ages, as stated above, for the Great Dyke. These concordant α-emitter ages for the Great Dyke are 2586±16 Ma (Sm-Nd whole-rock isochron), 2587±8 Ma (U-Pb mineral concordia), and 2596±14 Ma (Pb-Pb mineral and whole-rock isochrons).

The important observation derived from Beartooth andesitic amphibolite and the Bass Rapids diabase sill, verified by study of the

Great Dyke, is that α-emitters give older ages than β-emitters when applied to the same rocks. It is recommended that further similar studies of suitable rock units be undertaken to extend and confirm these findings. Further research on Precambrian sills and dikes, especially using Sm-Nd and Pb-Pb, should be conducted.

9. Conclusions

The distributions of parent and daughter radioisotopes in the Archean Beartooth amphibolite and in the middle Proterozoic Bass Rapids diabase sill reveal a significant problem with the assumptions of conventional radioisotope dating. Even though several lines of evidence confirm that the daughter isotopes were homogeneously mixed when the andesite was metamorphosed to amphibolite and the basaltic magma was intruded initially to form the sill, the four analyzed radioisotope systems yield discordant isochron "ages" for these geologic events. Although significant discordance exists between the K-Ar, Rb-Sr, Sm-Nd, and Pb-Pb radioisotope methods, each method appears to yield concordant "ages" internally between whole-rocks and minerals. Internal concordance is best illustrated by the diabase sill Rb-Sr whole-rock and mineral isochron "ages" of 1055 ± 46 Ma and 1060 ± 24 Ma, respectively. Furthermore, only limited evidence exists for open-system behavior. Open-system behavior is indicated by contamination of the whole-rock Sm-Nd radioisotope system in the granophyre at the top of the diabase sill immediately adjacent to the overlying hornfels wall rock. Therefore, it is concluded that it is the constant decay rates assumption of conventional radioisotope dating that is potentially invalid, and thus changing decay rates in the past could account for the demonstrated discordances between the resultant isochron "ages." Furthermore, our data are consistent with the possibilities that, at some time or times in the past, decay of the α-emitters (^{238}U, ^{235}U, and ^{147}Sm) was accelerated more than decay of the β-emitters (^{87}Rb and ^{40}K). Conventional radioisotope clocks need repair.

Acknowledgments

Andrew A. Snelling contributed significantly to sample collection, data analysis and writing of the manuscript. Without Andrew's significant help and encouragement during a fourteen-year period this research would not have been completed. William A. Hoesch assisted in laboratory analysis, especially mineral separations. Professor Lang Farmer assisted with attention to detail in the isotope analysis. Grand Canyon National Park provided special use permits allowing access to the remote site of the Bass Rapids sill and granting permission to collect rock samples. Private donors provided financial support through the RATE project, and the project preceding RATE, both administrated at the Institute for Creation Research.

References

Amelin, Y., and A. N. Zaitsev, Precise geochronology of phoscorites and carbonatites: the critical role of U-series disequilibrium in age interpretations, *Geochimica et Cosmochimica Acta, 66*, 2399–2419, 2002.

Austin, S. A., Mineral isochron method applied as a test of the assumption of radioisotope dating, in *Radioisotopes and the Age of the Earth: A Young-Earth Creationist Research Initiative*, edited by L. Vardiman, A. A. Snelling, and E. F. Chaffin, pp. 95–121, Institute for Creation Research, El Cajon, California and Creation Research Society, St. Joseph, Missouri, 2000.

Austin, S. A., and A. A. Snelling, Discordant potassium-argon model and isochron "ages" for Cardenas Basalt (Middle Proterozoic) and associated diabase of eastern Grand Canyon, Arizona, in *Proceedings of the Fourth International Conference on Creationism*, edited by R. E. Walsh, pp. 35–51, Creation Science Fellowship, Pittsburgh, Pennsylvania, 1998.

Babcock, R. S., Precambrian crystalline core, in *Grand Canyon Geology*, edited by S. S. Beus and M. Morales, first edition, pp. 11–28, Oxford University Press, New York, 1990.

Begemann, F., K. R. Ludwig, G. W. Lugmair, K. Min, L. E. Nyquist, P. J. Patchett, P. R. Renne, C. Y. Shih, I. M. Villa, and R. J. Walker, Call for improved set of decay constants for geochronological use, *Geochimica et Cosmochimica Acta, 65*, 111–121, 2001.

Bhattacharji, S., Scale model experiments on flowage differentiation in sills, in *Ultramafic and Related Rocks,* edited by P.J. Wyllie, pp. 69–70, John Wiley & Sons, New York, 1967.

Bhattacharji, S., and C.H. Smith, Flowage differentiation, *Science, 145*, 150–153, 1964.

Dalrymple, G.B., ^{40}Ar/^{36}Ar Analyses of historic lava flows, *Earth and Planetary Science Letters, 6*, 47–55, 1969.

Dalrymple, G.B., and M.A. Lanphere, *Potassium-Argon Dating: Principles, Techniques and Applications for Geochronology*, W.H. Freeman, San Francisco, 1969.

Davies, R.D., H.L. Allsopp, A. Erlank, and J.W.I. Manton, Sr isotopic studies on various layered mafic intrusions in Southern Africa, in *Symposium on the Bushveld Igneous Complex and Other Layered Intrusions*, pp. 576–593, Geological Society of South Africa, Special Publication 1, 1970.

Elston, D.P., Grand Canyon Supergroup, northern Arizona: stratigraphic summary and preliminary paleomagnetic correlations with parts of other North American Proterozoic successions, in *Geologic Evolution of Arizona*, edited by J.P. Jenney and S.J. Reynolds, pp. 259–272, Arizona Geological Society, Tucson, Digest 17, 1989.

Elston, D.P., and C.S. Grommé, Precambrian polar wandering from Unkar Group and Nankoweap Formation, eastern Grand Canyon, Arizona, in *Geology of Northern Arizona*, edited by T.N.V. Karlstrom, J.A. Swann, and R.L. Eastwood, pp. 97–117, Geological Society of America, Rocky Mountain Sectional Meeting, Flagstaff, Arizona, 1974.

Elston, D.P., and E.H. McKee, Age and correlation of the Late Proterozoic Grand Canyon disturbance, northern Arizona, *Geological Society of America Bulletin, 93*, 681–699, 1982.

Farmer, G.L., D.E. Broxton, R.G. Warren, and W. Pickthorn, Nd, Sr, and O isotopic variations in metaluminous ash-flow tuffs and related volcanic rocks at the Timber Mountain/Oasis Valley Caldera, Complex, SW Nevada: implications for the origin and evolution of large-volume silicic magma bodies, *Contributions to Mineralogy and Petrology, 109*, 53–68, 1991.

Ford, T.D., W.J. Breed, and J.S. Mitchell, Name and age of the Upper

Precambrian basalts in the eastern Grand Canyon, *Geological Society of American Bulletin, 81*, 223–226, 1972.

Giem, P. A. L., *Scientific Theology*, La Sierra University Press, Riverside, California, pp. 144–146, 1997.

Hamilton, J., Sr isotope and trace element studies of the Great Dyke and Bushveld mafic phase and their relation to early Proterozoic magma genesis in southern Africa, *Journal of Petrology, 18,* 24–52, 1977.

Harrison, T. M., and I. McDougall, Investigations of an intrusive contact, northwest Nelson, New Zealand—I. Thermal, chronological and isotopic constraints, *Geochimica et Cosmochimica Acta, 44,* 1985–2003, 1980.

Hendricks, J. D., *Younger Precambrian Basaltic Rocks of the Grand Canyon, Arizona*, Unpublished M. S. Thesis, Northern Arizona University, Flagstaff, 1972.

Hendricks, J. D., Petrology and chemistry of igneous rocks of Middle Proterozoic Unkar Group, Grand Canyon Supergroup, northern Arizona, in *Geology of the Grand Canyon, Northern Arizona (with Colorado River Guides)*, edited by D. P. Elston, G. H. Billingsley, and R. A. Young, pp. 106–116, American Geophysical Union, Washington, DC, 1989.

Hendricks, J. D., and I. Lucchitta, Upper Precambrian igneous rocks of the Grand Canyon, Arizona, in *Geology of Northern Arizona*, edited by T. N. V. Karlstrom, J. A. Swann, and R. L. Eastwood, pp. 65–86, Geological Society of America, Rocky Mountain Sectional Meeting, Flagstaff, Arizona, 1974.

Hendricks, J. D., and G. M. Stevenson, Grand Canyon Supergroup: Unkar Group, in *Grand Canyon Geology*, first edition, edited by S. S. Beus and M. Morales, pp. 29–47, Oxford University Press, New York, 1990.

Hendricks, J. D., and G. M. Stevenson, Grand Canyon Supergroup: Unkar Group, in *Grand Canyon Geology*, second edition, edited by S. S. Beus and M. Morales, second edition, pp. 39–52, Oxford University Press, New York, 2003.

Ilg, B. R., K. E. Karlstrom, D. P. Hawkins, and M. L. Williams, Tectonic evolution of Paleoproterozoic rocks in the Grand Canyon: insights into middle-crustal processes, *Geological Society of America Bulletin, 108,* 1149–1166, 1996.

Karlstrom, K. E., B. R. Ilg, M. L. Williams, D. P. Hawkins, S. A. Bowring, and S. J. Seaman, Paleoproterozoic Rocks of the Granite Gorges, in *Grand Canyon Geology*, edited by S. S. Beus and M. Morales, second edition, pp. 9–38, Oxford University Press, New York, 2003.

Larson, E. E., P. E. Patterson, and F. E. Mutschler, Lithology, chemistry, age and origin of the Proterozoic Cardenas Basalt, Grand Canyon, Arizona, *Precambrian Research, 65*, 255–276, 1994.

Ludwig, K. R., *Isoplot/Ex (Version 2.49): The Geochronological Toolkit for Microsoft Excel*, University of California Berkeley, Berkeley Geochronology Center, Special Publication No. 1a, 2001.

Maxson, J. H., *Preliminary Geologic Map of the Grand Canyon and Vicinity, Arizona, Eastern Section*, Grand Canyon Natural History Association, scale 1:62,500, 1967.

Maxson, J. H., *Preliminary Geologic Map of the Grand Canyon and Vicinity, Arizona, Western Section*, Grand Canyon Natural History Association, scale 1:62,500, 1968.

McKee, E. H., and D. C. Noble, Rb-Sr Age of the Cardenas Lavas, Grand Canyon, Arizona, *Geology of Northern Arizona*, edited by T. N. V. Karlstrom, G. A. Swann, and R. L. Eastwood, pp. 87–96, Geological Society of America, Rocky Mountain Sectional Meeting, Flagstaff, 1974.

McKee, E. H., and D. C. Noble, Age of the Cardenas Lavas, Grand Canyon, Arizona, *Geological Society of America Bulletin, 87*, 1188–1190, 1976.

Mueller, P. A., J. L. Wooden, K. Schulz, and D. R. Bowes, Incompatible-element-rich andesitic amphibolites from the Archean of Montana and Wyoming: evidence for mantle metasomatism, *Geology, 11*, 203–206, 1983.

Mueller, P. A., W. W. Locke, and J. L. Wooden, A study in contrasts: Archean and Quaternary geology of the Beartooth Highway, Montana and Wyoming, *Rocky Mountain Section of the Geological Society of America, Centennial Field Guide*, vol. 2, pp. 75–78, 1987.

Mueller, P. A., R. Shuster, M. Graves, J. Wooden, and D. Bowes, Age and composition of a Late Archean magmatic complex, Beartooth Mountains, Montana-Wyoming, Montana, in *Precambrian and Mesozoic Plate Margins, Montana, Idaho and Wyoming*, edited by S. Lewis and R. B. Berg, Montana Bureau of Mines and Geology, Special Publication 96, pp. 23–42, 1988.

Mueller, P. A., J. L. Wooden, A. P. Nutman, and D. W. Mogk, Early Archean crust in the northern Wyoming province: evidence from U-Pb ages of detrital zircons, *Precambrian Research, 91,* 295–307, 1998.

Mukasa, S. B., A. H. Wilson, and R. W. Carlson, A multielement geochronologic study of the Great Dyke, Zimbabwe: significance of the robust and reset ages, *Earth and Planetary Science Letters, 164,* 353–369, 1998.

Noble, L. F., Contributions to the geology of the Grand Canyon, Arizona: the geology of the Shinumo Area, *American Journal of Science, 29,* 369–386, 497–528, 1910.

Noble, L. F., The Shinumo quadrangle, Grand Canyon district, Arizona, *U.S. Geological Survey, Bulletin 549,* 1914.

Oberthür, T., D. W. Davis, T. G. Blenkinsop, and A. Höhndorf, Precise U-Pb mineral ages, Rb-Sr and Sm-Nd systematics for the Great Dyke, Zimbabwe—constraints on Late Archean events in the Zimbabwe craton and Limpopo belt, *Precambrian Research, 113,* 293–305, 2002.

Poitrasson, F., C. Pin, and J.-L. Duthou, Hydrothermal remobilization of rare earth elements and its effects on Nd isotopes in rhyolite and granite, *Earth and Planetary Science Letters, 130,* 1–11, 1995.

Renne, P. R., D. B. Karner, and K. R. Ludwig, Absolute ages aren't exactly, *Science, 282,* 1840–1841, 1998.

Simkin, T., Flow Differentiation in the picritic sills of North Skye, in *Ultramafic and Related Rocks,* edited by P. J. Wyllie, pp. 64–69, John Wiley & Sons, New York, 1967.

Snelling, A. A., S. A. Austin, and W. A. Hoesch, Radioisotopes in the diabase sill (Upper Precambrian) at Bass Rapids, Grand Canyon, Arizona: an application and test of the isochron dating method, in *Proceedings of the Fifth International Conference on Creationism,* edited by R. L. Ivey, Jr., pp. 269–284, Creation Science Fellowship, Pittsburgh, Pennsylvania, 2003.

Steiger, R. H., and E. Jäger, Subcommission on geochronology: convention on the use of decay constants in geo- and cosmochronology, *Earth and Planetary Science Letters, 36,* 359–362, 1977.

Teixeira, W., P. R. Renne, G. Bossi, N. Campal, and M. S. D'Agrella Filho, [40]Ar-[39]Ar and Rb-Sr geochronology of the Uruguayan dike swarm, Rio de la Plata craton and implications for Proterozoic intraplate activity in western Gondwana, *Precambrian Research, 93,* 153–180, 1999.

Timmons, M. J., K. E. Karlstrom, C. M. Dehler, J. W. Geissman, and M. T. Heizler, Proterozoic multistage (ca. 1.1 and 0.8 Ga) extension recorded in the Grand Canyon Supergroup and establishment of northwest- and north-trending tectonic grains in the southwestern United States, *Geological Society of America Bulletin, 113,* 163–180, 2001.

Warner, J. L., R. Lee-Berman, and C. H. Simonds, Field and petrologic relations of some Archean rocks near Long Lake, eastern Beartooth Mountains, Montana and Wyoming, in *Precambrian Geology of the Beartooth Mountains, Montana and Wyoming,* edited by P. A. Mueller and J. L. Wooden, pp. 56–68, Montana Bureau of Mines and Geology, Special Publication 84, 1982.

Weber, B., and H. Köhler, Sm-Nd, Rb-Sr and U-Pb geochronology of a Grenville Terrane in Southern Mexico: origin and geologic history of the Guichicovi Complex, *Precambrian Research, 96,* 245–262, 1999.

Weil, A. B., J. W. Geissman, M. Heizler, and R. Van der Voo, Paleomagnetism of Middle Proterozoic mafic intrusions and Upper Proterozoic (Nankoweap) red beds from the lower Grand Canyon Supergroup, Arizona, *Tectonophysics, 375,* 199–220, 2003.

Wooden, J. L., P. A. Mueller, D. K. Hunt, and D. R. Bowes, Geochemistry and Rb-Sr geochronology of the Archean rocks from the interior of the southeastern Beartooth Mountains, Montana and Wyoming, in *Precambrian Geology of the Beartooth Mountains, Montana and Wyoming,* edited by P. A. Mueller and J. L. Wooden, pp. 45–55, Montana Bureau of Mines and Geology, Special Publication 84, 1982.

York, D., Least squares fitting of a straight line with correlated errors, *Earth and Planetary Science Letters, 5,* 320–324, 1969.

Zhao, J., and M. T. McCulloch, Sm-Nd mineral isochron ages of Late Proterozoic dyke swarms in Australia: evidence for two distinctive events of mafic magmatism and crustal extension, *Chemical Geology, 109,* 341–354, 1993.

Chapter 6

Isochron Discordances and the Role of Inheritance and Mixing of Radioisotopes in the Mantle and Crust

Andrew A. Snelling, Ph.D.*

Abstract. New radioisotope data were obtained for ten rock units spanning the geologic record from the recent to the early Precambrian, five of these rock units being in the Grand Canyon area. All but one of these rock units were derived from basaltic magmas generated in the mantle. The objective was to test the reliability of the model and isochron "age" dating methods using the K-Ar, Rb-Sr, Sm-Nd, and Pb-Pb radioisotope systems. The isochron "ages" for these rock units consistently indicated that the α-decaying radioisotopes (^{238}U, ^{235}U, and ^{147}Sm) yield older "ages" than the β-decaying radioisotopes (^{40}K, ^{87}Rb). Marked discordances were found among the isochron "ages" yielded by these radioisotope systems, particularly for the seven Precambrian rock units studied. Also, the longer the half-life of the α- or β-decaying radioisotope, and/or the heavier the atomic weight of the parent radioisotope, the greater was the isochron "age" it yielded relative to the other α- or β-decaying radioisotopes respectively. It was concluded that because each of these radioisotope systems was dating the same geologic event for each rock unit, the only way this systematic isochron discordance could be reconciled would be if the decay of the parent radioisotopes had been accelerated at different rates at some time or times in the past, the α-decayers having been accelerated more than the β-decayers. However, a further complication to this pattern is that the radioisotope endowments of the mantle sources of basaltic magmas can sometimes be inherited by the magmas without resetting of the radioisotope

---

* *Geology Department, Institute for Creation Research, Santee, California*

"clocks" during ascent, intrusion, and extrusion in the earth's crust. This is particularly evident in recent or young rocks. Some evidence of open-system behavior was also found, and crustal contamination of some of the rock units was evident from their isotope geochemistry. Nevertheless, the overall systematic trend of radioisotope "ages" in the rock units according to their relative positions in the geologic record confirms that accelerated radioisotope decay was the dominant factor operating through earth history, with inheritance and mixing of radioisotopes from the mantle and crust as contributing factors in producing anomalous "ages." Within the Biblical framework of earth history, it is thus postulated that accelerated radioisotope decay accompanied the catastrophic geologic processes operating early in the Creation week and during the subsequent global Flood. Furthermore, because each of the three assumptions of conventional radioisotope dating—known initial conditions, closed-system behavior, and constancy of decay rates—have been clearly shown to be subject to failure, the radioisotope methods cannot, and should not, be relied upon to produce absolute "ages" for the earth's rock strata.

1. Introduction

It was in large part the discovery that modern lavas, particularly oceanic basalts, yielded old radioisotope "ages" which led to the recognition and definition of geochemical reservoirs in the earth's mantle where these lavas had been sourced. Thus *Zindler and Hart* [1986] delineated five end-member compositions in the mantle by which a variety of mixing processes were regarded as capable of explaining all the Sr-Nd-Pb isotope geochemical data on mid-ocean ridge and ocean-island basalts (MORBs and OIBs). Similarly, *Taylor et al.* [1984] had recognized three isotopic reservoirs in the continental crust, also characterized with respect to Sr, Nd, and Pb isotopes. What these mantle and crustal isotopic/geochemical reservoirs actually represent is still somewhat uncertain and very much a subject of current debate in the relevant literature as these reservoirs and their compositions have been linked in mantle-crust geodynamics models to the processes of plate tectonics [*Doe and Zartman*, 1979; *Allègre et al.*, 1983a,b; *Galer and O'Nions*, 1985; *Zindler and Hart*, 1986; *Allègre*, 1987; *Allègre et al.*, 1988; *Zartman and Haines*, 1988; *Kramers and Tolstikhin*, 1997; *Albarède*, 1998; *Nägler and Kramers*, 1998; *Phipps Morgan and Morgan*, 1999; *van Keken et al.*, 2002].

Snelling [2000a] concluded that the common thread among all the radioisotope systems is the role of these geochemical reservoirs in the mantle as the source of isotopic inheritance and mixing to give crustal rocks their isotopic signatures. This is now a well established explanation in the conventional literature, where mantle-crust geodynamics models have been used to link the characterized reservoir compositions to the different elements in the processes of plate tectonics. Thus it is envisaged that complex mixing has occurred through time as the upper and lower mantles have been stirred by subduction of plates, convection, and the ascent of plumes. Crustal growth has resulted. Defining what these mantle reservoirs represent is the subject of ongoing interpretation and debate. Even the so-called "Pb isotope paradox" seems to have been solved [*Murphy et al.*, 2003], with the proposal that subducted oceanic crust and associated continental sediment stored as slabs in the mantle Transition Zone or mid-lower mantle are the terrestrial reservoir that plots to the left of the meteorite isochron (or geochron).

However, vast time spans of slow-and-gradual uniformitarian plate tectonics are unnecessary to produce, and are indeed incapable of producing, the required mixing, crustal growth, and mantle stirring, whereas catastrophic plate tectonics has the potential to explain, and be consistent with, even more of the real-world data within a young-earth time frame [*Austin et al.*, 1994]. Indeed, state-of-the-art computer modeling of plate tectonics has demonstrated that the processes of subduction, plate movements, and mantle convection, and therefore crustal growth, occur catastrophically over a drastically shortened timescale [*Baumgardner*, 1994a, b, 2003].

Accelerated geological processes during Creation and the Flood, including catastrophic plate tectonics at least during the latter event, would have guaranteed that the present condition of the mantle and the crustal geologic record, which uniformitarians claim to have developed over 4.57 Ga, would have instead developed within a young-earth time frame of 6000–10,000 years.

Snelling [2000a] reviewed each of the major long-age radioisotope dating methods and showed that two of the three basic assumptions upon which these methods are based face easily demonstrated difficulties. First, open-system behavior is rife, being readily recognized in weathered and hydrothermally altered samples. However, it is also subtly present even in otherwise fresh rocks, often enough to suggest that all samples could be affected to varying degrees. All parent-daughter pairs suffer at least some fractionation and/or disturbance as a result of the mobility of these isotopes in crustal fluids (ground and hydrothermal waters) and during metamorphism, including even the Sm-Nd system which is usually claimed to be immobile even under metamorphic conditions. Furthermore, isotopic differences, migration, and gains or losses are found at all observational scales down to zones within mineral crystals and different crystal faces. Resetting of the radioisotope systems is therefore common.

Snelling [2000a] also found that the initial conditions can either be uncertain or variable for cogenetic suites of rock samples. In the K-Ar system, excess $^{40}Ar^*$ (radiogenic ^{40}Ar) occurs in modern lavas which thus yield anomalously old "ages," but this same problem now has been documented in volcanic and crustal rocks of all "ages." Because $^{40}Ar^*$ is indistinguishable from non-radiogenic ^{40}Ar, there is no way of knowing whether the $^{40}Ar^*$ measured in all samples has been produced by *in situ* radioactive decay of ^{40}K, whether it is primordial ^{40}Ar inherited from the mantle, or whether it is mobile $^{40}Ar^*$ acquired from other crustal rocks via fluid transport. Whereas the isochron technique is supposed to provide by extrapolation the initial ratios (and therefore initial conditions) for the Rb-Sr and Sm-Nd systems in cogenetic rock suites, significant problems do arise. The ranges of the $^{143}Nd/^{144}Nd$ ratios are usually so small compared to the analytical uncertainties of the samples that the necessary long extrapolations cause appreciable error margins for the determined initial ratios, and introduce substantial uncertainties. In any case, variations in initial $^{87}Sr/^{86}Sr$ or $^{143}Nd/^{144}Nd$ ratios for cogenetic suites of young lavas from single volcanoes have been found, meaning that the assumption of well-defined initial ratios for many suites of rocks is difficult to defend.

As a consequence of this inheritance and mixing of excess $^{40}Ar^*$ there have been numerous attempted explanations of the interaction of the geochemical reservoirs in the crust and mantle during plate tectonics processes throughout the earth's history [*Allègre et al.*, 1996; *O'Nions and Tolstikhin*, 1996; *Albarède*, 1998; *Phipps Morgan*, 1998; *Davies*, 1999]. However, of particular interest are the observations made by *Damon and Kulp* [1958], who found excess $^{40}Ar^*$ in beryl crystals recovered from pegmatites and other magmatic rocks of various uniformitarian "ages" and geological locations. Beryl is a mineral that usually contains no ^{40}K whatsoever, so all the $^{40}Ar^*$ measured (significant quantities in fact) had to have been inherited as excess $^{40}Ar^*$ from the magmas and magmatic/hydrothermal fluids present when the beryl crystallized. It would seem to be highly significant that they reported a 100-fold difference in excess $^{40}Ar^*$ content between beryl crystals formed in the early Precambrian (with an "age" of about 3 Ga) and those from the Paleozoic (with "ages" of 280–320 Ma). Furthermore, they found no significant variation in the total volume of the volatile constituents in the beryl crystals and thus eliminated formation pressure as a direct cause of this "age" correlation. In fact, there is a systematic trend in the data, between the absolute amounts of excess $^{40}Ar^*$ in the beryl crystals and the uniformitarian/radioisotope "ages" of the beryl crystals. *Damon and Kulp* [1958] therefore interpreted this correlation as due to a more extensive mobilization of the lower crust and mantle in the past (in the earlier phases of earth history), with a consequent greater rate of degassing of inert gases than at present.

Snelling [2000a] has discussed the Biblical framework of earth history, and the possibility of two clearly-stated periods of non-uniformitarian, accelerated geological processes—Creation and the Flood (2 Peter 3:3–7). It is conceivable that the apparent overall systematic trend of K-Ar and Ar-Ar radioisotope "ages" through the geologic record might be explained by systematic inheritance of excess $^{40}Ar^*$ during these periods of accelerated geological processes at Creation and the Flood when the vast majority of the geologic record was formed. A lot of outgassing would have occurred during Creation week, especially with crustal formation and associated catastrophic tectonics on Day 3 to produce the dry land, so rocks inheriting a lot of excess ^{40}Ar* at that time would now appear to be vastly older than rocks formed subsequently during the Flood when less outgassing was occurring. Similarly, there would have been more outgassing of excess ^{40}Ar* and inheritance at the beginning of the Flood, with the breaking up of the "fountains of the great deep" (Genesis 7:11), than during later phases of the Flood, so that early Flood rocks would now appear to be much older than late Flood rocks higher up the geologic record. The excess ^{40}Ar* in beryl data are consistent with this model.

Similarly, with the use of Sr, Nd, and Pb isotopes in modern lavas to define the mantle geochemical reservoirs from which the magmas were sourced, the source and history of other lavas and ancient magmatic rocks can also be described on the basis of their Sr-Nd-Pb isotope geochemistry (for example, *Snelling* [2003a, 2003b]). Indeed, mantle-crust geodynamics models have demonstrated that the radioisotope ratios in lavas and magmatic rocks interpreted as "ages" could conceivably have been derived from progressively tapping magmas from an increasingly stirred mantle with geochemical reservoirs consisting of compositional "plums" and melt residues [*Phipps Morgan and Morgan*, 1999], which included different U-Th-Pb, Rb-Sr, and Sm-Nd isotopic signatures, and excess ^{40}Ar* contents.

However, perhaps the most crucial observation made by *Snelling* [2000a] is that not all linear arrays on Rb-Sr, Sm-Nd, and Pb-Pb diagrams are true isochrons. Linear correlations are known to arise from mixing of the isotopic signatures of mantle and crustal sources, contamination, fractionation, and/or sampling bias. As already noted, recent lavas on ocean islands plot along Rb-Sr and Pb-Pb isochrons which correspond to exceedingly old "ages," so it is recognized that these inconsistent isotopic signatures represent characteristics of heterogeneous mantle sources rather than true "ages" of the lavas. The Pb-Pb system in these lavas is also totally at variance with all current models of Pb isotopic evolution built on the assumed primordial Pb isotopic composition of a mineral in one small meteoritic fragment which yields the earth's 4.57 Ga "age." Similarly, Sm-Nd "model ages" are based on the assumption that Nd isotopic evolution commenced with a bulk earth composition at its 4.6 Ga origin of the average chrondritic meteorite. Thus the edifice of radioisotope "dating" is ultimately built on the foundation of assumed earth accretion from the solar nebula at 4.57 Ga. Furthermore, what constitutes accepted "ages" within the uniformitarian time framework is determined by consistency with the stratigraphic and biostratigraphic settings and with other radioisotope "ages." Such concordances appear to occur systematically through the geologic record.

It logically follows that if modern lavas have radioisotope signatures which yield artificially old "ages" because the lavas have been sourced in heterogeneous mantle reservoirs, then it is possible, and entirely reasonable to suppose, that "ancient" lavas may likewise appear to be artificially old because of being similarly sourced from the mantle. Indeed, isotopic mixing from mantle and crustal reservoirs to produce crustal rocks has been demonstrated, for example, *Snelling* [2003a, b]. Thus, it is conceivable that the radioisotope "ages" in most crustal rocks are an artifact of systematic mixing of mantle and crustal sources which were supplied with fundamental radioisotope/geochemical signatures as a result of the accelerated crustal development processes operating during the fiat creation origin of the earth. Very different radioisotope signatures in successive flows from the same volcanoes would seem to be consistent with such mixing processes.

The quality and integrity of the radioisotope data may often be doubtful on the one hand, because of the demonstrated prevalent open-system behavior of the radioisotope systems in the surface samples from which the data are obtained. However, on the other hand, the concordances and a systematic consistency within the uniformitarian timescale edifice remain, so the solution to these may therefore involve the geochemical and catastrophic, tectonic (geodynamic) processes in the mantle and crust that have unmistakably produced their geochemical and radioisotope signatures in the earth's crustal rocks, signatures that have been wrongly interpreted as old "ages."

Nevertheless, some radioactive decay has occurred, sufficient to produce mature (fully-formed) ^{238}U radiohalos [*Snelling*, 2000b, 2005a;

S*nelling and Armitage*, 2003; *Snelling et al.*, 2003b], as well as some nuclear decay that has produced fission tracks [*Snelling*, 2005b]. But just how much radioisotope decay has occurred can really only be calculated from the physical evidence. Thus, for example, the development of fully-formed ^{238}U radiohalos would seem to require at least 100 million years of radioactive decay assuming constant decay rates at today's values [*Humphreys*, 2000; *Snelling*, 2000b], so the presence of fully-formed and overexposed ^{238}U radiohalos in granitic rocks at many levels throughout the Paleozoic-Mesozoic geologic record [*Snelling and Armitage*, 2003; *Snelling et al.*, 2003b; *Snelling*, 2005a] is consistent with hundreds of millions of years worth of radioisotope decay (at today's slow and constant rates) having occurred during accumulation of that portion of the Phanerozoic strata record. This conclusion is also confirmed by the quantities of fission tracks in selected Phanerozoic tuff beds corresponding to the accepted biostratigraphic and radioisotope "ages" of those strata [*Snelling*, 2005b].

The assumption of the uniformitarian timescale undergirds the interpretation of all radioisotope data, because consistency with that timescale distinguishes "dates" that are acceptable from "anomalies" that need to be explained by open-system behavior, inheritance, etc. Thus it is difficult to quantify just how significant are multiple radioisotope concordances and what appears to be a consistent overall trend of lower strata in the geologic record dating older than upper strata. However, the impression gained from the detailed examination by *Snelling* [2000a] of the primary radioisotope "dating" systems is that if the uniformitarian timescale assumption were removed, where more than one radioisotope system has been utilized to "date" specific rock strata, radioisotope discordances would be in the majority. That such discordances are often the case has already been discussed by *Austin* [2000], and has been thoroughly tested and documented on some specific strata by *Austin and Snelling* [1998], *Snelling et al.* [2003a], and *Austin* [2005]. Furthermore, it is highly significant that there are no practical geologic or geochemical explanations evident for these discordances, so if it weren't for the assumed appropriate uniformitarian "ages" used as a supposed objective "yardstick," all the discordant isochron "ages" could actually be "anomalous." Using the same reasoning, there is therefore no guarantee that even when and where radioisotope concordances do occur the resultant "dates" are somehow objectively correct. In any case, the "ages" derived from the radioisotope systems can really only be regarded as maximum ages because of the evidence of open-system behavior, mixing, inheritance, etc., and thus the true ages of the strata may be considerably, or even drastically, younger. Of course, this puts intolerable strain on the evolutionary timescale for uniformitarians, because it not only argues that the conventional interpretation of radioisotope dating is not secure, but that the evidence actually points towards a much younger earth. A very relevant example is the stark contrast between the U-Pb radioisotope "age" of 1500 Ma for the zircon grains in the Jemez granodiorite of New Mexico and the He (derived from U decay) diffusion age of the same zircon grains of only about 6000 years [*Humphreys et al.*, 2003a,b, 2004; *Humphreys*, 2005].

One definite possibility suggested by numerous lines of evidence is that there was a burst of accelerated nuclear decay during the Flood, and perhaps also a similar burst during the early part of the Creation week [*Humphreys*, 2000, 2005]. Thus, the radioisotope ratios produced, if interpreted in terms of today's slow radioisotope decay rates, would suggest that the rocks are very old, when in fact most of the radioisotope decay occurred extremely rapidly. If this occurred during the Flood, then the deepest strata would have more accelerated decay products accumulated in them than shallower strata deposited later in the Flood, and so would yield radioisotope "dates" that were much older. Furthermore, the physical evidence of radioisotope and nuclear decay provided by ^{238}U radiohalos and fission tracks respectively would thus be accounted for by the large amount of decay that actually occurred, albeit extremely rapidly. However, just how much decay occurred is constrained by the physical evidence of at least 500 million years worth (at today's decay rates) during the Flood [*Snelling*, 2005b]. Fission track ages of zircons in Precambrian granites of over 1000 million years are known [*Naeser et al.*, 1989], but much of that nuclear decay could be related to the Flood event, and 1000 million years is drastically short of the claimed 4.57 billion years of radioisotope decay from the origin of the earth interpreted from radioisotope ratios. Thus, there is ample scope for an alternative explanation for the radioisotope ratios measured in the earth's crustal rocks, but any alternative model must also still explain the apparent overall trend in radioisotope "dates" through the geologic record.

Uniformitarians assume the earth accreted from the solar nebula at 4.57 Ga, and that the earth's initial bulk geochemical composition was that of the average chondritic meteorite, which then becomes the starting condition for isotopic evolution through subsequent earth history. As argued by *Baumgardner* [2000], the plethora of geochemical data now available and the robustness of geochemical and geophysical modeling strongly suggest that at its creation the earth's bulk geochemical composition was probably that of the average chondritic meteorite. Of course, any associated inference about accretion from a solar nebula is totally rejected, given the unequivocal Biblical statements that the earth was in fact created before the Sun. Therefore, the quest to model the radioisotope data in the framework of catastrophic mantle-crust geodynamics is potentially greatly aided by starting with the same initial bulk geochemical composition and utilizing the same plate tectonics processes for stirring the mantle and extracting the crustal geologic record, but of course, in the context of catastrophic accelerated geological processes at Creation and during the Flood.

Therefore, in this concept of catastrophic mixing and inheritance to explain the radioisotope data, it is envisaged that the earth started after Creation with a radioisotope signature equivalent to an age approaching 4.57 Ga. Certainly, it is envisaged that some nuclear decay has occurred since Creation that has added to the initial radioisotope signature of the earth to now give it the uniformitarian "age" of 4.57 Ga, that nuclear decay having occurred at least during the Flood, as evidenced by mature ^{238}U radiohalos and fission tracks. This contribution may have been the equivalent of many millions, if not, hundreds of millions of years. Accelerated global tectonics processes during the Creation week to produce the dry land on Day 3 would then have extracted from the "primitive" mantle the necessary crustal material. Whether these processes were accompanied by some accelerated nuclear decay or not is uncertain. However, because sequential extraction to build the crust was involved, and thus progressively more fractionation and mixing, the resulting radioisotope signatures in the sequences of crustal rocks so formed during the Creation week could have conceivably displayed a "younging" trend. Then with catastrophic plate tectonics, and renewed mantle stirring and crustal growth, triggered by the breaking up of "the fountains of the great deep" at the outset of the Flood, the sequence of "new" crustal rocks progressively formed during the accompanying accelerated nuclear decay could conceivably have been endowed with even younger "ages" as the Flood event continued. However, radioisotope "age" anomalies would also have increasingly developed as oceanic crust and some ocean floor sediments were recycled back into the mantle, mixing their radioisotope signatures with those in the mantle, especially where melting occurred to produce magmas that then added new magmatic rocks to the crust again. Quite clearly, the "picture" that emerges is one of increasing complexity as these accelerated geological and tectonic processes continued. Repeated stirring of the mantle, extraction of the magmas from it, and also recycling of crustal rocks back into it, would have progressively complicated the pattern of radioisotope signatures in an increasingly "plum-pudding" mantle mixture. Migration of radioisotopes in crustal fluids would also have produced "age" anomalies.

This then is a description of the inheritance and mixing model proposed by *Snelling* [2000a], but it is still rudimentary and requires "fleshing out" with a more detailed description of the development through the earth's history of the radioisotope ratios found in crustal rocks. In this model, rather than the radioisotope systems being perturbed, complex, multi-faceted open-system behavior is proposed to explain how the radiogenic daughter isotopes are found in association with their radioactive parent isotopes in the proportions necessary to yield the false interpretation of long ages. Clearly, much research needs to be done to substantiate and refine this model if ever it is to become a viable explanation for the long "age" pattern of the radioisotopes in the earth's crustal rocks.

2. Rationale of the Present Study

The present study represents the first attempt to use radioisotope data derived from specific crustal rock units to test the inheritance and mixing model proposed by *Snelling* [2000a]. Of course, there is a huge volume of radioisotope data in the conventional literature for rock strata throughout the geologic record from all parts of the globe, so one approach would be to reprocess this huge volume of data to identify radioisotope discordances and the apparent overall trend in radioisotope "dates" through the geologic record, as well as focusing on the Sr-Nd-Pb isotope geochemistry of these rock units to explore if the data fit those rock units having been sourced in one of the identified mantle or crustal geochemical reservoirs. However, most rock units have only been subjected to selected radioisotope analyses, so often only limited radioisotope data are available for them. Yet even then there can be uncertainty, because sometimes only selected radioisotope data are published. If reasons are not given for why data were rejected, then one can't be sure whether they were simply rejected because they didn't fit the investigators' preconceived outcome, when in fact the rejected data may still be valid.

Thus a different approach was deemed more appropriate. Specific, strategic rock units whose geologic and tectonic contexts are well characterized were selected for exhaustive radioisotope "dating" studies. Fieldwork was undertaken to become familiar with these rock units, so as to then obtain carefully selected samples for the radioisotope analyses. The benefit of these "hands on" case studies is that the radioisotope data can then be compared with, and understood in the context of, field knowledge of the rock units, their petrography, mineralogy, and general geochemistry, as well as the history of those rock units in their context since their formation. The main radioisotope systems that are routinely used were targeted, namely, the K-Ar, Rb-Sr, Sm-Nd, and U-Th-Pb radioisotope systems. Once these radioisotope data were generated for the rock units in these case studies, it was then possible to compare the different radioisotope systems, the isochron "ages" and model "ages" (both whole-rock and mineral where possible) to test for radioisotope concordances and discordances, as well as to determine whether the overall trend in the radioisotope "dates" through the geologic record is only apparent or is real and can thus be fully accounted for by accelerated radioisotope decay, as argued by *Humphreys* [2000, 2005], or whether the radioisotope inheritance and mixing (catastrophic mantle-crust geodynamics) model can better explain the radioisotope data.

3. The Case Studies

The main criterion for the selection of the case studies for this present project was to target areas that are already well studied, both by the conventional community and by creationists, or the chosen areas are appropriate extensions to well-studied areas. This potentially maximizes the consequent benefits. Thus, the rock sequence in the Grand Canyon and the surrounding area is well studied by both the conventional scientific community and by creationists, and it offers a good cross-section through the geologic record of the Flood and into the pre-Flood rocks beneath. So it was logical to focus in this area as a "type section." Then an equally important criterion was to make sure the rock units studied spanned the geologic record and thus the conventional timescale. Furthermore, because there are a wide range of rock types on which radioisotope analyses can be made, it was important to hone the selection to a narrow band of rock types or compositions so that the same types of rocks could be compared at the different levels in the geologic record from the different episodes of earth history. This also had the additional advantage of removing the bulk chemistry of the rocks as a variable, potentially simplifying the interpretation of the resultant radioisotope data. The choice was thus made to primarily focus on mafic (basaltic) rock units, because the parent magmas were derived from the mantle, and thus the radioisotope and isotopic data obtained should coincide with one of the mantle geochemical reservoirs, or indicate mixing between them, or even crustal contamination during ascent of the magmas. When these additional criteria are applied to the Grand Canyon type section, it is evident that there are not mafic rock units evenly spaced within either the rock record or its associated conventional timescale, so additional choices were made to augment the selected Grand Canyon mafic rock units with case studies from adjoining or other suitable areas.

Thus, in the Grand Canyon type section the mafic units chosen were the Uinkaret Plateau basalts (Quaternary), the Cardenas Basalt and the related diabase sills (Middle Proterozoic), and the amphibolites (metamorphosed basalts) of the Brahma Schist in the Granite Gorge Metamorphic Suite (Lower Proterozoic). Even though it isn't of mafic composition, the Elves Chasm Granodiorite (Lower Proterozoic) was added to this selection from the Grand Canyon because it appears to be the oldest rock unit in the Grand Canyon sequence. To fill in the gaps in the span of these Grand Canyon rock units of the geologic record and its associated conventional timescale, several additional rock units were targeted, namely, the Mt. Ngauruhoe andesite flows, New Zealand (historic), the Somerset Dam layered mafic intrusion, Queensland, Australia (Jurassic-Triassic), the Apache Group basalts and diabase sills in central Arizona (Middle Proterozoic), and the Beartooth andesitic amphibolite in Wyoming (Archean). Additional reasons for selection of the Apache Group basalts and diabase sills, and the Beartooth andesitic amphibolite were that the former appear to be closely related to the Cardenas Basalt and diabase sills in the Grand Canyon, while the latter is regarded as one of the oldest rocks in the U. S. A.

Detailed descriptions of each of the rock units chosen for these case studies are provided in an Appendix. These descriptions include the geographical occurrence, petrography, and mineralogical and geochemical variations within each rock unit, and where available, observations relevant to understanding how it formed. Suitable location and geological maps are also provided as well as appropriate strata sequence diagrams. The sampling of each of the rock units is described, and where possible sample locations are shown on the maps and strata sequence diagrams. A total of one hundred and thirty-six samples were collected:-

• Mt. Ngauruhoe, New Zealand (historic)—11
• Uinkaret Plateau basalts, western Grand Canyon (Quaternary)—10

- Somerset Dam layered mafic intrusion, Queensland, Australia (Jurassic-Triassic)—15
- Cardenas Basalt, eastern Grand Canyon (Middle Proterozoic)—15
- Diabase sills, central Grand Canyon, including the Bass Rapids sill (Middle Proterozoic)—16
- Apache Group basalts and diabase sills, central Arizona (Middle Proterozoic)—30
- Brahma Schist amphibolites, central Grand Canyon (Lower Proterozoic)—27
- Elves Chasm Granodiorite, Grand Canyon (Lower Proterozoic)—8
- Beartooth andesitic amphibolite, Wyoming (Archean)—1

4. Radioisotope Analytical Procedures

Two procedures were used for the handling and processing of the collected samples, depending on where the initial handling occurred. After the initial handling of the samples, they were sent to various laboratories for the different analytical work required.

Those samples that were taken to the petrographic laboratory at the Institute for Creation Research were sawed to remove exterior surfaces which could be contaminated. Thin-sawed slices of each rock sample were dispatched for preparation of thin sections for petrographic analysis. Interior blocks representative of each rock sample were then washed, dried, and crushed in an iron mortar to be prepared as whole-rock powders for chemical and isotopic analyses. After milling and grinding, the powders were sieved. All equipment used was thoroughly cleaned and washed after processing of each sample in order to eliminate contamination between samples. Approximately 20 g of particles finer than 200 mesh were submitted for bulk geochemical analyses (66 elements) to the XRAL Laboratories of Don Mills, Ontario, Canada, where XRF (x-ray fluorescence), ICP (inductively coupled plasma), and ICP-MS (inductively coupled plasma–mass spectrometry) methods were used to analyze the whole-rock powders. Other splits of the whole-rock powders containing 80–200 mesh (0.18–0.075 mm) particles were sent for K-Ar radioisotope analyses to the Geochron Laboratories of Cambridge, Massachusetts, where they were analyzed under the direction of Dr. Richard Reesman, the K-Ar laboratory manager, who undertook standard K-Ar radioisotope analyses. The concentration of K_2O (weight %) was measured by the flame photometry method, and the ^{40}K concentration (ppm) was calculated from the terrestrial isotopic abundance using the measured concentration of K. The concentration in ppm of $^{40}Ar^*$, the supposed "radiogenic argon," was derived by the conventional formula from isotope-dilution measurements on a mass spectrometer by correcting for the presence of atmospheric Ar whose isotopic composition is known [*Dalrymple and Lanphere*, 1969]. Other splits of the powdered samples with particles <200 mesh (0.075 mm) were sent to the isotope laboratory at the University of Colorado at Boulder, where Professor G. Lang Farmer analyzed the samples by mass spectrometry for Rb-Sr, Sm-Nd, and Pb-Pb isotopes. These University of Colorado measurements of the Sr, Nd, and Pb isotopes were carefully calibrated by internationally recognized standards, and all the resultant isotopic data were then analyzed and isochrons plotted using the computer program called *Isoplot* [*Ludwig*, 2001]. For some of the rock units sampled, one or two of the samples were processed to split them into their mineral constituents. To do this, the −140 to +270 mesh grains were progressively concentrated into their various mineral constituents by centrifugation in different heavy liquids, followed by further cleaning using a strong magnet. X-ray diffraction (XRD) analysis and optical microscopy were used to confirm the identity and purity of the minerals concentrated. These mineral concentrates were then sent to the isotope laboratory at the University of Colorado at Boulder where Professor G. Lang Farmer undertook mass spectrometry measurements of the Sr, Nd, and Pb isotopes in the minerals. The resultant isotopic data were plotted as mineral isochrons for each radioisotope system, again using the *Isoplot* computer program.

Those samples whose processing was based in Brisbane, Australia, followed a slightly modified procedure. Split by hammering, a portion of each sample was sent for thin sectioning for subsequent petrographic analysis. Approximately 100 g splits of each of the samples were then dispatched to the Amdel laboratory in Adelaide, South Australia, where each sample was crushed and pulverized. Whole-rock analyses were then undertaken by total fusion of each powdered sample followed by digesting them before ICP-OES (inductively coupled plasma-optical emission spectrometry) for major and minor elements, and ICP-MS (inductively coupled plasma-mass spectrometry) for trace and rare earth elements. Separate analyses for Fe as FeO were also undertaken by wet chemistry methods that were also able to record the loss on ignition, primarily representing H_2O or any carbonate (given off as CO_2) in the samples. A second representative set of 100 g pieces of each of the samples was sent to the K-Ar dating laboratory at Activation Laboratories in Ancaster, Ontario, Canada, for whole-rock K-Ar dating under the direction of the laboratory manager, Dr. Yakov Kapusta. After crushing of the whole-rock samples and pulverizing them, the concentrations of K (weight%) were measured by the ICP technique. The ^{40}K concentrations (ppm) were then calculated from the terrestrial isotopic abundance using these measured concentrations of K. The concentrations in ppm of $^{40}Ar^*$, the supposed radiogenic ^{40}Ar, were derived using the conventional formula from isotope dilution measurements on a noble gas mass spectrometer by correcting for the presence of atmospheric Ar whose isotopic composition is known [Dalrymple and Lanphere, 1969]. Finally, a third representative set of 100 g pieces of each of these samples was sent to the PRISE laboratory in the Research School of Earth Sciences at the Australian National University in Canberra, Australia, where under the direction of Dr. Richard Armstrong whole-rock Rb-Sr, Sm-Nd, and Pb-Pb isotopic analyses were undertaken. After the sample pieces were crushed and pulverized, the powders were dissolved in concentrated hydrofluoric acid, followed by standard chemical separation procedures for each of these radioisotope systems. Once separated, the elements in each radioisotope system were loaded by standard procedures onto metal filaments to be used in the solid source thermal ionization mass spectrometer (TIMS), the state-of-the-art technology in use in this laboratory. Strontium isotopes were measured using the mass fractionation correction $^{86}Sr/^{88}Sr = 0.1194$, and the $^{87}Sr/^{86}Sr$ ratios were reported normalized to the NBS standard SRM 987 value of 0.710207.

Neodymium isotopes were corrected for mass fractionation using $^{146}Nd/^{144}Nd = 0.7219$ and were normalized to the present-day $^{143}Nd/^{144}Nd$ value of 0.51268 for standard BCR-1 (a Columbia River basalt, Washington, sample). Lead isotope ratios were normalized to NBS standard SRM 981 for mass fractionation. Again, all the resultant isotope data were analyzed and isochrons plotted for each radioisotope system using the *Isoplot* computer program [*Ludwig*, 2001].

5. Results

5.1 K-Ar Model and Isochron Dating

The results of the K-Ar radioisotope analyses on the samples from all of these case studies are summarized in Table 1. The K-Ar model "ages" were calculated for each sample analyzed using the standard model-age equation, which assumes that 10.5% of the ^{40}K atoms in each sample decay to $^{40}Ar*$ atoms. Furthermore, because ^{40}Ar is a common atmospheric gas which can leak into rocks and minerals making them appear older than their actual ages, in conventional K-Ar model age determinations it is assumed that a certain proportion of the ^{40}Ar in each rock sample is contamination, and therefore, a certain proportion of the total ^{40}Ar determined in the laboratory on each sample, in accordance with the ^{40}Ar to ^{36}Ar ratio of the present atmosphere, is subtracted so that only what is thus assumed to be the radiogenic ^{40}Ar in each sample is used in the model-age calculations [*Dalrymple and Lanphere*, 1969]. Furthermore, it is conventional to assume that no radiogenic ^{40}Ar (written as $^{40}Ar*$) was present in the rock when it initially formed, so that all the $^{40}Ar*$ now measured in the rock has been derived from *in situ* radioactive decay of ^{40}K. The reported error listed with each model "age" in Table 1 represents the estimated 1σ uncertainty due to the analytical equipment and procedure.

As already noted, the *Isoplot* computer program of *Ludwig* [2001], which is now commonly utilized by the geochronology community, was used to process the analytical data for each radioisotope system for each targeted rock unit. This program utilizes the least-squares linear

Table 1. K-Ar model and isochron "ages" obtained for the targeted rock units.

Rock Unit	Location	Conventional Age	Method	Number of Samples	Range of K-Ar Model Ages (Ma)		K-Ar Isochron Age (Ma)
					Minimum	Maximum	
Mt. Ngauruhoe andesites	Mt. Ngauruhoe, New Zealand	Historic flows (1949, 1954, 1975)	Direct observation	11 whole rocks (from 5 flows)	<0.27	3.5±0.2	Not applicable
Toroweap Dam	River Mile 179.4	1.16±0.18 Ma	K-Ar model	whole rock + 3 minerals	1.19±0.18 (whole rock)	20.7±1.3 (olivine)	Not applicable
Massive Diabase Dam	River Mile 202.5 Grand Canyon	0.443±0.041 Ma		whole rock + olivine	1.4±0.3 (whole rock)	46.5±4.3 (olivine)	
Somerset Dam layered mafic intrusion	Somerset Dam, southeast Queensland, Australia	216±4 Ma 225.3±2.3 Ma	K-Ar model composite Rb-Sr isochron	15 (whole rocks)	182.7±9	252.8±9	174±8
Cardenas Basalt	Eastern Grand Canyon, Arizona	1103±66 Ma	Rb-Sr isochron	15 (8 new, 7 existing)	577±12	1013±37	516±30
Bass Rapids diabase sill	Grand Canyon, Arizona	1070±30 Ma	Rb-Sr isochron	11 (whole rocks)	656±15	1053±24	841.5±164
Apache Group basalts	Central Arizona	1100 Ma	Assumed similar to diabase sills	9 (whole rocks)	513±13	968.9±25	Too much scatter
Apache Group diabase sills	Central Arizona	1120±10 Ma	zircon U-Pb	21 (whole rocks)	267.5±14	855.8±17	Too much scatter
Brahma amphibolites	Grand Canyon, Arizona	1140±40 Ma 1740–1750 Ma	biotite K-Ar zircon U-Pb concordia	27 (whole rocks)	405.1±10	2574.2±73	Too much scatter
Beartooth andesitic amphibolite	Northeast Wyoming	2790±35 Ma	Rb-Sr isochron	1 whole rock + 5 minerals	1520±31 (quartz-plag.)	2620±53 (hornblende)	Too much scatter

regression method of *York* [1969] to plot the isochron as the best-fit regression line through the data. The slope of the isochron is then used by the program to calculate the isochron "age" using the standard isochron-age equation. When plotted, each data point has assigned to it error bars that represent the estimated 2σ uncertainties due to the analytical equipment and procedure. The program also evaluates the uncertainties associated with the calculated isochron "age" using a statistic known as the "mean square of weighted deviates" (MSWD), which is roughly a measure of the ratio of the observed scatter of the data points from the best-fit line or isochron to the expected scatter from the assigned errors and error correlations (including, but not limited to, the analytical equipment). If the assigned errors are the only cause of scatter, so that the observed scatter approximates the expected scatter, then the value of the MSWD will tend to be near unity. MSWD values much greater than unity generally indicate either under-estimated analytical errors or the presence of non-analytical scatter [*Ludwig*, 2001], while MSWD values much less than unity generally indicate either over-estimated analytical errors or unrecognized error-correlations. Thus it is crucial to adequately estimate the analytical errors so that the observed scatter of the data points from the isochron line yields an MSWD near unity. This was the procedure adopted here, so that the isochron "ages" reported in Table 1 were calculated from isochrons with MSWDs near unity. The errors for each isochron age reported represent the estimated 2σ uncertainties. As *Ludwig* [2001] notes, this does not mean that the true age of the samples has a 95% probability of falling within the stated age interval, but rather only signifies that the mean of the infinitely-replicated regressions would yield an isochron age within this interval.

For recent and young rocks, such as the Mt. Ngauruhoe andesites and Toroweap Dam and Massive Diabase Dam basalts (Table 1), K-Ar isochrons simply could not be plotted to derive any meaningful K-Ar isochron "ages," so the K-Ar isochron method as expected is not applicable to these rocks. On the other hand, the oldest rock units in Table 1, their conventional ages being those reported in the geologic literature, yielded K-Ar isotope data that contained too much scatter to yield statistically viable K-Ar isochrons and isochron ages. This would suggest that a significant component in the observed scatter of the data points from the best-fit regression lines is due to factors other than the scatter due to analytical errors. Such factors would likely include contamination of the K-Ar radioisotope system by open-system behavior such as additions from the host wall rocks, and/or perturbing of the radioisotope systems by subsequent hydrothermal alteration and/ or during weathering.

The samples from most of the targeted rock units yielded large ranges of widely divergent or scattered K-Ar model "ages." The scatter of the model "ages" was often just as great in those rock units for which K-Ar isochron "ages" could be calculated as in those where there was too much scatter to yield statistically viable isochron "ages." Such scatter did not always prevent the fitting of isochrons to the data and calculation of isochron "ages." Nevertheless, it is highly likely that the same factors responsible for the excessive scatter of the data points from the best-fit regression lines, which prevented statistically viable isochron "ages" being calculated, were also responsible for the scatter in the model "ages," particularly as these factors would vary between the outcrops from which the samples were collected. Interestingly, in two of the three rock units for which K-Ar isochron "ages" could be determined, those isochron "ages" did not fall within the ranges of the K-Ar model "ages" for those rock units as might be expected, but were actually less than the lowest model "ages."

5.2 K-Ar, Rb-Sr, Sm-Nd, and Pb-Pb Isochron Dating

All the results of the K-Ar, Rb-Sr, Sm-Nd, and Pb-Pb isochron dating of the samples of the targeted rock units in this study are summarized in Table 2. As already indicated above, all the isotope data for each radioisotope system for each targeted rock unit was processed using *Isoplot* [*Ludwig*, 2001] to plot isochrons and calculate isochron "ages." Furthermore, all the comments above about the assessment of the 2σ uncertainties in both the isotope ratios obtained from each sample and in the calculated isochron "ages" are relevant to the data in Table 2.

Table 2. K-Ar, Rb-Sr, Sm-Nd, and Pb-Pb isochron "ages" obtained for the targeted rock units.

Rock Unit	Location	Conventional Age	Method	Number of Samples	K-Ar	Rb-Sr	Sm-Nd	Pb-Pb
Mt. Ngauruhoe andesites	Mt. Ngauruhoe, New Zealand	Historic flows (1949, 1954, 1975)	Direct observation	11 whole rocks (from 5 flows)	Not applicable	133±87 (5 samples)	197±160 (5 samples)	3908±390 (7 samples)
Uinkaret Plateau basalts	Western Grand Canyon, Arizona	<1.16±0.18 Ma	K-Ar model	8 (whole rocks)	None	1143±220 (7 samples)	916±570 (6 samples)	Not available
Somerset Dam layered mafic intrusion	Somerset Dam, southeast Queensland, Australia	216±4 Ma / 225.3±2.3 Ma	K-Ar model / composite Rb-Sr isochron	15 (whole rocks)	174±8 (15 samples)	393±170 (14 samples)	259±76 (13 samples)	1425±1000 (13 samples)
Cardenas Basalt	Eastern Grand Canyon, Arizona	1103±66 Ma	Rb-Sr isochron	26 (whole rocks) (14 new, 12 existing)	516±30 (14 samples)	1111±81 (19) / 892±82 (22)	1588±170 Ma (8 samples)	1385±950 Ma (4 samples)
Bass Rapids diabase sill	Grand Canyon, Arizona	1070±30 Ma	Rb-Sr isochron	11 whole rocks / D1-13 + minerals (6) / D1-15 + minerals (11) / magnetites (7)	841.5±164 / — / —	1055±46(11) / 1060±24 (7) / 1075±34 (12) / 1007±79 (7)	Too much scatter / 1379±140 (7) / 1330±360 (9) / 1336±380 (7)	1250±130 (11) / Too much scatter / 1584±420 (10) / 1327±230 (6)
Apache Group basalts	Central Arizona	1100 Ma	Assumed similar to diabase sills	9 (whole rocks)	Too much scatter	2295±300 (5)	Not enough spread	1304±69 (8)
Apache Group diabase sills	Central Arizona	1120±10 Ma / 1140±40 Ma	zircon U-Pb / biotite K-Ar	21 (whole rocks)	Too much scatter	2067±380(16)	Too much scatter	1142±98 (19) / 1146±59 (18)
Brahma amphibolites	Grand Canyon, Arizona	1740-1750 Ma	zircon U-Pb concordia	27 (whole rocks)	Too much scatter	840±86 (25) / 1240±84 (19)	1678±60 (24) / 1655±40 (21)	1864±78 (27) / 1883±53 (20)
Elves Chasm Granodiorite	Grand Canyon, Arizona	1840±1 Ma	zircon U-Pb	8 (whole rocks)	Not available	1512±140 (7 samples)	1664±200 (7 samples)	1933±220 (7 samples)
Beartooth andesitic amphibolite	Northeast Wyoming	2790±35 Ma	Rb-Sr isochron	1 whole rock + minerals (5)	Too much scatter	2515±110	2886±190	2689.4±8.6

Where possible, isochrons were fitted to the data so that the MSWD was close or equal to unity, so that the observed scatter from the best-fit regression lines or isochrons was equal to the assigned analytical errors. The 2σ uncertainties in the listed isochron "ages" in Table 2 were thus calculated on that basis. Where the 2σ uncertainties were so large as to render the calculated isochron "ages" statistically questionable, those isochron "ages" have been listed in italics. In one instance, the Cardenas Basalt, the large uncertainty in the Pb-Pb isochron "age" is probably due to the small sample set for which Pb-Pb isotope data is available. Otherwise, for several of the targeted rock units there was either not enough spread in the Sm-Nd isotope data to produce a valid isochron and isochron "age," or there was simply too much scatter in the data. This has already been noted above to also be the case with the K-Ar isotope data for some of the targeted Precambrian rock units.

Some of the data have already been published with full details, including isochron diagrams. The Mt. Ngauruhoe andesites have been discussed in detail by *Snelling* [1998, 2003a], the Somerset Dam layered mafic intrusion by *Snelling* [2003b], the Cardenas Basalt by *Austin and Snelling* [1998], the Bass Rapids diabase sill by *Snelling et al.* [2003] and *Austin* [2005], and the Beartooth andesitic amphibolite in *Austin* [2005]. The relevant isochron diagrams for the Brahma amphibolites are presented here in Figures 1, 2, and 3, while the isochron diagrams for the Elves Chasm Granodiorite are in Figures 4, 5, and 6. Many of the isochron "ages" listed in Table 2 are tightly constrained with large numbers of data points (samples) and excellent statistics. The isochrons for the Brahma amphibolites shown in Figures 1, 2, and 3 are excellent examples of this, with the Rb-Sr isochron defined by nineteen samples, the Sm-Nd isochron constrained by twenty-one samples, and the Pb-Pb isochron constrained by twenty samples (out of the twenty-seven analyzed). In each case the assigned analytical errors are low and yet the statistics are excellent because the observed scatter matches these low assigned analytical errors when the MSWD equals unity. The excellent statistics for these isochrons, coupled with the wide spread of the data points, yield isochron "ages" with low 2σ uncertainties. Table 2 also shows that for the Brahma amphibolites, if more samples

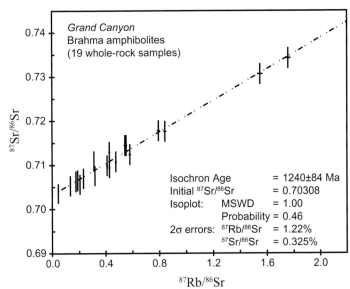

Figure 1. ^{87}Rb/^{86}Sr versus ^{87}Sr/^{86}Sr isochron diagram for the Brahma amphibolites in Grand Canyon. Nineteen of the twenty-seven whole-rock samples were used in the isochron and "age" calculations. The bars represent the 2σ uncertainties.

were included in the *Isoplot* analyses of the data, both the Sm-Nd and Pb-Pb isochron "ages" would essentially be the same apart from higher 2σ uncertainties, whereas the Rb-Sr isochron "age" would be significantly lower. Nevertheless, these three isochron "ages" for the Brahma amphibolites are very discordant. Indeed, most of the isochron "ages" listed in Table 2, when they are statistically valid, are discordant with one another for those rock units.

5.3 Sr-Nd-Pb Isotope Geochemistry

The Sr-Nd-Pb isotope geochemistry data obtained for the targeted rock units in this study are summarized in Table 3 and plotted on the respective isotope correlation diagrams in Figures 7–10. In these isotope correlation diagrams, where the isotope ratios of some of these samples plot beyond the margins of the diagrams, arrows point from the margins of the diagrams with the relevant sample symbols to indicate in which direction those data points plot. The mantle isotopic reservoirs plotted in Figures 7–10 have been defined primarily by the isotope ratios in countless thousands of samples of modern and recent oceanic basalts, while the regions of lower and upper continental crust Pb-Pb isotope values plotted on Figure 10 are well established from isotope analyses of many crustal rocks.

Only two of the rock units in this study plotted in or near these mantle isotopic reservoirs. The gabbros of the Somerset Dam layered mafic intrusion plotted in the HIMU field in Figure 7, in the MORB field in Figure 8, almost in the PREMA field in Figure 9, and on the edge of the MORB field in Figure 10, thus indicating that the magma for this intrusion was derived from the upper mantle without crustal contamination during its passage and intrusion into the upper crust. As a group the Mt. Ngauruhoe andesite samples plot together but outside the fields of these mantle isotopic reservoirs, which suggests that if

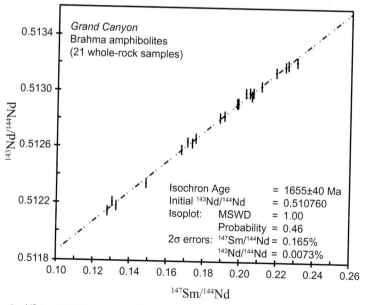

Figure 2. $^{147}Sm/^{144}Nd$ versus $^{143}Nd/^{144}Nd$ isochron diagram for the Brahma amphibolites in Grand Canyon. Twenty-one of the twenty-seven whole-rock samples were used in the isochron and "age" calculations. The bars represent the 2σ uncertainties.

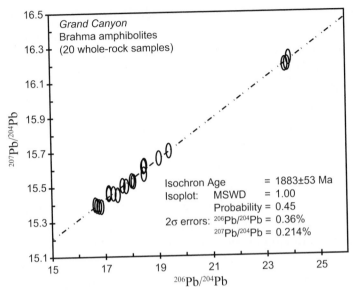

Figure 3. ^{206}Pb/^{204}Pb versus ^{207}Pb/^{204}Pb isochron diagram for the Brahma amphibolites in Grand Canyon. Twenty of the twenty-seven whole-rock samples were used in the isochron and "age" calculations. The ellipses represent the 2σ uncertainties.

this magma was sourced in the mantle, from where it would have been basaltic in composition, it was subsequently contaminated to produce its final andesitic composition. Otherwise, the samples from all of the other targeted rock units are scattered across these diagrams, though for some of the rock units some of these samples plot in and near the mantle array, suggesting a mantle component in their original magmas. This is even the case with the Elves Chasm Granodiorite, which would usually be regarded as being derived totally from magma sourced only in the lower crust. Furthermore, there appears to be a pattern to this scatter of the sample points plotted on these isotope correlation diagrams towards higher Sr isotope ratios in Figures 7–9, and towards higher Pb-Pb isotope ratios in Figure 10. The trend towards higher Sr isotope ratios, away from the mantle isotopic reservoirs, would appear to indicate significant crustal contamination in many of the rock units analyzed, while the strongly linear trend in the Pb-Pb isotope ratios in Figure 10 would appear to correlate with the respective Pb-Pb isochrons for some of these rock units. Thus it is abundantly clear from the data plotted in these isotope correlation diagrams that for those rock units whose magmas were sourced in the mantle they have inherited at least some of their isotope compositions from those mantle sources, while there has been some crustal contamination of these radioisotope systems, particularly the Rb-Sr radioisotope system, during the passage and intrusion of these magmas into the upper crust or onto the earth's surface.

6. Discussion

6.1 K-Ar Dating, Model Ages, and Excess ^{40}Ar*

The K-Ar model "ages" of up to 3.5 Ma obtained for the recent andesite lava flows at Mt. Ngauruhoe in New Zealand (Table 1) clearly indicate that excess ^{40}Ar* was present in those lavas when they erupted because

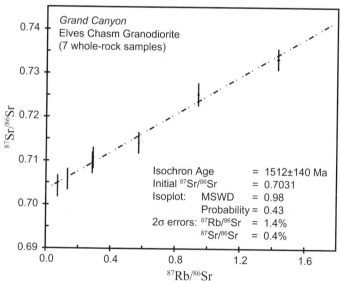

Figure 4. ^{87}Rb/^{86}Sr versus ^{87}Sr/^{86}Sr isochron diagram for the Elves Chasm Granodiorite in Grand Canyon. Seven of the eight whole-rock samples were used in the isochron and "age" calculations. The bars represent the 2σ uncertainties.

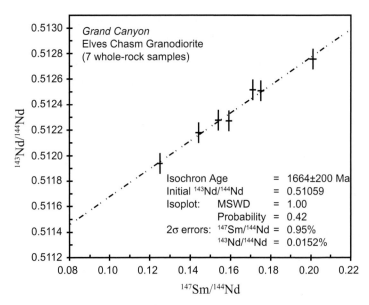

Figure 5. $^{147}Sm/^{144}Nd$ versus $^{143}Nd/^{144}Nd$ isochron diagram for the Elves Chasm Granodiorite in Grand Canyon. Seven of the eight whole-rock samples were used in the isochron and "age" calculations. The bars represent the 2σ uncertainties.

of being inherited from the mantle source of the magma [*Snelling*, 1998], and possibly also from the small component of crustal contamination [*Snelling*, 2003a]. Similarly, *Austin* [1996] found excess $^{40}Ar^*$ in dacite lava less than 10 years old at Mount St. Helens in Washington state, U. S. A. Furthermore, *Austin* [1996] found that the ferromagnesium mineral phases (amphibole and pyroxene) within that Mount St. Helens dacite yielded even larger anomalous K-Ar model "ages" than the whole rock, because the excess $^{40}Ar^*$ contained in them was supported by lower concentrations of parent ^{40}K. Similarly, when the minerals in the basalt of the Toroweap Dam in the western Grand Canyon were separated and analyzed, they yielded excessively older K-Ar model ages than the whole rock, especially the olivine with its low ^{40}K content ([*Rugg and Austin*, 1998] and Table 1). This is confirmed by the sample of the Massive Diabase Dam basalt, in which the excess $^{40}Ar^*$ in the olivine yielded an extraordinarily old K-Ar model "age" (Table 1). This problem of excess ^{40}Ar* being recognized and thus yielding anomalous old K-Ar model "ages" for historic, recent, and young volcanic rocks has now been widely documented, and has been extensively discussed by *Snelling* [1998, 2000a].

However, this begs the question: if excess ^{40}Ar* is so well recognized and documented in historic, recent, and young volcanic rocks due to mantle inheritance and crustal contamination, then could excess ^{40}Ar* likewise be present in ancient volcanic rocks, thus also producing anomalously old K-Ar model "ages" for them? This possibility, though, is easily dealt with by investigating the ancient rock units' K-Ar isochron diagrams, because if there is excess ^{40}Ar* in them the isochrons will intercept the ^{40}Ar* axes at positive ^{40}Ar* values where the ^{40}K is zero. In this study only three of the ancient rock units studied yielded statistically

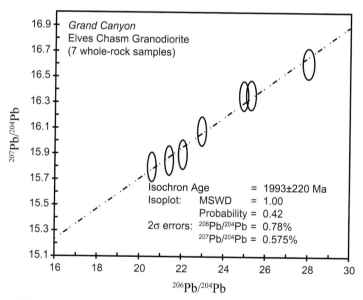

Figure 6. ^{206}Pb/^{204}Pb versus ^{207}Pb/^{204}Pb isochron diagram for the Elves Chasm Granodiorite in Grand Canyon. Seven of the eight whole-rock samples were used in the isochron and "age" calculations. The ellipses represent the 2σ uncertainties.

Table 3. Sr-Nd-Pb isotope geochemistry data obtained for the targeted rock units.

Rock Unit	Location	Conventional Age	Method	Number of Samples	Range of Isotope Ratios			
					$^{87}Sr/^{86}Sr$	$^{143}Nd/^{144}Nd$	$^{206}Pb/^{204}Pb$	$^{207}Pb/^{204}Pb$
Mt. Ngauruhoe andesites	Mt. Ngauruhoe, New Zealand	Historic flows (1949, 1954, 1975)	Direct observation	11 whole rocks (from 5 flows)	0.705153 (min) 0.705660 (max)	0.512704 (min) 0.512778 (max)	18.797 (min) 18.842 (max)	15.620 (min) 15.637 (max)
Uinkaret Plateau basalts	Western Grand Canyon, Arizona	<1.16±0.18 Ma	K-Ar model	8 (whole rocks)		0.512494 (min) 0.512751 (max)	Not available	Not available
Somerset Dam layered mafic intrusion	Somerset Dam, southeast Queensland, Australia	216±4 Ma; 225.3±2.3 Ma	K-Ar model; composite Rb-Sr isochron	15 (whole rocks)	0.702740 (min) 0.703138 (max)	0.512902 (min) 0.512990 (max)	18.393 (min) 18.861 (max)	15.562 (min) 15.702 (max)
Cardenas Basalt	Eastern Grand Canyon, Arizona	1103±66 Ma	Rb-Sr isochron	15 (whole rocks)	0.71270 (min) 1.72104 (max)	0.512187 (min) 0.512611 (max)	19.017 (min) 20.110 (max)	15.613 (min) 15.712 (max)
Cardenas related diabase sills	Grand Canyon, Arizona	1070±30 Ma	Rb-Sr isochron	18 (whole rocks)	0.704502 (min) 0.83703 (max)	0.511992 (min) 0.512700 (max)	17.255 (min) 25.432 (max)	15.452 (min) 16.135 (max)
Apache Group basalts	Central Arizona	1100 Ma	Assumed similar to diabase sills	9 (whole rocks)	0.709802 (min) 0.835571 (max)	0.512363 (min) 0.512707 (max)	17.634 (min) 23.071 (max)	15.455 (min) 15.971 (max)
Apache Group diabase sills	Central Arizona	1120±10 Ma; 1140±40 Ma	zircon U-Pb; biotite K-Ar	21 (whole rocks)	0.704807 (min) 0.75208 (max)	0.512155 (min) 0.512565 (max)	16.290 (min) 35.764 (max)	14.439 (min) 16.927 (max)
Brahma amphibolites	Grand Canyon, Arizona	1740-1750 Ma	zircon U-Pb concordia	27 (whole rocks)	0.703565 (min) 0.757016 (max)	0.512118 (min) 0.513242 (max)	16.696 (min) 25.473 (max)	15.384 (min) 16.318 (max)
Elves Chasm Granodiorite	Grand Canyon, Arizona	1840±1 Ma	zircon U-Pb	8 (whole rocks)	0.704174 (min) 0.73335 (max)	0.511938 (min) 0.512758 (max)	20.583 (min) 33.178 (max)	15.800 (min) 16.607 (max)
Beartooth andesitic amphibolite	Northeast Wyoming	2790±35 Ma	Rb-Sr isochron	1 whole rock + 5 minerals	0.70525 (titanite) 0.70988 (whole rock) 0.81352 (biotite)	0.509852 (biotite) 0.510492 (whole rock) 0.511381 (titanite)	14.455 (quartz-plag.) 16.306 (whole rock) 165.587 (titanite)	15.007 (quartz-plag.) 15.333 (whole rock) 42.666 (titanite)

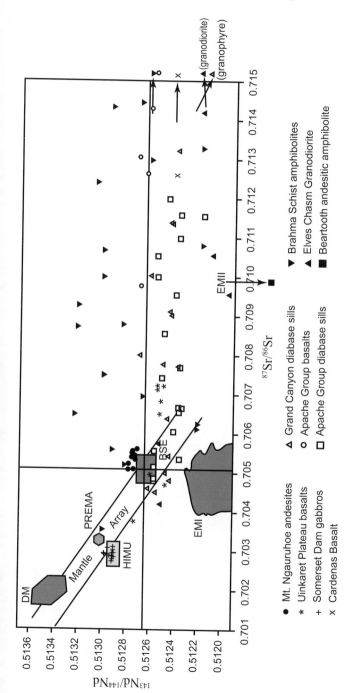

Figure 7. The $^{87}Sr/^{86}Sr$ versus $^{143}Nd/^{144}Nd$ isotope correlation diagram showing the main oceanic mantle reservoirs of *Zindler and Hart* [1986]: DM = depleted mantle; BSE = bulk silicate earth; EMI and EMII = enriched mantle; HIMU = mantle with high U/Pb ratio; PREMA = frequently observed PREvalent MAntle composition. The mantle array is defined by many oceanic basalts, and a bulk silicate earth value for $^{87}Sr/^{86}Sr$ can be obtained from this trend. The whole-rock isotope data for the samples from the rock units in this study are variously plotted and labeled on the diagram.

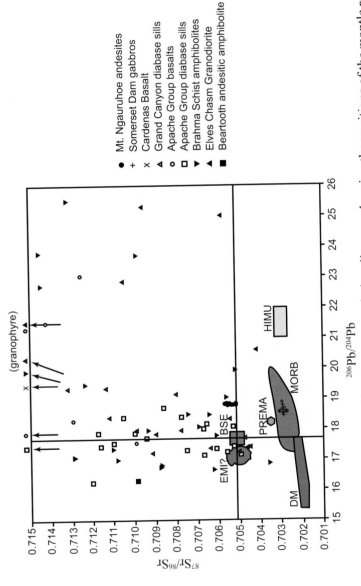

Figure 8. The $^{206}Pb/^{204}Pb$ versus $^{87}Sr/^{86}Sr$ isotope correlation diagram showing the positions of the mantle reservoirs identified by *Zindler and Hart* [1986]: DM = depleted mantle; BSE = bulk silicate earth; EMI and EMII = enriched mantle; HIMU = mantle with high U/Pb ratio; PREMA = frequently observed PREvalent MAntle composition. The $^{206}Pb/^{204}Pb$ value of the bulk silicate earth is taken from *Allègre et al.* [1988]. The whole-rock isotope data for the samples from the rock units in this study are variously plotted and labeled on the diagram.

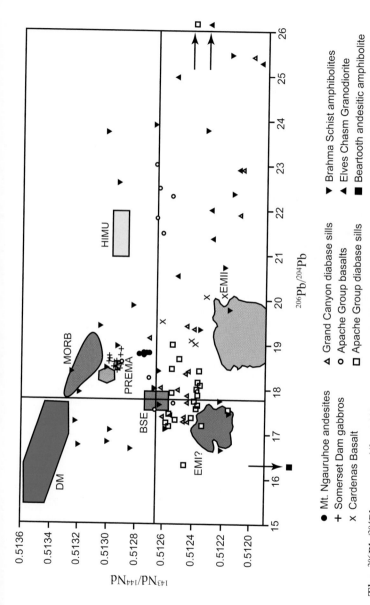

Figure 9. The $^{206}Pb/^{204}Pb$ versus $^{143}Nd/^{144}Nd$ isotope correlation diagram showing the positions of the mantle reservoirs identified by *Zindler and Hart* (1986): DM = depleted mantle; BSE = bulk silicate earth; EMI and EMII = enriched mantle; HIMU = mantle with high U/Pb ratio; PREMA = frequently observed PREvalent MAntle composition. The $^{206}Pb/^{204}Pb$ value of the bulk silicate earth is taken from *Allègre et al.* [1988]. The whole-rock isotope data for the samples from the rock units in this study are variously plotted and labeled on the diagram.

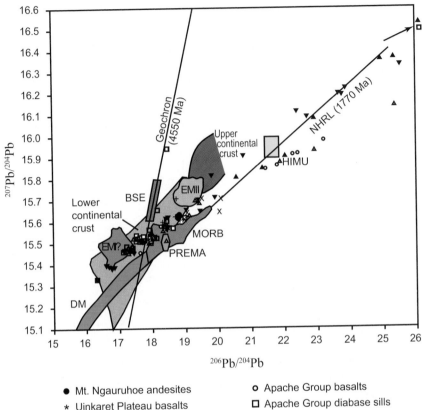

- ● Mt. Ngauruhoe andesites
- * Uinkaret Plateau basalts
- + Somerset Dam gabbros
- x Cardenas Basalt
- △ Grand Canyon diabase sills
- ○ Apache Group basalts
- □ Apache Group diabase sills
- ▼ Brahma Schist amphibolites
- ▲ Elves Chasm Granodiorite
- ■ Beartooth andesitic amphibolite

Figure 10. The $^{206}Pb/^{204}Pb$ versus $^{207}Pb/^{204}Pb$ isotope correlation diagram showing the position of the northern hemisphere reference line (NHRL), the slope of which has an age significance of 1770 Ma, and the geochron (4550 Ma). The mantle reservoirs of *Zindler and Hart* [1986] are: DM = depleted mantle; BSE = bulk silicate earth; EMI and EMII = enriched mantle; HIMU = mantle with high U/Pb ratio; PREMA = frequently observed PREvalent MAntle composition. The fields of the upper and lower continental crust, and of MORB (mid-ocean ridge basalts), are shown. The bulk silicate earth value is from *Allègre et al.* [1988]. The whole-rock isotope data for the samples from the rock units in this study are variously plotted and labeled on the diagram.

valid K-Ar isochrons (Table 1). In the K-Ar isochron diagrams for these three rock units, the isochron for the Bass Rapids diabase sill [*Snelling et al.*, 2003; *Austin*, 2005] intersected at the origin of both the ^{40}K and ^{40}Ar* axes, indicating no excess ^{40}Ar*, whereas the isochrons for the Somerset Dam layered mafic intrusion [*Snelling*, 2003b] and for the Cardenas Basalt [*Austin and Snelling*, 1998] both intersected the ^{40}Ar* axis very close to the origin of the ^{40}K axis, consistent with negligible excess ^{40}Ar* being in these rock units, certainly not enough to account for the radioisotope "ages."

However, *Snelling* [2000a] reported much evidence of the mobility of ^{40}Ar* in crustal rocks, resulting in some instances of ^{40}Ar* loss from some rock units and some minerals within rock units, and excess ^{40}Ar* in other rock units and minerals. Thus, even if a magma inherited excess ^{40}Ar* from its mantle source, and from crustal contamination during its ascent and intrusion into the upper crust or extrusion onto the earth's surface, once intruded or extruded the fact that Ar is an inert gas which does not chemically bond within the crystal lattices of minerals means that it would be free to migrate through rock units. Thus ^{40}Ar* could be lost from some rock units to surrounding rock units or the atmosphere, while in other rock units excess ^{40}Ar* would accumulate. Indeed, because of the mobility of the Ar gas, even within single rock units there could be areas and minerals whose ^{40}Ar* content has been depleted and other nearby areas and minerals where excess ^{40}Ar* has accumulated. This explanation might well account for the wide variations in the individual sample K-Ar model "ages" for each of the ancient rock units reported in Table 1. Of course, the different samples in any one of these rock units contain different quantities of K and therefore ^{40}K (sometimes vastly different quantities). Nevertheless, all samples from the same rock unit are supposed to be the same "age," and no matter what their ^{40}K concentrations are, the constant rate of ^{40}K decay should have yielded the same proportional quantities of ^{40}Ar*, so that all samples would give the same model "ages." Thus the wide ranges of K-Ar model "ages" recorded for these rock units must be due to some other cause, so the mobility of ^{40}Ar* would seem a likely explanation.

For example, samples of the Brahma amphibolites in Grand Canyon yielded an enormously wide range of K-Ar model "ages," from 405.1±10 Ma to 2574.2±73 Ma, for a rock unit that is supposed to be 1740–1750 Ma. Even samples only 0.84 m apart in the same outcrop yielded K-Ar model "ages" of 1205.3±31 Ma and 2574.2±73 Ma. These differences could be explained easily by ^{40}Ar* loss from one part of the outcrop and accumulation of excess ^{40}Ar* in the other part of the same outcrop. This would also explain why there is too much scatter in the K-Ar isotope data for this rock unit to produce a viable isochron and a statistically valid isochron "age" for it. Interestingly, for the three rock units in this study where valid K-Ar isochron ages were obtained (Tables 1 and 2), the isochron for the Bass Rapids diabase sill intersected the origin of the isochron diagram thus indicating no excess ^{40}Ar*, and the resultant K-Ar isochron age is mid-way within the range of K-Ar model "ages" for the individual samples. In comparison, the isochrons for the Somerset Dam layered mafic intrusion and Cardenas Basalt intersected the ^{40}Ar* axes above the origin in their respective isochron diagrams indicating very small quantities of excess ^{40}Ar*, and in both instances the resulting isochron "ages" were less than the youngest K-Ar model "ages" in the ranges of model "ages" for the individual samples. In other words, the excess ^{40}Ar* made the individual sample K-Ar model "ages" appear older than they should be. Thus this disparity between excessively wide ranges of K-Ar model "ages" and the corresponding K-Ar isochron "ages" where they can be validly obtained, plus the uncertainty over ^{40}Ar* mobility and the role of excess ^{40}Ar*, casts some doubt over the reliability of K-Ar radioisotope dating.

6.2 Isochron Dating and the Discordance Pattern

Because of the much longer half-lives of the parent ^{238}U, ^{87}Rb, and ^{147}Sm isotopes, compared to that of the parent ^{40}K isotope, it is not usually expected that young intrusive and volcanic rocks will yield valid Rb-Sr, Pb-Pb, and Sm-Nd isochron "ages." The isochron "ages" obtained for the targeted rock units in this study (Table 2) confirm this. Only by the judicious selection of the most suitable data from the recent Mt. Ngauruhoe andesite lava flows could a seemingly valid Rb-Sr isochron "age" of 133±87 Ma be obtained [*Snelling*, 2003a]. However, by comparison, the young Uinkaret Plateau basalts of the western Grand Canyon yielded a valid Rb-Sr isochron "age" of 1143±220 Ma. *Leeman* [1974] recognized that the $^{87}Sr/^{86}Sr$ ratios found in these basalts probably reflected their mantle origin. After *Sun and Hansen* [1975] found that the Rb-Sr data for fourteen different ocean island basalts when plotted on a isochron diagram yielded a positive correlation with a slope "age" of approximately 2000 Ma, *Brooks et al.* [1976a] called such "ages" "mantle isochrons." This mantle isochron concept was then extended to continental igneous rocks by *Brooks et al.* [1976b], who argued that these pseudo-isochrons were not mixing lines produced by crustal contamination of mantle-derived mafic magmas, but instead "dated" mantle differentiation events which had established domains of different Rb/Sr isotope ratios in the heterogeneous mantle sources of the magmas. Of course, a fundamental assumption of this mantle isochron model is that neither isotope nor elemental ratios are perturbed during magma ascent through the crust, an assumption that is now generally accepted as not being upheld with sufficient reliability to attribute age significance to such "erupted isochrons" [*Dickin*, 1995]. Nevertheless, *Leeman* [1982] and *Fitton et al.* [1988] have demonstrated conclusively that both the $^{87}Sr/^{86}Sr$ and $^{143}Nd/^{144}Nd$ isotope ratios in these western Grand Canyon basalts reflect the mantle source of their magma, compositional trends not being compatible with bulk crustal contamination but due to a heterogeneous mantle source. This is further confirmed by the Pb-Pb isotope data for these same basalts [*Alibert and Albarède*, 1986; *Austin*, 1994]. Thus the Rb-Sr isochron with its apparent 1143±220 Ma "age" obtained for these young basalts in the western Grand Canyon support the conclusion of *Zheng* [1989] that it is impossible to distinguish a valid isochron from an apparent isochron in the light of Rb-Sr isotope data alone, as an observed isochron does not necessarily define valid age information for a geological system, even if there is a good fit to the plotted data points.

However, it is certain that much radioactive decay has occurred throughout the earth's history, physical evidence for which is provided by [238]U radiohalos [*Snelling*, 2000b, 2005a; *Snelling and Armitage*, 2003; *Snelling et al.*, 2003b] and fission tracks [*Snelling*, 2005b]. This would thus imply that isochron "ages" yielded by ancient volcanic rocks should be due primarily to radioactive decay of parent radioisotopes. This is evident for the ancient intrusive and volcanic rock units targeted in this study whose isochron "ages" are listed in Table 2.

Austin [2005] has discussed the nature of the linear isotope plots for the Bass Rapids diabase sill and the Beartooth andesitic amphibolite. That discussion is equally relevant to the linear isotope plots obtained for the rock units listed in Table 2, and shown for the Somerset Dam layered mafic intrusion in *Snelling* [2003b], for the Cardenas Basalt in *Austin and Snelling* [1998], for the Brahma amphibolites in Figures 1–3, and for the Elves Chasm Granodiorite in Figures 4–6. All these isochron plots reveal an extraordinary linearity within the ^{40}K-^{40}Ar, ^{87}Rb-^{87}Sr, ^{147}Sm-^{143}Nd, and ^{207}Pb-^{206}Pb-^{204}Pb radioisotope systems. Of course, these are the successful isochron plots where the extraordinary linearity has produced statistically valid isochrons and isochron "ages," all the data points plotted following the linear trends within the error bars that represent the uncertainties assigned to each data point to account for analytical errors. As already indicated, the observed scatter in these plots has been fully accounted for by the assigned errors, as measured by the MSWD being at or near unity in each case. Not all attempted isochron plots using the *Isoplot* program [*Ludwig*, 2001] were successful, because as indicated in Table 2, either there was too much observed scatter to be accounted for by assigning reasonable analytical errors, or there was not enough spread in the data points to achieve statistically valid isochrons. This primarily occurred with respect to the ^{40}K-^{40}Ar radioisotope system for the reasons already discussed above. In several other instances the observed scatter was also too large in the Rb-Sr, Sm-Nd, and Pb-Pb radioisotope systems, which suggests that in those instances these radioisotope systems had been perturbed in those rock units by either contamination during their formation, or more likely, by post-formation alteration due to hydrothermal or metamorphic fluids, or groundwater and weathering.

For each of the ancient rock units listed in Table 2 it is clearly evident that, where the radioisotope data have provided statistically valid and robust isochron "ages," there is disagreement between the different radioisotope systems as to the "ages" of these rock units. This is not so evident for the Somerset Dam layered mafic intrusion which occurs in the Phanerozoic part of the geologic record, but it is strikingly obvious for the other listed ancient rock units that are situated in the Precambrian part of the geologic record. Indeed, in many instances the isochron discordances are pronounced. *Snelling et al.* [2003a] and *Austin* [2005] have discussed explanations for these discordances and have concluded that the only explanation that can account for them is that the radioisotope decay constants have not always been constant. *Austin* [2005] also cited several examples from the geologic literature that similarly report discordant isochron ages for other rock units, most notably for the Great Dyke in Zimbabwe [*Mukasa et al.*, 1998; *Oberthür et al.*, 2002], for the Stuart dyke swarm of central Australia [*Zhao and McCulloch*, 1993], and the Uruguayan dike swarm in South America [*Teixeira et al.*, 1999]. These examples in conjunction with the large number of rock units recorded in this study would strongly suggest that, where two or more of the commonly-used radioisotope pairs are applied to "date" rock units, discordances are the norm.

As already reported by *Austin* [2005], there is a pattern to the isochron discordances. The isochron "ages" listed in Table 2 consistently indicate that the α-emitters (^{238}U, ^{235}U, ^{147}Sm) yield older ages than the β-emitters (^{87}Rb and ^{40}K) when used to date the same geologic event, that is, the formation of each listed rock unit—for example, the extrusion of the Cardenas Basalt lavas, and the intrusion of the Bass Rapids diabase sill and Elves Chasm Granodiorite. In the case of the Brahma amphibolites, none of the listed isochron "ages" "date" the eruption of the original basalt lavas at 1740–1750 Ma. That "date" is based on U-Pb concordia dating of zircon grains in metamorphosed felsic volcanic lavas within the associated Brahma and Rama Schists that are believed to have survived the metamorphism without the U-Pb radioisotope system being reset [*Hawkins et al.*, 1996; *Ilg et al.*, 1996]. Nor do the isochron "ages" obtained "date" the metamorphism of the original basalt lavas to form the amphibolites, which has been determined as 1690–1710 Ma based on U-Pb concordia dating of metamorphic monazite, xenotime, and titanite in the overlying Vishnu Schist and underlying Rama Schist [*Hawkins et al.*, 1996; *Hawkins and Bowring*, 1999]. Nevertheless, assuming the isochron "ages" listed in Table 2 for each of the rock units are "dating" the same geologic event for each rock unit, then a logical explanation of these data is that the radioisotope decay of the various parent isotopes has not always proceeded at the rates described by the present-day decay "constants." Thus the discordances would instead be due to the different parent radioisotopes decaying at different rates over the same time periods since the geologic events represented by each rock unit. In other words, the decay of these parent radioisotopes was accelerated by different amounts. Thus the data in Table 2 are consistent with the possibility that α-decay was accelerated more than β-decay at some time or times in the past.

The correlation between the present radioactive decay "constants" for these α- and β-emitters and the isochron "ages" they have yielded for the geologic events associated with three of the targeted rock units is illustrated for the Cardenas Basalt in Figure 11, and for the Brahma amphibolites in Figure 12. *Austin* [2005] provides a similar isochron "age" versus mode of decay diagram for the radioisotope systems within the Bass Rapids diabase sill. In each of these examples the α-decaying isotopes (^{238}U and ^{147}Sm) yielded older isochron "ages" than the β-decaying isotopes (^{40}K and ^{87}Rb). Among the β-decaying isotopes, ^{87}Rb has the smaller decay constant and thus the longer half-life, yet it consistently yields the older "ages," double the K-Ar isochron "age" of the Cardenas Basalt in Figure 11. On the other hand, even though ^{147}Sm has the smaller decay constant (and thus the longer half-life) of the α-decaying isotopes, it does not always yield the older isochron "ages." It does for the Cardenas Basalt (Figure 11), for the Bass Rapids diabase sill, and for the Beartooth andesitic amphibolite [*Snelling et al.*, 2003a; *Austin*, 2005], but not for the Brahma amphibolites (Figure 12) and the Elves Chasm Granodiorite (Table 2). Perhaps the metamorphism of the original basalt lavas may have reset the Sm-Nd radioisotope system in the resulting Brahma amphibolites but not perturbed the U-Pb radioisotope pairs. Similarly, the Elves Chasm Granodiorite may

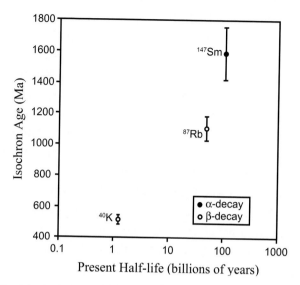

Figure 11. The isochron "ages" yielded by three radioisotope systems for the Cardenas Basalt, Grand Canyon, plotted against the present half-lives of the parent radioisotopes according to their mode of decay.

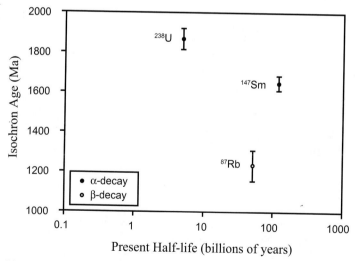

Figure 12. The isochron "ages" yielded by three radioisotope systems for the Brahma amphibolites, Grand Canyon, plotted against the present half-lives of the parent radioisotopes according to their mode of decay.

have suffered late-stage hydrothermal alteration and the subsequent effects of the same metamorphic event that produced the Brahma amphibolites, so again the Sm-Nd radioisotope system may have been perturbed relative to the U-Pb radioisotope pairs. On the other hand, if these isochron "ages" are plotted against the atomic weights of the respective parent isotopes (Figure 13), then there appears to be a trend of older isochron "ages" with increasing atomic weight that would seem to partly resolve this enigma over which α-decaying parent isotope might consistently give the older isochron "ages."

In any case, it is clear that the different radioisotope systems produced discordant isochron "ages" for the same geologic events, suggesting that their decay was accelerated at different rates over the same time periods since those geologic events, the α-decaying parent isotopes being accelerated more than the β-decaying parent isotopes. It is also possible that the longer the half-life of the α- or β-emitter, and/or the heavier its atomic weight, the more its decay has been accelerated relative to the other α- or β-emitters at some time or times in the past. Obviously, the isochron dating method cannot be relied upon to give true absolute "ages."

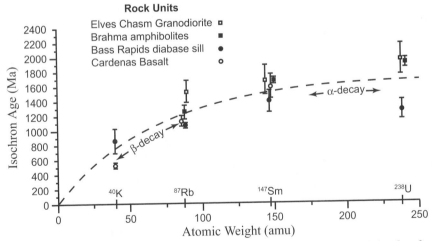

Figure 13. Composite plot of isochron age versus atomic weight for four radioisotope pairs and four Precambrian formations in Grand Canyon from *Austin* [2005] and this study.

6.3 Inheritance and Mixing of Sr, Nd, and Pb Isotopes

As already discussed, there is very clear evidence that modern, historic, and recent volcanic rocks have inherited radioisotope signatures of the mantle sources of the magmas that produced them, and this is now well documented in the geologic literature. For example, radioisotope analyses of the young Uinkaret Plateau basalts of the western Grand Canyon yield Rb-Sr, Sm-Nd, and Pb-Pb isochron "ages" that reflect isotopic heterogeneities inherited by their magma from its mantle source (Table 2) [*Leeman*, 1974, 1982; *Alibert et al.*, 1986; *Fitton et al.*, 1988; *Austin*, 1994]. This is also true of the historic andesite flows at Mt. Ngauruhoe, New Zealand, although the isochron "ages" in Table 2 were derived by selective manipulation of the data and have large errors due to the statistics of the observed scatter in the data [*Snelling*, 2003a]. Furthermore, these andesite flows yield depleted mantle Nd model "ages" ranging from 724.5 Ma to 1453.3 Ma, and even though their isotope data plot as tight clusters in Figures 7–10, they plot outside the fields of the mantle isotopic reservoirs. This indicates that even though the isotopic signature of these andesite lavas was inherited from the mantle source of what would have been originally a basaltic magma, when crustal contamination modified the mantle composition to produce these andesite lavas their isotopic signature was also modified by the crustal contamination [*Snelling*, 2003a].

Graham et al. [1992] demonstrated on an Sr-Nd isotope correlation diagram how the Ngauruhoe andesites would have been derived from a parent basalt magma sourced in the mantle below, but then contaminated with a small quantity (up to 10%) of the Torlesse metasedimentary strata that underlie the volcano. However, whereas *Graham and Hackett* [1987] and *Graham et al.* [1992] regarded this crustal contamination as thus being a secondary process in which the basalt magma composition was modified by assimilation of crustal rocks *en route* through the crust to the surface, *Gamble et al.* [1996] proposed that the crustal contamination was primary due to a source-modifying process of sediment subduction into the mantle under the volcano. Using combinations of the MORB (mid-ocean ridge basalt)-

source typical for the basalt magmas of the Taupo-Kermadec Volcanic Arc system to which the Ngauruhoe volcano belongs, with sediments typical of the adjacent offshore Kermadec Trench-Hikurangi Trough and with the Torlesse metasediments, *Gamble et al.* [1996] calculated bulk mixing curves based on the isotope pairs $^{206}Pb/^{204}Pb$ versus $^{143}Nd/^{144}Nd$ and $^{87}Sr/^{86}Sr$ (Figure 14). Thus they found that the incorporation of a relatively small amount (around 5%) of New Zealand continental sediment (equivalent to the average Torlesse metasediment [*Graham et al.*, 1992]) to basalt magma from a MORB-source could have brought about massive shifts in the isotopic composition of the magma, the sediment-hosted Pb having a "swamping" affect on the "mantle Pb." Therefore, it could be reasonably concluded that the Ngauruhoe andesite lavas have resulted from the contamination of a basalt magma from a MORB-source with around 5% trench sediment consisting of eroded Torlesse basement metasediments subducted into the mantle under the Ngauruhoe volcano. This petrogenetic model favored by *Gamble et al.* [1996] envisages a zone of melt formation approximately below the volcanic front (which includes Mt. Ngauruhoe) in a region delimited by the interface of the subducting slab (of the Pacific Plate) with the mantle wedge under the arc lithosphere of continental New Zealand (Figure 15). Subducted trench sediment scraped from the upper surface of the slab is incorporated into the mantle wedge along the slab-mantle interface. Fluids liberated from the descending slab as it progressively dehydrates ascend into the mantle wedge, causing partial melting of both the mantle peridotite and the subducted sediment being mixed with it. The resulting lower density melt, now andesitic in composition, then rises and pools in an upwelling melt column, to eventually penetrate upwards into the overlying crust to fill magma chambers that then erupt when full.

If isotopic signatures are inherited from mantle sources of magmas and subsequently suffer crustal contamination during ascent and extrusion of modern and recent volcanic rocks, are these effects also evident in the case of ancient volcanic and intrusive rocks and their associated isochron "ages"? As already noted, the Phanerozoic gabbros of the Somerset Dam layered mafic intrusion plot in the isotope correlation diagrams of

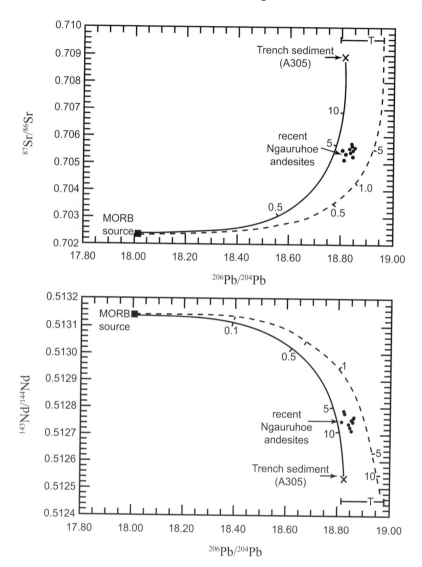

Figure 14. Plots of $^{87}Sr/^{86}Sr$ and $^{143}Nd/^{144}Nd$ versus $^{206}Pb/^{204}Pb$ for the recent Ngauruhoe andesites. Calculated bulk mixing curves for MORB-sediment A305 (continuous line) and MORB-Torlesse basement (dashed line) are shown [*Gamble et al.*, 1996]. T is the average composition of the Torlesse metasediments and the horizontal bar delineates the range of their compositions [*Graham et al.*, 1992]. Tick marks are percent of sediment added to the MORB-source end-member.

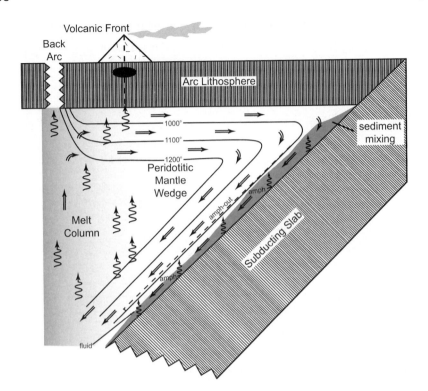

Figure 15. Dynamic petrogenetic model for andesite magma genesis beneath the Kermadec-Taupo Volcanic Arc subduction system [*Tatsumi*, 1986; *Davies and Stevenson*, 1992; *Gamble et al.*, 1996]. Flow lines (arrows with double lines) show mantle flowing from the back-arc region into the mantle wedge, where the isotherms are inverted owing to the cooling effect of the cold subducting "Cretaceous" slab [*Mortimer and Parkinson*, 1996]. Sediment that was deposited on the oceanic crust and thus also subducted is mixed into the wedge assemblage along the interface. Progressive dehydration reactions in the slab lead to fluid transfer from the slab into the mantle wedge. In the juxtaposed wedge, amphibole (amph) is stabilized, but then breaks down over the depth range 112±19 km [*Tatsumi*, 1986], inducing partial melting. In the resulting melt column, the first formed melts accumulating closest to the slab-mantle interface will be most susceptible to fluxing from the slab. Above this zone, melting will continue. The rising melts will eventually pool in the melt column, and the resulting magma finally ascends into the overlying arc lithosphere along fracture conduits, filling magma chambers and triggering eruptions.

Figures 7–10 within, or very close to, the fields of the defined mantle isotopic reservoirs, suggesting that there has been no crustal contamination of the intrusion's magma after having been sourced in the mantle. However, the magma not only inherited the isotopic signature of its mantle source, but also depleted mantle Nd model "ages" ranging from 432.3 Ma to 2923.0 Ma [*Snelling*, 2003b]. The three statistically viable isochron "ages" reported in Table 2 for the Phanerozoic Somerset Dam intrusion are essentially concordant, whereas the isochron "ages" for the Precambrian rock units targeted in this study are discordant, as already noted. Their isotope data plotted in Figures 7–10 are somewhat scattered, largely not coinciding with the fields of the defined mantle isotopic reservoirs. Nevertheless, some trends appear to be apparent in these isotope correlation diagrams. So for ease of visualizing these trends only the isotope ratios for the mafic Precambrian rock units in the Grand Canyon and central Arizona areas are plotted in Figures 16–19, minus the data for the Brahma amphibolites because of the excessive scatter in them, which is probably due to the effects of the metamorphism of the original basalt lavas.

Some obvious trends are evident in the data plotted in Figures 16–19. The effect of the inheritance by the Uinkaret Plateau basalts of the Sr-Nd isotopic signature of their magma's mantle source can be seen in Figure 16 as a linear trend from the field of the mantle array towards increasing $^{87}Sr/^{86}Sr$ ratios. This trend in the $^{87}Sr/^{86}Sr$ ratios obviously coincides with the apparent Rb-Sr isochron defined by the inherited mantle isotopic signature in these Uinkaret Plateau basalts. What is then obvious in Figure 16 is that the data points for the Cardenas Basalt, Grand Canyon diabase sills, Apache Group basalts, and Apache Group diabase sills follow the same poorly defined linear trend as the Uinkaret Plateau basalt data points, except that the Precambrian basalts and diabase sills yield some extremely high $^{87}Sr/^{86}Sr$ isotope ratios. A similar trend towards higher $^{87}Sr/^{86}Sr$ ratios is also evident in Figure 17, while in Figures 18 and 19 the trend is towards higher Pb isotope ratios. Now if the linear trend in the Uinkaret Plateau basalt data in Figure 16 reflects the inherited mantle Rb-Sr isochron whose "age" listed in Table 2 is 1143±220 Ma, then the obvious question is whether the same linear

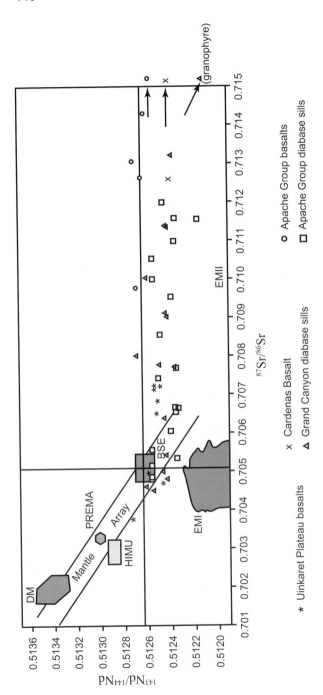

Figure 16. The $^{87}Sr/^{86}Sr$ versus $^{143}Nd/^{144}Nd$ isotope correlation diagram showing the main oceanic mantle reservoirs of *Zindler and Hart* [1986]: DM = depleted mantle; BSE = bulk silicate earth; EMI and EMII = enriched mantle; HIMU = mantle with high U/Pb ratio; PREMA = frequently observed PREvalent MAntle composition. The mantle array is defined by many oceanic basalts, and a bulk silicate earth value for $^{87}Sr/^{86}Sr$ can be obtained from this trend. The whole-rock isotope data for the samples from the selected rock units in this study are variously plotted and labeled on the diagram.

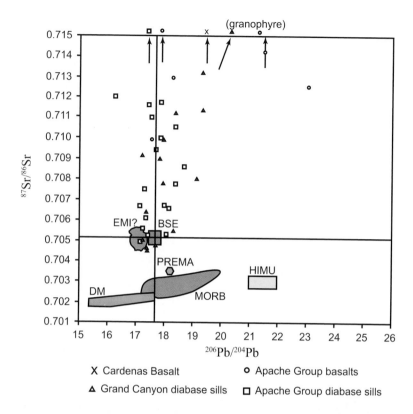

Figure 17. The $^{206}Pb/^{204}Pb$ versus $^{87}Sr/^{86}Sr$ isotope correlation diagram showing the positions of the mantle reservoirs identified by *Zindler and Hart* [1986]: DM = depleted mantle; BSE = bulk silicate earth; EMI and EMII = enriched mantle; HIMU = mantle with high U/Pb ratio; PREMA = frequently observed PREvalent MAntle composition. The $^{206}Pb/^{204}Pb$ value of the bulk silicate earth is taken from *Allègre et al.* [1988]. The whole-rock isotope data for the samples from the selected rock units in this study are variously plotted and labeled on the diagram.

trend in the Precambrian basalts and diabase sills data also reflects their isochron "ages"? Therefore, it is not clear as to whether it is significant that the Rb-Sr isochron "ages" of the Cardenas Basalt (1181±81 Ma [Table 2] or 1103±66 Ma [*Larson et al.*, 1994]) and Bass Rapids diabase sill (1060±24 Ma [Table 2] or 1070±30 Ma [*Elston and McKee*, 1982])

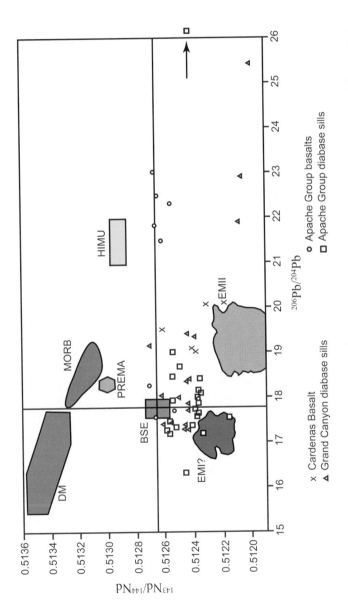

Figure 18. The $^{206}Pb/^{204}Pb$ versus $^{143}Nd/^{144}Nd$ isotope correlation diagram showing the positions of the mantle reservoirs identified by *Zindler and Hart* [1986]: DM = depleted mantle; BSE = bulk silicate earth; EMI and EMII = enriched mantle; HIMU = mantle with high U/Pb ratio; PREMA = frequently observed PREvalent MAntle composition. The $^{206}Pb/^{204}Pb$ value of the bulk silicate earth is taken from *Allègre et al.* [1988]. The whole-rock isotope data for the samples from the selected rock units in this study are variously plotted and labeled on the diagram.

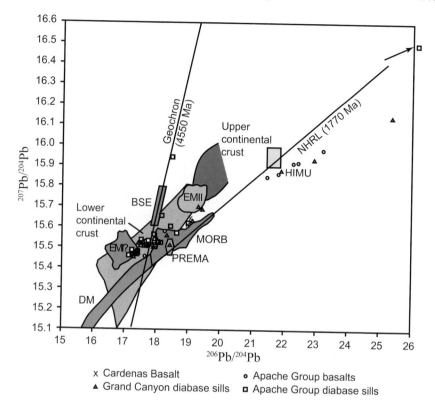

x Cardenas Basalt   o Apache Group basalts
▲ Grand Canyon diabase sills   □ Apache Group diabase sills

Figure 19. The ^{206}Pb/^{204}Pb versus ^{207}Pb/^{204}Pb isotope correlation diagram showing the position of the northern hemisphere reference line (NHRL), the slope of which has an age significance of 1770 Ma, and the geochron (4550 Ma). The mantle reservoirs of *Zindler and Hart* [1986] are: DM = depleted mantle; BSE = bulk silicate earth; EMI and EMII = enriched mantle; HIMU = mantle with high U/Pb ratio; PREMA = frequently observed PREvalent MAntle composition. The fields of the upper and lower continental crust, and of MORB (mid-ocean ridge basalts) are shown. The bulk silicate earth value is from *Allègre et al.* [1988]. The whole-rock isotope data for the samples from the selected rock units in this study are variously plotted and labeled on the diagram.

in the eastern and central Grand Canyon are essentially identical with this Rb-Sr mantle isochron "age" for the Uinkaret Plateau basalts in the western Grand Canyon. Given that all these magmas were sourced in the same general area of the mantle beneath the Grand Canyon, it could be argued that these Rb-Sr isochron "ages" for the Cardenas Basalt and Bass Rapid diabase sill are also the result of their inheritance of the isotopic signature of their magmas' mantle source. On the other hand, the linear trend in the Pb isotope data in Figure 19, which is roughly coincident for these four groups of Precambrian basalts and diabase sills, must reflect their Pb-Pb isochrons, because the isochrons also are all plotted on $^{206}Pb/^{204}Pb$ versus $^{207}Pb/^{204}Pb$ diagrams. This conclusion is confirmed by the agreement between, or concordance of, the Pb-Pb isochron "ages" for these rock units listed in Table 2. But again, given that these magmas were sourced in the same area of the mantle, these Pb-Pb isochron "ages" may also be in some measure the product of the mantle isotopic signature their magmas inherited.

However, the most extreme isotope ratios for the Grand Canyon diabase sills in Figures 16–19 belong to the granophyre layer at the top of the Bass Rapids diabase sill. Because this felsic granophyre is compositionally distinct from the diabase in the body of the sill, it is usually regarded as having separated by in-place differentiation of the parent basaltic magma after intrusion of the sill. But this does not explain how the parent basaltic magma acquired this substantial felsic component, which represents 6–7% of the sill's volume. The granophyre's extremely high isotope ratios, principally $^{87}Sr/^{86}Sr$ and $^{206}Pb/^{204}Pb$, are consistent with the granophyre being derived by crustal contamination of the parent basaltic magma, just as the demonstrated crustal contamination of a basalt magma to produce the Mt. Ngauruhoe andesite lavas is likewise reflected in higher isotope ratios (Figures 7–10). Continental crustal rocks of felsic composition typically have higher isotope ratios, and this includes sedimentary and metamorphosed sedimentary rocks such as those intruded by the Bass Rapids diabase sill. Figure 20 is the diagrammatic section through the Bass Rapids sill showing the granophyre capping on the diabase and the contact hornfels above and beneath the sill. Selected whole-rock geochemical and isotope data are shown beside the respective samples of the diabase and granophyre, plus two samples from the contact hornfels beneath the sill. It is immediately apparent that the high $^{87}Sr/^{86}Sr$ and $^{206}Pb/^{204}Pb$ ratios present in the granophyre are matched by similar

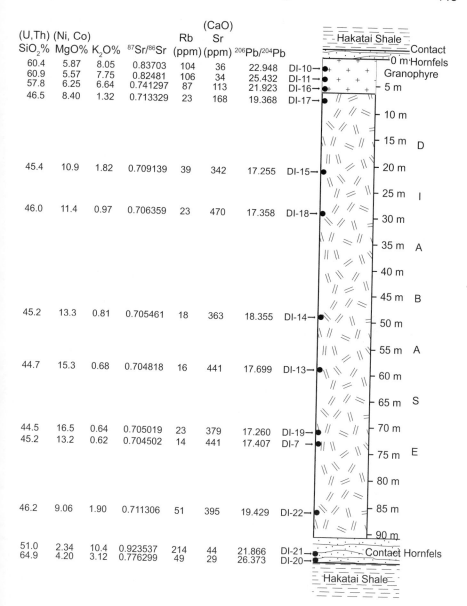

(U,Th) SiO₂%	(Ni, Co) MgO%	K₂O%	⁸⁷Sr/⁸⁶Sr	Rb (ppm)	(CaO) Sr (ppm)	²⁰⁶Pb/²⁰⁴Pb	
60.4	5.87	8.05	0.83703	104	36	22.948	DI-10→
60.9	5.57	7.75	0.82481	106	34	25.432	DI-11→
57.8	6.25	6.64	0.741297	87	113	21.923	DI-16→
46.5	8.40	1.32	0.713329	23	168	19.368	DI-17→
45.4	10.9	1.82	0.709139	39	342	17.255	DI-15→
46.0	11.4	0.97	0.706359	23	470	17.358	DI-18→
45.2	13.3	0.81	0.705461	18	363	18.355	DI-14→
44.7	15.3	0.68	0.704818	16	441	17.699	DI-13→
44.5	16.5	0.64	0.705019	23	379	17.260	DI-19→
45.2	13.2	0.62	0.704502	14	441	17.407	DI-7→
46.2	9.06	1.90	0.711306	51	395	19.429	DI-22→
51.0	2.34	10.4	0.923537	214	44	21.866	DI-21→
64.9	4.20	3.12	0.776299	49	29	26.373	DI-20→

Figure 20. Diagrammatic section through the Bass Rapids sill showing the granophyre "capping" on the diabase, the contact hornfels, the location of samples, and selected whole-rock geochemical and isotope data.

isotope ratios in the contact hornfels. Indeed, the values of these isotope ratios closely correlate with some of the major and trace elements in these rocks, which in turn reflect the minerals that host these elements and therefore the isotopes. For example, the diabase is characterized by the mineral olivine, which is reflected in the diabase's MgO content (and high levels of Ni and Co), compared with the high quartz and K-feldspar content of the granophyre, reflected in its high SiO_2 and K_2O (and high trace U and Th) contents. Because Rb substitutes for K in the K-feldspar crystal lattice, there are higher trace amounts of Rb in the granophyre. In contrast, the diabase is dominated by plagioclase, which is Ca-dominated feldspar, and because Sr substitutes for Ca in the plagioclase crystal lattice, the diabase has a higher trace Sr content. It can thus be seen that the higher isotope ratios follow these mineralogical and geochemical differences between the diabase and the granophyre. But the contact hornfels beneath the sill has similar contents of these major and trace elements, and isotopes, to those in the granophyre. The hornfels, of course, represents the host Hakatai Shale intruded by the basaltic magma which was metamorphosed in contact with the diabase as it crystallized, due primarily to the heat of the magma. That there has been some isotopic contamination of the diabase by both the contact hornfels and the granophyre is evident from the intermediate values of the isotope ratios in the diabase samples adjacent to the granophyre and hornfels respectively. This could perhaps suggest that some of the crustal contamination was provided in-place from the Hakatai Shale wall rock to the sill. The contact hornfels zone is thicker below the sill than above it, but the granophyre is at the top of the sill exclusively, due to its lighter density that would have caused it to float to the top of the basaltic magma as it crystallized and cooled.

The Cardenas Basalt lavas, which are regarded as the extrusive equivalent of the same magma responsible for the Bass Rapids and other diabase sills in Grand Canyon, similarly exhibit very high $^{87}Sr/^{86}Sr$ isotope ratios (Figures 16 and 17), though not as high $^{206}Pb/^{204}Pb$ isotope ratios (Figures 17–19). Figure 21 shows the type section of the Cardenas Basalt with the relative locations of the samples used in this study and selected whole-rock geochemical and isotope data obtained

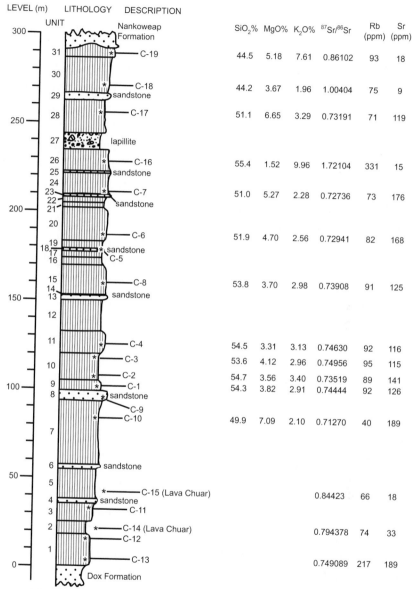

Figure 21. The measured type section of the Cardenas Basalt in Basalt Canyon, eastern Grand Canyon (after *Hendricks and Lucchitta* [1974]). Their unit numbers are shown. The relative locations of the samples collected are also shown, including two samples from nearby Lava Chuar Canyon. Selected whole-rock geochemical and isotope data are also shown.

from them. Of course, there is no felsic equivalent of the granophyre capping in the Bass Rapids diabase sill among the lava flows of the Cardenas Basalt, simply because differentiation and flotation of any felsic crustal contamination requires some time to occur as in the intrusive sill with its coarse-grained diabase, whereas the fine-grained basalt lavas cooled very rapidly. Thus any felsic crustal contamination in the basalt magma when it was extruded would have been retained in-place within the resultant basalt lavas, making them compositionally more felsic than the pure basalt magma that crystallized to form the diabase in the sills. That this is the case can be seen by comparing the selected major and trace elements in the Cardenas Basalt listed in Figure 21 with those in the diabase of the Bass Rapids sill listed in Figure 20. It is immediately apparent that the basalt lavas have higher SiO_2 and K_2O contents and a lower MgO content than the diabase in the sill. Thus the upper member flows of the Cardenas Basalt, for which these elements are listed in Figure 21, are mostly classified as basaltic andesites. Their higher trace Rb content compared with the diabase in the sill parallels their higher K_2O contents and results in higher $^{87}Sr/^{86}Sr$ isotope ratios similar to those in the granophyre and the contact hornfels of the Bass Rapids sill. Even the lower member flows of the Cardenas Basalt, which are alkali basalt lavas that more truly reflect the original mantle-derived basalt magma, contain the same high $^{87}Sr/^{86}Sr$ isotope ratios, indicative of crustal isotopic contamination during ascent of the basalt magma through the crust via conduits. Another possibility is that the crustal isotopic contamination occurred as a result of post-crystallization alteration of the lava flows, given that their high K_2O content and low Sr content could reflect the sericitization (alteration to the fine-grained white mica sericite) of their plagioclase, as observed in thin sections. However, as the bulk geochemistry and mineralogy of these lava flows define them as basaltic andesites, regardless of any post-crystallization alteration, so the crustal contamination they contain is a primary feature, due to such crustal contamination being incorporated in the basalt magma during its passage through the crust from the mantle where it was sourced.

One other means of demonstrating that crustal contamination of the basaltic magma occurred during intrusion of the Bass Rapids diabase sill is to show that there has been interaction of the basaltic magma as it was intruded and crystallized with the sill's Hakatai Shale wall rock. The two samples of the contact hornfels below the Bass Rapids sill (Figure 20) were also submitted for radioisotope analyses. The resultant data were then included with all the radioisotope data for the diabase sill and granophyre "capping," and further regression analyses were undertaken using the *Isoplot* program [*Ludwig*, 2001] to plot isochrons and obtain isochron "ages." Figures 22–25 are the resultant isochron plots, with a K-Ar isochron "age" of 847±110 Ma (Figure 22), a Rb-Sr isochron "age" of 1082±33 Ma (Figure 23), and a Pb-Pb isochron "age" of 1280±100 Ma (Figure 25). In each of these three cases the isochron regression lines have excellent statistics, with the MSWD at or near unity, meaning the assigned errors match the observed scatter.

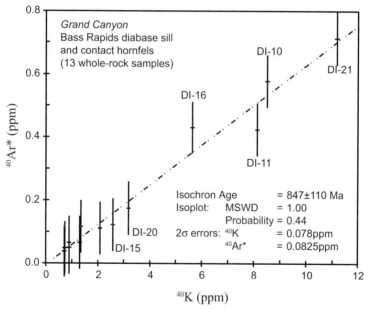

Figure 22. ^{40}K versus ^{40}Ar* isochron diagram for the Bass Rapids sill (diabase and granophyre) and its contact hornfels in Grand Canyon. All thirteen whole-rock samples (some labeled as per Figure 20) were used in the isochron and "age" calculations. The bars represent the 2σ uncertainties.

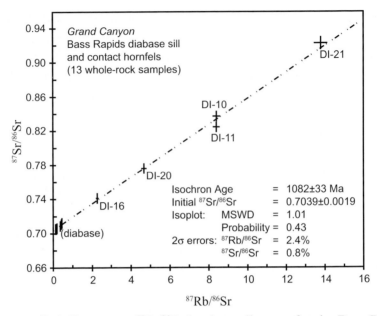

Figure 23. ^{87}Rb/^{86}Sr versus ^{87}Sr/^{86}Sr isochron diagram for the Bass Rapids sill (diabase and granophyre) and its contact hornfels in Grand Canyon. All thirteen whole-rock samples (some labeled as per Figure 20) were used in the isochron and "age" calculations. The bars represent the 2σ uncertainties.

Furthermore, these isochron "ages" are concordant with the isochron "ages" obtained for the respective radioisotope systems using just the diabase and granophyre samples from the sill itself (Table 2), and the 2σ uncertainties of these isochron "ages" that include the two hornfels samples are overall significantly smaller. In other words, including the hornfels samples with the sill samples in the *Isoplot* analyses yields even better isochron "ages," with the same pattern of discordancy between the radioisotope systems. Furthermore, the hornfels samples plot with the granophyre samples for all of the radioisotope systems, including the Sm-Nd radioisotope system in Figure 24. Indeed, the two hornfels samples combined with the three granophyre samples yield their own five-point Sm-Nd isochron distinct from the DI-13 mineral Sm-Nd isochron that can be fitted to the eight diabase samples [*Snelling et al.*, 2003a; *Austin*, 2005]. The "age" obtained from this granophyre plus hornfels isochron of 626±280 Ma does not have the best statistics and does not appear to coincide with any known geologic event. However, this obvious relationship between the contact hornfels and the granophyre does confirm that there has been interaction between the granophyre and the contact hornfels as a result of the hydrothermal alteration of the granophyre occurring during the contact metamorphism with the Hakatai Shale to produce the hornfels. Hydrothermal conditions have been shown to cause rare earth element mobility in rhyolite and granite [*Poitrasson et al.*, 1995], to which the granophyre is compositionally identical. Thus, as suggested by *Snelling et al.* [2003a] and *Austin* [2005], the Nd isotopes were obviously perturbed during this hydrothermal

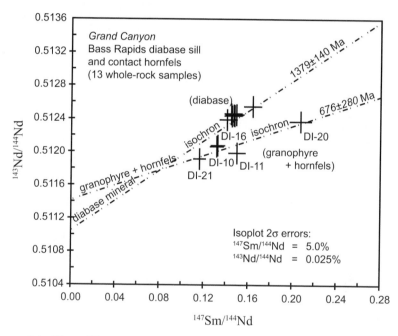

Figure 24. $^{147}Sm/^{144}Nd$ versus $^{143}Nd/^{144}Nd$ isochron diagram for the Bass Rapids sill (diabase and granophyre) and its contact hornfels in Grand Canyon. All thirteen whole-rock samples (some labeled as per Figure 20) are plotted, with the bars representing the 2σ uncertainties. The diabase mineral isochron of sample DI-13 [*Snelling et al.*, 2003; *Austin*, 2005] passes through the eight diabase samples. An apparent isochron can be fitted to the five granophyre and hornfels samples.

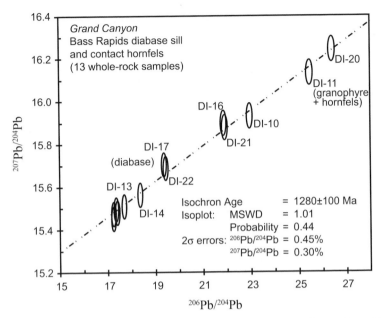

Figure 25. $^{206}Pb/^{204}Pb$ versus $^{207}Pb/^{204}Pb$ isochron diagram for the Bass Rapids sill (diabase and granophyre) and its contact hornfels in Grand Canyon. All thirteen whole-rock samples (many labeled as per Figure 20) were used in the isochron and "age" calculations. The ellipses represent the 2σ uncertainties.

alteration by exchange between the hornfels and the granophyre. It is also clear from Figures 22, 23, and 25 that there has also been exchange in the other radioisotope systems between the granophyre and the hornfels on the one hand, and the granophyre and hornfels with the diabase on the other, because otherwise the radioisotope data for the hornfels, granophyre, and diabase would not have plotted on the same respective isochrons. Indeed, this radioisotope equilibration between the sill and the hornfels is to be expected, because it would have been the heat from the intruding basaltic magma that combined with the connate water in the wall-rock shale that resulted in the contact metamorphism which produced the hornfels between the sill and the shale both above and below the sill. Thus there was crustal contamination of the basaltic magma as it intruded into the shale, that crustal contamination being contributed from the shale itself. The process could have also included sufficient felsic contamination into the basaltic magma at both the lower and upper contacts of the sill from the shale wall rock itself to produce the granophyre that "floated" to the top of the basaltic magma as it crystallized and cooled to accumulate as the "capping" on the sill. The fact that the contact metamorphism and this crustal contamination coincided with the sill intrusion event would explain why, as would be expected, the hornfels samples plot on the same isochrons as the diabase and granophyre samples from the sill itself.

It is the coincidence of the granophyre and hornfels radioisotope data with the diabase radioisotope data on the same isochrons in the K-Ar (Figure 22), Rb-Sr (Figure 23), and Pb-Pb (Figure 25) radioisotope systems that provides the overall spread in the radioisotope data to yield good isochrons and isochron "ages" with excellent statistics. Indeed, it is because the granophyre and hornfels Sm-Nd radioisotope data are not consistent with the Sm-Nd radioisotope data for the diabase samples that a whole-rock Sm-Nd isochron cannot be plotted for the sill in Sm-Nd radioisotope system (Figure 24). Furthermore, as already noted, in the K-Ar, Rb-Sr, and Pb-Pb radioisotope systems it is the spread in the radioisotope data provided by the granophyre and hornfels samples that actually make the isochrons and isochron "ages" possible, so this implies that the crustal contamination of the basaltic magma to produce the sill with its granophyre "capping" and contact hornfels adjoining it was crucial for the radioisotope methods to succeed in "dating" the sill. However, because it is clear from the isochron diagrams (Figures 22–25) that the isochrons representing the isochron "ages" of the sill do fit with the respective radioisotope data for the diabase samples only, this would imply that radioisotope decay was still necessary to produce these isochrons and isochron "ages." Nevertheless, the 6–7% crustal contamination of the basaltic magma (determined by the volume of the granophyre as a proportion of the total volume of the sill) contributed significantly to the respective radioisotope systematics, and thus to the resultant "statistically robust" isochrons and isochron "ages" for the sill. Of course, if the basaltic magma inherited this radioisotope signature from its mantle source, it may be that a significant quantity of the radioisotope decay indicated by the isochron "ages" occurred in the mantle source, this mantle radioisotope signature then equilibrating by exchange with the crustal contamination of the basaltic magma in the sill during the contact metamorphism. However, this does not preclude some significant radioisotope decay then occurring in the sill subsequent to its intrusion, crystallization and cooling.

6.4 Resultant Implications for Radioisotope Dating

There are several observations that are clearly evident from the foregoing discussion of radioisotopes in the Precambrian Bass Rapids sill. First, the sill's Rb-Sr isochron "age" is virtually identical to the mantle Rb-Sr isochron "age" of the recent Uinkaret Plateau basalts that outcrop in the western Grand Canyon not all that far from the Bass Rapids sill. Because the basaltic magma that intruded to form the Bass Rapids sill was sourced in the same area of the mantle under the Grand Canyon region as was the basaltic magma for the Uinkaret Plateau basalts, this similarity in Rb-Sr isochron "ages" could be interpreted to mean that the Rb-Sr isochron for the Bass Rapids sill is similarly an inherited mantle isochron. However, it could equally be valid to interpret the similarity in the Rb-Sr isochron "ages" to imply that after the basaltic magma for the Bass Rapids diabase sill separated from the mantle source, the parent Rb isotopes in both the sill and the magma's mantle source experienced the same amount of radioisotope decay, the signature of which was then inherited very recently by the magma which was extruded as the Uinkaret Plateau basalt flows when it was sourced in the same mantle area.

Second, the isochron "ages" for the Bass Rapids sill obtained from the four radioisotope systems are discordant, with the α-decaying isotopes yielding older isochron "ages" than the β-decaying isotopes, and the longer the half-life (and/or the heavier the atomic weight) of the α- or β-decaying isotope the greater the isochron "age" compared to that derived from the other respective α- or β-decaying isotopes. If all four radioisotope systems are "dating" the same geologic event (the formation of the sill), then this pattern is consistent with the four parent radioisotopes decaying at different accelerated rates, the α-decaying parent isotopes having their radio-decay accelerated more than that of the β-decaying parent isotopes. However, this pattern of discordance is not also evident in the limited data available for the other radioisotope systems in the Uinkaret Plateau basalts. It might be argued that there is some similarity in the Sm-Nd isochron "ages," but the 2600 Ma Pb-Pb isochron "age" for the Uinkaret Plateau basalts [*Austin*, 1994] is more than double the Pb-Pb isochron "age" of the Bass Rapids sill. Furthermore, even though there is no comparative K-Ar isochron "age" available for the Uinkaret Plateau basalts, their K-Ar model "ages" are very recent and contrast markedly with the K-Ar model "ages" for the Bass Rapids sill. However, whereas the Cardenas Basalt is regarded as the extrusive equivalent of the intrusive diabase sills derived from the same basaltic magma, even though the Cardenas Basalt and Bass Rapids sill yield essentially the same Rb-Sr isochron "age," the other radioisotope systems yield different isochron "ages" for the Cardenas Basalt and Bass Rapids sill. Indeed, the K-Ar isochron "age" for the Cardenas Basalt is much less than that for the Bass Rapids sill, even though the former may have been affected by excess ^{40}Ar* when the latter was not.

Third, there is unequivocal evidence of both the Bass Rapids sill and the Cardenas Basalt having been affected by crustal contamination which had to be responsible for some perturbing of the radioisotope systems, especially the Rb-Sr and Sm-Nd radioisotope systems. That this crustal contamination involved radioisotope exchange between the intruding basaltic magma and the shale wall rock to the sill is evident from the fact that the contact hornfels and granophyre "capping" within the sill both plot on the same isochrons as the diabase, dramatically improving the compositional spread in the radioisotopes and thus resulting in excellent statistics for the isochron fits and isochron "ages" in the K-Ar, Rb-Sr, and Pb-Pb radioisotope systems. Nevertheless, this radioisotope exchange during contact metamorphism of the shale wall rock by the intruding basaltic magma must have equilibrated in both the granophyre and the contact hornfels, because in both the Rb-Sr and Pb-Pb radioisotope systems the mineral isochrons yielded by diabase samples are essentially identical to the whole-rock isochrons obtained using both the diabase samples and the granophyre and hornfels samples. Nevertheless, the crustal contamination did affect the mantle-derived magma, with its inherited radioisotopes, of both the Cardenas Basalt and Bass Rapids diabase sill, and the differences between their isochron "ages" in some of the radioisotope systems may be due to the crustal contamination remaining mixed in the rapidly-cooled Cardenas Basalt compared to its separation into the distinct granophyre phase "capping" the slower-cooled Bass Rapids diabase sill.

All these considerations—isochron discordances, inheritance of mantle source isotopic signatures, and mixing of crustal contamination—must render radioisotope "dating" highly questionable at best, and useless at worst, as the absolute "dating" method it is so unanimously and forthrightly claimed to be. Obviously, if radioisotope decay was accelerated at some time or times in the past, and the decay of the different parent radioisotopes was accelerated at different rates, then the radioisotope decay "clocks" could never be relied upon to provide absolute "dates" for rocks in terms of hundreds of millions of years. Furthermore, if some of the radioisotope decay occurred in the mantle, from where magmas were subsequently sourced and inherited the resultant radioisotope signatures, then measuring the radioisotopes today in the lavas or intrusions could not provide "dates" for when the lavas were erupted and the magmas intruded, because it would be unclear just how much of the radioisotope decay had occurred since eruption or intrusion. And finally, if crustal contamination of magmas occurs during their ascent, intrusion and extrusion, modifying the radioisotope content of the magmas, then unless it was known how much modification of the radioisotopes occurred, it would be impossible to be sure whether measurements performed today were actually providing correct absolute "dates" for the formation of the volcanic and intrusive rocks. Indeed, even as volcanic, intrusive and metamorphic rocks are cooling, hydrothermal alteration by fluids expelled from the cooling rocks and/or the groundwaters from surrounding rocks can modify mineralogy, geochemistry, and radioisotope contents of the rocks being "dated" with radioisotopes.

Given that any or all of these complex factors will have affected each of the radioisotope systems, often differently, then it is misleading to "date" rocks with just one of the radioisotope pairs. As has been shown here, discordancy between the radioisotope systems is the norm, and therefore without a knowledge of the complex history of the rocks being "dated," it is impossible to decide which of the radioisotope pairs is actually truly "dating" the rocks. These three demonstrated effects on the history of the radioisotope systems in rocks, namely, inheritance from the mantle sources and magmas, crustal contamination, and accelerated radioisotope decay, totally discredit the three assumptions on which the radioisotope "dating" methods are based, namely, known initial conditions, the rock remains a closed system, and a constant rate of radioisotope decay, respectively. Thus radioisotope "dating" methods, which have underpinned uniformitarian geology for nearly a century, are totally discredited and are therefore worthless as absolute geologic chronometers.

6.5 Towards a Model for the Behavior of Radioisotopes in Rocks through Earth History

At best, therefore, the radioisotope methods can only provide relative "dates." Thus, the absolute time framework for earth history into which the sequences of rock units and their relative "dates" can be placed and systematized must be sought from another, more reliable source. In endeavoring to piece together the historic past, evidence in the present can only be circumstantial, subject to interpretation based on the assumptions of the researcher. The best and most reliable sources to validate the details of historic events are reputable eyewitness accounts, a similar procedure to the testimonies of eyewitnesses being used in a courtroom to establish what happened at the crime scene. However, no human observers or researchers were present during the earth's early history, so historical geology is conventionally based only on circumstantial evidence. On the other hand, the Bible provides an eyewitness account of the earth's early history, validated by the character and testimony of the Creator Himself (Jesus Christ), followed by the testimonies of subsequent human observers. The early chapters of Genesis that are the Creator's eyewitness account of the earth's earliest history are unmistakably historical narrative [*Boyd*, 2005].

The unequivocal testimony of the Biblical record is that the earth, universe and life were created by God in six literal days only 6000–7000 years ago, and that subsequently there was a global catastrophic Flood which destroyed pre-Flood life and buried it in the strata that accumulated as the earth was totally reshaped. Thus the behavior of radioisotopes in rocks through the earth's history needs to be understood and modeled within this Biblical framework with its 6000–7000 year absolute timescale.

In the Bible framework of earth history there were two clearly-stated periods of non-uniformitarian, accelerated geological processes—Creation and the Flood (2 Peter 3:3–7). Early in the Creation week before life was created, and during the Flood when life was preserved on the Ark, the bulk of the earth's present geologic record would have been produced by catastrophic processes not now in operation, and this must have included accelerated radioisotope decay. It is likely that by the end of Day 1 of the Creation week, the early earth that had been created beneath the globe-covering water had already been differentiated internally into its core, mantle, and initial crust divisions [*Austin et al.*, 1994]. It is not inconceivable that accelerated radioisotope decay was part of the creative means God used to produce this internal differentiation of the initial earth [*Baumgardner*, 2000]. This accelerated radioisotope decay would have meant that by the end of Day 1, the earth's mantle and crustal rocks would have already acquired a radioisotope signature that if measured then and interpreted by present-day uniformitarian assumptions would have been already as much as 1000 Ma or more "old." This should not be confused with any day-age concept, but should be recognized as only an apparent long-"ages" history during a single literal day if the catastrophic processes involved are ignored. Crustal formation would have continued through Day 2 and reached its climax accompanied by catastrophic global tectonic processes during the first half of Day 3 when the first dry land surface was produced. With the earth now ready for the creation of plant and animal life to populate the earth, the bulk of God's geologic creative work would have been finished during Day 3, so that with the curtailment of catastrophic geologic processes during Day 3 the burst of accelerated radioisotope decay would also have stopped, leaving some mantle and crustal rocks with apparent radioisotope "ages" already as much as 3000–4000 Ma. Other strata that had progressively developed during this period of catastrophic crustal formation and tectonics would have acquired progressively younger relative radioisotope "ages," due to the radioisotope systems often having been reset as these rock strata formed.

Through the remainder of the Creation week, and through the pre-Flood period, both geological processes and radioisotope decay would probably have occurred at rates similar to today's rates for these processes. This was necessary for the well-being and proliferation of plants and animals on the earth's surface. However, with the onset of the Flood, uniformitarian conditions were replaced by catastrophic geologic processes and plate tectonics, again accompanied by a burst of accelerated radioisotope decay [*Austin et al.*, 1994; *Humphreys*, 2000]. The physical evidence for this second episode of accelerated radioisotope and nuclear decay includes the abundant radiohalos and fission tracks respectively in granites and volcanic layers formed during the Flood [*Snelling*, 2000b, 2005a, b; *Snelling and Armitage*, 2003; *Snelling et al.*, 2003b]. Again, as the geologic record of the Flood accumulated, those volcanic and intrusive rocks that were progressively erupted and intruded often had their radioisotope systems reset during their formation to provide apparent relative "ages" of less than approximately 600 Ma.

A by-product of radioisotope decay is heat, so these bursts of accelerated radioisotope decay would have produced enormous quantities of heat that would need to be dissipated quickly to avoid vaporizing the rocks, as pointed out by *Snelling* [2005a]. *Humphreys* [2000, 2005] has tentatively suggested a process that might be capable of quickly dissipating this unwanted excessive heat, but an adequate viable mechanism is yet to be fully elucidated.

In the light of the evidence of prolific isochron discordances between the radioisotope systems, inheritance of radioisotope signatures by magmas from their mantle sources, and the changes in the radioisotope contents of magmas due to some mixing in some of them of crustal contamination, many anomalies in this relative "age" progression during the early Creation week and Flood accumulation of the geologic record would have occurred. Indeed, inheritance and mixing of radioisotopes from mantle and crustal sources continue to be evident in modern and recent volcanic rocks. It would seem that the isochron discordances between the radioisotope systems are most pronounced in Precambrian rock units, though that conclusion may be heavily biased by the majority of the rock units targeted in this study being of Precambrian designation. More pronounced isochron discordances in Precambrian rock units are consistent with many of the rocks so designated having had their origin during the early part of the Creation week, when the burst of accelerated radioisotope decay would seem to have been equivalent to perhaps as much as 3000–4000 Ma worth at today's decay rates. Such a large amount of accelerated radioisotope decay would have increased potential for discordances between the radioisotope systems, the α-decayers being accelerated more than the β-decayers, and in general the longer the half-life, and/or the heavier the atomic weight, of the parent isotope the greater the acceleration. In contrast, if the second burst of accelerated radioisotope decay during the Flood was only equivalent to approximately 600 Ma worth at today's rates, then the potential for isochron discordances between the radioisotope systems would be much diminished, and this is certainly reflected in the Phanerozoic rock unit targeted in this study. Furthermore, just how often the radioisotope signatures inherited by magmas from their mantle sources are not reset during magma ascent, intrusion and extrusion is very difficult to gauge, because of the apparent dominating effect of accelerated radioisotope decay.

Similarly, it is not always apparent that magmas had crustal contamination mixed into them, because where such crustal contamination is recognizable it only amounts to the equivalent of 5–10% by volume of the magma. Thus, even if crustal contamination of a magma was equivalent to up to 20% of the magma volume, and the crustal contamination was not easily recognized because of being mixed and homogenized in the magma, the effect of accelerated radioisotope decay would dominate overall and still produce isochron discordances between the radioisotope systems. Furthermore, the nature and composition of the crustal contamination can result in one or more of the radioisotope systems being perturbed more than the others, so this might explain where the patterns of isochron discordances are not the same, instead of any trend according to atomic weights of the parent isotopes. For example, in several of the targeted rock units the Pb-Pb isochron "ages" are older than the Sm-Nd isochron "ages," whereas according to the dominant pattern of isochron discordances the longer half-life α-decay of ^{147}Sm should have been accelerated more, and thus should have produced older isochron "ages" than the shorter half-life α-decayers ^{238}U and ^{235}U. And finally, the mobility of ^{40}Ar* within rocks can often result in either its loss or accumulation in excess of that produced by *in situ* radioisotope decay of its parent ^{40}K, so that widely divergent K-Ar model "ages" may result even in adjacent samples from the same outcrop, and K-Ar isochron "ages" can also be perturbed. Thus, superimposed on an overall younging trend in the relative "ages" upwards through the geologic record are many anomalies due to these various factors.

In conclusion, while all the observations made and issues discussed by *Snelling* [2000a], and summarized in the introduction to this report, have been vindicated in this overall study, the radioisotope "ages" measured in the earth's crustal rocks cannot be simply explained solely by a model in which inheritance and mixing of radioisotopes in the mantle and crust have occurred due to the two catastrophic episodes of mantle-crust geodynamics (early in the Creation week and during the Flood). The weight of the available evidence favors the conclusion that accelerated radioisotope decay has been the dominant influence on the behavior of radioisotopes in rocks through earth history, "swamping" any effects of inheritance and mixing of radioisotopes in the mantle and crust. And the quantity of the accelerated radioisotope decay appears to equate to that conventionally measured. Not only do the radiohalos and fission tracks in Flood rocks provide physical evidence of 500 million years worth of accelerated radioisotope decay in these rocks equivalent to conventional determinations using radioisotope "dating," but Precambrian (pre-Flood) strata yield radioisotope "ages" of the right order of magnitude commensurate with the claimed "age" of the earth based on concordant radioisotope isochron "ages" for meteorites [*Dalrymple*, 1991; *Austin*, 2000]. Thus, because of these two bursts of accelerated radioisotope decay being the apparent time contributor to the resultant radioisotope "ages" obtained for the earth's crustal rocks, the systematic trend of radioisotope "dates" in the geologic record can still be used for relative dating. Nevertheless, there will also be anomalous "ages" due to the contributions of inheritance and mixing of radioisotopes in and from mantle and crustal sources. However, the only reliable framework for understanding the earth's geologic history is that provided in the Bible, and that emphasizes a young created earth and a subsequent global Flood, the two events which have catastrophically built the earth's crustal geologic record and shaped its surface.

7. Conclusions

Potassium-Ar, Rb-Sr, Sm-Nd, and Pb-Pb radioisotope analyses of ten targeted rock units that span the geologic record from the recent to the early Precambrian demonstrate that pronounced discordancy between model and isochron "ages," and between isochron "ages," is always present, contrary to the perception that when two or more radioisotope dating methods are applied to the same rocks they yield the same radioisotope "ages." This indicates that there is a fatal problem with the radioisotope "dating" methods, and with the assumptions on which they are based.

For the seven Precambrian rock units studied there is a clear pattern to the significant discordances that exist between the different radioisotope pairs, the K-Ar and Rb-Sr isochron "ages" always being younger than the Sm-Nd and Pb-Pb isochron "ages." In other words, the β-decayers yield younger isochron "ages" than the α-decayers. Furthermore, within each decay mode it is also generally true that the longer the half-life, and/or the heavier the atomic weight, of the parent radioisotope the older the isochron "age" yielded. Therefore, it is obvious that the constant-decay-rates assumption of conventional radioisotope "dating" must be invalid, because for any of these rock units all four radioisotope pairs are supposed to be "dating" the same geologic event. The only way to reconcile these systematic discordances between the radioisotope pairs is changing decay rates in the past. Thus it is concluded that at some time or times in the past the decay of the α-emitters (^{238}U, ^{238}U, and ^{147}Sm) had to have been accelerated more than the decay of the β-emitters (^{87}Rb and ^{40}K), and in general, the longer the present half-life and/or the heavier the atomic weight of the α- or β-emitter, the more its decay was accelerated relative to the other α- or β-emitters.

However, a further complication to this pattern is that the radioisotope endowment of the mantle sources of basaltic magmas can sometimes be inherited by the magmas without resetting of the radioisotope "clocks" during ascent, intrusion, and extrusion in the earth's crust, thus producing anomalous radioisotope "ages." Furthermore, the radioisotope systems may also be perturbed by crustal contamination during ascent, intrusion, and extrusion, by actual mixing of crustal rock into the magma, or by the transfer of radioisotopes and other trace elements into the magma by hydrothermal and other forms of alteration, again producing anomalous "ages." Thus the known initial conditions and closed system assumptions foundational to the radioisotope "dating" methods are also demonstrably subject to failure, so that together with non-constant accelerated decay rates in the past, radioisotope dating cannot possibly yield absolute "ages" for the earth's crustal rocks.

The dominant process to have affected the radioisotope systems is the accelerated radioisotope decay, which has produced a systematic younging trend of relative ages upwards through the geologic record, with anomalous "ages" occasionally superimposed on the trend by mantle inheritance of radioisotopes by magmas and/or by crustal contamination mixing radioisotopes into magmas. But such effects appear to have only been limited, crustal contamination perhaps only being 5–10% (up to 20% at most) of magma volumes. Additionally, the mobility of ^{40}Ar* within rocks often results in either its loss or accumulation in excess of that produced by *in situ* radioisotope decay of ^{40}K, so that widely divergent K-Ar model "ages" may result, even in adjacent samples from the same outcrop, and K-Ar isochron "ages" can be perturbed.

Within the Biblical framework of a young created earth and a subsequent global Flood, there would have been two bursts of accelerated radioisotope decay accompanying catastrophic geological processes. These would have been during the early part of the Creation week and during the Flood, with upwards of four billion years worth (at today's rates) of radioisotope decay at the beginning of earth history, and about 600 million years worth subsequently during the Flood. Thus the relative "ages" provided by radioisotope "dating" methods may still be useful, except the demonstrated discordances can make it difficult to decide which is the "correct" relative "age."

8. Future Work

While the ten targeted rock units in this study have been adequate to draw the above conclusions with confidence, radioisotope studies of more rock units would undoubtedly enhance the demonstration that isochron discordances are systematically present and destroy the viability of the radioisotope "dating" methods. Because of so few Phanerozoic rock units being targeted in this present study, further radioisotope studies should include several more Phanerozoic rock units, particularly some from the Paleozoic. This could be useful in determining whether there is a difference in the isochron discordance pattern in rock units formed during the Flood compared with those formed pre-Flood and during the Creation week. Because of the expense of radioisotope analyses it may also be worthwhile to conduct literature searches to obtain radioisotope data on rock units that have already been "dated" by three or four of the main radioisotope dating methods. Furthermore, where possible radioisotope data from relevant rock units should be obtained for the Lu-Hf and Re-Os radioisotope "dating" methods. Because ^{176}Lu and ^{187}Re are β-decayers, it would be possible to thus demonstrate whether they follow the pattern of the longer the half-life, and/or the heavier the atomic weight, the older the isochron "age." In building a comprehensive radioisotope database for each selected rock unit, if literature searches only provide radioisotope data for several of the radioisotope systems, then such data could be supplemented by collecting samples of those rock units and submitting them for analyses of the other radioisotope systems. And finally, the copious radioisotope data on meteorites needs to be compiled in order to closely examine the claimed concordance of isochron "ages" for them. It remains a puzzle as to why the meteorite isochron "ages" are apparently concordant, when those for the Precambrian rock units tested in this study are discordant. The meteorite radioisotope data are also relevant to the question of just how much accelerated radioisotope decay has occurred during the earth's history.

Acknowledgments

Many people contributed to this research, and their help and support is gratefully acknowledged. Dr. Kurt Wise and Dr. Steve Austin assisted with some of the sampling of many of the rock units targeted in this study, and access and support of many of the sampling programs were provided by various raft crews on a number of trips through the Grand Canyon. The Grand Canyon National Park granted permission to collect rock samples and undertake the analyses of them. Answers in Genesis (Australia) provided logistical support for the Mt. Ngauruhoe and Somerset Dam fieldwork. William (Bill) Hoesch helped with the processing of many rock samples in the ICR rock laboratory. Of course, the analytical work undertaken by the various laboratories used in this research was crucial, and the excellent analytical data they provided are appreciated and acknowledged. Even though they may not agree with some aspects of the interpretation of the data and the conclusions of this study, the help and the work of Dr. Richard Reesman at Geochron Laboratories in Cambridge, Massachusetts, of Dr. Yakov Kapusta at Activation Laboratories in Ancaster, Ontario, of Dr. Richard Armstrong of the PRISE Laboratory in the Research School of Earth Sciences at the Australian National University in Canberra, and of Professor G. Lang Farmer at the University of Colorado at Boulder were all appreciated. Of course, none of the field or analytical work required for this study would have been possible without the donations to the RATE project from many supporters, and they are profusely thanked for those donations. Finally, the advice and encouragement of the other members of the RATE group, especially Dr. Steve Austin, is also acknowledged.

Appendix: The Case Studies—Descriptions and Sampling

A1. Mt. Ngauruhoe, New Zealand

Mt. Ngauruhoe is an andesite stratovolcano within the Tongariro volcanic massif of the Tongariro Volcanic Center of the Taupo Volcanic Zone, North Island, New Zealand (Figure 26) [*Cole et al.*, 1986;

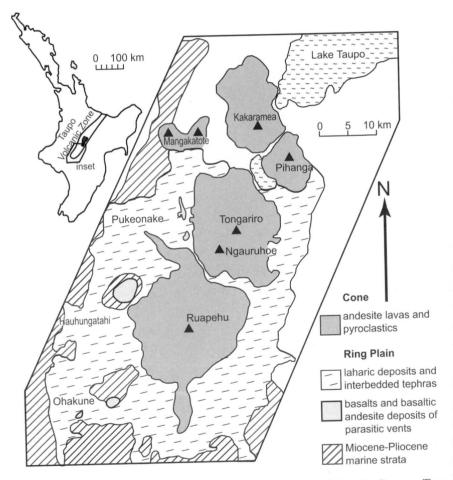

Figure 26. Location and deposits of the Tongariro Volcanic Center, Taupo Volcanic Zone, North Island, New Zealand (after *Cole et al.* [1986]; *Hackett and Houghton* [1987, 1989]). Note the location of Mt. Ngauruhoe.

Graham and Hackett, 1987; *Hackett and Houghton,* 1987]. *Snelling* [1998, 2003a] has summarized the geological setting of the Tongariro Volcanic Center that includes the still active Ruapehu volcano. The Tongariro volcano itself is a large volcanic massif that consists of at least twelve composite cones, Ngauruhoe being the youngest and most active for at least the last 2500 years [*Grindley,* 1965; *Topping,* 1973; *Cole et al.,* 1986; *Nairn and Wood,* 1987; *Williams,* 1994]. Ngauruhoe has been one of the most active volcanoes in New Zealand, with more than seventy eruptive episodes since 1839, when the first steam eruption was recorded by European settlers [*Gregg,* 1960; *Nairn and Wood,* 1987; *Williams,* 1994]. The first lava eruptions seen by European settlers occurred in 1870, and then there were pyroclastic (ash) eruptions every few years, with major explosive activity in 1948. The next lava extrusion was in February 1949, when a series of hot block and ash flows down the northwestern slopes of the volcano was followed by lava flows with a subsequently estimated volume of about 575,000 m^3 [*Battey,* 1949; *Gregg,* 1960] (Figure 27).

The eruption from May 13, 1954 to March 10, 1955 began with an explosive ejection of ash and blocks, followed by an estimated volume of almost 8 million m^3 of lava that flowed from the volcano's crater from June through September 1954. It was claimed to be the largest flow of lava observed in New Zealand (by European settlers) [*Gregg,* 1956, 1960; *Nairn and Wood,* 1987; *Williams,* 1994]. The lava was actually dispelled from the crater in a series of 17 distinct flows on the northwestern and western slopes of the volcano (Figure 27). After the 1954–1955 eruption, Ngauruhoe steamed semi-continuously with numerous small eruptions of ash. Then on February 19, 1975 a series of nine, cannon-like, individual eruptions, accompanied by clearly visible atmospheric shock waves and condensation clouds, followed a 1.5 hour period of voluminous gas-streaming emission which formed a convecting eruption plume between 11 km and 13 km high [*Nairn,* 1976; *Nairn and Self,* 1978; *Nairn and Wood,* 1987; *Williams,* 1994]. Numerous pyroclastic avalanches were also generated by fallback from the continuous eruption column, and these turbulent mixtures of ash, bombs, and larger blocks rolled swiftly down Ngauruhoe's sides at

about 60 km per hour. It was estimated that a minimum bulk volume
of 3.5 million m³ of pyroclastic material was erupted in seven hours on
that day, accumulating as sheets of debris on the northwestern slopes
of the volcano and in the valley below (Figure 27). There have been no
further eruptions since February 1975.

Most of the flows from Ngauruhoe are labradorite (plagioclase)-
pyroxene andesite with phenocrysts of labradorite, hypersthene, and
rare augite in a hyalopilitic (needle-like microlites set in a glassy

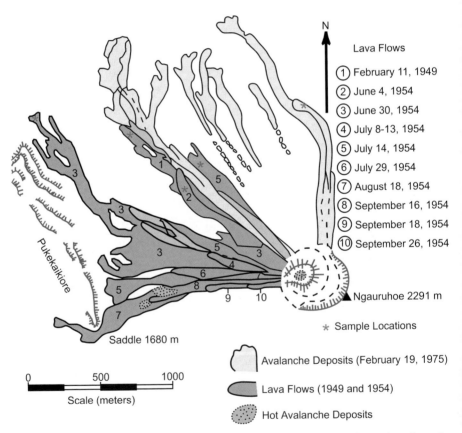

Figure 27. Map of the northwestern slopes of Mt. Ngauruhoe showing the
lava flows of 1949 and 1954, and the 1975 avalanche deposits (after *Battey*
[1949]; *Gregg* [1956, 1960]; *Nairn and Self* [1978]; *Nairn and Wood* [1987]).
The locations of samples collected for this study are marked.

mesostasis) groundmass containing abundant magnetite [*Clarke*, 1960]. However, all lavas, lapilli, and incandescent blocks that have been analyzed from the eruptions in the twentieth century also contain olivine, so that chemically they can be classified as low-silica (or basaltic) andesites, using the classification scheme of *Gill* [1981]. All published analyses show only trivial changes in the compositions of the lavas and pyroclastics between 1928 and 1975 [*Steiner*, 1958; *Clark*, 1960; *Ewart and Stipp*, 1968; *Nairn et al.*, 1976; *Cole*, 1978; *Cole et al.*, 1983, 1986; *Graham and Hackett*, 1987; *Hackett and Houghton*, 1987; *Nairn and Wood*, 1987]. The porphyritic texture of these andesite lavas consists of phenocrysts consistently amounting to 35–40% by volume, the phenocryst assemblage being dominated by labradorite, but also orthopyroxene (hypersthene) and clinopyroxene (augite) are always major components, with olivine and magnetite present in trace amounts. All the lavas usually contain xenoliths that are usually rounded and invariably consist of fine-grained quartzose material with relict gneissic structure [*Battey*, 1949; *Steiner*, 1958]. Additionally, the andesite lavas contain glomerocrysts and mafic nodules consisting of plagioclase, orthopyroxene, and clinopyroxene with occasional olivine [*Graham et al.*, 1995], which probably represent clumps of crystals that formed early in the magma chamber below the volcano.

Eleven samples were collected for the present study—two each from the February 11, 1949, June 4, 1954, and July 14, 1954 lava flows, and from the February 19, 1975 avalanche deposits, as well as three from the June 30, 1954 lava flow [*Snelling*, 1998, 2003a]. The sample locations are marked on Figure 27.

A2. Uinkaret Plateau Basalts, Western Grand Canyon, Arizona

The basaltic rocks of the western Grand Canyon are part of the Uinkaret Volcanic Field on the Uinkaret Plateau (Figure 28). This volcanic field extends northward from the Colorado River approximately 80 km to near the Vermilion Cliffs, and consists of up to 160 volcanic cones ranging in height from 15 to 250 m [*Koons*, 1945]. The lava flows from these volcanic cones are generally less than 8 m thick and cover

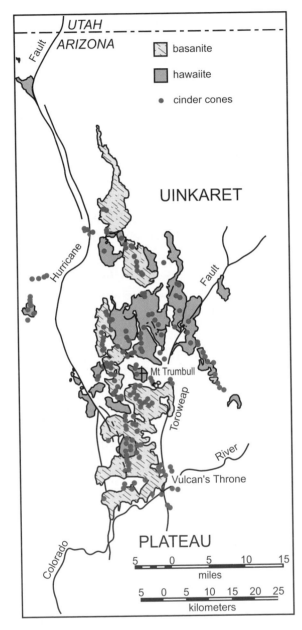

Figure 28. Generalized geologic map of the Uinkaret Plateau in the western Grand Canyon region, showing the distribution of the basaltic rocks (after *Best and Brimhall* [1974]; *Leeman* [1974]).

an area of several hundred km². They erupted in association with two north-south trending fissures on the Uinkaret Plateau, which extend north from near the rim of the inner gorge of Grand Canyon [*Maxson*, 1949]. Flows average between approximately 1–2 m thick, and some individual flows cover areas of up to several km². The thin and extensive lateral coverage of the flows indicates that they were highly fluid upon eruption. Only a few relatively small eruptive sources occur on the platform south of the inner gorge of Grand Canyon.

More than 150 of these lava flows poured southward into the inner gorge of Grand Canyon as lava cascades [*Hamblin*, 1989, 1990, 1994, 2003]. The most spectacular cascades are found on the north wall of the inner gorge between miles 179 and 182 of the Colorado River (downstream from Lees Ferry), having spilled over the rim of the inner gorge just to the west of Vulcan's Throne, a prominent cinder cone near the north rim of the inner gorge (Figures 28 and 29). One of

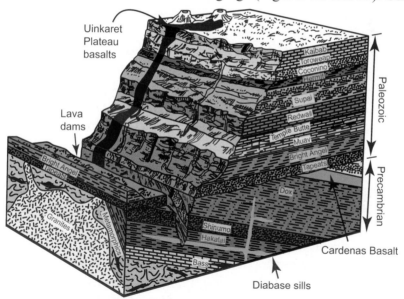

Figure 29. Generalized geologic block diagram showing most of the strata sequence and topographic form below the north rim of Grand Canyon (after *Austin* [1994]). The stratigraphic positions and relationships are shown for the Middle Proterozoic Cardenas Basalt and the likely related diabase sills, and for the Quaternary Uinkaret Plateau basalts and the related lava dams.

these cascades today almost reaches the bank of the Colorado River [*Billingsley and Huntoon*, 1983], while many of the other lava flows once reached the river, where the lavas crystallized and formed dams that temporarily filled the inner gorge of Grand Canyon to different heights, blocking the flow of the Colorado River. Today only erosion remnants of these lava dams remain within the inner gorge of Grand Canyon. When first studied, *McKee and Schenk* [1942] concluded that the lava-dam remnants were part of a large solitary dam structure. However, after more detailed study, *Maxson* [1949] concluded that up to three separate dams, two of which coexisted, once filled the inner gorge. Nevertheless, *Hamblin* [1994], in the most detailed study to date, has concluded that at least thirteen separate lava dams, none of which coexisted, filled the inner gorge during a period between 1.8 Ma to 0.4 Ma of the Pleistocene [*Hamblin*, 1994; *Dalrymple and Hamblin*, 1998]. However, *Rugg and Austin* [1998] argue that the entire span of time from the formation of the first dam to the destruction of the last could have been less than 2000 years.

   Maxson [1949] described the volcanic rocks of the Uinkaret Plateau as olivine basalt flows and basaltic cinders. More detailed geochemical and mineralogical analyses by *Best and Brimhall* [1974] showed that the lavas of the western Grand Canyon region comprise a fairly broad and essentially continuous spectrum of compositions within the alkali basalt suite. The recent geologic mapping [*Billingsley and Huntoon*, 1983] has recognized older and younger flows on the Uinkaret Plateau on the basis of strata sequence and filling of valleys. Furthermore, petrographic and geochemical studies [*Best and Brimhall*, 1974] have distinguished two types of alkali basalts—basanites and hawaiites. The most widespread flows on the Uinkaret Plateau (Figure 28) are the hawaiites which are hypersthene (orthopyroxene)-normative [*Best and Brimhall*, 1974; *Fitton*, 1989; *Austin*, 1992]. All the basalt types contain some olivine, including those that form the remnants of the lava dams inside the inner gorge of Grand Canyon. *Austin* [1992] collected a suite of hawaiite samples from scattered locations across the Uinkaret Plateau for radioisotope analyses.

   Furthermore, *Rugg and Austin* [1998] collected a sample from the lava remnants of the Toroweap Dam about 300 m downstream from the site sampled by *McKee et al.* [1968]. The sample was taken from the north side of the Colorado River just above Lava Falls Rapid (mile 179.4) at a somewhat higher elevation than the *McKee et al.* [1968] sample. *Rugg and Austin* [1998] described it as very fine-grained and uniform black, without phenocrysts and without xenoliths, and thus classifiable as a basanite. Subsequently, on another river trip, a sample of the Massive Diabase Dam was collected on March 30, 1999, at mile 202.5 on the north side of the Colorado River, from a basal colonnade about 4 m above the exposed base of the flow, approximately the same site sampled by *Dalrymple and Hamblin* [1998]. The basalt sample was coarse-grained with visible phenocrysts of plagioclase, augite and olivine, devoid of xenoliths, and free of obvious effects of weathering.

A3. Somerset Dam Layered Mafic Intrusion, Queensland, Australia

The Somerset Dam layered mafic intrusion is situated immediately west of the village of Somerset Dam, some 65 km northwest of the city of Brisbane in southeast Queensland on Australia's east coast (Figure 30). The outcrop is somewhat oval shaped, covering an area of about 4 km² with a diameter of about 1.5 km (Figure 31) [*Mathison*, 1964, 1967, 1970]. It is a small layered gabbro intrusion with an exposed stratigraphic thickness of 500 m on a steep hillside. It is a well-preserved, well-exposed, steep-sided, discordant intrusion which is undeformed and unmetamorphosed. The roof and floor of the intrusion are not exposed, and an unknown thickness of layered gabbros of the intrusion have been eroded from the top, and are concealed below the exposed sequence. The location and nature of the feeder zone are unknown, yet it probably represents a small, relatively shallow (3–5 km depth), sub-volcanic magma chamber [*Mathison*, 1967, 1987].

Within this gabbro intrusion there is an exposed sequence of twenty-two saucer-shaped macrolayers, 3–50 m thick generally dipping inwards at 10–20° (Figure 31) [*Mathison*, 1967]. The contacts between these prominent layers are sharply defined, generally to within 10 cm, and

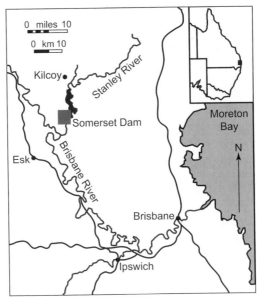

Figure 30. Location map for the Somerset Dam layered mafic intrusion near Brisbane on Australia's east coast (after *Mathison* [1967]).

are phase, modal mineralogy, and textural contacts. These macrolayers appear to be stratigraphically homogeneous. The repetition of these macrolayers has allowed the recognition of at least six well-developed cyclic units, ranging from 30 to 150 m thick (average about 80 m thick). The macrolayers are limited to only four main rock types, which are defined in terms of their essential cumulus mineral phases (distinguished texturally from the intercumulus mineral phases) [*Wager et al.*, 1960; *Irvine*, 1982] (Figures 31 and 32). These four rock types constituting the macrolayers are leucogabbro or anorthosite (plagioclase cumulate), troctolite (plagioclase + olivine cumulate), olivine gabbro (plagioclase + augite + olivine cumulate), and oxide (or ferri-) gabbro (plagioclase + augite ± olivine + magnetite + ilmenite cumulate) [*Mathison*, 1967, 1987].

The definition of these cyclic units and which of these macrolayers commences each cycle is strongly influenced by what is expected to be the order of crystallization and the magma fractionation pattern, because there is commonly no clear field evidence to identify the base or top of a cyclic unit. In the Somerset Dam layered gabbro intrusion, *Mathison* [1964, 1967, 1970, 1975] chose to define each cyclic unit to be the sequence troctolite–olivine gabbro–oxide gabbro–leucogabbro, because troctolite was considered the least fractionated rock type, and cryptic trends generally suggested a reversal at the bases of the

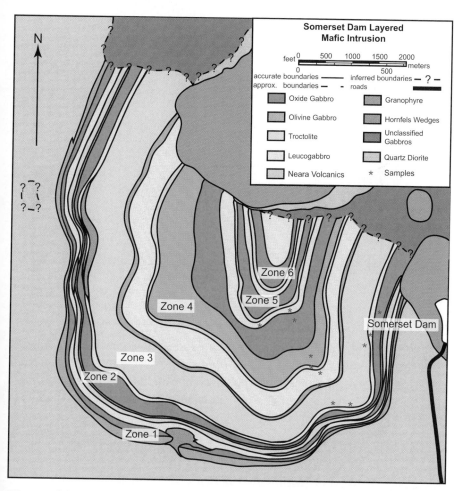

Figure 31. Detailed geologic map of the Somerset Dam layered mafic intrusion, southeast Queensland, Australia (after *Mathison* [1967]).

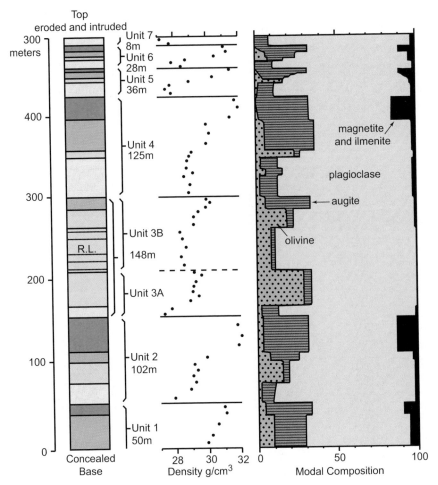

Figure 32. Stratigraphic column for the exposed portion of the Somerset Dam layered mafic intrusion (after *Mathison* [1987]) showing its inferred cyclic units, rock densities, and modal compositions. [▢ =leucogabbro/ anorthosite; ▢ =troctolite; ▨ =olivine gabbro; ▨ =oxide (ferri-) gabbro; R.L.=best developed zone of rhythmic layering]

troctolites. However, *Mathison* [1987] revised this choice of sequence in each cyclic unit so that anorthosite was defined as the basal layer and oxide gabbro as the top layer, the choice subsequently followed by

Walker [1998] (Figure 32). This interpretation better fits the inferred order of crystallization, the oxide gabbro being the most fractionated rock type. Of course, the mineralogy, and therefore the whole-rock compositions, of these macrolayers show marked changes between these rock types in this cyclical sequence [*Mathison*, 1967, 1987; *Walker*, 1998; *Snelling*, 2003b]. Despite the remarkable similarity of successive cyclic units, significant differences exist between them in the sequences of macrolayers, thicknesses of individual macrolayers and of the cyclic units, mineral compositions and cryptic patterns, average level of fractionation, and the sizes of reversals (Figure 32).

A total of eighteen whole-rock samples were collected along a farm road that traverses through the intrusion, commencing with samples of the oxide gabbro at the top of cyclic unit 2, and continuing progressively with samples of all the successive macrolayers for units 3 and 4 up to two samples of the anorthosite macrolayer at the base of unit 5 [*Snelling*, 2003b]. The locations of these samples are marked on Figure 31. Details of the petrography of the different macrolayers and the compositions of the minerals in them are provided by *Mathison* [1967, 1987] and are summarized by *Snelling* [2003b]. The samples collected for this study were comparable in major and trace element geochemistry to previous studies [*Mathison*, 1967, 1987; *Walker*, 1998; *Snelling*, 2003b].

A4. Cardenas Basalt, Eastern Grand Canyon

Mafic igneous rocks occur as sills, dikes, and flows in the thick succession of sedimentary strata making up the Middle Proterozoic Unkar Group of the Grand Canyon, Arizona (Figures 29 and 33). The Unkar Group sedimentary sequence is comprised of four formations—in ascending order, the Bass Limestone, Hakatai Shale, Shinumo Quartzite, and the Dox Formation—which are overlain by the 300 m+ thick flow sequence of lavas comprising the Cardenas Basalt [*Hendricks and Stevenson*, 1990, 2003]. The Upper Proterozoic sedimentary strata of the Nankoweap Formation and the Chuar Group overlie this Unkar Group succession, which unconformably rests on the Lower Proterozoic metamorphic and igneous crystalline basement [*Babcock*, 1990; *Ilg et*

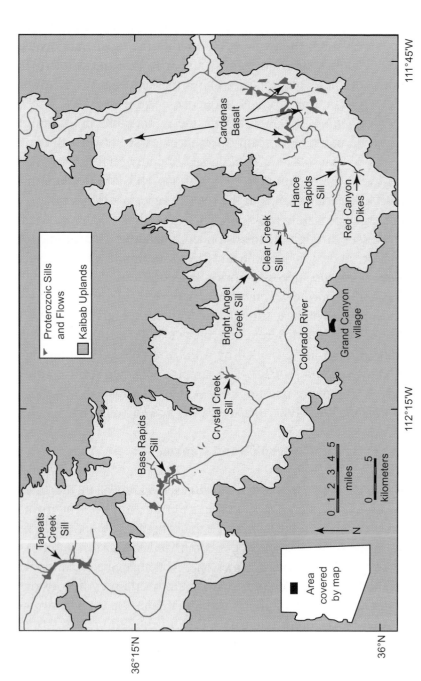

Figure 33. Location of the Cardenas Basalt and the related Middle Proterozoic named diabase sills and dikes in Grand Canyon, northern Arizona (after *Hendricks and Lucchitta* [1974]).

al., 1996; *Karlstrom et al.*, 2003] (Figure 29).

The Cardenas Basalt crops out over an area of about 120 km² in the eastern Grand Canyon (Figure 33). Most of the Cardenas Basalt lavas are so little altered that primary flow and depositional features are well preserved [*Lucchitta and Hendricks*, 1983]. Several distinctive units within the lavas are good indicators of the depositional environment, and these units are laterally persistent, making it possible to correlate between individual sections. In the type section at Basalt Canyon (Figure 21, p. 447) [*Hendricks and Lucchitta*, 1974; *Hendricks*, 1989; *Larson et al.*, 1994], the Cardenas Basalt consists of a 100 m-thick lower member composed of about six, coarsely ophitic flows of olivine basalt which vary in thickness from about 3 to 25 m. Beds of siltstone and sandstone 1.5 to 3 m thick occur between some of the flows. All flows possess vesicular tops and bottoms, and massive to columnar-jointed central portions. Typically this lower member is poorly exposed, weathering to spheroidal masses surrounded by granular debris. Before alteration, this medium-grained olivine basalt was similar in texture and mineralogy to the diabase sills and dikes intruded into the lower Unkar Group sedimentary strata in the central Grand Canyon (Figures 29 and 33). Petrological and geochemical data also appear to suggest that this lower member was originally a spilitic hyaloclastite, which would have been the altered effusive equivalent of those mafic intrusives. However, the spheroidal masses may simply have resulted from onion-skin weathering rather than being suggestive of pillow structures (and underwater extrusion), and therefore, the field evidence could indicate subaerial extrusion of these lower member basalts in a series of low-viscosity pahoehoe flows.

In contrast, the 200 m-thick upper member of the Cardenas Basalt comprises four to six aphyric, intersertal to intergranular flows that change sequentially from basaltic andesite to basalt and then back to basaltic andesite upward through the section (Figure 21). The dramatic change from the easily weathered, greenish ophitic flows of the lower member to the resistant, less-green, finer-grained flows of the upper member is indicative of this abrupt change in magma chemistry. Individual flows vary in thickness from about 20 to 50 m, each flow being separated from adjacent flows by laterally persistent siltstone and sandstone beds that generally range in thickness from 0.3 to 3 m. The 40 to 50 m-thick lowermost flow displays both large-scale flow banding and rather abrupt thickness variations of about 8–10 m. Amygdaloidal zones, from 2 to 5 m thick, are common near the bases and tops of the flows, and scoriaceous flow breccias are conspicuous at the tops of several of them. Some of the flows exhibit crude columnar jointing in their middle to upper portions, but most also display irregular, hackly fractures. None of the flows exhibits any evidence (pillow structures, hyaloclastites) of interaction with water. Overall, the extent of the lava flow remnants outcropping in the eastern Grand Canyon (Figure 33) suggests an initial volume for the Cardenas Basalt of about 60 km^3. The relationship of the diabase sills and dikes (Figure 33) to the Cardenas Basalt flows remains obscure because direct feeders to the flows and sills have never been recognized.

Hendricks and Lucchitta [1974], Hendricks [1989], and Larson et al. [1994] describe in detail the petrography and chemistry of the Cardenas Basalt flows. All lower member flows appear to originally have consisted of 10–14 vol.% olivine, 45–50 vol.% plagioclase (labradorite), 18–20 vol.% augite (in subequant ophitic grains that enclose the plagioclase), 5 vol.% titanomagnetite and ilmenite, and 15–20 vol.% glass and crystallites (mesostasis). This mineral association and the ophitic texture mean the rock is appropriately classified as an olivine basalt. All these flows have been affected to some degree by post-extrusion alteration. Whereas it could be expected that this alteration may have changed the original rock chemistry, Larson et al. [1994] used an isocon (short for "same concentration") plot to show that these rocks have probably undergone minimal enrichment or depletion of individual major-element oxides during hydration, an important observation relevant to the suitability of these lava flows for radioisotope analyses. Otherwise, the chemistry of these lower member lava flows suggests a tholeiite, but is also compatible with a high-alumina basalt of shoshonitic affinities.

Flows of the upper member vary in texture from intersertal to intergranular, and are much finer grained than those of the lower member. Larson et al. [1994] concluded from sporadic occurrence of pigeonite (clinopyroxene), the aphyric texture, and the modal olivine content ranging from a trace to 10 vol.%, that all of the flows can be classified as tholeiitic olivine basalts or basaltic andesites. The variable chemical alteration of the upper member flows is generally similar to that of the lower member flows, but is often less extensive. *Larson et al.* [1994] also concluded that some of the major element chemical variations between the upper member flows appear to be related to initial differences in the magma composition. SiO_2 and K_2O steadily decrease upwards for the lower four upper-member flows and then increase abruptly in the upper two, whereas CaO and MgO display the opposite behavior. The lowermost upper-member flow, which is the most felsic, corresponds to an andesite, while the three flows above it can be classified as basaltic andesite to basalt, as they become progressively less felsic upward in the sequence. The two uppermost flows also appear to be andesites. Alternately, based on the normative compositions, the more mafic flows are quartz tholeiites, while the more SiO_2-rich flows are tholeiitic andesites (or icelandites).

A total of nineteen samples of the Cardenas Basalt were collected, all but two of them from the Basalt Canyon type section (Figure 21), one of the best and most studied outcrops. Because the Basalt Canyon section has poor exposure of the lower third of the Cardenas Basalt, two samples were collected from the superior exposure of the lower 15 m at Lava Chuar Canyon (Figure 21) [*Austin and Snelling*, 1998].

A5. Diabase Sills, Central Grand Canyon

The diabase sills and dikes of the central Grand Canyon (Figure 33) are believed to be the intrusive equivalents of the Cardenas Basalt lava flows, but they are not found in direct association with them [*Hendricks and Lucchitta*, 1974; *Hendricks*, 1989]. Thus the relationship between them is obscure, because the direct feeders to the flows have never been recognized among the available diabase outcrops. The diabase sills are, in fact, confined to the lower part of the Unkar Group, particularly intruding near the contact between the Bass Limestone and Hakatai Shale, while the related dikes are intruded into all the formations above the sills along faults that predate, or are contemporaneous with, the sills (Figure 29). These mafic sills crop out in seven locations along a 70–80 km length of the Grand Canyon (Figure 33), whereas the Cardenas Basalt flows are restricted to the area around Basalt Canyon in the eastern Grand Canyon. The sills range in thickness from about 20 m (about 65 ft) near Hance Rapids in the east to more than 200 m (655 ft) near Tapeats Creek in the west. Thicknesses of the other sills include 23 m along Clear Creek, 140 m along Bright Angel Creek, a minimum of 100 m along Crystal Creek, and 100–150 m in the vicinity of Bass Rapids and Shinumo Creek, while nearby in Hakatai Canyon, the latter sill is reported to be 300 m thick [Noble, 1914].

All of these diabase sills are composed chiefly of medium-grained ophitic olivine-rich diabase that is uniform in texture and mineralogy, as well as in chemistry, from sill to sill through the Canyon [Hendricks and Lucchitta, 1974; Hendricks, 1989]. The dikes have a similar composition but are finer grained. All the diabase sills have fine-grained chilled margins about 30 cm to less than 1 m thick, which suggests that the magma was highly fluid at the time of intrusion [Hendricks and Stevenson, 1990, 2003]. All the sills show varying amounts of early in-place differentiation and crystal settling that is evidenced by syenite lenses up to 10 m thick and felsite dikes, as well as by layers which are richer in olivine. The sill in the Bass Rapids-Shinumo Creek area is unique in that it displays distinct layers of differentiation and segregation products, with a well-defined 6 m (20 ft) thick granophyre layer on top of the 85 m (280 ft) thick diabase. Contact metamorphism caused by intrusion of the diabase sills resulted in the formation of chrysotile asbestos above the sills where the magma intruded the Bass Limestone. On the other hand, where the sills intrude the Hakatai Shale, it has been altered into a knotted hornfels.

The diabase sills and dikes are mineralogically similar to the lower member flows of the Cardenas Basalt [Hendricks and Lucchitta, 1974; Hendricks, 1989]. Chemical variation diagrams also indicate a potential common parentage for the diabase in the sills and the lower member flows of the Cardenas Basalt. However, the upper member flows of the Cardenas Basalt are much more silicic than the diabase sills, and therefore, it has been concluded that they probably were not emplaced during the same phase of igneous activity. Nevertheless, the similarity in mineral composition of the unaltered lower member basalt flows and of the diabase sills suggests that the lavas and the diabase sills were co-magmatic and probably coeval. Indeed, *Larson et al.* [1994] found that the main observable difference between the lower-member basalt flows and the diabase sills is in the color of the augite in thin section, being commonly pink-brown to purplish brown in the diabase due to a content of about 2.5 wt% TiO_2, compared to being colorless to light grey in the basalt due to a content of <1 wt% TiO_2. Thus it has been concluded that the upper member lavas of the Cardenas Basalt (the top two-thirds of the sequence) were extruded after differentiation of the parent magma, which would account for their higher silica content. This conclusion is supported by paleomagnetic observations that suggest the diabase sills may be slightly older than the Cardenas Basalt flows [*Elston and Grommé*, 1974; *Elston*, 1989]. Indeed, *Elston* [1986] indicated that the paleomagnetic evidence suggests the majority of the sills were intruded at the same time that the upper Dox Formation was being deposited. Nevertheless, some of the diabase dikes in the eastern Grand Canyon have paleomagnetic pole positions similar to the Cardenas Basalt and may represent feeders. However, these dikes are not seen connected to either the Cardenas Basalt flows or to the nearby Hance Rapids sill (Figure 33). Nevertheless, the diabase sills and dikes, and the Cardenas Basalt flows are still regarded overall as representing a single volcanic episode, in which the earliest phases were the intrusion of the diabase sills, followed by a period of quiescence during continued deposition of the Dox Formation before the later phases when eruptions of basalt and basaltic andesite flows occurred via a network of thin dikes [*Hendricks and Stevenson*, 1990, 2003].

Larson et al. [1994] also found that, whereas the major-element chemistry of the diabase sills exhibited similarities and dissimilarities with the lower-member flows of the Cardenas Basalt [*Hendricks and Lucchitta*, 1974], the trace and rare earth element data from a sample of the Hance Rapids sill shows very similar variation patterns to those in the lower-member flows of the Cardenas Basalt. Only the Ti and P contents were markedly higher in the sill, and the negative Eu (europium) anomaly for the sill was smaller than that for the lower-member Cardenas Basalt flows. Thus, *Larson et al.* [1994] suggested a common origin for the diabase of the sills and the basalt of the lower-member flows similar to continental flood basalts, except that the higher Ti and P contents of the diabase may indicate that the magma that fed the intrusions did not also directly feed the flows of the lower member. Alternately, they suggested that the higher silica (SiO_2), Ti, and P contents of the basalt flows were due either to greater crustal contamination of the basalt magma on its passage to the earth's surface, or heterogeneity in the mantle source.

A total of nineteen samples from these diabase sills were collected for this study [*Austin and Snelling*, 1998; *Snelling et al.*, 2003a]. These included two samples from the Hance Rapids sill (Figure 33), two samples from the Red Canyon dikes, a single sample from the Bright Angel Creek sill, three samples from the Tapeats Creek sill, and eleven samples from the Bass Rapids sill. The eleven samples collected through the sill at Bass Rapids (north bank of the Colorado River at mile 107.6–108.0) were from a composite section, the same section sampled by *Hendricks and Lucchitta* [1974] some 800 m east of Shinumo Creek. The samples were chosen to represent the overall petrographic variability within the complete thickness of the sill, as depicted in Figure 20 (p. 445), with three samples from the 6 m thick granophyre layer at the top of the sill, and eight samples from the 85 m thick main body of the diabase sill.

The Bass Rapids sill is similar to the other sills within the Unkar Group being composed of olivine diabase, but it is uniquely capped by granophyre (Figure 20), making this sill a classic example of in-place differentiation of a basaltic magma. The 6 m-thick granophyre consists predominantly of K-feldspar (55–60%) and quartz (12–25%), with biotite, plagioclase, some clinopyroxene, and titanomagnetite making up the remaining 20–28%. The rock is holocrystalline, coarse-grained, and has a well-developed granophyric texture in which quartz, plagioclase, biotite, clinopyroxene, and titanomagnetite fill interstices between the orthoclase crystals. The transition between the granophyre and diabase below occurs over a vertical distance of <1 m and is a zone rich in biotite and accessory minerals [*Hendricks*, 1989]. Apatite makes up as much as 5–10% of the rock, while ilmenite and sphene are prominent, and zircon with reaction halos occurs within the biotite grains.

The olivine diabase interior of the sill is medium- to coarse-grained, containing plagioclase (30–45%), olivine (20–35%), clinopyroxene (15–20%), titanomagnetite and ilmenite (5%), and biotite (1%), with accessory apatite and sphene. The texture is diabasic to subophitic, although a crude alignment of feldspar laths can be seen in many places. The olivine concentration tends to increase towards the center of the sill, whereas the clinopyroxene decreases. Immediately below the granophyre the diabase contains about 5% modal olivine, which increases rapidly to 20–30% through the central part of the sill [*Hendricks and Lucchitta*, 1974]. About 15 m above the base of the sill is an olivine-rich layer that contains about 50% modal olivine, and then the olivine content of the diabase decreases to about 10% near the base. *Hendricks and Lucchitta* [1974] and *Hendricks* [1989] have suggested that this distribution of the olivine in the sill can be explained by the process of flow differentiation, which involves the movement of early-formed olivine grains away from the margins of the sill during flow of the intruding magma [*Bhattacharji and Smith*, 1964; *Bhattacharji*, 1967; *Simkin*, 1967]. It is envisaged that, as the magma intruded up through the conduit and then outward to form the sill, fluid-dynamic forces concentrated toward the center of the moving mass the olivine crystals that had formed early in the cooling history of the magma, even before the emplacement of the sill. As the magma also moved laterally, gravity acting on the olivine crystals would have produced a gradational change in the olivine content from the lower contact upward, while causing an abrupt change in olivine from the upper contact downward. Once emplaced, crystallization of the remaining liquid magma within the sill would then have yielded the remaining minerals in relatively constant proportions [*Simkin*, 1964]. Although there is a general uniformity of the diabase throughout the sill, there are two types of textural variation, first described by *Noble* [1914]. First, there are "lumps" or "balls" similar in mineralogy to the surrounding diabase, but the plagioclase laths in the lumps are up to 7.5 mm in length and fill embayments in large olivine crystals. Second, pegmatite veins consisting of plagioclase and augite with a very similar texture are found in the upper part of the sill. These textural variations undoubtedly represent segregation features produced during crystallization of the sill.

The lower chilled margin and contact of the Bass Rapids sill with the underlying Hakatai Shale is covered, but is probably similar to the fine-grained chilled margins found in most of the other sills intruding the Unkar Group in Grand Canyon. The upper contact of the sill is marked by the 6 m-thick capping of granophyre, the contact with the overlying Hakatai Shale is sharp (Figure 20), and no xenoliths of Hakatai Shale are found in the granophyre, suggesting that it was not produced by assimilation of the shale. Instead, the transition zone between the granophyre and the diabase beneath it in the sill suggests that the granophyre was a residual magma that "floated" to the top of the sill as the diabase crystallized, so that there was little late-stage mixing of it with the diabase part of the sill [*Hendricks and Lucchitta*, 1974].

Contact metamorphism of the Hakatai Shale has occurred above and below the sill, the shale being altered to a knotted hornfels (Figure 20). This contact metamorphism is greater below the sill than above it. The hornfels below the sill extends for 5 m below the contact and forms a prominent outcrop, from which two samples were collected. No recrystallization of the shale has occurred beyond 5 m below the sill contact, while the mineralogy of the metamorphism (biotite, andalusite, and cordierite[?] porphyroblasts) suggests that it was of low–medium grade.

A6. Apache Group Basalts and Diabase Sills, Central Arizona

In a large area of central and southern Arizona, Middle Proterozoic rocks are represented by the Apache Group, the Troy Quartzite, and co-extensive diabase sills (Figure 34) [*Shride*, 1967; *Wrucke*, 1989]. These sedimentary strata, basalt flows, and diabase sills are regarded, due to their stratigraphic position and lithologic similarities, as correlative

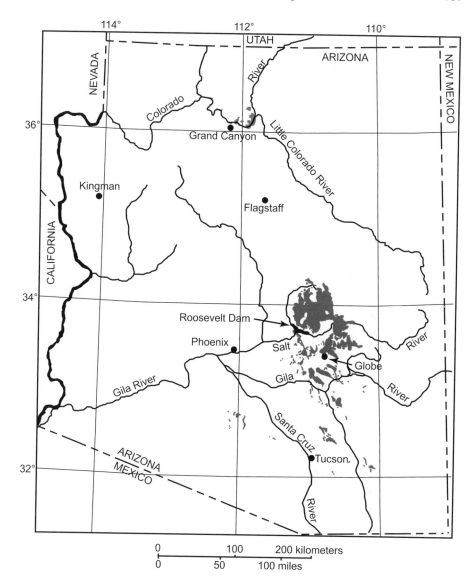

Figure 34. Outcrop areas of the Middle Proterozoic Apache Group, Troy Quartzite, and associated basalts and diabase sills in central and southern Arizona (red), and of the Middle Proterozoic Unkar Group (including the Cardenas Basalt) and associated diabase sills in Grand Canyon, northern Arizona (green) (after *Shride* [1967]; *Wrucke* [1989]).

with the Unkar Group sedimentary strata, Cardenas Basalt, and the related diabase sills in Grand Canyon [*Shride*, 1967; *Elston*, 1989; *Wrucke*, 1989; *Hendricks and Stevenson*, 1990, 2003; *Larson et al.*, 1994] (Figure 34). Indeed, *Elston* [1986, 1989] reviewed the correlation of various Middle and Upper Proterozoic sequences on a paleomagnetic basis and found that a paleomagnetic pole from the Mescal Limestone of the Apache Group correlates with poles from the Dox Formation. Furthermore, the diabase sills that intrude both the Apache Group and Troy Quartzite are similar paleomagnetically to the diabase sills in the Unkar Group of Grand Canyon, their respective paleomagnetic poles also correlating with the paleomagnetic poles from mafic intrusions in the Keweenawan Supergroup of the Lake Superior region of the U.S.A. Thus, *Larson et al.* [1994] correlate the diabase sills in the Unkar Group of Grand Canyon and the Apache Group of central Arizona with a number of other Middle Proterozoic mafic and related intrusions around the southwest U.S.A., and in the Belt Supergroup of the northwest U.S.A. and southwestern Canada, as well as those in the Midcontinent Rift System across to the northeastern U.S.A.

The Apache Group and Troy Quartzite crop out in a roughly triangular area of about 20,000 km² in central and southern Arizona (Figure 34). The Apache Group sedimentary strata range in thickness from 380 to 490 m and consist, in ascending order, of the Pioneer Shale, the Dripping Spring Quartzite, the Mescal Limestone, and unnamed basalt flows (Figure 35), while the Troy Quartzite has a maximum thickness of 365 m [*Shride*, 1967; *Wrucke*, 1989]. The Pioneer Shale consists of a basal conglomerate overlain by silty mudstone, siltstone, and arkose. The dominant silty mudstone is characteristically greyish-red to dusk red-purple because it largely consists of water-laid rhyolitic tuff [*Gastil*, 1954]. The unconformably overlying Dripping Spring Quartzite also consists of a basal conglomerate overlain by a mostly thick-bedded arkose that grades through a 1–2 m interval into a largely thin-bedded siltstone. The Mescal Limestone unconformably overlies the Dripping Spring Quartzite (Figure 35), and comprises three members: a lower thin- to medium-bedded member of cherty dolomite, or of calcitic limestone that is its metamorphic equivalent, a middle partly massive

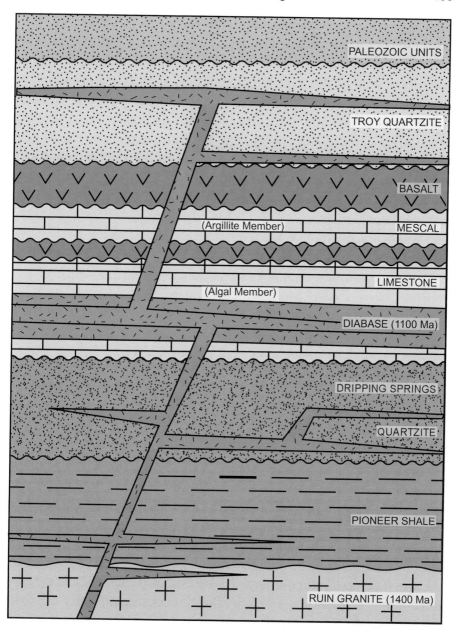

Figure 35. Schematic stratigraphic column of the Apache Group, Troy Quartzite, and associated basalts and diabase sills in central Arizona (modified from *Shride* [1967]; *Wrucke* [1989]).

algal member of similar carbonate, and an upper argillite member. The algal member rests conformably on the lower cherty dolomite member and consists of a thick-bedded dolomite containing columnar branching colonies of stromatolites and biostromes having great lateral continuity, that are overlain by a thin-bedded dolomite with chert that contains filamentous chains and spherules identified as replacements of blue-green algae [*McConnell*, 1974]. The argillite member of the Mescal Limestone (Figure 35) mostly rests directly on the algal member with a disconformable contact, except in a few places where an angular unconformity is evident. It consists of a basal unit of chert, chert breccia, and chert conglomerate overlain by argillite that makes up most of the unit and contains minor amounts of silicified limestone.

Basalt flows occur at two stratigraphic positions high in the Apache Group sequence. Throughout the region the principal occurrences separate the overlying Troy Quartzite from the Mescal Limestone of the Apache Group. At two localities, in the Sierra Ancha mountains north of the Salt River and at Roosevelt Dam (Figure 34), petrographically similar basalt flows with a maximum thickness of 34 m are found between the algal and argillite members of the Mescal Limestone. The two sequences of basalt flows in their juxtaposition below and above the argillite member of the Mescal Limestone are best exposed in cliff faces in the southern part of the Sierra Ancha [*Shride*, 1967]. The sequence of basalt flows stratigraphically above the Mescal Limestone is commonly 10–25 m thick, but locally reaches 75–115 m. Though abundant hematite is disseminated throughout these lava flows they are still recognizable as basalt due to their dark aphyric appearance and evidence of an intersertal to intergranular texture defined by tiny plagioclase laths. The basalt has a highly altered, fine-grained groundmass of albite, chlorite, and other minerals, and sparse to abundant tabular former plagioclase phenocrysts. Vesicles and amygdules are especially abundant in the tops and bottoms of the flows, with ropy flow breccias being conspicuous in places. Thus the basalt formed as subaerial flows which were very fluid. No feeder dikes for these lavas have been found.

The angular relations of the unconformity that separates the Troy Quartzite from the Apache Group are apparent only on a regional scale.

The Apache Group strata were broadly warped, then eroded before deposition of the Troy Quartzite, which thus rests in different places on the different formations of the Apache Group. The Troy Quartzite consists from the base upward of an arkose member, a prominent sandstone member, and a quartzite member, which together obtain a maximum thickness of 365 m.

In nearly every locality where the Apache Group and Troy Quartzite are exposed, diabase sills are associated with them, and dikes, although volumetrically insignificant, are locally numerous. The diabase sills and dikes were emplaced in the Apache Group almost to the exclusion of other formations, but in places extensive bodies also intruded the Troy Quartzite and the older Precambrian basement consisting of metamorphic rocks and the Ruin Granite. Paleozoic formations rest unconformably on the diabase sills, indicating some erosion of the overlying strata after emplacement, and/or a shallow depth of emplacement. Over large areas along the Salt River Canyon and in the Sierra Ancha, the aggregate volume of the diabase sills is as great as the combined volume of the exposed Apache Group and Troy Quartzite strata.

The diabase sills typically are tens of meters thick. The maximum verified thickness of a single diabase sill is about 400 m in the Sierra Ancha [Shride, 1967]. Diabase sills as much as 1000 m thick have been reported, but they almost certainly are compound bodies consisting of two or more separate intrusive sheets. Laterally extensive diabase bodies formed by multiple sill intrusions are known throughout the region (exposed in the walls of one of the large open cast mines and of the Salt River Canyon), and can be recognized by the chilled margins of the younger rock against the older, and locally by tabular septa of host strata that commonly remain where a second intrusion was emplaced approximately along the contact with the first. The second intrusion passed around and isolated the remnants of country rock.

All the diabase sills are locally discordant to the host strata. Some cross the layering of the host rocks at low angles as simple tabular bodies having planar contacts, while others have discordant step-like breaks across strata and relatively short vertical and horizontal segments. Sills commonly end at high-angle contacts that can be distinguished between faults by the chilled diabase along the steep termination, although faults may extend above or below and contain dikes. The diabase sills tend to follow certain stratigraphic horizons with remarkable persistence. For example, sills 0.5 m thick are traceable for 1.5 km, while some thicker sills crop out for at least 30 km. Commonly the diabase sills occur along horizons that separate strata of contrasting competency or along nearby horizons in incompetent rocks. Great volumes of diabase invaded the Ruin Granite at shallow depth below the Apache Group, at horizons a few meters below the top of the Pioneer Shale, within the upper siltstone member of the Dripping Spring Quartzite, within the lower cherty dolomite member of the Mescal Limestone at positions about 12 and 40 m below the upper contact, and between the algal and argillite members of the Mescal Limestone [*Bergquist et al.*, 1981]. Diabase sills are widespread along the unconformity between the Mescal Limestone and the Troy Quartzite, and between the Troy Quartzite and the basalt that locally overlies the Mescal Limestone. One thick sill in the Sierra Ancha is in the quartzite member of the Troy Quartzite. Possibly the stratigraphic horizon having the greatest volume of diabase is that near the top of the Pioneer Shale.

The diabase typically is a dark-grey to greenish-black rock that is aphanitic to fine-grained at chilled margins and medium- to coarse-grained and subophitic to ophitic in the interior of the sills. Plagioclase, clinopyroxene, and olivine are the common minerals, so the rock is best classified as an olivine diabase. The distinguishing characteristic of the diabase in these sills compared to similar mafic rocks elsewhere is the unusually coarse grain size of the ophitic and subophitic phases. The plagioclase laths are commonly 1–4 mm long (sometimes 4–8 mm long), and the pyroxene crystals are commonly 5–20 mm across (often 30–50 mm across), in contrast to plagioclase crystals 0.25–2 mm long and pyroxene crystals less than 5 mm across in the well-known Palisade diabase sill in New Jersey [*Walker*, 1940].

Most petrographic studies of the Apache Group diabase have been based on the principal intrusion, the 400 m thick Sierra Ancha sill, emplaced in the upper member of the Dripping Spring Quartzite

[*Nehru and Prinz*, 1970; *Smith*, 1970]. The sills have almost knife-sharp contacts with their host rocks, but the effects of chilling of the diabase can sometimes be seen as far as 10 m from the margins of the sills. The chilled diabase is very fine grained, and progressing to the interior of the sills the diabase becomes a fine-grained felted mat of plagioclase laths and interstitial mafic grains which grade rapidly into subophitic diabase. In the interiors of the sills the ophitic and subophitic diabase consists of plagioclase (labradorite) (45–70%), clinopyroxene (10–40%), orthopyroxene (0–7%), olivine (0–20%), and accessory minerals (3–15%). Augite is the most abundant clinopyroxene and pigeonite is present in small amounts. Hypersthene (orthopyroxene) is sparse, while olivine occurs as small equant grains. Biotite is present in accessory amounts with magnetite, and other accessory minerals include ilmenite, apatite, sphene, zircon, and sparse pyrite and chalcopyrite. Olivine is generally dispersed throughout the sills, although in some of the thicker sills it is concentrated slightly below the middle of the intrusions, similar to the Bass Rapid diabase sill in Grand Canyon.

Felspathic rocks locally are conspicuous in the diabase, and such differentiates include microtroctolite (a plagioclase-olivine rock), aplite (microgranite), pegmatite, and granophyre. Generally these differentiates make up only a small fraction of any sill, except in the 400 m thick Sierra Ancha sill where the microtroctolite that occupies the middle part of the sill is 70 m thick [*Nehru and Prinz*, 1970]. The fair-to-good alignment of the plagioclase crystals parallel to the top and bottom of the microtroctolite zone indicates that the mass was emplaced by flowage differentiation of a crystal mush during the main crystallization phase of the diabase [*Smith*, 1970]. Otherwise, the largest feldspathic masses associated with the Sierra Ancha diabase sill are discontinuous pods of granitic rocks up to 50 m thick at the top of the sill. These consist of various proportions of microgranite and granophyre, and there is some evidence to suggest that, rather than being the result of differentiation of the parent magma during crystallization of the sill, the granophyre represents felspathic country rock material that has become fused at the contact with the diabase [*Smith and Silver*, 1975].

Thermal contact metamorphism resulting from emplacement of the diabase sills affected the carbonate rocks of the Apache Group on a regional scale, and in many localities caused widespread changes in siliceous rocks [*Wrucke*, 1989]. The dolomite of the Mescal Limestone nearly everywhere was converted to limestone (by removal of Mg, probably by hydrothermal fluids), but the stratification and other sedimentary structures were preserved sufficiently to mask the metamorphosed character of the rocks. Chrysotile asbestos was locally produced in veins by the alteration processes during emplacement of the diabase sills, similar to that produced in the Bass Limestone of Grand Canyon. In the feldspar-rich sedimentary rocks contact metamorphism produced granophyre, and with increased induration, hornfels and spotted hornfels. Where the diabase sills are thin, felspathic rocks were metamorphosed for only a meter or so adjacent to the contact, but where the sills are thick or numerous, entire formations have been affected. Even the basalt flows have been albitized, recrystallized, and veined by epidote adjacent to some diabase sills, confirming that the diabase sills are younger.

Based on chemical analyses of samples from the sills, most of the diabase would be classified as olivine tholeiite with normative hypersthene and olivine, but a few minor sills consist of diabase that is quartz tholeiite, due to having normative quartz. It has been suggested that an original olivine tholeiite magma produced by partial melting in the mantle could have then differentiated at depths of 30–35 km into the high-alumina olivine tholeiite resembling the olivine diabase in most of the sills. However, if the same original olivine tholeiite magma fractionated at shallow crustal depths, a quartz-normative tholeiite magma would have been produced to be emplaced as quartz tholeiite diabase sills. Because the older basalt flows appear to have originally been olivine basalts, it is possible they were derived from the same olivine tholeiite magma that subsequently was intruded as the diabase sills. Emplacement of the diabase sills is thought to have been generally passive, as evidenced by the persistent planar strata above and below both thick and thin sills. Local small-scale folds and minor bedding-plane faults and thrusts found along and near discordant contacts indicate that some shouldering action took place in response to the intrusive activity. It is envisaged that the diabase magma welled up along feeder dikes and seeped out along bedding planes, inflating the tabular masses of strata by hydraulic action of the magma aided by the buoyancy of the host rocks compared to the denser diabase magma. At some localities, such as now exposed in the Salt River Canyon, continued flooding of the magma caused two or more infiltrations of the diabase to produce adjacent sills, or even sills intruded into other sills. Whether diabase magma inflation was relatively continuous (although episodic at a given locality), or was accomplished in several stages, is not known.

For the purposes of this present study both the Apache Group basalts and the diabase sills were sampled from road cuts along highways. The basalt flows between the algal and argillite members of the Mescal Limestone (Figure 35) were sampled in a road cut south of Globe, and near the wall of the Roosevelt Dam (Figure 34). At the latter location the full sequence of basalt flows was exposed and five samples were collected. Similarly, the basalt flows between the Mescal Limestone and Troy Quartzite (Figure 35) were found exposed in a road cut between the town of Superior and the Ray copper mine, and three samples were collected. Samples of diabase sills intruded into the Apache Group sedimentary strata and the Ruin Granite were sampled from road cuts on State Route 60 north of Globe. Three samples of diabase sills intruded into the Ruin Granite, a sample of a diabase sill intruded near the base of the Pioneer Shale, a sample of a diabase sill intruded into the lower member of the Mescal Limestone, and three samples of a diabase sill intruded into the Dripping Springs Quartzite, as well as samples of diabase dikes cross-cutting the Dripping Springs Quartzite and the Pioneer Shale, were collected. Additionally, twenty-three samples were collected on State Route 60's traverse from the Salt River up the north wall of the Salt River Canyon, where the sills are thick and multiple injections of diabase magma have occurred. These sills intrude between the lower cherty dolomite and algal members of the Mescal Limestone, and between the algal member of the Mescal Limestone and the overlying Devonian Martin Formation, the Troy

Quartzite being missing in this section [*Wrucke*, 1989].

A7. Brahma Schist Amphibolites, Grand Canyon

The east-west trending Grand Canyon transect presents spectacular exposures of the Lower Proterozoic (Paleoproterozoic) rocks that represent the crystalline basement under the Colorado Plateau [*Karlstrom et al.*, 2003]. In the Upper Granite Gorge, these rocks are continuously exposed from river mile 78 to 120, while there are discontinuous exposures in the Middle Granite Gorges from mile 127 to mile 137 (Figure 36) ([*Ilg et al.*, 1996; *Karlstrom et al.*, 2003]. *Powell* [1876] was the first to identify the Precambrian "granite" and "Grand Canyon schist." *Walcott* [1894] identified the Vishnu "terrane" as a complex of schist and gneiss. Subsequently, *Campbell and Maxson* [1938] identified different mappable units called the Vishnu "series" and Brahma "series" [*Maxson*, 1968]. However, Campbell and Maxson under-estimated the structural complexities and probably over-estimated the stratigraphic thickness when they proposed that the combined stratigraphic sequence of these metasedimentary and metavolcanic rocks was 8–16 km thick. This stratigraphic approach was called into question by *Ragan and Sheridan* [1970], and subsequently *Brown et al.* [1979] also emphasized the complex deformational features, so they lumped all of the metasedimentary and metavolcanic rocks together under the name "Vishnu Complex," the approach continued by *Babcock* [1990], who used the term "Vishnu Metamorphic Complex."

More recent detailed field mapping, based on the approach that recognizes the need to simultaneously pursue both tectonic and stratigraphic subdivisions of these Lower Proterozoic rocks, has resulted in a new geologic map (Figure 36) [*Ilg et al.*, 1996; *Karlstrom et al.*, 2003]. Thus, *Ilg et al.* [1996] and *Karlstrom et al.* [2003] have proposed the new name of Granite Gorge Metamorphic Suite for the entire sequence of metamorphosed volcanic and sedimentary rocks in the Grand Canyon. Furthermore, the new names assigned to the mappable rock units in the Upper and Middle Granite Gorges (Figure 36), as well as the Lower Granite Gorge, are Brahma Schist for the mafic metavolcanic rocks (after the Brahma "series" of *Campbell and Maxson* [1938]), the Rama Schist for the felsic metavolcanic rocks, and Vishnu Schist for the metamorphosed sedimentary rocks, as probably intended by *Walcott* [1894], recommended by *Noble and Hunter* [1916] (their Vishnu schist), and proposed by *Campbell and Maxson* [1938] (their Vishnu "series"). These metasedimentary and metavolcanic rocks of the Granite Gorge Metamorphic Suite make up about half of the exposed rocks in the Granite Gorges of Grand Canyon, the rest being intrusive rocks (granites, granodiorites, tonalites, and gabbros). Descriptive metamorphic rock names are used for the rocks seen in outcrop and in thin section, and the original sedimentary or volcanic "protoliths" are inferred from rock compositions and a limited number of primary structures that have survived the deposition and metamorphism. Primary structures such as relict pillows and graded bedding show that the original sedimentary rocks were locally deposited on a volcanic sequence, and that the mafic and felsic metavolcanic rocks are commonly interlayered. However, because similar volcanogenic sequences could have been deposited at different times or in separate basins, and such differences would be difficult to unravel due to the subsequent tectonism, this terminology can be considered mainly as lithologic, rather than necessarily stratigraphic.

The Rama Schist consists of quartzofeldspathic schist and gneiss with locally preserved phenocrysts of quartz and feldspar, and possible relict lapilli, that suggest a felsic to intermediate volcanic origin [*Ilg et al.*, 1996; *Karlstrom et al.*, 2003]. It is dominated by massive fine-grained quartzofeldspathic rocks, but also contains metarhyolites and interlayered micaceous quartzofeldspathic schists and gneisses. The Rama Schist is commonly complexly injected with pegmatite and contains leucocratic layers that may in part reflect preferential partial melting of these rocks due to the peak metamorphic conditions of about 720°C and 6 kbar [*Ilg et al.*, 1996; *Hawkins and Bowring*, 1999]. It is also locally interlayered with the mafic Brahma Schist.

The Brahma Schist consists of amphibolite, hornblende-biotite-plagioclase schist, biotite-plagioclase schist, orthoamphibole-bearing schist and gneiss, and metamorphosed sulfide deposits [*Ilg et al.*,

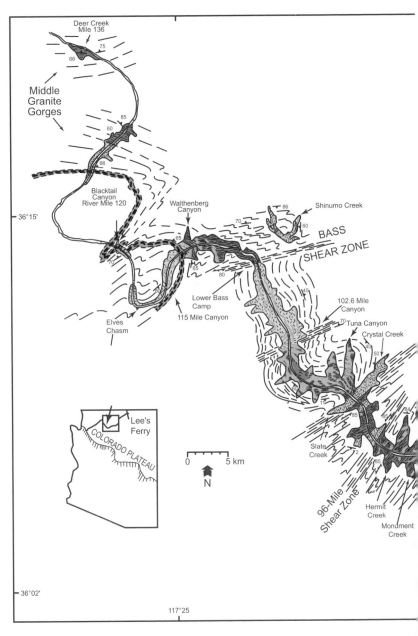

Figure 36. Simplified geologic map of Paleoproterozoic (Lower Proterozoic) rocks in the Upper and Middle Granite Gorges, Grand Canyon, northern Arizona (after *Ilg et al.* [1996]; *Karlstrom et al.*, [2003]). Form lines outside

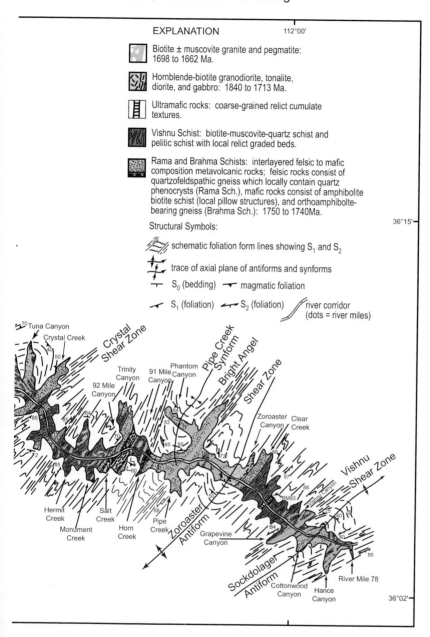

EXPLANATION

Biotite ± muscovite granite and pegmatite: 1698 to 1662 Ma.

Hornblende-biotite granodiorite, tonalite, diorite, and gabbro: 1840 to 1713 Ma.

Ultramafic rocks: coarse-grained relict cumulate textures.

Vishnu Schist: biotite-muscovite-quartz schist and pelitic schist with local relict graded beds.

Rama and Brahma Schists: interlayered felsic to mafic composition metavolcanic rocks; felsic rocks consist of quartzofeldspathic gneiss which locally contain quartz phenocrysts (Rama Sch.), mafic rocks consist of amphibolite biotite schist (local pillow structures), and orthoamphibolte-bearing gneiss (Brahma Sch.): 1750 to 1740Ma.

Structural Symbols:

schematic foliation form lines showing S_1 and S_2

trace of axial plane of antiforms and synforms

S_0 (bedding) magmatic foliation

S_1 (foliation) S_2 (foliation) river corridor (dots = river miles)

the Paleoproterozoic exposures show their interpretation of the trace of the regional foliation on the map surface. The transect is divided into metamorphic domains that are generally separated by shear zones.

1996]. The petrology and geochemistry of Brahma Schist amphibolites were studied by *Clark* [1978, 1979], who divided the amphibolites and mafic schists into five groups based on field occurrence and mineral assemblage: (1) anthophyllite-bearing and cordierite-anthophyllite-bearing rocks (orthoamphibole schist), (2) "early amphibolites," (3) the Granite Park mafic body (Lower Granite Gorge area), (4) hornblende-bearing dikes, and (5) tremolite-bearing dikes. *Ilg et al.* [1996] agreed with Clark's interpretation that the orthoamphibole-bearing (group 1) rocks are metamorphosed, hydrothermally altered, mafic marine volcanic rocks, and that the "early amphibolites" (group 2) are metamorphosed basalts and basaltic tuffs. Clark's groups 1 and 2 compose the supracrustal Brahma Schist, following *Campbell and Maxson's* [1938] original usage of the term.

Massive amphibolites (part of Clark's group 2) make up 30–40% of the Brahma Schist. This unit does not typically preserve primary igneous features, but relict pillow structures are present at a number of localities. Massive amphibolites occur in units several meters to tens of meters thick, and are composed of plagioclase and hornblende, plus subordinate quartz, biotite, clinopyroxene, and epidote (plus accessories) [*Clark*, 1978, 1979]. Furthermore, these massive amphibolites have a tholeiitic character and trace element compositions consistent with an island-arc environment. The biotite-plagioclase and hornblende-biotite-plagioclase schists (the remainder of Clark's group 2) make up approximately 50% of the Brahma Schist in the Upper Granite Gorge. Although strong tectonic layering has mostly obscured primary igneous textures, in several locations original textures are preserved, such as subangular quartz + plagioclase + biotite fragments entrained in an amphibolitic matrix, which suggests that some of these rocks may have been volcaniclastic breccias. Interlayered with the biotite schists are discontinuous meter-scale lenses of garnet + diopside + epidote + calcite rocks, the protoliths of these lenses possibly being relatively thin layers of calcareous shale or algal mats interbedded with submarine sediments [*Babcock*, 1990]. The Brahma Schist also contains exposures of orthoamphibole-bearing rocks (Clark's group 1) (Figure 36). They are interpreted to be hydrothermally altered, mafic marine volcanic rocks [*Vallance*, 1967]. The presence of relict pillow basalt, orthoamphibolite rocks, and associated sulfide mineralization indicates that the Brahma Schist was a product of dominantly mafic submarine volcanism. The Rama and Brahma metavolcanic schists can be complexly interlayered so that contact relationships support variable relative ages between mafic and intermediate metavolcanic rocks. However, in the Upper Granite Gorge, the Rama Schist is underneath and older than the Brahma Schist.

The Vishnu Schist consists of pelitic schist and quartz-biotite-muscovite schists that are interpreted as meta-lithic-arenites and metagreywackes (metamorphosed sandstones and mudstones), with numerous calc-silicate lenses and pods that are interpreted to be concretions [*Ilg et al.*, 1996; *Karlstrom et al.*, 2003]. Several-kilometer thick sections of meta-lithic-arenite and metagreywacke sequences exhibit rhythmic banded (centimeter- to meter-scale) coarser and finer layers, with locally well-preserved bedding and graded bedding [*Walcott*, 1894; *Brown et al.*, 1979] suggesting deposition as submarine turbidites. The original grain sizes in the Vishnu Schist metasedimentary rocks probably range from medium-grained sand to silt and clay, while conglomerates are conspicuously absent, all of which suggests a lack of high-energy proximal facies. The preserved relict graded bedding, association with metavolcanic rocks containing pillow structures, lack of coarse sediments, and geochemical data [*Babcock*, 1990] indicate that these Vishnu metasedimentary units were deposited in submarine conditions on the flanks of eroding oceanic islands (an oceanic island-arc environment). The preserved graded bedding indicates that the Vishnu Schist was deposited stratigraphically above the Brahma Schist, and the accessible exposures indicate that the contact between them is generally concordant, although there is some interlayering of the contact in some places.

For the purposes of this study twenty-seven Brahma Schist amphibolite samples were collected in the Upper and Middle Granite Gorges: (1) three samples from the Cottonwood Canyon area, (2) nine samples from the Clear Creek area, including seven samples from a single 50 m long and 2 m wide amphibolite body just upstream from the mouth of Clear Creek, (3) one sample from the Cremation Creek area, (4) one sample from near the mouth of Pipe Creek, (5) seven samples from outcrops just upstream of Blacktail Canyon, and (6) six samples from outcrops along the Colorado River between miles 126.5 and 129. All these locations are evident on Figure 36. The small tabular body of amphibolite near the mouth of Clear Creek was intensively sampled because it appeared to show mineralogical variation through its width, perhaps suggesting that it may have been a thin sill rather than a lava flow. Otherwise, all the other samples were of massive amphibolite. In the area just upstream of Blacktail Canyon, there was clear field evidence that the amphibolites represented a series of basaltic lava flows, there being well defined competent layers 3–10 m thick in succession along the outcrop separated by structural breaks accompanied by leaching of the rock (possibly paleoweathering), or in one instance by what appeared to be a thin inter-flow sandstone layer. That sequence of metamorphosed basalt flows was thus systematically sampled.

A8. Elves Chasm Granodiorite, Grand Canyon

All sedimentary and volcanic rocks must be deposited on some older substrate or "basement." However, such "basement" and its "sedimentary cover" often get detached from each other and tectonically interlayered during subsequent deformation, while high-grade metamorphism also obscures the nature of the origin sedimentary and volcanic protoliths, and the original contact relationships. Thus, *Noble and Hunter* [1916] posed this problem and speculated that some of the gneisses of the Grand Canyon might be basement for the schists. However, subsequent investigations recognized that the gneisses are deformed intrusive rocks [*Campbell and Maxson*, 1938; *Brown et al.*, 1979; *Babcock*, 1990]. Indeed, the Granite Gorge Metamorphic Suite is intruded by Lower Proterozoic (Paleoproterozoic) granitoid plutons, mafic dikes, and granitic pegmatite dike swarms that together make up about one-half of the crystalline rocks exposed in the Upper Granite Gorge (Figure 36). *Campbell and Maxson* [1938] thought there was a single major period of igneous "invasion," and this led to the convention of lumping all plutonic rocks of the Grand Canyon under a single name, the Zoroaster Gneiss. This name was subsequently changed to Zoroaster Granite by *Maxson* [1968], and then to the Zoroaster Plutonic Complex by *Babcock et al.* [1979]. However, new mapping by *Ilg et al.* [1996] and geochronology investigations [*Hawkins et al.*, 1996] have shown that these plutonic rocks represent a long and complex record of crustal development of the Grand Canyon crystalline basement. As such, these plutonic rocks range widely in conventional ages, in composition from gabbro to granite, in morphology from large plutons to stocks, dikes, and sills, and in tectonic significance.

However, early studies in the Grand Canyon suggested that the quartzofeldspathic Elves Chasm Gneiss and Trinity Gneiss were basement to the supracrustal rocks [*Noble and Hunter*, 1916]. On the other hand, *Babcock et al.* [1974, 1979] suggested that the Elves Chasm and the Trinity Gneisses were formed either by the "granitization" of Vishnu Schist or that they were orthogneisses (metamorphosed intrusives). Later, *Babcock* [1990] interpreted the Trinity Gneiss to be a metamorphosed sequence of interbedded dacitic to andesitic tuffs and flows and sedimentary strata deposited prior to deposition of the Vishnu sediments on top of them. Similarly, *Babcock* [1990] suggested that the orthoamphibole-bearing schist horizon identified by *Clark* [1978, 1979] could be interpreted as a paleosol (former soil horizon), and thus the Elves Chasm Gneiss might be the basement to the supracrustal Vishnu rocks. However, the new mapping by *Ilg et al.* [1996] and the geochronology investigations by *Hawkins et al.* [1996] have shown that the Trinity Gneiss is definitely not basement, but is intrusive into the Granite Gorge Metamorphic Suite. Whereas some layers do have geochemical signatures consistent with a sedimentary parentage [*Babcock*, 1990], they can be interpreted as screens of country rock because the Trinity Gneiss is clearly intrusive into some of them.

However, the Elves Chasm Gneiss is still interpreted as most likely being part of the basement on which the volcanics and sediments were deposited that were then metamorphosed to become the Granite Gorge Metamorphic Suite. Consistent with this interpretation, *Hawkins et al.* [1996] reported a 1840 Ma crystallization age for the Elves Chasm pluton and interpreted the Elves Chasm Gneiss as therefore an older granodioritic pluton. This conventional age makes the Elves Chasm Granodiorite the oldest rock known in the southwestern United States. The contact around this pluton, which based on radioisotope dating is much older than the Granite Gorge Metamorphic Suite and the plutons that intrude it, is tectonized, but is defined by the high-grade orthoamphibole-bearing gneiss horizon that is exposed adjacent to the Elves Chasm pluton in the Middle Granite Gorge (Figure 36). The contact is gradational over an interval of several meters between the foliated pluton and the distinctive orthoamphibole-bearing gneiss. This orthoamphibole-bearing gneiss suggests a zone of early alteration of the contact zone, possibly a metamorphosed and sheared paleosol as proposed by *Babcock* [1990], or possibly a zone of hydrothermal alteration of mafic marine volcanic rocks [*Vallance*, 1967]. The Elves Chasm pluton itself is dominantly hornblende-biotite tonalite to quartz diorite and is distinguished geochemically from other plutons in the Grand Canyon by its lower concentration of large ion lithophile elements (LILE) and its lower concentration of light rare earth elements relative to heavy rare earth elements [*Karlstrom et al.*, 2003].

Eight samples of the Elves Chasm pluton were collected from the outcrops along the river corridor between river miles 112.5 and 117.5 (Figure 36). Samples were carefully selected to be representative of mineralogical and rock type variations within the Elves Chasm pluton.

A9. Beartooth Andesitic Amphibolite, Wyoming

The Beartooth Mountains of southern Montana and northwestern Wyoming are a large uplifted block of Precambrian metasedimentary and metaigneous rocks [*Baadsgaard and Mueller*, 1973; *Mueller and Rogers*, 1973]. The predominant rock types are granitic gneisses and migmatites, but amphibolite, schist, quartzite, and ironstone occur in minor amounts in the southern Beartooth Mountains straddling the Montana-Wyoming border (Figure 37 inset). The amphibolites included in the granitic gneisses were originally interpreted as metamorphosed diabase dikes and small intrusions because of their mapped field

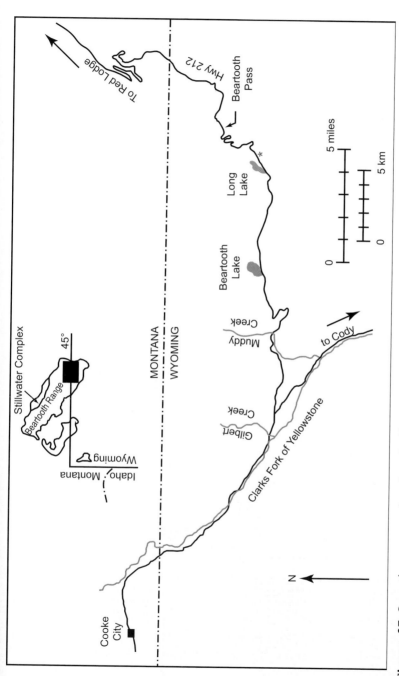

Figure 37. Location maps, showing the Beartooth Mountains of Montana and Wyoming (inset) and the Long Lake-Beartooth Pass area on U.S. Highway 212 (after *Baadsgaard and Mueller* [1973]; *Wooden et al.* [1982]). The location from which the andesitic amphibolite sample was collected is shown *.

relationships as long, narrow, dike-like bodies [*Baadsgaard and Mueller*, 1973]. These amphibolite bodies were easily recognized as older than the unmetamorphosed diabase dikes that clearly cross-cut all the older metamorphosed granitic and mafic rocks. Initial radioisotope dating of all these mafic rocks [*Baadsgaard and Mueller*, 1973] determined that the amphibolites (interpreted as metadiabase dikes) were Archean, whereas the unambiguous dikes of unmetamorphosed diabase were determined to be probably Middle Proterozoic. This distinction was also evidenced from petrographic and geochemical investigations [*Prinz*, 1964; *Mueller and Rogers*, 1973].

More recent detailed mapping and fieldwork, and petrological and geochemical investigations, have clarified the relationship between these amphibolites and the granitic rocks [*Warner et al.*, 1982; *Wooden et al.*, 1982]. Outcrops were examined and sampled along U. S. Highway 212 west of Beartooth Pass (Figure 37), and a small area beside the highway

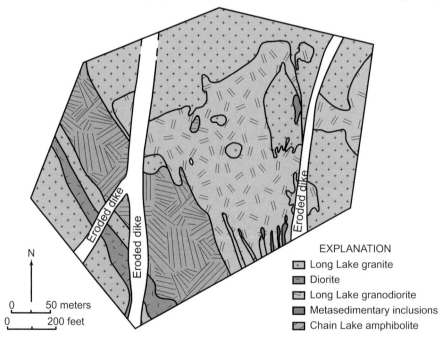

Figure 38. Simplified geologic map of an area adjacent to, and southeast of, Long Lake and U. S. Highway 212, southern Beartooth Mountains, Wyoming (after *Warner et al.* [1982]).

near Long Lake was mapped in detail to elucidate the relationships between the major rock types (Figure 38). The rock units mapped, described and informally named include a basaltic to dioritic unit referred to as the Chain Lake andesitic amphibolite, a series of foliated granitic to tonalitic rocks referred to as the Long Lake granodiorite, and a more massive leucocratic granitic to tonalitic unit referred to as the Long Lake granite. Unnamed diorite and metasedimentary units also occur in the mapped area. The Chain Lake andesitic amphibolite consists of quartz, plagioclase (oligoclase), biotite, and hornblende with accessory sphene (titanite), apatite, epidote, and magnetite with an equigranular texture. It is a metamorphic rock with quartz and plagioclase forming a matrix of equant crystals in which are set pencil-shaped aggregates of biotite and prisms of hornblende. The quartz-plagioclase net consists of approximately $300\,\mu m$ crystals in fine-grained samples, and approximately $2\,mm$ crystals in coarse-grained samples. Biotite aggregates and hornblende prisms have an aspect ratio between 1:3 and 1:4, with their short dimension approximately $100\,\mu m$ in fine-grained samples and approximately $500\,\mu m$ in coarse-grained samples. Hornblende is generally about twice as large as biotite. Grain boundaries are smooth or smoothly scalloped and tend to meet at $120°$ angles in triple junctions. The crystals do not display zoning. Biotite and hornblende prisms tend to be aligned in a parallel to subparallel array that reflects the hand sample and outcrop lineation. Banding, where present, is defined by variations in the mafic mineral content. This andesitic amphibolite has a relatively restricted composition, with SiO_2 between 55 and 61%, FeO (total) of between 5 and 10%, 2–5% MgO, 3–4% Na_2O, and 0.9–2.6% K_2O. Thus the major element composition is similar to that of many modern andesites, except for slightly lower Al_2O_3 contents. The composition of this andesitic amphibolite is thus very close to that of the original igneous rock and is not the result of alkali metasomatism of basaltic rocks as suggested by *Armbrustmacher and Simons* [1977]. The general homogeneity of the andesitic amphibolite's composition over a large geographic area, the preservation of igneous fractionation trends within the unit, and the survival of many amphibolites of basaltic composition in the same area support this conclusion [*Wooden et al.*, 1982].

This andesitic amphibolite is the dominant type of inclusion in the foliated granitic rocks in the central and southeastern Beartooth Mountains [*Wooden et al.*, 1982]. There has been some chemical interaction between the andesitic amphibolites and the foliated granites, with the most common example being the introduction of small (1–5 cm) leucocratic veins into the andesitic amphibolite. There is no obvious evidence of any major metasomatic reaction whereby the andesitic amphibolite could have been produced by interaction between rocks of original basaltic composition and a component of the foliated granites. The andesitic amphibolite is generally well foliated and, as indicated by examination of thin sections, has textures that indicate recrystallization. The interpretation of this andesitic amphibolite unit is that it is definitely older than the foliated granites, and this is confirmed by the field observations which indicate that the andesitic amphibolite has been intruded by the Long Lake granodiorite, which in turn has been intruded by the Long Lake granite [*Warner et al.*, 1982]. It has had a more extensive metamorphic-deformational history, its original igneous character being transformed to a metamorphic texture by later deformations. Mineral analyses [*Warner et al.*, 1982] suggest final equilibration temperatures of approximately 400°C, a temperature equivalent to metamorphism at the epidote-amphibolite facies, which is confirmed by the presence of epidote in most samples of it. *Wooden et al.* [1982] plotted a composite Rb-Sr isochron for samples of the Long Lake granite, Long Lake granodiorite, and this andesitic amphibolite, which yielded an isochron "age" of 2790±35 Ma. However, they suggested that the Rb-Sr data for the andesitic amphibolite indicated a maximum age of 3100–3000 Ma, and a minimum age of 2800 Ma corresponding to its intrusion by the Long Lake granite. This "age" for the andesitic amphibolite places it among some of the oldest rocks in the continental U. S. A.

A sample of this andesitic amphibolite unit was collected from a prominent outcrop in a road cut on U. S. Highway 212, west of Beartooth Pass, 1.3 km east-northeast of Long Lake (Figure 37). The outcrop sampled is on the east side of the highway, where it has been exposed by a deep excavation engineered for the highway. Subsequent careful laboratory work to separate the rock into its constituent minerals enabled its mineral composition to be determined as quartz and plagioclase (oligoclase) about 71% of the rock, biotite about 17%, hornblende about 7%, magnetite about 3%, and titanite about 2%.

References

Albarède, F., Time-dependent models of U-Th-He and K-Ar evolution and the layering of mantle convection, *Chemical Geology, 145*, 413–429, 1998.

Alibert, A., and F. Albarède, Isotope and trace element geochemistry of the Colorado Plateau volcanics, *Geochimica et Cosmochimica Acta, 50*, 2735–2750, 1986.

Allègre, C. J., Isotope geodynamics, *Earth and Planetary Science Letters, 86*, 175–203, 1987.

Allègre, C. J., S. R. Hart, and J.-F. Minster, Chemical structure and evolution of the mantle and continents determined by inversion of Nd and Sr isotopic data, I. Theoretical models, *Earth and Planetary Science Letters, 66*, 177–190, 1983a.

Allègre, C. J., S. R. Hart, and J.-F. Minster, Chemical structure and evolution of the mantle and continents determined by inversion of Nd and Sr isotopic data, II. Numerical experiments and discussion, *Earth and Planetary Science Letters, 66*, 191–213, 1983b.

Allègre, C. J., A. Hofmann, and R. K. O'Nions, The argon constraints on mantle structure, *Geophysical Research Letters, 23*, 3555–3557, 1996.

Allègre, C. J., E. Lewin, and B. Dupre, A coherent crust-mantle model for the uranium-thorium-lead isotope system, *Chemical Geology, 70*, 211–234, 1988.

Armbrustmacher, T. J., and F. S. Simons, Geochemistry of amphibolites from the central Beartooth Mountains, Montana-Wyoming, *U. S. Geological Survey Journal of Research, 5*, 53–60, 1977.

Austin, S. A., Isotope and trace element analysis of hypersthene-normative basalts from the Quaternary of Uinkaret Plateau, western Grand Canyon, *Geological Society of America, Abstracts with Programs, 27*(7), A261, 1992.

Austin, S. A. (editor), *Grand Canyon: Monument to Catastrophe*, Institute for Creation Research, Santee, California, 1994.

Austin, S. A., Excess argon within mineral concentrates from the new dacite lava dome at Mount St Helens volcano, *Creation Ex Nihilo Technical Journal*, *10*(3), 335–343, 1996.

Austin, S. A., Mineral isochron method applied as a test of the assumptions of radioisotope dating, in *Radioisotopes and the Age of the Earth: A Young-Earth Creationist Research Initiative*, edited by L. Vardiman, A. A. Snelling, and E. F. Chaffin, pp. 95–121, Institute for Creation Research, El Cajon, California, and Creation Research Society, St. Joseph, Missouri, 2000.

Austin, S. A., Do radioisotope clocks need repair? Testing the assumptions of isochron dating using K-Ar, Rb-Sr, Sm-Nd, and Pb-Pb isotopes, in *Radioisotopes and the Age of the Earth: Results of a Young-Earth Creationist Research Initiative*, edited by L. Vardiman, A. A. Snelling, and E. F. Chaffin, pp. 325–392, Institute for Creation Research, El Cajon, California, and Creation Research Society, Chino Valley, Arizona, 2005.

Austin, S. A., and A. A. Snelling, Discordant potassium-argon model and isochron 'ages' for Cardenas Basalt (Middle Proterozoic) and associated diabase of eastern Grand Canyon, Arizona, in *Proceedings of the Fourth International Conference on Creationism*, edited by R. E. Walsh, pp. 35–51, Creation Science Fellowship, Pittsburgh, Pennsylvania, 1998.

Austin, S. A., J. R. Baumgardner, D. R. Humphreys, A. A. Snelling, L. Vardiman, and K. P. Wise, Catastrophic plate tectonics: a global flood model of earth history, in *Proceedings of the Third International Conference on Creationism*, edited by R. E. Walsh, pp. 609–621, Creation Science Fellowship, Pittsburgh, Pennsylvania, 1994.

Baadsgaard, H., and P. A. Mueller, K-Ar and Rb-Sr ages of intrusive Precambrian mafic rocks, southern Beartooth Mountains, Montana and Wyoming, *Geological Society of America Bulletin*, *84*(11), 3635–3644, 1973.

Babcock, R. S., Precambrian crystalline core, in *Grand Canyon Geology*, first edition, edited by S. S. Beus and M. Morales, pp. 11–28, Oxford University Press, New York, and Museum of Northern Arizona Press, Flagstaff, Arizona, 1990.

Babcock, R. S., E. H. Brown, and M. D. Clark, Geology of the older Precambrian rocks of the Upper Granite Gorge of the Grand Canyon, *Geology of the Grand Canyon*, edited by W. S. Breed, pp. 2–10, Grand Canyon Natural History Association, Grand Canyon, Arizona, 1974.

Babcock, R. S., E. H. Brown, M. D. Clark, and D. E. Livingston, Geology of the older Precambrian rocks of the Grand Canyon: Part II. The Zoroaster Plutonic Complex and related rocks, *Precambrian Research, 8*, 243–275, 1979.

Battey, M. H., The recent eruption of Ngauruhoe, *Records of the Auckland Institute and Museum, 3*, 389–395, 1949.

Baumgardner, J. R., Computer modeling of the large-scale tectonics associated with the Genesis Flood, in *Proceedings of the Third International Conference on Creationism*, edited by R. E. Walsh, pp. 49–62, Creation Science Fellowship, Pittsburgh, Pennsylvania, 1994a.

Baumgardner, J. R., Runaway subduction as the driving mechanism for the Genesis Flood, in *Proceedings of the Third International Conference on Creationism*, edited by R. E. Walsh, pp. 63–75, Creation Science Fellowship, Pittsburgh, Pennsylvania, 1994b.

Baumgardner, J. R., Distribution of radioactive isotopes in the earth, in *Radioisotopes and the Age of the Earth: A Young-Earth Creationist Research Initiative*, edited by L. Vardiman, A. A. Snelling, and E. F. Chaffin, pp. 49–94, Institute for Creation Research, El Cajon, California, and Creation Research Society, St. Joseph, Missouri, 2000.

Baumgardner, J. R., Catastrophic plate tectonics: the physics behind the Genesis Flood, in *Proceedings of the Fifth International Conference on Creationism*, edited by R. L. Ivey, Jr., pp. 113–126, Creation Science Fellowship, Pittsburgh, Pennsylvania, 2003.

Bergquist, J. R., A. F. Shride, and C. T. Wrucke, *Geologic Map of the Sierra Ancha Wilderness and Salome Study Area, Gila County, Arizona*, U. S. Geological Survey, Miscellaneous Field Studies Map MF-1162A, Scale 1:48,000, 1981.

Best, M. G., and W. H. Brimhall, Late Cenozoic alkali basaltic magmas in the western Colorado Plateau and the Basin and Range Transition Zone, U. S. A., and their bearing on mantle dynamics, *Geological Society of America Bulletin, 85*, 1677–1690, 1974.

Bhattacharji, S., Scale model experiments on flowage differentiation in sills, in *Ultramafic and Related Rocks*, edited by J. Wyllie, pp. 69–70, John Wiley & Sons, New York, 1967.

Bhattacharji, S., and C. H. Smith, Flowage differentiation, *Science, 145*, 150–153, 1964.

Billingsley, G. H., and P. W. Huntoon, *Geologic Map of Vulcan's Throne and Vicinity, Western Grand Canyon, Arizona*, Grand Canyon Natural History Association, Grand Canyon, Arizona, scale 1:48,000, 1983.

Boyd, S. W., Statistical determination of genre in Biblical Hebrew: evidence for a historical reading of Genesis 1:1–2:3, in *Radioisotopes and the Age of the Earth: Results of a Young-Earth Creationist Research Initiative*, edited by L. Vardiman, A. A. Snelling, and E. F. Chaffin, pp. 631–734, Institute for Creation Research, El Cajon, California, and Creation Research Society, Chino Valley, Arizona, 2005.

Brooks, C., S. R. Hart, A. Hofmann, and D. E. James, Rb-Sr mantle isochrons from oceanic regions, *Earth and Planetary Science Letters, 32*, 51–61, 1976a.

Brooks, C., D. E. James, and S. R. Hart, Ancient lithosphere: its role in young continental volcanism, *Science, 193*, 1086–1094, 1976b.

Brown, E. H., R. S. Babcock, M. D. Clark, and D. E. Livingston, Geology of the older Precambrian rocks of the Grand Canyon: Part I. Petrology and structure of the Vishnu Complex, *Precambrian Research, 8*, 219–241, 1979.

Campbell, I., and J. H. Maxson, Geological studies of the Archean rocks at Grand Canyon, *Carnegie Institution of Washington Year Book, 37*, 359–364, 1938.

Clark, M. D., Amphibolitic rocks from the Precambrian of Grand Canyon: mineral chemistry and phase petrology, *Mineralogical Magazine, 42*, 199–207, 1978.

Clark, M. D., Geology of the older Precambrian rocks of the Grand Canyon: Part 3. Petrology of mafic schists and amphibolites, *Precambrian Research, 8*, 277–302, 1979.

Clark, R. H., Petrology of the volcanic rocks of Tongariro subdivision, in *The Geology of the Tongariro Subdivision*, D. R. Gregg, New Zealand Geological Survey Bulletin, n.s. 40, 107–123, 1960.

Cole, J. W., Andesites of the Tongariro Volcanic Centre, North Island, New Zealand, *Journal of Volcanology and Geothermal Research, 3*, 121–153, 1978.

Cole, J. W., K. V. Cashman, and P. C. Rankin, Rare-earth element geochemistry and the origin of andesites and basalts of the Taupo Volcanic Zone, New Zealand, *Chemical Geology, 38*, 255–274, 1983.

Cole, J. W., I. J. Graham, W. R. Hackett, and B. F. Houghton, Volcanology and petrology of the Quaternary composite volcanoes of Tongariro Volcanic Centre, Taupo Volcanic Zone, in *Late Cenozoic Volcanism in New Zealand*, edited by I. E. M. Smith, pp. 224–250, Royal Society of New Zealand, Bulletin 23, 1986.

Dalrymple, G. B., *The Age of the Earth*, Stanford University Press, Stanford, California, 1991.

Dalrymple, G. B., and W. K. Hamblin, K-Ar ages of Pleistocene lava dams in the Grand Canyon, Arizona, *Proceedings of the National Academy of Sciences USA, 95*, 9744–9749, 1998.

Dalrymple, G. B., and M. A. Lanphere, *Potassium-Argon Dating: Principles, Techniques and Applications to Geochronology*, W. H. Freeman, San Francisco, 1969.

Damon, P. E., and J. L. Kulp, Excess helium and argon in beryl and other minerals, *American Mineralogist, 43*, 433–459, 1958.

Davies, G. F., Geophysically constrained mantle mass flows and the ^{40}Ar budget: a degassed lower mantle?, *Earth and Planetary Science Letters, 166*, 149–162, 1999.

Davies, J. H., and G. J. Stevenson, Physical model of source region of subduction volcanics, *Journal of Geophysical Research, 97*, 2037–2070, 1992.

Dickin, A. P., *Radiogenic Isotope Geology*, Cambridge University Press, Cambridge, England, 1995.

Doe, B. R., and R. E. Zartman, Plumbotectonics, in *Geochemistry of Hydrothermal Ore Deposits*, second edition, edited by H. L. Barnes, pp. 22–70, John Wiley & Sons, New York, 1979.

Elston, D. P., Magnetostratigraphy of Late Proterozoic Chuar Group and Sixtymile Formation, Grand Canyon Supergroup, Northern Arizona: correlation with other Proterozoic strata of North America, *Geological*

Society of America, Abstracts with Programs (Rocky Mountain Section), *18*, 353, 1986.

Elston, D.P., Grand Canyon Supergroup, northern Arizona: stratigraphic summary and preliminary paleomagnetic correlation with parts of other North American Proterozoic sessions, in *Geologic Evolution of Arizona*, edited by J.P. Jenney and S.J. Reynolds, pp. 259–272, Arizona Geological Society, Tucson, Digest 17, 1989.

Elston, D.P., and C.S. Grommé, Precambrian polar wandering from Unkar Group and Nankoweap Formation, eastern Grand Canyon, Arizona, in *Geology of Northern Arizona*, edited by T.N.V. Karlstrom, J.A. Swann, and R.L. Eastwood, pp. 97–117, Geological Society of America, Rocky Mountain Sectional Meeting, Flagstaff, Arizona, 1974.

Elston, D.P., and E.H. McKee, Age and correlation of the Late Proterozoic Grand Canyon disturbance, northern Arizona, *Geological Society of America Bulletin, 93*, 681–699, 1982.

Ewart, A., and J.J. Stipp, Petrogenesis of the volcanic rocks of the central North Island, New Zealand, as indicated by a study of $^{87}Sr/^{86}Sr$ ratios, and Sr, Rb, K, U and Th abundances, *Geochimica et Cosmochimica Acta, 32*, 699–736, 1968.

Fitton, J.G., Petrology and geochemistry of Late Cenozoic basalt flows, western Grand Canyon, Arizona, in *Geology of Grand Canyon, Northern Arizona (with Colorado River Guides)*, edited by D.P. Elston, G.H. Billingsley, and R.A. Young, pp. 186–189, American Geophysical Union, Washington, DC, 1989.

Fitton, J.G., D. James, P.D. Kempton, D.S. Ormerod, and W.P. Leeman, The role of lithospheric mantle in the generation of Late Cenozoic basic magmas in the western United States, *Journal of Petrology, Special Lithosphere Issue*, 331–349, 1988.

Galer, S.J.G., and R.K. O'Nions, Residence time of thorium, uranium and lead in the mantle with implications for mantle convection, *Nature, 316*, 778–782, 1985.

Gamble, J.A., J.D. Woodhead, I. Wright, and I. Smith, Basalt and sediment geochemistry and magma petrogenesis in a transect from ocean island arc to rifted continental margin arc: the Kermadec-Hikurangi margin, S.W. Pacific, *Journal of Petrology, 37*(6), 1523–1546, 1996.

Gastil, R. G., Late Precambrian volcanism in southeastern Arizona, *American Journal of Science, 252,* 436–440, 1954.

Gill, J. B., *Orogenic Andesites and Plate Tectonics,* Springer-Verlag, Berlin, 1981.

Graham, I. J., and W. R. Hackett, Petrology of calc-alkaline lavas from Ruapehu volcano and related vents, Taupo Volcanic Zone, New Zealand, *Journal of Petrology, 28*(3), 531–567, 1987.

Graham, I. J., J. W. Cole, R. M. Briggs, J. A. Gamble, and I. E. M. Smith, Petrology and petrogenesis of volcanic rocks from the Taupo Volcanic Zone: a review, *Journal of Volcanology and Geothermal Research, 68,* 59–87, 1995.

Graham, I. J., B. L. Gulson, J. W. Hedenquist, and K. Mizon, Petrogenesis of Late Cenozoic volcanic rocks from the Taupo Volcanic Zone, New Zealand, in the light of new Pb isotope data, *Geochimica et Cosmochimica Acta, 56,* 2797–2819, 1992.

Gregg, D. R., Eruption of Ngauruhoe 1954–55, *New Zealand Journal of Science and Technology, B37,* 675–688, 1956.

Gregg, D. R., *The Geology of Tongariro Subdivision,* New Zealand Geological Survey Bulletin, n.s. 40, 1960.

Grindley, G. W., Tongariro National Park: stratigraphy and structure, *New Zealand Department of Scientific and Industrial Research Information Series, 50,* 79–86, 1965.

Hackett, W. R., and B. F. Houghton, Active composite volcanoes of Taupo Volcanic Zone, in *Central North Island Volcanism,* New Zealand Geological Survey, Record 21, pp. 61–114, 1987.

Hackett, W. R., and B. F. Houghton, A facies model for a Quaternary andesitic composite volcano: Ruapehu, New Zealand, *Bulletin of Volcanology, 51,* 51–68, 1989.

Hamblin, W. K., Pleistocene volcanic rocks of the western Grand Canyon, Arizona, in *Geology of Grand Canyon, Northern Arizona (with Colorado River Guides),* edited by D. P. Elston, G. H. Billingsley, and R. A. Young, pp. 190–204, American Geophysical Union, Washington, DC, 1989.

Hamblin, W. K., Late Cenozoic lava dams in the western Grand Canyon, in *Grand Canyon Geology,* first edition, edited by S. S. Beus and M. Morales, pp. 385–433, Oxford University Press, New York, and Museum of Northern

Arizona Press, Flagstaff, Arizona, 1990.

Hamblin, W.K., *Late Cenozoic Lava Dams in the Western Grand Canyon*, Geological Society of America, Memoir 183, 1994.

Hamblin, W.K., Late Cenozoic lava dams in the western Grand Canyon, in *Grand Canyon Geology*, second edition, edited by S.S. Beus and M. Morales, pp. 313–345, Oxford University Press, New York, 2003.

Hawkins, D.P., and S.A. Bowring, U-Pb monazite, xenotime and titanite geochronological constraints on the prograde to post-peak metamorphic thermal history of Paleoproterozoic migmatites from the Grand Canyon, Arizona, *Contributions to Mineralogy and Petrology, 134*, 150–169, 1999.

Hawkins, D.P., S.A. Bowring, B.R. Ilg, K.E. Karlstrom, and M.L. Williams, U-Pb geochronological constraints on the Paleoproterozoic crustal evolution of the Upper Granite Gorge, Grand Canyon, Arizona, *Geological Society of America Bulletin, 108*(9), 1167–1181, 1996.

Hendricks, J.D., Petrology and chemistry of igneous rocks of Middle Proterozoic Unkar Group, Grand Canyon Supergroup, Northern Arizona, in *Geology of the Grand Canyon, Northern Arizona (with Colorado River Guides)*, edited by D.P. Elston, G.H. Billingsley, and R.A. Young, pp. 106–116, American Geophysical Union, Washington, DC, 1989.

Hendricks, J.D., and I. Lucchitta, Upper Precambrian igneous rocks of the Grand Canyon, Arizona, in *Geology of Northern Arizona*, edited by T.N.V. Karlstrom, G.A. Swann, and R.L. Eastwood, pp. 65–86, Geological Society of America, Rocky Mountain Sectional Meeting, Flagstaff, 1974.

Hendricks, J.D., and G.M. Stevenson, Grand Canyon Supergroup: Unkar Group, in *Grand Canyon Geology*, first edition, edited by S.S. Beus and M. Morales, pp. 29–47, Oxford University Press, New York, and Museum of Northern Arizona Press, Flagstaff, Arizona, 1990.

Hendricks, J.D., and G.M. Stevenson, Grand Canyon Supergroup: Unkar Group, in *Grand Canyon Geology*, second edition, edited by S.S. Beus and M. Morales, pp. 39–52, Oxford University Press, New York, 2003.

Humphreys, D.R., Accelerated nuclear decay: a viable hypothesis?, in *Radioisotopes and the Age of the Earth: A Young-Earth Creationist Research Initiative*, edited by L. Vardiman, A.A. Snelling, and E.F. Chaffin, pp. 333–379, Institute for Creation Research, El Cajon, California, and Creation Research Society, St. Joseph, Missouri, 2000.

Humphreys, D. R., Young helium diffusion age of zircons supports accelerated decay, in *Radioisotopes and the Age of the Earth: Results of a Young-Earth Creationist Research Initiative*, edited by L. Vardiman, A. A. Snelling, and E. F. Chaffin, pp. 25–100, Institute for Creation Research, El Cajon, California, and Creation Research Society, Chino Valley, Arizona, 2005.

Humphreys, D. R., S. A. Austin, J. R. Baumgardner, and A. A. Snelling, Helium diffusion rates support accelerated nuclear decay, in *Proceedings of the Fifth International Conference on Creationism*, edited by R. L. Ivey, Jr., pp. 175–195, Creation Science Fellowship, Pittsburgh, Pennsylvania, 2003a.

Humphreys, D. R., S. A. Austin, J. R. Baumgardner, and A. A. Snelling, Recently measured helium diffusion rate for zircon suggests inconsistency with U-Pb age for Fenton Hill granodiorite, *EOS, Transactions of the American Geophysical Union, 84*(46), Fall Meeting Supplement, Abstract V32C-1047, 2003b.

Humphreys, D. R., S. A. Austin, J. R. Baumgardner, and A. A. Snelling, Helium diffusion age of 6000 years supports accelerated nuclear decay, *Creation Research Society Quarterly, 41*, 1–16, 2004.

Ilg, B. R., K. E. Karlstrom, D. P. Hawkins, and M. L. Williams, Tectonic evolution of Paleoproterozoic rocks in the Grand Canyon: insights into middle-crustal processes, *Geological Society of America Bulletin, 108*(9), 1149–1166, 1996.

Irvine, P. N., Terminology for layered intrusions, *Journal of Petrology, 23*, 127–162, 1982.

Karlstrom, K. E., B. R. Ilg, M. L. Williams, D. P. Hawkins, S. A. Bowring, and S. J. Seaman, Paleoproterozoic rocks of the Granite Gorges, in *Grand Canyon Geology*, second edition, edited by S. S. Beus and M. Morales, pp. 9–38, Oxford University Press, New York, 2003.

Koons, D. E., Geology of the Uinkaret Plateau, northern Arizona, *Geological Society of America Bulletin, 56*, 151–180, 1945.

Kramers, J. D., and I. N. Tolstikhin, Two terrestrial lead isotope paradoxes, forward transport modeling, core formation and the history of the continental crust, *Chemical Geology, 139*, 75–110, 1997.

Larson, E. E., P. E. Patterson, and F. E. Mutschler, Lithology, chemistry, age and origin of the Proterozoic Cardenas Basalt, Grand Canyon, Arizona,

Precambrian Research, 65, 255–276, 1994.

Leeman, W.P., Late Cenozoic alkali-rich basalt from the western Grand Canyon area, Utah and Arizona: isotopic composition of strontium, *Geological Society of America Bulletin, 85*, 1691–1696, 1974.

Leeman, W.P., Tectonic and magmatic significant of strontium isotopic variations in Cenozoic volcanic rocks from the western United States, *Geological Society of America Bulletin, 93*, 487–503, 1982.

Lucchitta, I., and J.D. Hendricks, Characteristics, depositional environment, and tectonic interpretations of the Proterozoic Cardenas Lavas, eastern Grand Canyon, Arizona, *Geology, 11*(3), 177–181, 1983.

Ludwig, K.R., *Isoplot/Ex (Version 2.49): The Geochronological Toolkit for Microsoft Excel*, University of California Berkeley, Berkeley Geochronology Center, Special Publication No. 1a, 2001.

Mathison, C.I., *Variation in the Somerset Dam Layered Basic Complex*, Unpublished B.Sc. Honours Thesis, University of Queensland, Brisbane, 1964.

Mathison, C.I., The Somerset Dam layered basic intrusion, south-eastern Queensland, *Journal of the Geological Society of Australia, 14*(1), 57–86, 1967.

Mathison, C.I., *The Somerset Dam Layered Basic Intrusion*, Unpublished Ph.D. Thesis, University of Queensland, Brisbane, 1970.

Mathison, C.I., Magnetites and ilmenites in the Somerset Dam layered basic intrusion, south-eastern Queensland, *Lithos, 8*, 93–111, 1975.

Mathison, C.I., Cyclic units in the Somerset Dam layered gabbro intrusion, south-eastern Queensland, Australia, *Lithos, 20*, 187–205, 1987.

Maxson, J.H., Lava flows in the Grand Canyon of the Colorado River, Arizona, *Geological Society of America Bulletin, 61*, 9–16, 1949.

Maxson, J.H., *Geologic Map of the Bright Angel Quadrangle, Grand Canyon National Park, Arizona*, revised, Grand Canyon Natural History Association, Grand Canyon, Arizona, scale 1:48,000, 1968.

McConnell, R.L., Preliminary report of microstructures of probable biologic origin from the Mescal Formation (Proterozoic) of central Arizona, *Precambrian Research, 1*, 227–234, 1974.

McKee, E.D., W.K. Hamblin, and P.E. Damon, K-Ar age of lava dam in Grand Canyon, *Geological Society of America Bulletin, 79*, 133–136, 1968.

McKee, E. D., and E. T. Schenk, The lower canyon lavas and related features at Toroweap in Grand Canyon, *Journal of Geomorphology, 5,* 245–273, 1942.

Mortimer, N., and D. Parkinson, Hikurangi Plateau: a Cretaceous large igneous province in the southwest Pacific Ocean, *Journal of Geophysical Research, 161,* 687–696, 1996.

Mueller, P. A., and J. J. W. Rogers, Secular chemical variation in a series of Precambrian mafic rocks Beartooth Mountains, Montana and Wyoming, *Geological Society of America Bulletin, 84*(11), 3645–3652, 1973.

Mukasa, S. B., A. H. Wilson, and R. W. Carlson, A multielement geochronologic study of the Great Dyke, Zimbabwe: significance of the robust and reset ages, *Earth and Planetary Science Letters, 164,* 353–369, 1998.

Murphy, D. T., B. S. Kamber, and K. D. Collerson, A refined solution to the first terrestrial Pb-isotope paradox, *Journal of Petrology, 44,* 39–53, 2003.

Naeser, C. W., I. R. Duddy, D. P. Elston, T. A. Dumitru, and P. F. Green, Fission-track dating: ages for Cambrian strata and Laramide and post-Middle Eocene cooling events from the Grand Canyon, Arizona, in *Geology of Grand Canyon, Northern Arizona (with Colorado River Guides),* edited by D. P. Elston, G. H. Billingsley, and R. A. Young, pp. 139–144, American Geophysical Union, Washington, DC, 1989.

Nägler, T. F., and J. D. Kramers, Nd isotope evolution of the upper mantle during the Precambrian: models, data and the uncertainty of both, *Precambrian Research, 91,* 233–252, 1998.

Nairn, I. A., Atmospheric shock waves and condensation clouds from Ngauruhoe explosive eruptions, *Nature, 259,* 190–192, 1976.

Nairn, I. A., C. A. Y. Hewson, J. H. Latter, and C. P. Wood, Pyroclastic eruptions of Ngauruhoe volcano, central North Island, New Zealand, 1974 January and March, in *Volcanism in Australasia,* edited by R. W. Johnson, pp. 385–405, Elsevier, Amsterdam, 1976.

Nairn, I. A., and S. Self, Explosive eruptions and pyroclastic avalanches from Ngauruhoe in February 1975, *Journal of Volcanology and Geothermal Research, 3,* 39–60, 1978.

Nairn, I. A., and C. P. Wood, Active volcanoes of Taupo Volcanic Zone, in *Active Volcanoes and Geothermal Systems, Taupo Volcanic Zone,* New Zealand Geological Survey, Record 22, pp. 5–84, 1987.

Nehru, C. E., and M. Prinz, Petrologic study of the Sierra Ancha sill complex, Arizona, *Geological Society of America Bulletin, 81*(6), 1733–1766, 1970.

Noble, L. F., The Shinumo quadrangle, Grand Canyon district, Arizona, *U. S. Geological Survey, Bulletin 549*, 1914.

Noble, L. F., and J. F. Hunter, Reconnaissance of the Archean Complex of the Granite Gorge, Grand Canyon, Arizona, *U. S. Geological Survey, Professional Paper 98-I*, 95–113, 1916.

Oberthür, T., D. W. Davis, T. G. Blenkinsop, and A. Höhndorf, Precise U-Pb mineral ages, Rb-Sr and Sm-Nd systematics for the Great Dyke, Zimbabwe—constraints on Late Archean events in Zimbabwe craton and Limpopo belt, *Precambrian Research, 113*, 293–305, 2002.

O'Nions, R. K., and I. N. Tolstikhin, Limits on the mass flux between lower and upper mantle and stability of layering, *Earth and Planetary Science Letters, 139*, 213–222, 1996.

Phipps Morgan, J., Thermal and rare gas evolution of the mantle, *Chemical Geology, 145*, 431–445, 1998.

Phipps Morgan, J., and W. J. Morgan, Two-stage melting and the geochemical evolution of the mantle: a recipe for mantle plum-pudding, *Earth and Planetary Science Letters, 170*, 215–239, 1999.

Poitrasson, F., C. Pin, and J.-L. Duthou, Hydrothermal remobilization of rare earth elements and its effects on Nd isotopes in rhyolite and granite, *Earth and Planetary Science Letters, 30*, 1–11, 1995.

Powell, J. W., *Exploration of the Colorado River of the West*, Smithsonian Institution, Washington, DC, 1876.

Prinz, M., Geologic evolution of the Beartooth Mountains, Montana and Wyoming: Part V. Mafic dike swarms of the southern Beartooth Mountains, *Geological Society of America Bulletin, 75*, 1217–1248, 1964.

Ragan, D. N., and M. F. Sheridan, The Archean rocks of the Grand Canyon, Arizona, *Geological Society of America, Abstracts with Programs, 2*(2), 132–133, 1970.

Rugg, S. H., and S. A. Austin, Evidences for rapid formation and failure of Pleistocene "lava dams" of the western Grand Canyon, Arizona, in *Proceedings of the Fourth International Conference on Creationism*, edited by R. E. Walsh, pp. 475–486, Creation Science Fellowship, Pittsburgh, Pennsylvania, 1998.

Shride, A. F., Younger Precambrian geology in southern Arizona, *U. S. Geological Survey, Professional Paper 566*, 1967.

Simkin, T., Flow differentiation in the picritic sills of North Skye, in *Ultramafic and Related Rocks*, edited by P. J. Wyllie, pp. 64–69, John Wiley & Sons, New York, 1967.

Smith, D., Mineralogy and petrology of the diabasic rocks in a differentiated olivine diabase sill complex, Sierra Ancha, Arizona, *Contributions to Mineralogy and Petrology, 27*, 95–113, 1970.

Smith, D., and L. T. Silver, Potassic granophyre associated with Precambrian diabase, Sierra Ancha, central Arizona, *Geological Society of America Bulletin, 86*, 503–513, 1975.

Snelling, A. A., The cause of anomalous potassium-argon "ages" for recent andesite flows at Mt Ngauruhoe, New Zealand, and the implications for potassium-argon "dating," in *Proceedings of the Fourth International Conference on Creationism*, edited by R. E. Walsh, pp. 503–525, Creation Science Fellowship, Pittsburgh, Pennsylvania, 1998.

Snelling, A. A., Geochemical processes in the mantle and crust, in *Radioisotopes and the Age of the Earth: A Young-Earth Creationist Initiative*, edited by L. Vardiman, A. A. Snelling, and E. F. Chaffin, pp. 123–304, Institute for Creation Research, El Cajon, California, and Creation Research Society, St. Joseph, Missouri, 2000a.

Snelling, A. A., Radiohalos, in *Radioisotopes and the Age of the Earth: A Young-Earth Creationist Research Initiative*, edited by L. Vardiman, A. A. Snelling, and E. F. Chaffin, pp. 381–468, Institute for Creation Research, El Cajon, California, and Creation Research Society, St. Joseph, Missouri, 2000b.

Snelling, A. A., The relevance of Rb-Sr, Sm-Nd and Pb-Pb isotope systematics to elucidation of the genesis and history of recent andesite flows at Mt Ngauruhoe, New Zealand, and the implications for radioisotopic dating, in *Proceedings of the Fifth International Conference on Creationism*, edited by R.L. Ivey, Jr., pp. 285–303, Creation Science Fellowship, Pittsburgh, Pennsylvania, 2003a.

Snelling, A. A., Whole-rock K-Ar model and isochron, and Rb-Sr, Sm-Nd and Pb-Pb isochron, "dating" of the Somerset Dam layered mafic intrusion, Australia, in *Proceedings of the Fifth International Conference on Creationism*, edited by R. L. Ivey., Jr, pp. 305–324, Creation Science Fellowship, Pittsburgh, Pennsylvania, 2003b.

Snelling, A. A., Radiohalos in granites: evidence for accelerated nuclear decay, in *Radioisotopes and the Age of the Earth: Results of a Young-Earth Creationist Research Initiative*, edited by L. Vardiman, A. A. Snelling, and E. F. Chaffin, pp. 101–207, Institute for Creation Research, El Cajon, California, and Creation Research Society, Chino Valley, Arizona, 2005a.

Snelling, A. A., Fission tracks in zircons: evidence for abundant nuclear decay, in *Radioisotopes and the Age of the Earth: Results of a Young-Earth Creationist Research Initiative*, edited by L. Vardiman, A. A. Snelling, and E. F. Chaffin, pp. 209–324, Institute for Creation Research, El Cajon, California, and Creation Research Society, Chino Valley, Arizona, 2005b.

Snelling, A. A., and M. H. Armitage, Radiohalos—a tale of three granitic plutons, in *Proceedings of the Fifth International Conference on Creationism*, edited by R. L. Ivey, Jr., pp. 243–267, Creation Science Fellowship, Pittsburgh, Pennsylvania, 2003.

Snelling, A. A., S. A. Austin, and W. A. Hoesch, Radioisotopes in the diabase sill (Upper Precambrian) at Bass Rapids, Grand Canyon, Arizona: an application and test of the isochron dating method, in *Proceedings of the Fifth International Conference on Creationism*, edited by R. L. Ivey, Jr., pp. 269–284, Creation Science Fellowship, Pittsburgh, Pennsylvania, 2003a.

Snelling, A. A., J. R. Baumgardner, and L. Vardiman, Abundant Po radiohalos in Phanerozoic granites and timescale implications for their formation, *EOS, Transactions of the American Geophysical Union, 84*(46), Fall Meeting Supplement, Abstract V32C-1046, 2003b.

Steiner, A., Petrogenetic implications of the 1954 Ngauruhoe lava and its xenoliths, *New Zealand Journal of Geology and Geophysics, 1*, 325–363, 1958.

Sun, S. S., and G. N. Hansen, Evolution of the mantle: geochemical evidence from alkali basalt, *Geology, 3*, 297–302, 1975.

Tatsumi, Y., Formation of the volcanic front in subduction zones, *Geophysical Research Letters, 13*, 717–720, 1986.

Taylor, T. M., N. W. Jones, and S. Moorbath, Isotopic assessment of relative contributions from crust and mantle sources to magma genesis of

Precambrian granitoid rocks, *Philosophical Transactions of the Royal Society of London, A310*, 605–625, 1984.

Tiexeira, W., P. R. Renne, G. Bossi, N. Campal, and M. S. D'Agrella Filho, [40]Ar-[39]Ar and Rb-Sr geochronology of the Uruguayan dike swarm, Rio de la Plata craton and implications for Proterozoic intraplate activity in western Gondwana, *Precambrian Research, 93*, 153–180, 1999.

Topping, W. W., Tephrostratigraphy and chronology of Late Quaternary eruptives from the Tongariro Volcanic Centre, New Zealand, *New Zealand Journal of Geology and Geophysics, 16*, 397–423, 1973.

Vallance, T. G., Mafic rock alteration and isochemical development of some cordierite-anthophyllite rocks, *Journal of Petrology, 8*, 84–96, 1967.

Van Keken, P. E., E. H. Hauri, and C. J. Ballentine, Mantle mixing: the generation, preservation and destruction of chemical heterogeneity, *Annual Review of Earth and Planetary Sciences, 30*, 493–525, 2002.

Wager, L. R., G. M. Brown, and W. J. Wadsworth, Types of igneous cumulates, *Journal of Petrology, 1*, 73–85, 1960.

Walcott, C. D., Precambrian igneous rocks of the Unkar Terrane, Grand Canyon of the Colorado, *U. S. Geological Survey, 14th Annual Report for 1892/93, Part 2*, 497–519, 1894.

Walker, F., The differentiation of the Palisade diabase, New Jersey, *Geological Society of America Bulletin, 51*, 1059–1106, 1940.

Walker, T. B., *The Somerset Dam Igneous Complex, South-East Queensland*, Unpublished B.Sc. Honours Thesis, The University of Queensland, Brisbane, 1998.

Warner, J. L., R. Lee-Berman, and G. H. Simonds, Field and petrologic relations of some Archean rocks near Long Lake, eastern Beartooth Mountains, Montana and Wyoming, in *Precambrian Geology of the Beartooth Mountains, Montana and Wyoming*, compiled by P. A. Mueller and J. L. Wooden, pp. 56–68, Montana Bureau of Mines and Geology, Special Publication 84, 1982.

Williams, K., *Volcanoes of the South Wind: A Field Guide to the Volcanoes and Landscape of the Tongariro National Park*, Tongariro Natural History Society, Turangi, New Zealand, 1994.

Wooden, J. L., P. A. Mueller, D. K. Hunt, and D. R. Bowes, Geochemistry and Rb-Sr geochronology of Archean rocks from the interior of the southeastern

Beartooth Mountains, Montana and Wyoming, in *Precambrian Geology of the Beartooth Mountains, Montana and Wyoming*, compiled by P.A. Mueller and J.L. Wooden, pp.45–55, Montana Bureau of Mines and Geology, Special Publication 84, 1982.

Wrucke, C.T., The Middle Proterozoic Apache Group, Troy Quartzite and associated diabase in Arizona, in *Geologic Evolution of Arizona*, edited by J.P. Jenney and S.J. Reynolds, pp.239–258, Arizona Geological Society, Tucson, Digest 17, 1989.

York, D., Least squares fitting of a straight line with correlated errors, *Earth and Planetary Science Letters, 5*, 320–324, 1969.

Zartman, R.E., and S.M. Haines, The plumbotectonic model for Pb isotopic systematics among major terrestrial reservoirs—a case for bidirectional transport, *Geochimica et Cosmochimica Acta, 52*, 1327–1339, 1988.

Zhao, J., and M.T. McCulloch, Sm-Nd mineral isochron ages of late Proterozoic dyke swarms in Australia: evidence for two distinctive events of magma magmatism and crustal extension, *Chemical Geology, 109*, 341–354, 1993.

Zheng, Y.-F., Influences of the nature of the initial Rb-Sr system on isochron validity, *Chemical Geology, 80*, 1–16, 1989.

Zindler, A., and S.R. Hart, Chemical geodynamics, *Annual Review of Earth and Planetary Sciences, 14*, 493–571, 1986.

Chapter 7

Accelerated Decay: Theoretical Considerations

Eugene F. Chaffin, Ph.D.*

Abstract. I discuss the possibility of variation of coupling constants and particle masses within modern physics. Quantum mechanical calculations are presented giving the decay constant for α-decay and its variation with depth of the nuclear potential well. Concrete, numerical approaches are considered for the possible variation of the Fermi constant and strong coupling constant over the history of the earth. The dependence of forbidden β-decays on the decay energies is considered as a mechanism which affects the sensitivity of the half-life to changes in coupling constants. For double β-decay data, evidence from experimental data for ⁸²Se, gathered from both geochemical and direct laboratory detection methods, is considered which indicates possible accelerated decay episodes. In addition, data from the Oklo natural reactor are considered as to whether they constrain the possible variation of half-lives.

1. Introduction

The subject of *accelerated* radioactive decay is the study of the possibility that radioisotope half-lives had smaller values earlier in history than today. This chapter will concern itself mainly with physical ideas which may serve as viable models of accelerated decay. In recent times, new understandings of mathematics and physics have enabled reasons and explanations to be given in particle physics which had not been previously possible. Attempting to take advantage of these new descriptive capabilities, we wish to consider the possibility that modern quantum theory, field theory, Kaluza-Klein theory, and string theory

* *Physics Department, Bob Jones University, Greenville, South Carolina*

may prove relevant to the age of the earth question. Various concepts from these theories lead to possible mechanisms for changing half-lives. One of these concepts is the idea that gravitational, electromagnetic, weak nuclear, and strong nuclear forces may fit into a single theoretical framework. In field theory, a Feynman diagram is used to facilitate the construction of expressions for probabilities of various particle reaction processes. For each vertex of the Feynman diagram, a coupling constant is inserted, depending on the type of interaction taking place at that vertex. In this chapter we will advance the hypothesis that the coupling constants for the strong and possibly the weak force are actually not constants but variables. We shall point out many instances in the scientific literature where physicists have considered this as a real possibility. In order to avoid confusion about which terms we are actually describing, we shall continue to call these quantities constants even though they are being considered as variables. Because they are variables, rates of nuclear decay may vary over time and actually shrink the timescale that is indicated by isotopic abundance measurements.

Alpha decay, in modern theory, is described in terms of tunneling of a preformed α-particle out through a barrier which classical physics forbids it to cross. In a preliminary section of this chapter, we will consider this theory, plus an assumption that the strength of the nuclear force could change during Creation week, during the Flood year, or at various other points in history. We shall see that changes in the number of nodes in α-particle wavefunctions are very important in determining half-lives. If the age of the earth is measured in thousands rather than billions of years, then how does one explain the isotopic abundances of, for example, U, as found in geologic samples? If half-lives have varied over earth history, then nuclear physics must be altered in some way, and the altered theories could lead to new explanations for the isotopic abundance variations with time [*Chaffin*, 2000a,b, 2001]. We shall spend a section examining the concept of radioactive equilibrium in this light, and also a section on the Oklo natural reactor and the constraints it provides on the variations. Then some of the mathematical aspects of string theory will be discussed and the relations of diameter and shapes of compactified extra dimensions to the values of gauge coupling constants, Yukawa coupling constants, and particle masses. It will be hypothesized that the electron mass is constant and that changes in the electromagnetic force have been minimal; changes in the proton mass have been relatively small but probably not zero, whereas changes in the strong coupling constant have been large. Reasons will be given why the weak interaction coupling constant may also have changed, but not as much as the strong coupling constant. As a possible experimental support for these ideas, we will end by discussing forbidden β-decays and double β-decays.

2. Alpha-Decay and Variation of the Nuclear Force Strength

Historically, the numerical treatment of α-decay has relied on quantum mechanics and the tunneling theory [*Preston*, 1947; *Pierronne and Marquez*, 1978]. Figure 1 shows the usual scheme where the potential felt by an α-particle is modeled by a square well for the interior of the nucleus and a Coulomb repulsion outside. For heavy nuclei, the well depth appropriate for an α-particle is over 100 MeV [*Pierronne and Marquez*, 1978; *Buck et al.*, 1990, 1992]. Classically, a particle could

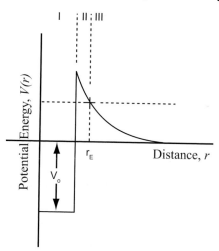

Figure 1. The square-well potential with Coulomb barrier. *V(r)* is the potential energy of the α-particle due to the nucleus, and *r* is the distance from the nuclear center.

not occupy region II of the figure. When a particle is in region II it is under the barrier and thus has a large positive potential energy. Thus it would have to have negative kinetic energy in order to have the same total energy of only a few MeV as when it escapes to infinity. However, a wave such as that used in quantum theory can leak through, even though a particle would have a negative kinetic energy for radius less than the r_E value shown in the figure.

Although the changes in physical "constants" suggested in recent physics literature are very small [*Chaffin*, 2000b], α-decay rates are very sensitive to small changes in well depths or well shapes. *Chaffin* [1994, 2003] discussed results of a numerical study, using a simple computer program, which allowed the depth of the nuclear potential well to vary. The radius of the nucleus and the depth of the potential well represent two variables which are tied to the energy of the emitted α-particle and the decay constant. In this simple model a constraint is needed, which may be taken to be the approximate constancy of radioactive halo radii [*Gentry*, 1986; *Chaffin*, 1994, 2000b; *Humphreys*, 2000; *Snelling*, 2000]. If the energy of the α-particle is held constant, then the halo radius will also be constant. Since the radius of a halo ring is slightly dependent on the dose of radiation and the size of the halo inclusions, an exact constraint on the α-particle energy cannot be maintained. For a 5 MeV change in the potential well depth, with the α-energy held exactly constant the computer program showed that the decay constant will change by only one power of ten. If the α-energy is allowed to change by 10% or so, then the decay constant changes by about 10^5. If the accelerated decay needed to explain the data is restricted to about one year or so, then a change in the decay constant of 10^9 or so may be required [*DeYoung*, 2000]. Thus these considerations seemed to indicate that a one-year episode of accelerated decay at the time of the Flood may not be enough.

To test the variability of the decay constant, the computer program mentioned above, which was a Fortran program, was rewritten using *Mathematica*, a very powerful, modern software package which facilitates numerical work of this sort. For the square well potential on the inside of the nucleus, the *Mathematica* notebook gave essentially the same answers as the earlier work. In collaboration with Gothard and Tuttle [*Chaffin et al.*, 2001], Chaffin modified the notebook to use a harmonic oscillator potential for the interior region, where the nuclear potential is felt by the α-particle. In the course of this work, it was discovered that, as the nuclear potential well depth is changed, and the nuclear radius changes slightly, it is possible to have a sudden change in the number of nodes of the real part of the α-particle's wavefunction (Figure 2). This was modeled for both the harmonic oscillator and square well potentials, with nearly the same results for either notebook.

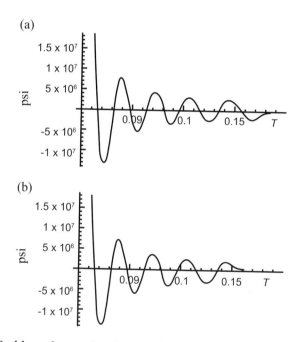

Figure 2. Sudden change in the number of nodes (zero crossings). The harmonic oscillator wavefunction for well depths of 58 MeV (a) and 54 MeV (b). The *x*-axis is the radial coordinate of the α-particle, $T=\rho/(2\eta)$, where ρ and η are defined in *Green and Lee* [1955]. Figure 2a shows the harmonic oscillator wave function for a well depth of 58 MeV. Figure 2b shows what happens when the well depth is changed to 54 MeV, without changing the α-particle energy. If one counts the number of nodes in Figure 2a, there are nine, not counting the ones at zero and infinity. For Figure 2b, there are eight nodes, a reduction by one.

Eugene F. Chaffin

The change in the number of nodes causes the probability of tunneling to change by about a factor of ten, as shown by the discontinuity in the graph of Figure 3. Tunneling probabilities depend on the size of the wavefunction at infinity. The two graphs of Figure 2a, b show the wavefunction decreasing to zero at infinity. The x-axis shows a dimensionless variable T (defined in [*Fröberg*, 1955]), whose size represents the distance from the nucleus. The graph appears to decrease to near zero for large distances from the nucleus. However, the probability of α-decay for a nucleus such as ^{238}U is very low, hence the wavefunction will have small oscillation of both its real and imaginary parts, too small to show on this scale. Figure 4 shows a plot of the real part of the wavefunction for well depth parameter of 54 MeV, produced with *Mathematica* simulations. This plot (Figure 4) shows only the wavefunction outside the nucleus, because the scale needed to be changed to show the very small oscillations found there is too small to see on Figure 2. Such very small oscillations would be typical of a nucleus which has a very long half-life.

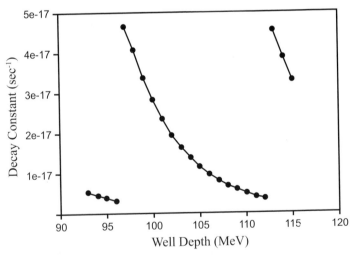

Figure 3. The decay constant versus well depth for the harmonic oscillator interior potential. The graph shows a discontinuity, which occurs when the wavefunction changes the number of nodes as the radius slowly increases.

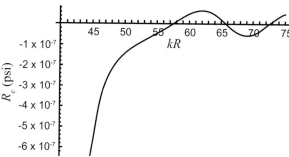

Figure 4. The real part of the Coulombic wavefunction outside the Coulomb barrier. The oscillatory behavior shows that the probability of escape is not zero for the α-particle. The x-axis is the dimensionless radial coordinate $\rho = kR$. The equations needed to give a precise definition of ρ are given in *Green and Lee* [1955] or *Fröberg* [1955].

The use of potentials with a sharp boundary between the interior and exterior of the nucleus is not realistic. Consequently, in collaboration with Banks [*Chaffin and Banks*, 2002], a *Mathematica* notebook was written to use the exponentially diffuse boundary square well for the interior of the nucleus. This interior potential was originally investigated in a classic work by *Green and Lee* [1955], although they did not apply it to α-decay. Figure 5 shows the potential well and the corresponding wavefunction for this case.

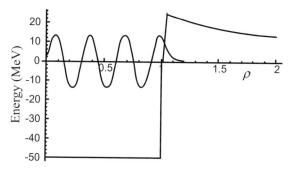

Figure 5. The exponentially diffuse boundary potential and the corresponding wavefunction. The vertical axis is energy in MeV and the horizontal axis is the radius ρ, in units where 1 is about ten fermis (one fermi is the same as one femtometer or 10^{-15} m). For the wavefunction, the vertical axis is the real part of the wavefunction scaled by a factor of ten.

The use of this potential allows the potential energy to increase gradually as the distance increases outward and the nuclear force yields to the Coulomb repulsion. The treatment is somewhat complicated, in that now the wavefunction is a spherical Bessel function in the interior of the well, whose logarithmic derivative is matched to a Bessel function of non-integral order in the changeover (or barrier) region, and then to a Coulomb wavefunction for the exterior region. The non-integral order of the wavefunction is a decimal fraction which is determined from the matching by iterative procedure [*Chaffin and Banks*, 2002]. There is now an interior radius for the changeover region, as well as an exterior radius. Either one can be varied to see what the effect is. In the case of the square well potential with sharp edges, the uncertainty in the radii of ancient radiohalos led to an uncertainty in the α-particle emission energies. For the square well potential, it was found that if the α-energy is allowed to change by 10% or so, then the decay constant changes by about 10^5. For the diffuse boundary potential, it is found that variations in the decay constant of the order of magnitude of 10^5 to 10^8 occur in some cases for a small change in the well depth parameter, when the number of nodes in the wavefunction changes. Thus this is about what we obtained for the simpler cases of the square well or harmonic oscillator well, when the α-particle energy was varied, but now the diffuse boundary allows such variations without changes in α-energy. More specifically, when the well depth was 96 MeV the *Mathematica* notebook runs showed a change from $\lambda = 2.4 \times 10^{-4} \mathrm{s}^{-1}$ to $7.98 \times 10^{-12} \mathrm{s}^{-1}$ when the number of nodes changed from thirteen to twelve.

In these calculations I have tried to use realistic values of the nuclear parameters. However, when we are considering these hypothetical changes in the nuclear force in ancient times, it is not a matter of fitting data that has been measured in a modern laboratory, but instead one must consider a range of possible parameters. Modern scattering data [*Gils and Rebel*, 1976] show that the nuclear potential in a heavy nucleus drops to zero within a distance of about two fermis. Hence the diffuseness of the nuclear surface must reflect a variation of this order of magnitude and not a bigger one.

Experimental data on α-particle and heavy ion scattering [*Wildermuth and McClure*, 1966; *Anyas-Weiss et al.*, 1974; *DeVries et al.*, 1975; *Buck*, 1976; *Davies et al.*, 1976] have long been known to validate a cluster model in which an α-particle moves in the average field provided by the rest of the nucleus. Four-nucleon transfer reactions were observed on target nuclei that are the daughters of an α-emitter. The comparison of reaction rates with the corresponding α-decay rates indicates the tendency for the four transferred particles to form a true α-particle. The data give evidence that nodes in the α-particle wavefunction do in fact exist. When the nuclear potential seen by the α-particle is represented by a square well, the effect of changing the depth of the well is to change the α-particle wavefunction. Usually this change is slight, but at certain critical values the number of nodes in the wavefunction can change precipitously, with a corresponding change of more than an order of magnitude in the decay constant.

One might ask whether the α-particle wavefunction, when the α-particle is first formed in the nucleus, might be better represented by a Gaussian wavefunction with no nodes rather than an eigenstate of the approximate potential of the α-particle due to the rest of the nucleus? This could cause the α-particle wavefunction to change progressively in a manner somewhat different than that advocated here, perhaps even causing departures from exponential decay. However, such a treatment would ignore the very large transition rates between a Gaussian wavefunction and the eigenstates. For instance, *Shankar* [1994] in chapter 18 of his **Quantum Mechanics** book has discussed the inadequacy of a treatment of spontaneous decay which ignores the quantum nature of the electromagnetic field.

The depth of the nuclear potential well is determined directly by the strength of the strong nuclear force, hence by the "strong coupling constant." A coupling constant is a number inserted in a theory to fix the strength of a force. We determine it experimentally, but theories exist which indicate that it may not be a constant over the history of the universe. Hence, we will discuss the relevant parts of these theories in other sections of this chapter.

3. Isotopic Distributions of U

Uranium isotopes ^{238}U, ^{235}U, and ^{234}U occur in the percent abundances of 99.27%, 0.72%, and 0.0055%, with other isotopes only occurring in trace amounts. The half-lives of these isotopes are 4.47×10^9 years for ^{238}U, 7.04×10^8 years for ^{235}U, and 2.47×10^5 years for ^{234}U. A condition known as *radioactive equilibrium* occurs when the activities of successive members of a decay chain are equal. The activity is defined as the decay constant (which is the natural logarithm of two divided by the half-life) times the number of atoms in the sample.

Figure 6 shows an analogy between fluid flow and the decay of the atoms in the ^{238}U to ^{234}U series. The level of the fluid in a bucket is a result of a balance between the rate of inflow and the rate of outflow. For a given level of fluid in the bucket, a proportional amount of pressure is produced at the bottom of the bucket, where the valves are

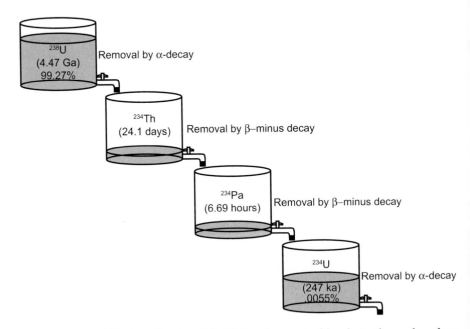

Figure 6. Equilibrium levels of fluid flowing out of buckets through valves that are not opened to the same setting. This forms an analogy to radioactive equilibrium of the ^{238}U decay series.

located. This is analogous to the amounts of radioactive parent atom present. However, the rate of decay also depends on how wide open the valve is, which is analogous to the half-life. The most probable decay mode of ^{238}U is α-decay, which produces ^{234}Th. Thorium-234 undergoes β minus decay with a half-life of 24.1 days, producing ^{234}Pa. Protactinium-234 then also undergoes β minus decay with a half-life of 6.69 hours producing ^{234}U. Thus ^{234}U is in the decay chain of ^{238}U, and radioactive equilibrium does exist because 0.0055 times the decay constant of ^{234}U is the same as 99.27 times the decay constant of ^{238}U. Departures from radioactive equilibrium exist in some samples [*Thurber*, 1962; *Chalov et al.*, 1966; *Chalov and Merkulova*, 1966, 1968] but the departures are relatively small.

The variations may possibly be explained in terms of the difference in relative solubility of ^{234}U and ^{238}U starting from hexavalent and tetravalent U in compounds and their decomposition products [*Chalov and Merkulova*, 1966; 1968]. Thus, a fraction of the ^{234}U atoms present in a mineral lattice will have formed by radioactive decay starting from ^{238}U. Due to the recoil of a nucleus during α-decay, a significant number of daughter nuclei will lose their former link with the mineral lattice. These daughter ^{234}U nuclei will as a result be, on the average, found in different linkages as compared to the ^{238}U nuclei. This was Chalov and Merkulova's explanation for why they found different rates of dissolution of ^{234}U and ^{238}U in their laboratory experiments. Working together with Tuzova, Chalov and Merkulova attempted to use this difference in solubility to obtain an age of the Aral Sea (southern Kazakhstan and northern Uzbekistan) [*Chalov et al.*, 1996]. Their result was 150±30 ka. However, some fragile assumptions were needed to arrive at this number, and such ages are not well accepted even among evolutionists.

From a young-earth viewpoint, it is easy to point to these fragile assumptions to invalidate age determinations such as those just mentioned. However, with an earth of only some thousands of years old, it is difficult to explain the bulk of the approximately equal ratios without an episode of accelerated decay. Starting from an arbitrary initial state, it takes more than one half-life of ^{234}U to establish equilibrium, implying an age of the samples very much larger than straightforward Biblical interpretation would indicate.

Figure 7 shows the graph of the ^{234}U abundance versus time, assuming the ^{234}U starts with a 100% abundance, or was equal in abundance to that of ^{238}U. One sees that, for this starting assumption, and assuming no accelerated decay, an age of the earth of at least four million years is implied. A possible alternative assumption is to assume that there was no ^{234}U at all at the start.

Figure 8 shows the result of that calculation. Assuming no accelerated decay, this assumption thus implies an earth age of at least 1.2 million years.

To justify the young-earth viewpoint, one would be logically correct in claiming that the rocks may have been created already in a state of radioactive equilibrium, with no time needed to reach that state. However, a more natural explanation seems to be provided by accelerated radioactive decay. We do not know the original ratio of ^{234}U to ^{238}U in the created materials of the early earth, but if we make some reasonable guesses, then a period of accelerated decay would adjust this ratio to the 0.0055% ratio presently found in the bulk of earth

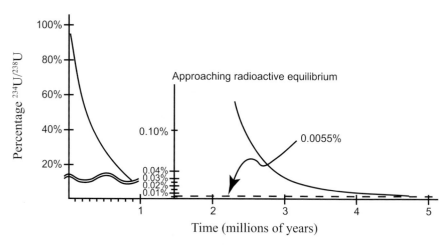

Figure 7. The percentage ^{234}U/^{238}U as a function of time, assuming that ^{234}U/^{238}U begins at 100%. The timescale shown assumes that no accelerated decay occurred.

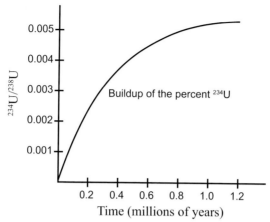

Figure 8. The percentage $^{234}U/^{238}U$ as a function of time, assuming that it begins at 0%.

materials. This may be evidence that such accelerated decay did, in fact, occur. Furthermore, by the time of the end of the acceleration episode, radioactive equilibrium would have been in existence, and decay rates of U much smaller, possibly even zero. It could even be that the decays of ^{234}U and ^{238}U were accelerated by different amounts, as long as the ratios of their decay rates approached the present-day values late in the episode. This would ensure that the 0.0055% value was reached. The intermediate stages in the path from ^{238}U to ^{234}U involve the relatively short half-lives of the β-decays of ^{234}Th and ^{234}Pa. Thus, acceleration of these intermediate stages produces a negligible effect, since they are already almost instantaneous on the timescales of interest.

The ^{235}U abundance, compared to ^{238}U, also seems to support this point of view. If the initial abundances of these two isotopes were of the same order of magnitude, then several half lives of ^{235}U are needed to establish the present 0.72% and 99.27% isotopic abundances, implying sample ages of a few billion years [*Chaffin*, 1985]. As in the ^{234}U cases, we do find slight variations in ^{235}U percent abundances between different minerals collected at different sites (see for example [*Malyshev et al.*, 1977]). However, the variations are small. To advocate a young earth without accelerated decay or very rapid initial decay after the creation of the elements, one seems forced to assume that the U isotopes were created in isotopic percent abundances approximating those found today [*Chaffin*, 1985].

4. The Oklo Data—A Constraint on Accelerated Decay?

In 1976, a Russian physicist published a letter to *Nature* which pointed out the relevance of the Oklo data to constraining possible variations of the nuclear force over the history of the earth [*Shlyakhter*, 1976]. More detailed discussions of the problem have since been published by other authors [*Damour and Dyson*, 1996; *Fujii et al.*, 2000]. Along with Molgaard, I have also done some recent work on the subject [*Chaffin and Molgaard*, 2003]. Oklo is a location in Gabon, Africa where some French scientists discovered more than a dozen reaction zones. In these zones fission product elements and depleted U led to the inescapable conclusion that former nuclear reactors existed in this Precambrian geological formation. The formations have been fitted into a Precambrian interpretation according to uniformitarian ideas about the geological setting, and would correspond to an age of about 2 billion years on the uniformitarian timescale. The abundances of ^{149}Sm, ^{238}U, and other isotopes have been measured in core samples. A development by *Fujii et al.* [2000] leads to the equation:

$$\frac{N_{147}(t_1) + N_{148}(t_1)}{N_{149}(t_1)} =$$

$$\frac{\dfrac{\sigma_{f235} k Y_{147}}{\sigma_a}\left[1 - exp\left(\sigma_a \phi t_1\right)\right] + \left(R_{147}^{nat} + R_{148}^{nat}\right)}{\dfrac{k\sigma_{f235} Y_{149}}{\sigma_a - \sigma_{149}}\left[exp\left(-\sigma_{149}\phi t_1\right) - exp\left(-\sigma_a \phi t_1\right)\right] + R_{149}^{nat} exp\left(-\sigma_{149}\phi t_1\right)} \quad (1)$$

In the equation, $N(t)$ represents the measured isotopic abundances of the various Sm isotopes indicated by the subscripts, the σ values are the present-day cross-sections of the isotopes for absorption (a) or fission (f), the Y values are the fractional fission yields, the R values are the relative fractional natural abundances of the Sm isotopes, and t is the time. For more details, see the paper by *Fujii et al.* [2000]. It happens that the cross-section for absorption of neutrons by ^{149}Sm has a very large resonance peak at $E_r = 0.0958325$ eV. If this peak's position had shifted by more than about 0.01 eV, the calculated Sm cross-section would no longer match the data [*Chaffin and Molgaard*, 2003]. It cannot be ruled out, however, that two or more factors may have changed concurrently, causing one factor to cancel out the effect of the other. In any case, the Oklo data may indicate that coupling strengths could not have been too much different from today's values at the time of the reactions.

Table 1, column 2, shows the values of the effective cross-section σ_{149} which satisfies the above equation (1). These values were found by *Chaffin and Molgaard* [2003] by an iterative procedure using *Mathematica*. Column 3 shows the results of *Fujii et al.* [2000] for comparison. The results were obtained using data for Oklo reactor zone 10. One sees that the various samples give an average value of 90.3 ± 7.4 kilobarns (1 barn $= 10^{-24}$ cm^2). Here the 7.4 kilobarns is the standard deviation of the four sample results.

Table 1. Results of calculations for Oklo samples.

Sample	σ_{149} (kb)	Fujii *et al.* Results
SF84-1492	98.1	99.0
SF84-1485	83.0	83.8
SF84-1480	95.0	96.5
SF84-1469	85.0	85.6
Standard Deviation	7.4	7.6
Average	90.3	91.2

In a simple nuclear model in which a square well is used for the potential seen by the neutron inside the nucleus, the ^{149}Sm cross-section is related to the depth V_0 of the potential well. As *Weber et al.* [1982] showed, the resonant energy E_r is a constant minus V_0. Hence, a change in the nuclear force coupling constant is equivalent to a change in V_0, which is equivalent to a change in E_r. An adequate model for the ^{149}Sm neutron absorption cross-section as a function of energy is given by the Breit-Wigner shape:

$$\sigma_r = A \frac{\Gamma_n \Gamma_r}{\left(E - E_r\right)^2 + \Gamma_{tot}^2/4} \tag{2}$$

In this expression the widths Γ do not depend directly on the depth V_0 of the potential well, so the spread in values of 7.4 kilobarns can be related to a spread in values of V_0. For ^{149}Sm, E_r is 0.095835 eV, hence calculations show that a change of 7.4 kilobarns in σ_r corresponds to a change in E_r of ±0.0102 eV.

Assuming that the change in the nuclear force is due to a change in the strong coupling constant, a change in E_r of ±0.0102 eV for ^{149}Sm would correspond to a change of the same order of magnitude in the V_0 for the ^{238}U. For ^{238}U, the half-life for α-decay is 4.47×10^9 years and the V_0 is 110.5 MeV.

As discussed earlier, and represented in Figure 3, slight changes in the depth of the nuclear potential can cause a precipitous change in the α-decay half-life. The precipitous change is due to the change in the number of nodes in the α-particle wavefunction. This can cause a change in the decay constant λ by a factor of 13.5, or more than one order of magnitude. Hence, the Oklo data do provide a constraint on the difference in the half-life at the time of the Oklo reactions and the present. Half-life differences of more than one order of magnitude would seem to be ruled out, unless two or more factors may have changed concurrently, with each effect canceling the other. Since the Oklo rocks are interpreted as Precambrian this brings up the question of when the reactions may have occurred. They could have occurred long after the deposition had occurred, but since the deposits are sedimentary it seems unlikely that they could have been from early in Creation week.

In *Chaffin* [2000b] it was pointed out that radiohalos provide a constraint on possible variations in the energies of α-particles emitted in radioactive decay. *Gentry* [1986] has pointed out the constancy of the halo radii gathered from various geologic strata. Since the radii of halo rings are slightly dependent on the dose of radiation and the size of halo inclusions, an exact constraint on the α-particle energy cannot be maintained. Using the variable well depth models proposed here (discussed in Section 2), it is possible to show that, relaxing the requirement of exactly the same halo radii, a change in α-particle emission energy of 10% or so corresponds to a change in decay constant by a factor of about 10^5. Using a more realistic diffuse boundary potential, variations in the decay constant or 10^5 to 10^8 can occur in some cases. Contrary to what the combination of halo data with these simulations show, the Oklo data seem to be more restrictive and to dictate a change of decay constant by not more than about one order of magnitude. However, that would only correspond to the time in earth history when the Oklo chain reactions were occurring, or at least to the last stages in those reactions when the Sm absorption occurred. At other times the possibility of larger decay rate changes (more accelerated decay) remains open.

In the next few sections we will explore the theory of how the changes in coupling constants might have occurred.

5. Topology and Strings

Multidimensional string theories lead to a branch of mathematics known as *topology*. This, of necessity, is what happens when one considers these extra coordinates, or dimensions. An *n-dimensional manifold* is a space which can be transformed into a connected polyhedron, and such that every point can be surrounded by a collection of other points which is equivalent to the interior of an n-dimensional ball [*Alexandroff*, 1961; *Nash and Sen*, 1983; *Pontryagin*, 1999]. For example, the surface of a sphere is a two-dimensional manifold, which mathematicians write as S^2 (pronounced *S-two*, not *S-squared*). One needs two numbers to specify a point on this manifold, hence the number 2 means it is two-dimensional. Another two-dimensional manifold is the surface of a torus, T^2. For precise, mathematical purposes, the sphere S^2 and the torus T^2 are distinct entities, and should not be confused.

For example, suppose we are trying to describe the motion of a pendulum (Figure 9). Initially, let us suppose that the pendulum is swinging back and forth, staying perfectly within the confines of a vertical plane. Then we could draw a line, or projection, down to the point on a flat, horizontal surface directly below the pendulum ball. A single

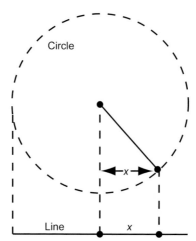

Figure 9. The position of a pendulum bob, confined to move in a single vertical plane, can be completely specified by a single linear coordinate x, provided the pendulum does not swing over the support's level. If the pendulum is free to swing higher than the support, then the circular topology is needed to specify the position. (Figure drawn after *Rourke and Stewart* [1986].)

coordinate x would then suffice to specify the position of the pendulum ball, this coordinate specifying the position on a *straight line*. However, for large oscillations of the pendulum, and if the pendulum was fixed by a universal joint at the top, the pendulum could swing over the top. Our single coordinate would then not suffice to distinguish positions above the support from positions below the support. Hence, a more correct mathematical model for the pendulum would be the *circle*. If, in addition, the pendulum were now able to swing in all directions, and not confined to one vertical plane, then the circular topology becomes inadequate, and a more correct model would be the *sphere*, S^2.

Suppose now that the problem is that of two pendulums, each confined to move in a vertical plane but allowed to swing over the top. The two pendulums move *independently* of each other, assuming positions on two different circles. The combined coordinates now have a different topology, the topology of the torus, T^2.

One of the early pioneers of topology was Henri Poincaré, whose active work on the subject occurred during the 1890s up to his death in 1912. Poincaré analyzed different surfaces by thinking in terms of deformations of loops, which links to what are now called *homology* and *homotopy*. In mathematical topology, homology theory concerns itself with the question of the number of *holes* in the space. Shown in Figure 10 are three curves, *a*, *b*, and *c* on the surface of a torus. The curves *a*, *b*, and *c* have something in common; they cannot be shrunk to a point by continuous sequence of deformations. For curves *a* and *b* it is because the hole is there. For curve *c* it is because the curve is wound around a closed circumference and cannot be shrunk unless one cuts the curve, moves it, and then pastes the ends together. In topology, this is described by stating that *a* and *b* belong to the same homology class, whereas *c* belongs to a different class. Similarly, the concept of homotopy concerns itself with deforming loops. Two loops are homotopic if they can be continuously deformed into each other. These concepts, and others, become important tools in analyzing topology and ultimately multidimensional string theory.

Within the last five to ten years, research has uncovered numerous *dualities* relating different limits and formulations of string and membrane theories. *Duff* [1998] and *Greene* [2000] have discussed the duality between ordinary vibrational modes and winding modes of a string (see Figure 11).

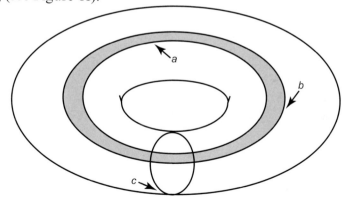

Figure 10. Three closed curves on the surface of a doughnut (torus) illustrate inequivalent and equivalent closed paths. Curves *a* and *b*, which bound the hatched area, can be smoothly distorted into each other, whereas curve *c* winds around a different direction and cannot be distorted into *a* or *b*, without cutting and pasting the ends. (Figure drawn after *Eguchi et al.* [1980].)

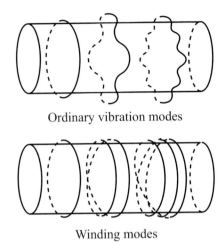

Ordinary vibration modes

Winding modes

Figure 11. The ordinary vibration modes of closed strings (top) and the winding modes (bottom). In the equations of string theory, these two modes carry energy, and exchange roles when the radius of the compactified dimension moves from small to large.

A value of the radius for compactified dimensions leads to the same results or equivalent results for a different radius, in which the winding modes and ordinary vibrational modes change roles in the equations of the theory [*Dai et al.*, 1989]. Another type of duality relates the *strong coupling* limit of one theory to the *weak coupling* limit of another. A *coupling constant* is a number giving the strength with which an elementary particle is coupled to the field that it experiences. For example, the coupling constant for interaction with the electromagnetic field is the electric charge. In some work by *Lykken* [1996] and *Witten* [1996], these authors speculated that, contrary to previous thought (see *Kaplunovsky* [1988, 1992]), strong coupling limits of certain string theories were more relevant to accelerator physics. This led to some more realistic applications of string theory than had previously been possible (see *Nath and Yamaguchi*, [1999]).

6. Compact Circumferences and Coupling Constants

Weinberg [1983a] used generalized Kaluza-Klein models having

4+N dimensions to find a relation between coupling constants and the root-mean-square (rms) circumferences of the compactified dimensions. As discussed by *Chaffin* [2000a], the original Kaluza-Klein model had only one extra dimension besides the usual four of ordinary spacetime. *Witten* [1981] discussed the generalization to the case where there are more compact dimensions. Weinberg applied this idea to reduce some assumed higher-dimensional equations of gravitation theory to the four-dimensional case, and worked out the results of his equations for some simple examples. These examples assign an assumed topology to the compactified dimensions, and then calculate the rms circumferences. For one example, he assumed that the topology corresponded to the symmetry group **SO(N+1)**, the group of rotations, contiguous to the "leave-it-alone" or identity rotation, in N+1 dimensional space. (A *group* is a set of elements plus a rule of combination of pairs of elements, satisfying certain requirements, including that every element has an inverse.) This gave the result for the SO(N+1) coupling constant:

$$g = \left(\frac{\kappa}{R}\right)\left[\frac{1}{2}(N+1)\right]^{1/2} \tag{3}$$

Here, $\kappa^2 = 16\pi G$, where G is Newton's gravitational constant, R is the radius of this (N+1)-dimensional shape with topology analogous to that of a sphere. Thus, for a highly symmetrical topology such as this, all the coupling constants would be the same. In the real world, we know that the strong, electroweak, and gravitational constants are different, but here we are dealing with a simplified example to illustrate possible "real" behaviors.

Weinberg [1983a] also considered an example having the symmetry SU(3), the group of all unitary 3×3 matrices with determinant of plus one. In this example there are two different possible values for coupling constants g and g',

$$g = \frac{\sqrt{2\kappa}}{R} \tag{4a}$$

and

$$g' = \sqrt{\frac{2}{3}}\frac{\kappa}{R} \tag{4b}$$

Thus, the ratio of the two coupling constants is the square root of 3, and does not depend on the radius R of the extra dimensional shape.

Candelas and Weinberg [1984] generalized these results to include the effects of quantum fluctuations of matter fields on the vacuum, and found slightly modified versions of the earlier relations between the radii R of the compactified dimensions and the coupling constants. They also generalized some considerations of *Rubin and Roth* [1983] which attempted to relate the radii of the compactified dimensions to the average temperature of the matter fields contained in the universe. The change of the compactified radii with temperature can be understood physically through the Casimir effect [*Hawking*, 1996; *Chaffin*, 2000a]. In modern quantum field theory there is a zero-point energy, which can be thought of as a sea of virtual particles arising from the vacuum, and which cannot be eliminated. The Casimir effect is a force between two parallel conducting plates caused by differences in zero-point energy of the electromagnetic field. In a similar manner, at zero temperature, the gravitational zero-point energy of the Kaluza-Klein ground state leads to the collapse of the fifth dimension, but in that case we deal with the topology of the compactified dimensions, not with parallel plates. In the parallel-plate case, if a gas of photons at fixed temperature is introduced between the plates, the net pressure on the plates will be the sum of two contributions: the positive pressure from thermal photons, of constant magnitude, and the negative Casimir pressure, varying in inverse proportion to the fourth power of the plate separation. The negative Casimir pressure arises because the short distance between the plates prevents standing waves of certain wavelengths from existing between the plates. In particular, it excludes long wavelengths. If the plates start out close together, the negative Casimir pressure is stronger than that of the thermal photons and the plates collapse. If they start out at a distance such that the Casimir pressure is weaker, then the plates will fly apart with nothing to stop the separation. The thermal photon pressure changes as the plate separation changes, but only as (separation)$^{-4/3}$; that is, much more slowly than the Casimir pressure.

Candelas and Weinberg [1984], and before them *Rubin and Roth* [1983], attempted to extrapolate from the parallel-plate case to a realistic Kaluza-Klein model. Such a model would remove the artificial constraints of an assumed external geometry and an assumed time-independent internal geometry. Realistic models would also involve more than just one compact dimension, with compactification brought about by vacuum expectation values (VEVs) for non-gravitational fields, and would include fermionic (half-integral spin) fields. The presence of curvature in both the compact and non-compact dimensions, the response of the VEVs to changes in temperature, and fermion degeneracy pressure might well all contribute to behavior very different from that observed in the parallel-plate case.

This idea provides a possible mechanism for changing the radii of the compact dimensions as the universe expands and its background temperature changes. Early in Creation week, it may be that the mechanism could also work in a young-earth model.

7. Manifolds and Coupling Constants in Superstring Theory

In superstring theory, we need to link a 10-dimensional "manifold," which is simply a framework which can be smoothly described by ten independent coordinates, with our observed four-dimensional spacetime. If the extra six dimensions are curled up into a compact space, this simply means that every point of four-dimensional spacetime has one of these compact six-dimensional spaces associated with it. (In more recent theory, eleven-dimensional membranes are wrapped up to make ten-dimensional superstrings, but that is just an unneeded complication as far as we will be concerned.) If the size of the compactified six-dimensional space is small compared to the scale of everyday life, we would not directly detect the effect of these extra dimensions [*Chaffin*, 2000a; *Hawking*, 2001].

At high enough energies, higher even than those of the abortive superconducting supercollider, the SSC (which began but did not complete construction in Texas), a particle accelerator would be likely to detect the presence of the so-called Kaluza-Klein excitations or Kaluza-Klein modes. In quantum mechanics, waves are associated with all particles. When we consider string theory, we find that if a spatial dimension is curled up, then the momentum p associated with the waves wrapping around this dimension will be quantized, with values $p = nh/(2\pi R)$, $n = 0, 1, 2, 3, \ldots$, and h is Planck's constant, while R is the radius of the compactified dimension. In this picture the masses of the quantized excitations, the masses m_n of the particles, are given by $m_n^2 = m_0^2 + n^2h^2/(4\pi^2R^2c^2)$, where m_0 is the mass of the mode with zero momentum and c is the speed of light.

Particles can be divided into fermions (half-integral spin) and bosons (integral spin). It is possible that the fermions, or some of the fermions, may not have Kaluza-Klein excitations [Dienes et al., 1999]. This is dependent on exactly how the extra dimensions are compactified. If the fermion corresponds to excitations located at the fixed points of an *orbifold*, then no Kaluza-Klein excitations exist. In mathematically precise formulations of topology, an *orbifold* is a way of smoothing over or "blowing up" certain fixed points at which different coordinates must be joined [Dixon et al.,1985].

The term *orbifold* originated in a graduate mathematics class taught by William P. Thurston in 1976–1977 [Thurston, 1997, 2002]. For an n-dimensional space R^n, an *orbifold* is a structure constructed by using a finite group G, and considering equivalence classes of points in R^n modulo group G. The equivalence classes are then considered as the points of the orbifold. The technical definition is given by Thurston [1997, 2002], but we will not go into the details here. A simple, rough example is formed by considering the finite group Z_2 and its action on R^3. The group Z_2 has two elements, the identity element and the operation of reflection through the y-z plane. A point (x, y, z) is reflected to the point $(-x, y, z)$. One could imagine a mirror in the y-z plane (Figure 12). The two points (x, y, z) and $(-x, y, z)$ are considered part of an equivalence class, and the space of the orbifold is thus the half-space $x \geq 0$ (see Figure 12). Orbifolds were introduced into string theories in the mid 1980s. It is difficult to trace who first introduced them, but they were used in a Ph. D. thesis by Dixon [1986].

In the actual multidimensional string theories, we need to make contact with the "real" world of four spacetime dimensions. The ten-dimensional superstring theory must compactify six of the

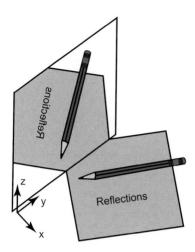

Figure 12. Considering each point (x, y, z) as equivalent to its reflection $(-x, y, z)$ leads to the quotient space.

dimensions on a six-dimensional compact manifold. Particle physicists have, in the last fifteen years, spent a great deal of time studying just how to do this. Fortunately, mathematicians have been studying topology since the time of Poincaré in the late 1800s. While they have not fully developed all the machinery needed by the string theorists, two mathematicians, Eugenio Calabi and Shing-Tung Yau had studied a type of six-dimensional space, known as a Calabi-Yau space (pronounced *cah-lah'-bee-yah'-oo*) which particle theories needed [*Greene*, 2000]. The topology of this space, with the requisite number of "holes," seems to be right to allow the known quarks and leptons to be described in terms of string theory. The quarks and leptons are grouped into three "families," which are allowed by these Calabi-Yau shapes. They allow description in terms of representations of the $SU(3) \times SU(2) \times U(1)$ group of the so-called *standard model*.

The Calabi-Yau spaces have "holes," and in superstring theory the sizes of coupling constants are related to the diameters of these holes [*Greene*, 2000]. Figure 13 shows a cross-section through a Calabi-Yau space. In some cases, Calabi-Yau manifolds have been constructed for which it has been possible to find the coupling constants from first

principles [*Arnowitt and Nath*, 1989; *Nath and Arnowitt*, 1989a, b].
Through their effects on the possible vibrations of strings, Calabi-
Yau shapes influence the detailed properties of the existing particles.
Strominger and Witten [1985] showed that the way that the various
multidimensional holes intersect and overlap with each other actually
determines Yukawa couplings and hence the masses of the matter
particles. *Yukawa couplings* are numbers in field theory equations
which determine the strengths of fermion interactions with scalar
fields such as the Higgs fields or string theory fields called the dilaton
or moduli fields. Their specification is needed for a complete theory,
over and above the specification of the gauge coupling constants of
the symmetry groups **SU**(3), **SU**(2), and **U**(1) of the standard model
[*Bailin and Love*, 1986, p. 248]. According to the Higgs boson theory
of the standard model, the Yukawa coupling constant multiplied by the
vacuum expectation value of the Higgs field gives the mass of a particle
of matter. Thus we find that string theory provides us with a framework
for answering some very important questions.

The new theory of recent years is called M-theory, where M may stand

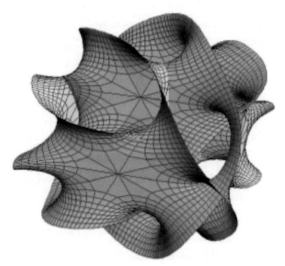

Figure 13. A cross-section through a six-dimensional Calabi-Yau shape,
generated with *Mathematica*.

for membranes, matrices, and other things. Protagonists seem to prefer to leave the meaning of the "M" open. This theory involves membranes rather than strings of zero diameter. This means that six-dimensional Calabi-Yau shapes are replaced by seven-dimensional manifolds known as Joyce manifolds, after *Joyce* [1996a, b, c] who is credited with finding the techniques for their mathematical description.

Up to the present, a glaring failure of string theory has been found in superstring theory. It has been impossible, starting from first principles, to calculate which Joyce manifold, or in the limit where membranes shrink to strings, which Calabi-Yau manifold is a solution to the basic Lagrangian equations. Stated in other language, the theorist cannot determine which vacuum is the true vacuum. Instead the approach used is *phenomenological*. One searches for manifolds that seem to provide correct particle properties, but these manifolds are found from guesses rather than by solving the equations.

Also, it is sometimes stated that there is only one parameter in superstring theory. *Dabholkar and Harvey* [1989] wrote: "In string theory, the only really fundamental constant is the string tension μ." *Witten* [1984] wrote:

> An observation that is not essentially new, but still worth mentioning, is that—as befits a possible unification of all interactions—the superstring theory has no adjustable parameter.

Witten called attention to what is called the dilaton field in superstring theory [*Damour*, 2003]. Witten went on to speculate that, when someday it became possible to calculate the vacuum states from first principles, the minimum of a non-trivial potential for the massless scalar dilaton field would represent the true vacuum and leave no free parameters at all. However, these authors assume that there is only one unique vacuum solution of the string theory equations, and that it is immutable, unchangeable over the history of the universe. While it appears that this issue is yet to be decided [*Duff et al.*, 2002], it seems likely that there could also be solutions in which the strong force coupling constant changes relative to other coupling constants. In particular, the size of the extra dimensions is tied to the dilaton field [*Veneziano*, 2004], but the assumption is sometimes made that all of the compactified dimensions must be the same size. This need not be the case.

Other string theorists may be quoted to show this alternative viewpoint. *Page* [1987] wrote:

The superstring theory itself might predict only certain combinations of the physical constants, leaving several independent combinations that could be predicted only by the WAP *[Weak Anthropic Principle]* (and then probably only within a certain range allowed by the existence of observers).

In his discussion, Page thus advocates what many evolutionary proponents advocate, the WAP which is that we observe the constants and other values that we do because if these constants did not have these values then no intelligent life could have evolved or could exist and there would be no observers. To a Biblical creationist, this evolutionary paradigm is replaced by the realization that God has designed our world so that we will exist in accordance with His design. Creationists who take the Bible's statements about history as being factual do believe in a young earth and that man was created by a direct act of God. But this is leading us away from Page's other point, which is that the string theory may allow solutions which are richer in variation than Witten, Dabholkar, Harvey, etc. seem to advocate.

8. Unified Theories: Food for Thought?

In 1974 the SU(5) theory of combined strong, weak, and electromagnetic interactions was proposed (see *Georgi and Glashow*, [1974] and *Georgi et al.*, [1974]). The SU(5) theory receives its name because it is modeled after five by five special unitary matrices (hence the nickname SU standing for special unitary), *special* meaning they have determinant of plus one. This theory allowed all the families of quarks and leptons to be combined into representations of the SU(5) group, which means that we only needed particles called gluons, W^+, W^-, Z^0 bosons, and the photon to describe the forces between the quarks and leptons. (*Georgi* [1989] has given a popular-level description of how this theory was formulated.) Basically, the SU(5) theory had only one "coupling constant." In accord with previous discussion, the "coupling constant" may be thought of as a number which describes how much force originates from placing particles of known type a certain distance apart. Each type of force has its own coupling constant, but the **SU**(5) theory implied that the coupling constants for strong, weak and electromagnetic forces all originated from a single constant, diverging into their various values as the energy of the interactions is lowered from high energies down to low energies. The reason for the divergence of these values has to do with what is called *renormalization*, and with the *effective field theory* which results from performing the renormalization appropriate to a given energy scale. In quantum field theory, a particle is surrounded by a cloud of virtual particles, which cloud will be penetrated to varying degrees by a second particle interacting with it [*Georgi*, 1989]. A more energetic particle penetrates further. For example, a real particle with positive electric charge will be surrounded by pairs of virtual electrons and positrons. On the average, the virtual positrons are pushed farther away from the real particle, while the virtual electrons are nearer to it. So on the average, the real particle has more negative charge near to it than far from it. A second real particle, depending on its energy, will penetrate this cloud to a lesser or greater degree. For this reason, the effective interaction depends on the particle energy, and the coupling constant of electromagnetic interactions is less for smaller energies. In the case of the strong force, the gluons cause the force to get weaker at larger energies [*Georgi*, 1989, p. 432; *Dimopoulos et al.*, 1991; *Franklin*, 2005, p. 452]. The fine structure constant, which is approximately 1/137 at low energies, has been experimentally measured as about 1/128 at an energy of 58 GeV [*Levine et al.*, 1997]. Similarly, the strong coupling constant α_s has been measured as about 0.119 at 91 GeV (the mass-energy of the Z-boson), whereas it decreases to about 0.110 at 206 GeV [*Bethke*, 2002].

Renormalization theory says that not only the coupling constants, but also the masses of particles appear to vary on different energy scales ['*t Hooft*, 1980; *Nelson*, 1985]. While quantum theory connects this effect to varying energy scales, the basic ideas are actually much older. J. J. Thomson discovered the so-called electromagnetic mass in 1881 [*Thomson*, 1881]. Thomson correctly noted that a charge moving through a dielectric experiences a resistance, which is non-dissipative, and hence is best described by an additional contribution to the mass. The resistance is comparable to that of a sphere moving through a perfect fluid. Motion of the sphere is impeded by the presence of the fluid. Using James Clerk Maxwell's theory of electricity and magnetism, Thomson showed that the charged sphere, moving through the dielectric, would experience an additional mass. Thomson's equation for the new mass m is:

$$m = m_0 + \frac{4}{15} \frac{\mu_0 e^2}{a} \tag{5}$$

where e is the charge, a is the radius of the sphere, and μ_0 is the magnetic permeability. While quantum theory does not assign a radius to the electron, the "vacuum polarization" effect is nevertheless a real effect [*Bjorken and Drell*, 1964, section 8.2; *Georgi*, 1989, p. 434]. In many laboratory experiments, the particles have low energy and are nowhere near the large energies that bring out these effects. However, for experiments involving modern particle accelerators, these effects become evident: the effective coupling constants and effective masses vary with energy.

The **SU**(5) theory of Georgi and colleagues had an unfortunate failure. It predicted the decay of the proton, with a half-life greater than 10^{29} years. As a result of this prediction, experiments were set up to detect this proton decay, and no conclusive evidence for such decays was found. The half-life of the proton, if not infinite, was shown to be higher than the range which the **SU**(5) theory seems to allow. Other unified theories based on other groups or on string theory are possible, and this is still an active field of research. For example, *Shiu and Tye* [1998] discussed the possible suppression of proton decay by an additional symmetry, while *Dienes et al.* [1998a, b] discussed a *higher-dimensional* mechanism involving selection rules for the Kaluza-Klein excitations which allow all proton-decay processes to have vanishing probability. In the **SU**(5) theory and in similar theories allowing proton decay, there are particles, either X-bosons or Higgs particles, which are responsible for the proton's decay. In the *Dienes et al.* theory, however, the proton does not have Kaluza-Klein excitations, which leads to a zero probability for its decay. (Technically, the proton is said to be restricted to the fixed points of an orbifold, at which point the probability for interacting with the X-bosons or Higgs particles is zero.) *Emmanuel-Costa and Wiesenfeldt* [2003], noting that the original considerations assumed the equality of two Yukawa coupling constants, have speculated that these couplings might be different, which could possibly save the **SU**(5) theory from extinction. Of course, these theories are untested at present, so the correct explanation for the lack of proton decay is still undecided.

Unfortunately, this also leaves open the question of whether or not the **SU**(5) theory was correct in predicting that there is only one gauge coupling constant at high energies. If the radii of compactified dimensions varied over the early history of Creation, then a related question also seems to be unanswered for us. Could the rates of α- and β-decay vary relative to each other over the history of the universe? This is an interesting question, and needs to be answered in order to correctly interpret radioisotope data. A start in this direction will be provided in the next section.

9. Kaluza-Klein Excitations, Technicolor, and the Fermi Coupling Constant

Gauge field theories by themselves provide no mechanism for giving the values of the coupling constants, because the coupling constants are just numbers which must be measured experimentally and inserted in the equations [*Weinberg*, 1983b]. We can measure how the coupling constants "run" with energy, as we have already discussed, but the basic starting values are not provided by the gauge field theory and no mechanism is provided for their time variation. Hence, in order to provide mechanisms for variations of coupling constants, one is forced to consider more ambitious theories, such as Kaluza-Klein theory or string theory. This means discussing theories which are at present somewhat speculative.

Nath and Yamaguchi [1999], considered the question of whether Kaluza-Klein excitations contribute to the so-called Fermi constant, which determines the fundamental rates of β-decays. Enrico Fermi, the

Italian-American of the Manhattan project, was responsible for the first realistic theories of β-decay, so this constant G_F, as applied in β-decay theory, is named after him. For the case of one extra dimension, Nath and Yamaguchi showed that to leading order in the ratio of the W boson mass M_W to the mass proportional to $1/R$ (the compactification scale mass M_R), the effective Fermi constant G_F^{eff} is given by

$$G_F^{eff} \cong G_F^{SM} \left(1 + \frac{\pi^2}{3} \frac{M_W^2}{M_R^2} \right) \tag{6}$$

Here, G_F^{SM} is the value of the Fermi constant, which may be calculated from the standard model of quantum field theory. *Nath and Yamaguchi* [1999] comment that the standard model agrees very well with experiment without any assumptions about extra dimensions. For the case of more than one extra dimension, Nath and Yamaguchi derived a simple formula similar to the above but depending on the extra dimensions. From the results of standard model calculations, plus experimental measurements [*Abachi et al.*, 1996; *van Ritbergen and Stuart*, 1999], Nath and Yamaguchi showed that the energy $M_R c^2$ was at least 1.6 TeV. This encourages particle physicists to hope that, with the completion of the Large Hadron Collider (LHC), expected in 2007 or so, evidence for these extra dimensions may be found (see *Kane* [1998] for a semi-fictitious account of expectations).

Now, because we are interested in the possibility of accelerated decay in the early universe, we need to take the discussion a step further than Nath and Yamaguchi did. In their paper, they only considered present-day measurements. Because of our interest in explaining radioisotope data in terms of a young earth, we may think as follows. If, over the early history of the universe, the radius of compact dimensions should change, then so would the mass scale M_R, and hence the value of the Fermi constant. Under the simplifying assumption that other factors in the equation do not change as radically as M_R does, decreases in the sizes of extra dimensions would increase M_R, and hence decrease the values of G_F. This in turn would mean that half-lives for β-decays of nuclei would become larger as the extra dimensions became smaller. Thus, one would expect accelerated decay to have occurred early in the history of the creation.

In particle physics today, there are rival theories including some called Technicolor models [*Chivukula et al.*, 2004]. In these models extra gauge bosons, with the same properties as the W and Z bosons except larger masses, should appear at the higher energies that should become available when and if the CERN accelerator upgrade is completed in about 2007. These models have extra coupling constants besides those of the standard model, and lead to equations for the Fermi constant very similar to the one given above, except that a scale parameter f plays the role of the M_R of equation (6) given above. Hence, time variation of the Fermi constant is possible in many different ways which will have to be sorted out when more data become available sometime after 2007.

10. Variation of Particle Masses: A Problem?

The depth of the nuclear potential well is determined directly by the strength of the strong nuclear force, hence by the "strong coupling constant." A coupling constant is a number inserted in a theory to fix the strength of a force. We determine it experimentally, but theories exist which indicate that it may not be a constant over the history of the universe. The principal coupling constants in modern physics are those of the strong, weak, electromagnetic, and gravitational interactions. Particles may be divided into sets according to the types of force to which they respond. The leptons include the neutrinos, the electron, muon, and tau particles. The neutrinos have no electric charge and hence do not experience the electromagnetic interaction. The electron, muon, and tau experience the weak and electromagnetic interactions but not the strong interaction. Hadrons are the types of particles which experience the strong interactions. The hadrons include the proton and neutron, as well as various heavier particles such as hyperons and mesons.

In considering possible variations in the strengths of the various forces, as indicated by changes in the coupling constants, it soon becomes evident that the masses of the particles could also possibly change. In fact, consistent modern theories seem to *demand* that such changes be a by-product of the changes in force strengths.

For instance, consider the mass of the proton and/or neutron (which are called nucleons). While significant unanswered questions still remain, theories of the nucleon mass have been formulated, based on the quark model plus some assumptions about the nature of the forces between quarks. These assumptions include that the force is basically due to the exchange of eight particles called gluons, plus contributions from exchange of pions and other bosons for larger distances. Xiangdong Ji, then a physicist at Massachusetts Institute of Technology, published in 1995 a separation of the nucleon mass into the contributions of the quark and gluon kinetic energies, the quark masses, and other contributions [*Ji*, 1995]. For instance, Ji's work shows that the contributions of the valence and sea quark masses amount to a contribution of 160 MeV out of the total of 939 MeV of mass-energy of the nucleon. Here the "valence quarks" are the two up quarks and one down quark that compose a proton or the two down quarks and one up quark that compose a neutron. The sea quarks are the virtual quarks that exist as virtual particles at any one instant of time. Ji's calculation ignored the small contribution of electromagnetic forces to the mass of a nucleon. According to *Calmet and Fritzsch* [2000], the nucleon mass "receives also a small contribution from electromagnetism of the order of 1%…" Both the neutron and proton have these electromagnetic contributions, even though the neutron is neutral, because the quarks inside the neutrons have non-zero charge, with a total of zero.

If one considers the mass of the electron, one soon notices that since the electron does not experience the strong force, then changes in the strong coupling constant would not affect the mass of the electron. This in turn would mean that as a result of a change in the nuclear force, the chemistry of everyday life could continue to operate nearly as it had before. The atom is largely empty space, with most of the mass concentrated in the small nucleus at its center. In the approximation that the nucleus does not move, energy levels of atoms and molecules are not affected by the nuclear force, only the energy levels of the nucleus. To calculate atomic energy levels, the fact that the nucleus does move is taken into account by replacing the mass of the electron by the so-called reduced mass, equal to:

$$\frac{m_e M_N}{m_e + M_N} \tag{7}$$

where m_e is the mass of the electron and M_N the mass of the nucleus. The present value of the proton-to-electron mass ratio μ is 1836.1526645. Hence, the reduced mass differs from the mass of the electron by a factor of 0.9994557. Past values can be inferred from studying molecular spectra such as those of H_2 molecules in distant gaseous clouds, which absorb the light coming to earth from distant quasar light sources. *Potekhin et al.* [1998] reported results indicating a larger value of the proton to electron mass ratio in light from the quasar PKS 0528-250. If $\mu = M_p/m_e$, the fractional change $\Delta\mu/\mu$ was found to be:

$$\frac{\Delta\mu}{\mu} = \left(8.3^{+6.6}_{-5.0}\right) \times 10^{-5} \tag{8}$$

Since the given limits of variation are one standard deviation errors, this result is also consistent with no change at all. More seriously, it illustrates that changes in the reduced mass have measurable consequences, if we assume that changes occurring on earth were also occurring elsewhere in the cosmos. Since light from distant stars originated in the past, then measurements should show such differences if they occurred throughout the universe.

A more recent analysis of light from the quasar Q 0347-382 yielded a similar result [*Ivanchik et al.*, 2003]:

$$\frac{\Delta\mu}{\mu} = (5.02 \pm 1.82) \times 10^{-5} \tag{9}$$

Here the error does not exceed three standard deviations, so the result hints at a variation but is also consistent with no variation.

However, a change of the mass of the proton by 0.08% would lead to transformation of protons into neutrons by electron capture. This would occur if the proton mass-energy increased from its present value of 938.28 MeV to a value greater than the neutron mass-energy of 939.57 MeV. The electromagnetic contribution to the nucleon mass can be calculated, as for example by *Genovese et al.* [1997]. The principal contributions are the Coulomb attractions and repulsions between the various quarks and the interactions of their magnetic moments. However, the neutron differs from the proton by the replacement of one down quark by an up quark. Hence, the difference in masses of the up and down quarks is another source of the neutron-proton mass difference. In this case, the masses of the quarks might not vary in the way that a naïve model might predict. Hence, variations in the strong coupling constant would not necessarily upset the fine balance between the masses of the neutron and proton.

Calmet and Fritzsch [2000] proposed a theory in which the masses of the light quarks, including the up and down quarks, would not vary at all, only the mass of the top quark. If this theory is correct, and the gluons have zero rest mass as commonly believed, then variation of the strong force could possibly occur without a noticeable change in either the quark or the nucleon masses. The changes would not likely be zero due to various higher-order effects, but they could be small enough so that the reduced mass was not noticeably changed.

In standard electroweak theory, the Higgs boson is responsible for most of the mass of observed particles [*Taylor*, 1989]. The theory requires the Higgs particle to interact with all particles which have mass—the bigger the mass the stronger the interaction. The Higgs mass is at present unknown, since conclusive evidence for its existence does not yet exist [*Renton*, 2004]. In 2002, the electron-positron collider, LEP, at CERN in Geneva, Switzerland, was collecting data consistent with a possible Higgs particle with a mass-energy of 115 GeV. However, the accelerator had to be shut down to prepare for the construction of a new, more powerful accelerator, expected to be completed in 2007. As *Renton* [2004] discusses, indirect methods give an estimate of 92^{+130}_{-48} GeV for the Higgs mass-energy, a value which is consistent with the hint from CERN of 115 GeV. However, the confirmation of the Higgs particle awaits the construction of the new CERN accelerator.

In extended versions of electroweak theory, more than one Higgs boson exists. Such theories include the minimal supersymmetric standard model (MSSM) and grand unified theories (GUTs). In particular, some versions include, in addition to two Higgs particles with mass-energies of about 100–200 GeV, other Higgs particles with mass-energies between 10^{14} and 10^{16} GeV. Such particles have allegedly played a role in inflationary models of the universe [*Linde*, 1979, 1984, 1997], in which some driving force was needed to cause a rapid expansion of the universe. The fact that some Higgs particles are so much heavier than the others is called the *gauge hierarchy problem*, and although various solutions have been proposed [*Randall and Csaki*, 1996; *Witten*, 2002], the correct one is not known. Although CERN found some evidence for one Higgs particle near 115 GeV, the existence of these other Higgs particles is not known and is not likely to be known in the near future. If the heavier Higgs particles exist, it may be that their influence on the quark masses is also negligible, as in the Calmet and Fritzsch theory. On the other hand, they may not exist at all, and firm conclusions based on the properties of Higgs particles are not possible.

In *Calmet and Fritzsch* [2000] theory, the 100–200 GeV Higgs boson and its production of mass for quarks was considered. It was pointed out that the coupling of the light mass quarks and the electron to the Higgs field is an unknown which could even be zero. The theory becomes inconsistent unless the $W^{\pm}$ and Z^0 gauge bosons couple to the Higgs field, via the gauge coupling constants and the weak mixing parameter (which will be explained below in Section 12). However, the Yukawa coupling constant of the light quarks and the electron to the Higgs field could be very small, possibly even zero. *Quigg* [1997] assumed a Higgs vacuum expectation value of 176 GeV to get a value of about 3×10^{-6} for the electron Yukawa coupling and approximately 1.0 for the top quark Yukawa coupling. This interprets the very heavy top quark (mass-energy 178 GeV) as the only quark which couples strongly to the Higgs field. Other physicists [*Weinberg*, 1982] have also concluded that the Yukawa couplings of light quarks and leptons must be very small. This would explain why these quarks and leptons are much lighter than the W-particles.

In conclusion, it seems likely that the mass of the nucleon does vary with the strength of the nuclear force. However, the size of the variation may be small if theories similar to the Calmet-Fritzsch idea are true. In the standard model, it is thought that contributions to the masses of both leptons and quarks arise from electroweak interactions. The masses of the quarks, but not the leptons, would also receive contributions from the strong interactions. Since quarks are confined inside nucleons and mesons, and are not observed as free particles, an exact measurement of their masses is not available. In particle physics, the *current quark mass* is a term used for the mass the quarks would have in the high-energy limit, in which limit they would not be hindered by their interactions with clouds of virtual particles in their environment. One cannot go to the laboratory and change the strength of the nuclear force. However, one can observe what happens with particle accelerators for various beam energies. At different beam energies, experiment shows that coupling constants "run," which means they change with energy because of their varying interactions with the clouds of virtual particles surrounding targets they may encounter. This change in coupling constants with energy also means that the effective mass of particles such as quarks should change with energy. Inside a nucleon, the three valence quarks are not at high energy, hence they have a somewhat higher effective mass called the *constituent quark mass*. The current quark masses, in energy units, of the up and down quarks are thought to be about 3 MeV and 7 MeV, respectively, while their constituent quark masses are thought to be about 315 MeV and 318 MeV, respectively. By comparison, the mass-energy of the top quark is very large, at 174 GeV [*Liss and Tipton*, 1997]. Thus, it seems that the strong force should have some influence on the masses of nucleons and nuclei, although how much seems to be model-dependent and/or uncertain at present.

11. The Conserved Vector Current (CVC) Hypothesis

When we bind protons and neutrons together into a complex nucleus, the charge on the complex nucleus is exactly Z times that of an isolated proton. In fact, the coupling constant e is the same for all particles which have electric charge. No matter what the environment is, whether surrounded by clouds of virtual pions or whatever, the value of this coupling constant does not appear to be disturbed. Of course the distribution of charge is disturbed, so that scattering of high energy beams off a nucleus depends on the actual distribution of the nucleons. However, the coupling in the low energy limit, which is what we call the electric charge, is not changed. We could say then that the charge of a nucleon is not renormalized when it is included in a nucleus.

In a similar way, the conserved vector current hypothesis [*Feynman and Gell-Mann*, 1958; *Feynman*, 1960; *Wilkinson*, 1978] asserts that there is a part of the weak interaction, the so-called vector interaction, whose coupling constant does not depend on whether the nucleon is free or bound in a nucleus. Also, the coupling constant is the same for a muon as for a nucleon. In other words, for low-energy transitions, β-decays proceeding by the vector interaction channel are unchanged by the interaction of pions and nucleons. On the other hand, there is another coupling constant involved in β-decays, the so-called axial vector interactions, which is renormalized by a factor of 1.2 for nucleons in nuclei.

This all has a consequence if the strength of the strong nuclear force changes. The constancy of electric charge means that, to the first approximation, changing the coupling constant for the strong nuclear force will not change the electronic orbitals of atoms, and the everyday chemistry of life could be unaffected by accelerated decay episodes that involve the strong force changing but not the electric force. Would a change in the strength of the strong nuclear force change the rates of β-decays? The CVC hypothesis would indicate that the vector part of the coupling constant is not changed, however, in β-decay the decay rate depends on the size of the energy release (the so-called Q-value). Hence, the rates of β-decays are changed by changes in the strong force.

12. Forbidden Decays and Radioisotope Dating

Beta-minus decay, according to modern ideas, proceeds when one of the down quarks which make up a neutron emits a W⁻ particle. The down quark is thereby changed into an up quark, which also changes the neutron into a proton. Since the rest energy of the W⁻ particle is 80 GeV, which is more than the available energy, the W^- is a virtual particle and cannot escape but decays into an electron and an antineutrino. *Chaffin et al.* [2004] proposed that the process can be modeled as a tunneling of the system through an 80 GeV potential barrier. This is similar to the modeling of pair production as a tunneling which was proposed long ago by *Schwinger* [1951] and developed further by *Brezin and Itzykson* [1970] and *Casher et al.* [1979]. Slight variations in the strong force or other parameters then could lead to pronounced changes in the β-decay half-life similar to those found by modeling α-decay as a tunneling. In the case of β-decay, however, the dominant decay modes are forbidden decays, a factor not encountered for α-decay.

It seems that radioisotope dating of rocks using β-decay is always done with isotopes which decay via "forbidden decays." Forbidden decays are not impossible ones but they are of much lower probability than "allowed" or "superallowed" decays. The word "forbidden" is here borrowed from its usage in atomic spectroscopy, where a transition between two electronic states of an atom is "allowed" if certain "selection rules" for the changes in the quantum numbers n, ℓ, j, μ, m_ℓ, m_s are obeyed, corresponding to so-called electric dipole transitions. However, just because a transition is not allowed does not mean that it never occurs. Higher-order processes such as "magnetic dipole" and "electric quadrupole" transitions may be possible, although at a much reduced rate. In the case of nuclear energy levels, there are selection rules operable in the β-decay transitions which are of interest. For the mathematically inclined it means that the matrix elements involve a different operator, but these matrix elements are small and do not become important unless the normal matrix elements vanish. But in the case of radioisotope dating we are usually using decays of this type because otherwise the half-life would not be very long. Nuclei with "allowed" β-decays invariably have a relatively short half-life and hence are not often used in radioisotope dating. A second factor is that the decay energy is usually small for decays of this type. Some examples are:

- ^{40}K: 3rd forbidden transition for the β^- transition (89.33%), decay energy 1.3 MeV

- ^{87}Rb: 2nd forbidden transition, decay energy 0.275 MeV
- ^{187}Re: 1st forbidden transition with a large atomic number $Z=75$, and small decay energy 0.0026 MeV
- ^{176}Lu: 1st forbidden transition, decay energy $=0.57$ MeV,
- ^{14}C: allowed transition, decay energy $=0.156$ MeV
- ^{10}Be: 2nd forbidden transition, decay energy 0.556 MeV.

It might be pointed out that allowed decays of short half-life typically have decay energies of several MeV, unlike those listed above. The small values of the decay energies also contribute to the sensitivity of the isotope half-lives to changes in nuclear parameters.

In the 1940s, before the theory was very well developed, the classification of transitions as "2nd forbidden," "allowed," etc. was usually done on an empirical basis, by looking at various graphs involving so-called "ft values" [*Konopinski and Uhlenbeck*, 1935, 1941; *Konopinski*, 1943; *Alburger*, 1950; *Brodzinski and Conway*, 1965; *Berenyi*, 1968; *Sastry*, 1969]. Back then, ^{14}C was thought to be a forbidden transition, but now we know that it is an allowed transition with a nuclear spin change of +1 and no parity change. On the time scale of interest here, the half-life of ^{14}C is also relatively short, at 5715 years [*Parrington et al.*, 1996].

The theory of forbidden β-decays is discussed in nuclear physics textbooks, or in sources such as *Konopinski* [1943] or *Behrens and Bühring* [1982]. In the limit of small decay energy Δ, the fraction of all the radioactive atoms decaying per unit time, called the decay constant, is given by:

$$\lambda = \frac{0.693}{T_{\frac{1}{2}}} = \begin{cases} G_F^2\, K \Delta^{L+3}, \textit{for } Z \textit{ small} \\ G_F^2\, K \Delta^{2+\left(1-\alpha^2 Z^2\right)^{\frac{1}{2}}}, Z \textit{ not small} \end{cases} \quad (10)$$

Here G_F is the Fermi constant, K is a constant, Z is the atomic number, λ is the decay constant, and L is the degree of "forbiddenness" of the decay. Notice that the degree of "forbiddenness" appears in an exponent, so that highly forbidden decays are very sensitive to the values of the decay energies Δ, particularly when Δ is small. Defining p as the exponent that occurs as the power of Δ in equation (10) above, *Dyson*

[1967, 1972] defined a "sensitivity" of the decay constant to changes in the fine-structure constant as shown in Table 2. We are here not interested in variations in the fine-structure constant but in variations in the strong coupling constant. However, since the changes caused by either one are considered to enter through changes in Δ, the sensitivities are very similar.

Table 2. Sensitivity of various forbidden β-decays to changes in decay energy (after *Dyson*, [1972]).

Nucleus	Half-life (years)	Δ (MeV)	p	u	Sensitivity
^{40}K	1.30×10^9	1.31	6	-5	-30
^{87}Rb	5.00×10^{10}	0.275	5	-36	-180
^{123}Te	1.23×10^{13}	0.06(EC)	6	210	1260
^{187}Re	4.00×10^{10}	0.0025	2.8	-6400	-18000

In the theory of β-decay, there is a quantity called the "Weinberg angle" named after a Nobel Prize winner [*Behrens and Bühring*, 1982]. In more recent discussions it is just called "the weak mixing angle," since it was actually Glashow who introduced it, not Weinberg. It measures a mixing between the weak coupling and the electromagnetic coupling. Due to this mixing, it would be very difficult to formulate a successful theory in which the weak coupling constant could change but not the charge of the electron, at least for post-Creation week accelerated decay episodes. Hence, Noah's body could be negatively affected by such a change, if it were large enough. In the standard theory for the Fermi constant, the electroweak equations involve coupling constants g and g' which cancel out of the expression for the Fermi constant [*Kimberly and Magueijo*, 2004]. However, they do not cancel out of the expressions for the electronic charge, as Kimberly and Magueijo showed. Hence, if the Fermi constant is to vary in a realistic manner, models such as those considered above in Section 9 involving Kaluza-Klein excitations or technicolor are needed .

A possible better alternative is to allow large changes in the strong coupling constant, the one which has the biggest influence on the nuclear force and nuclear masses. This coupling is effectively decoupled from the others at the low energies of ordinary life. Also, a change in the strong coupling would not just change α-decay and spontaneous fission, but also the β-decays. According to equation (10) above, the half-life for β-minus decay depends on the decay energy Δ raised to some power. That power is approximately the degree of forbiddenness plus three, at least for nuclei lighter than about those with a proton number $Z = 50$. Small changes in the decay energy, caused by small changes in the strong coupling constant, could thus cause relatively large changes in half-life for these forbidden decays.

Potassium-Ar dating depends primarily on the β-minus decay to ^{40}Ca to remove the ^{40}K. That decay involves a spin change of −4 with a parity change, and is third forbidden. Rubidium-Sr decay on the other hand is a spin change of +3 with a parity change, a second forbidden transition. The powers of the decay energy involved are therefore different, since one is third forbidden while the other is second forbidden. This should help explain the differences between K-Ar results and Rb-Sr results which Austin and Snelling have been finding [*Austin and Snelling*, 1998; *Snelling et al.*, 2003; *Snelling*, 2003a, b; *Austin*, 2005; *Snelling*, 2005a, b].

Furthermore, the mathematics shows that Re-Os decays should be the most sensitive of all to accelerated decay, by a factor of about 100 over Rb-Sr and 600 over K-Ar (see Table 2). However, samples suitable for Re-Os dating appear to be less common than for other techniques.

13. Using Double β-Decay Data to Test for Variability of the Fermi Constant

Double β-decay was first studied from a theoretical standpoint by *Goeppert-Mayer* [1935]. Important information can be extracted from the study of this rare type of decay. Not only can it be used to check whether the Fermi constant G_F varies with time, but has some interesting ties to some other questions [*Levi*, 1987].

Ordinary β-minus decay is proportional to the Fermi constant squared.

Double β-decay is a higher order process in which two electrons are emitted in the same decay (not just two β-decays in succession), and has a probability proportional to the fourth power of the Fermi constant [*Barabash*, 1998]. Two neutrinos may be emitted in double β-decay, but it has been proposed that a rarer form of double β-decay occurs in which no neutrinos are emitted may also exist. Since this form of β-decay is rarer, we will not discuss it further here. A double β-decay is not just two β-decays in succession. For example, Figure 14 shows the level scheme for double β-decay of ^{130}Te. A single β-decay cannot occur since the ground state of ^{130}I is higher in energy than that of ^{130}Te. However, double β-decay occurs since the ground state of ^{130}Xe is lower than that of the other two.

The only useful isotope for which the half-life for double β-decay has been directly measured is ^{82}Se. Tellurium-130 and ^{128}Te, have been measured by inferring the half-life from measuring the decay products in geological samples, but the half-life is too long for direct measurement in the laboratory, at least so far. The double β-decay half-life of ^{116}Cd has been measured as $(3.75\pm0.35(\text{stat.})\pm0.21(\text{syst.}))\times10^{19}$ years, but geochemical measurements have not been successful [*Arnold et al.*, 1996]. Similar situations exist for ^{100}Mo and ^{76}Ge [*Dassié et al.*, 1995; *Günther et al.*, 1997]. According to *Kirsten* [1983] "only double β-decays leading to rare gas isotopes are accessible to the 'geochemical' method."

A useful laboratory for fundamental research on double β-decay has turned out to be the Fréjus Underground Laboratory. It was constructed in 1980, to perform an experiment for detecting the decay of the proton. At the time the **SU**(5) theory said that the half-life of the proton might be

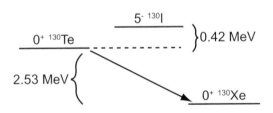

Figure 14. The double-β-decay scheme of ^{130}Te.

10^{29} years. When the proton proved to be stable to the available accuracy, the research activities were expanded to include other projects. Fréjus Underground Laboratory is located at approximately 1700 m under the top of Fréjus mountain, in the medium of the road tunnel of the same name, which eases travel between France and Italy. The about 1600 m of solid rock provided by the Fréjus mountain reduces the cosmic ray background by more than six orders of magnitude (1/2,000,000) compared to the intensity at the earth's surface. Various shields of paraffin, lead, and copper are used to reduce radioactive emissions coming from surrounding rocks and building materials. Thus far, double β-decay observations for ^{100}Mo, ^{76}Ge, ^{82}Se, ^{116}Cd, ^{130}Te, ^{96}Zr, ^{48}Ca, and ^{150}Nd have been planned or already completed.

In 1998, the NEMO (an acronym for Neutrino Ettore Majorana Observatory—named after the physicist Ettore Majorana) collaboration of about 50 French, Russian, Finnish, and American scientists used the Fréjus Underground Laboratory to measure the double β-decay half-life of ^{82}Se, reporting $T_{1/2} = (0.83 \pm 0.10(\text{stat.}) \pm 0.07(\text{syst.})) \times 10^{20}$ years [*Arnold et al.*, 1998]. This agrees with an earlier, but less accurate, measurement at University of California, Irvine, which gave $T_{1/2} = (1.1 \,^{+0.8}_{-0.3}) \times 10^{20}$ years [*Elliott et al.*, 1987].

With these results, it is possible to compare geochemical data to see if accelerated decay is indicated. If the Fermi constant G_F is changing, then the half-life for double β-decay should change relative to that for ordinary β-decay. Hence, what is needed is a suite of samples for which ^{82}Se and its decay product ^{82}Kr have been measured, and also some other measurements such as K/Ar or Rb/Sr have been performed.

At a 1986 conference in Osaka, Japan, *Kirsten et al.* [1986] reported K/Ar and ^{82}Se/^{82}Kr measurements for various geological samples, Precambrian samples from Boliden, Sweden (Revesund), late Cretaceous or early Tertiary samples from Pakajaka, Bolivia, and some described as Variscan Orogeny from Bukov and Rozna, western Moravia, a region of Czechoslovakia. The Varsican Orogeny was the late Paleozoic (Carboniferous through Permian) mountain-building event in Europe. It appears to correspond with the "Appalachian Orogeny" in eastern North America. In a 1983 American Institute of Physics conference volume, *Kirsten* [1983] also gave some useful data for some clausthalite from Paleozoic rocks from Cacheuta, Argentina. In these samples, the K concentrations are very small, of the order of parts per million, but nevertheless measurable.

Using the raw data, given in the paper by *Kirsten et al.* [1986], model ages for K/Ar can be calculated along with model ages using double β-decay of ^{82}Se to ^{82}Kr. Assuming that contaminant ^{36}Ar is 0.337% of all Ar, and ^{40}Ar is 99.6%, we may find the amount of ^{40}Ar* for each sample. Assuming ^{84}Kr is 56.9% of all "normal" Kr, and 11.56% is ^{82}Kr, we may similarly subtract out the non-radiogenic Kr. Then by dividing (radiogenic ^{82}Kr/^{82}Se) by (^{40}Ar*/^{40}K) we get the dimensionless ratios R shown in the Table 3 for each sample.

Table 3. Data on the ratios R for each sample.

Sample	R
Moravian Be-Bu 1	$(6.47\pm7.41) \times 10^{-8}$
Moravian Be-Bu 2	$(13.84\pm15.36) \times 10^{-8}$
Moravian Be-Ro	$(11.47\pm13.62) \times 10^{-8}$
Bolivian Bl-Pa	$(10.32\pm26.3) \times 10^{-8}$
Swedish Sk-Bo a	$(3.40\pm1.27) \times 10^{-10}$
Swedish Sk-Bo b	$(9.32\pm4.05) \times 10^{-10}$
Argentine clausthalite	$(0.948\pm0.846) \times 10^{-10}$

Assuming the NEMO collaboration's value for the ^{82}Se half-life, the 1.277×10^9 year half-life for ^{40}K, and that 10.67% of ^{40}K decays produce ^{40}Ar instead of ^{40}Ca, we may plot what the ratio R should look like as a function of time. This graph is shown Figure 15.

The time axis units are billions of years. Thus "20" means 20×10^8 years or 2 billion years. All of the samples except the Swedish, and possibly the Argentine samples, have unacceptable limits of error, causing the R value to come out on a scale of 10^{-7}, but with the error bars bracketing a value of the order of 100% to 200%. However, the error bars for the Swedish samples were smaller, the $(3.40\pm1.27) \times 10^{-10}$ value giving results consistent with an age between 1.54 and 5.5 billion years.

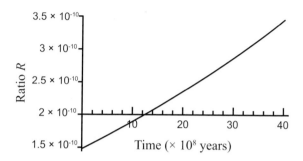

Figure 15. The ratio R of (radiogenic $^{82}Kr/^{82}Se$) divided by ($^{40}Ar*/^{40}K$) versus time.

Precambrian rocks of Boliden, central Sweden, give their name to an ore formation located there. The Revesund Granite is found there and over a large area of central Sweden. It is assigned a uniformitarian age of 1.75 billion years. The data for the Swedish Boliden rocks are interesting in that the above R value derived from the data indicate a somewhat older age for the formations than the uniformitarian age of 1.75 billion years for these Precambrian rocks. Does this show whether the Fermi constant varied over time? *Barabash* [1998, 2000, 2003, 2004] interpreted the data as indicating such a variation. However, his analysis of the geochemical data assumed that the uniformitarian geologic timetable is correct. If the Boliden rocks are supposed to be 1.75×10^9 years old, then the mean R ratio of 3.40×10^{-10} is too big according to Figure 15, possibly indicating accelerated decay had to occur to produce this large value of R. This shows that this method has promise, but more accuracy is needed. Perhaps more data will appear in the literature which would make better determinations possible and show whether accelerated decay occurred in this way. The NEMO-3 detector is now operating, and may produce a laboratory result for ^{130}Te. This would then enable the large body of geochemical data that exist in the literature for ^{130}Te to be compared with present-day laboratory results. If the Fermi constant is not varying, but the strong interaction coupling did vary, these analyses should help show that this is the case. If both vary, these data should still be valuable to sort out the mechanisms that are responsible.

14. Conclusion

Because God is the Creator of physical principles, it would be wrong to state that He must act in a certain way. However, Scripture is a reliable record of His actual Creation. The models considered here merely point out some unnecessary assumptions involved in interpreting radioactive decay: half-lives may not have been constant.

In our studies of α-decay, it is found that small changes in the strength of the nuclear force can lead to large changes in the half-life of a nucleus such as U^{238}. Using realistic values for the strength and range for the nuclear force it was found that a small change in the depth of the nuclear potential well can cause a change in the number of nodes in the α-particle wavefunction, resulting in a change in the half-life that in some cases could be as much as a factor of 10^8.

It was found that these models are consistent with the U isotope distributions found in nature, and their approach to radioactive equilibrium. These results enable one to conjecture about how much the variation in nuclear force must have been in order to explain present-day isotopic abundances. Since there is no precise number to match with theory, and since various approaches to the final, present-day abundances are possible, these results remain exploratory in nature. In the case of the Oklo natural reactors, a study of the resonance absorption of neutrons by ^{149}Sm was found to place some constraints on the time during earth history when the reactions could have occurred, and/or the type of model that is consistent with the data.

Borrowing some ideas from Kaluza-Klein theory and string theory, we found that changes in the radii of compact extra dimensions can lead to a change in the effective coupling constant for the strong force, hence in the strength of the nuclear force. Although extended Kaluza-Klein and string theories must be considered as highly tentative theories, in this work we find some explicit equations showing the possible variation of the strong and weak coupling constants. We discussed the connection between coupling constants and the sizes of the holes in a Calabi-Yau shape. We also discussed modern unified theories of the strong, weak and electromagnetic forces and the implications of changes in coupling constants and Yukawa couplings as far as the effect on particle masses is concerned. We conclude that, although all the relevant measurements and theories are not yet available, consistent theories which allow accelerated decay seem to be possible. It seems that the best models, the ones which would be most likely to be successful, would involve a variation in the strong force rather than the electromagnetic force. Whether the weak force can vary in a way consistent with observation seems doubtful.

We discussed the idea of a forbidden transition in β-decay theory, and found that most of the nuclei that are of interest in radioisotope dating problems undergo forbidden transitions with a comparatively small decay energy (the Q-value). The sensitivity of a theoretical value of the half-life of a β-decay was found to be increased by a smallness of the relevant Q-value. A change in the strong force could therefore affect the β-decays of these nuclei through change in the Q-value.

Double β-decay promises to provide a check on whether accelerated decay has occurred. The double β-decay of ^{82}Se already gives some evidence of this type, but more data will possibly become available in the next few years if direct measurements of the half-life of ^{130}Te are successful. Perhaps future studies will be able to connect more precisely with the data.

References

Abachi, S., et al. (D0 collaboration), Search for right-handed W bosons and heavy W' in p-pbar collisions at $\sqrt{s}$ = 1.8 TeV, *Physical Review Letters, 76,* 3271–3276,1996.

Alburger, D. E., Beta-ray spectrum of ^{40}K, *Physical Review, 78,* 629–630, 1950.

Alexandroff, P., *Elementary Concepts of Topology,* Dover, New York, 1961.

Antoniadis, I., and M. Quirós, Large radii and string unification, *Physics Letters B, 392,* 61–66, 1997.

Anyas-Weiss, N., J. C. Cornell, P. S. Fisher, P. N. Hudson, A. Menaca-Rocha, D. J. Millener, A. D. Panagiotou, D. K. Scott, D. Strottman, D. M. Brink, B. Buck, P. J. Ellis, and T. Engeland, Nuclear structure of light nuclei using the selectivity of high energy transfer reactions with heavy ion, *Physics Reports, C12*(3), 201–272, 1974.

Arkani-Hamed, N., S. Dimopoulos, and G. Dvali, The hierarchy problem and new dimensions at a millimeter, *Physics Letters B, 429*, 263–272, 1998.

Arnold, R., *et al.*, Double-β decay of ^{116}Cd, *Zeitschrift für Physik C Particles and Fields, 72*(2), 239–247, 1996

Arnold, R., *et al.*, Double-β decay of ^{82}Se, *Nuclear Physics B, 636*, 209–223, 1998.

Arnowitt, R., and P. Nath, Proton decay in three-generation matter-parity-invariant superstring models, *Physical Review Letters, 62*, 2225–2228, 1989.

Austin, S.A., and A.A. Snelling, Discordant potassium-argon model and isochron "ages" for Cardenas Basalt (Middle Proterozoic) and associated diabase of eastern Grand Canyon, Arizona, in *Proceedings of the Fourth International Conference on Creationism*, edited by R.E. Walsh, pp. 35–51, Creation Science Fellowship, Pittsburgh, Pennsylvania, 1998.

Austin, S.A., Do radioisotope clocks need repair? Testing the assumptions of isochron dating using K-Ar, Rb-Sr, Sm-Nd, and Pb-Pb isotopes, in *Radioisotopes and the Age of the Earth: Results of A Young-Earth Creationist Research Initiative*, edited by L. Vardiman, A.A. Snelling, and E. Chaffin, pp. 325–392, Institute for Creation Research, El Cajon, California, and Creation Research Society, Chino Valley, Arizona, 2005.

Bailin, D., and A. Love, *Introduction to Gauge Field Theory*, Institute of Physics Publishing, Bristol and Philadelphia, 1986.

Barabash, A.S., Does the weak interaction constant depend on time? *JETP Letters, 68*(1) (10 July), 1–6, 1998.

Barabash, A.S., Is the weak interaction constant really constant? *European Physical Journal A, 8*, 137–140, 2000.

Barabash, A.S., Possible evidence of time variation of weak interaction constant from double beta decay experiments, *Astrophysics and Space Science, 283*, 607–612, 2003.

Barabash, A.S., Double-beta-decay experiments: present status and prospects for the future, *Physics of Atomic Nuclei, 67*(3), 438–452, 2004.

Behrens, H., and Bühring, W., *Electron Radial Wave Functions and Nuclear Beta-Decays*, Clarendon Press, Oxford, 1982.

Berenyi, D., Recent results on electron capture, *Reviews of Modern Physics, 40*, 390–398, 1968.

Bethke, S., α_s 2002, in a talk at the *QCD 02 High Energy Physics International Conference on Quantum Chromodynamics,* Montpellier (France) July 2–9, 2002, hep-ex/0211012, 2002.

Bjorken, J. D., and S. D. Drell, *Relativistic Quantum Mechanics,* McGraw-Hill, New York, 1964.

Brezin, E., and C. Itzykson, Pair production by an alternating field, *Physical Review D, 2,* 1191–1199, 1970.

Brodzinski, R. L., and D. C. Conway, Decay of Rhenium-187, *Physical Review, 138*(6B), 1368–1371, 1965.

Buck, B., Nuclear-structure information from several-nucleon transfer reaction, in *Nuclear Spectroscopy and Nuclear Reactions with Heavy Ions,* International School of Physics Enrico Fermi course 62, North Holland, Amsterdam, 1976.

Buck, B., A. C. Merchant, and S. M. Perez, New look at alpha decay of heavy nuclei, *Physical Review Letters, 65*(24), 2975–2977, 1990.

Buck, B., A. C. Merchant, and S. M. Perez, Alpha decay calculations with a realistic potential, *Physical Review C, 45,* 2247–2253, 1992.

Calmet, X., and H. Fritzsch, The cosmological evolution of the nucleon mass and the electroweak coupling constants, *European Physical Journal C, 24,* 639–642, 2000.

Calmet, X., and H. Fritzsch, The Higgs boson might not couple to B quarks, *Physics Letters B, 496,* 190–194, 2002.

Candelas, P., and S. Weinberg, Calculation of gauge couplings and compact circumferences from self-consistent dimensional reduction, *Nuclear Physics B, 237,* 397–441, 1984.

Casher, A., H. Neuberger, and S. Nussinov, Chromoelectric-flux-tube model of particle production, *Physical Review D, 20,* 179–188, 1979.

Chaffin, E. F., The Oklo natural uranium reactor: evidence for a young earth, *Creation Research Society Quarterly, 22,* 10–16, 1985.

Chaffin, E. F., Are fundamental "constants" of physics really variables?, in *Proceedings of the Third International Conference on Creationism,* edited by R. E. Walsh, pp. 143–150, Creation Science Fellowship, Pittsburgh, Pennsylvania, 1994.

Chaffin, E. F., A mechanism for accelerated radioactive decay, *Creation Research Society Quarterly, 37*, 3–9, 2000a.

Chaffin, E. F., Theoretical mechanisms of accelerated radioactive decay, in *Radioisotopes and the Age of the Earth: A Young-Earth Creationist Research Initiative*, edited by L. Vardiman, A. A. Snelling, and E. F. Chaffin, pp. 305–331, Institute for Creation Research, El Cajon, California, and Creation Research Society, St. Joseph, Missouri, 2000b.

Chaffin, E. F., A model for the variation of the Fermi constant with time, *Creation Research Society Quarterly, 38*(3), 127–138, 2001.

Chaffin, E. F., and D. S. Banks, A *Mathematica* program using exponentially diffuse boundary square well eigenstates to model alpha-particle tunneling half life variability, *nucl-th/0206020*, 2002.

Chaffin, E. F., and J. Molgaard, The Oklo constraints on alpha-decay half-lives, *nucl-th/0307007*, 2003.

Chaffin, E. F., N. W. Gothard, and J. P. Tuttle, A *Mathematica* program using isotropic harmonic oscillator eigenstates to model alpha-particle tunneling half life variability, *nucl-th/0105070*, 2001.

Chaffin, E. F., S. Moody, and D. Rebar, A semiclassical model for the decay of the neutron, *Bulletin of the American Physical Society, 49*(7), 13, 2004.

Chalov, P. I., and K. I. Merkulova, Comparative rate of oxidation of U-234 and U-238 atoms in certain materials, *Doklady of the Academy of Sciences USSR, Earth Sciences Section, 167*(3), 146–148, 1966.

Chalov, P. I., and K. I. Merkulova, Effects of oxidation on the separation of uranium isotopes during leaching from minerals, *Geokhimiya*, Number 7 (A Supplement to *Geochemistry International, 5*)7, 391–397, 1968.

Chalov, P. I., K. I. Merkulova, and T. Z. Tuzova, Absolute age of the Aral Sea as determined from non-equilibrium uranium, *Doklady of the Academy of Sciences USSR, Earth Sciences Section, 169*(1), 1–3, 1966.

Chivukula, R. S., H.-J. He, J. Howard, and E. H. Simmons, The structure of electroweak corrections due to extended gauge symmetries, *Physical Review D, 69*, 015009-1 to 015009-7, 2004.

Dabholkar, A., and J. A. Harvey, Nonrenormalization of the superstring tension, *Physical Review Letters, 63*(3), 478–481, 1989.

Dai, J., R. G. Leigh, and J. Polchinski, New connections between string theories, *Modern Physics Letters A, 4*, 2073–2083, 1989.

Damour, T., String theory, cosmology, and varying constants, *Astrophysics and Space Science, 283,* 445–446, 2003.

Damour, T., and F.J. Dyson, The Oklo bound on the time variation of the fine-structure constant revisited, *Nuclear Physics B, 480,* 37–54, 1996.

Dassié, D., *et al.,* Two-neutrino double-*beta* decay measurement of ^{100}Mo, *Physical Review D, 51,* 2090–2100, 1995.

Davies, W.G., R.M. DeVries, G.C. Ball, J.S. Forster, W. McLatchie, D. Shapira, J. Toke, and R.E. Warner, A comparison of alpha-transfer and alpha-decay in the lead region, *Nuclear Physics A, 269,* 477–492, 1976.

DeVries, R.M., D. Shapira, W.G. Davies, G.C. Ball, J.S. Forster, and W. McLatchie, Inverse alpha decay via the reaction ^{208}Pb(^{16}O, ^{12}C)^{212}Po, *Physical Review Letters, 35*(13), 835–838, 1975.

DeYoung, D., Radioisotope dating review, in *Radioisotopes and the Age of the Earth: A Young-Earth Creationist Research Initiative,* edited by L. Vardiman, A.A. Snelling, and E.F. Chaffin, pp.27–47, Institute for Creation Research, El Cajon, California, and Creation Research Society, St. Joseph, Missouri, 2000.

Dienes, K.R., E. Dudas, and T. Gherghetta, TeV-Scale GUTs, *hep-ph/9807522,* 1998a.

Dienes, K.R., E. Dudas, and T. Gherghetta, Extra spacetime dimensions and unification, *Physics Letters B, 436,* 55–65, 1998b.

Dienes, K.R., E. Dudas, and T. Gherghetta, Grand unification at intermediate mass scales through extra dimensions, *Nuclear Physics B, 537,* 47–108, *hep-ph/9806292,* 1999.

Dimopoulos, S., S.A. Raby, and F. Wilczek, Unification of couplings, *Physics Today, 44*(1), 25–33, 1991.

Dixon, L.J., *Symmetry Breaking in String Theories via Orbifolds,* Unpublished Ph.D. thesis, Princeton University, *UMI-86-27933-mc,* 163 pp., 1986.

Dixon, L., J.A. Harvey, C. Vafa, and E. Witten, Strings on orbifolds, *Nuclear Physics B, 261,* 678–686, 1985.

Duff, M.J., The theory formerly known as strings, *Scientific American, 278*(2), 64–69, 1998.

Duff, M.J., L.B. Okun, and G. Veneziano, Trialogue on the number of fundamental constants, *Journal of High Energy Physics, 23,* 1–20 [*http://jhep.sissa.it/archive/papers/jhep032002023 /jhep032002023.pdf*], 2002.

Dyson, F. J., Time variation of the charge of the proton, *Physical Review Letters, 19*(22), 1291–1293, 1967.

Dyson, F. J., The fundamental constants and their time variation, in *Aspects of Quantum Theory*, edited by A. Salam and E. P. Wigner, pp. 213–236, Cambridge University Press, 1972.

Eguchi, T., P. B. Gilkey, and A. J. Hanson, Gravitation, gauge theories and differential geometry, *Physics Reports, 66*, 213–393, 1980.

Elliot, S. R., S. R. Hahn, and M. K. Moe, Direct evidence for two-neutrino double-beta decay in ^{82}Se, *Physical Review Letters, 59*(18), 2020–2023, 1987.

Emmanuel-Costa, D., and S. Wiesenfeldt, Proton decay in a consistent supersymmetric SU(5) GUT model, *Nuclear Physics B, 661*, 62–82, 2003.

Feynman, R. P., The status of the conserved vector current hypothesis, in *Proceedings of the 1960 Annual International Conference on High Energy Physics at Rochester*, edited by E. C. G. Sudarshan, J. H. Tinlot, and A. C. Melissinos, The University of Rochester, New York, August 25–September 1, 1960, Interscience, New York, pp. 501–507, 1960.

Feynman, R. P., and M. Gell-Mann, Theory of the Fermi interaction, *Physical Review, 109*, 193–198, 1958.

Franklin, J., *Classical Electromagnetism*, Addison Wesley, San Francisco, 2005.

Fröberg, C.-E., Numerical treatment of Coulomb wavefunctions, *Reviews of Modern Physics, 27*(4), 399–411, 1955.

Fujii, Y., A. Iwamoto, T. Fukahori, T. Ohnuki, M. Nakagawa, H. Hidaka, Y. Oura, and P. Möller, The nuclear interaction at Oklo 2 billion years ago, *Nuclear Physics B, 573*, 377–401, 2000.

Genovese, M., H.-M. Richard, B. Silvestre-Brac, and K. Varga, Baryons electromagnetic mass splittings in potential models, *Proceedings of the ISS*, Tashkent, 6–13 October, 1997, *hep-ph/9710482*, 1997.

Gentry, R. V., *Creation's Tiny Mystery*, Earth Science Associates, Knoxville, Tennessee, 1986.

Georgi, H. M., Grand unified theories, in *The New Physics*, edited by P. Davies, pp. 425–445, Cambridge University Press, New York and Cambridge, 1989.

Georgi, H., and S. L. Glashow, Unity of all elementary-particle forces,

Physical Review Letters, 32(8), 438–441, 1974.

Georgi, H., H. R. Quinn, and S. Weinberg, Hierarchy of interactions in unified gauge theories, *Physical Review Letters, 33*(7), 451–454, 1974.

Gils, H. J., and H. Rebel, Differences between neutron and proton density rms radii of $^{204, 206, 208}$Pb determined by 104 MeV α particle scattering, *Physical Review C, 13*(6), 2159–2165, 1976.

Goeppert-Mayer, M., Double beta-disintegration, *Physical Review, 48*, 512–516, 1935.

Green, A. E. S., and K. Lee, Energy eigenvalues for a spherical well with an exponentially diffuse boundary, *Physical Review, 99*, 772–777, 1955.

Greene, B., *The Elegant Universe*, Vintage Books, New York, 2000.

Günther, M., *et al.*, Heidelberg-Moscow *beta beta* experiment with ^{76}Ge: full setup with five detectors, *Physical Review D, 55*, 54–67, 1997.

Guth, A., and P. Steihhardt, The inflationary universe, in *The New Physics*, pp. 34–60, edited by P. Davies, Cambridge University Press, New York, 1989.

Hawking, S., *A Brief History of Time*, updated and expanded tenth anniversary edition, Bantam Books, New York, 1996.

Hawking, S., *Universe in a Nutshell*, Bantam Books, New York, 2001.

Humphreys, D. R., Accelerated nuclear decay: a viable hypothesis?, in *Radioisotopes and the Age of the Earth: A Young-Earth Creationist Research Initiative*, edited by L. Vardiman, A. A. Snelling, and E. F. Chaffin, pp. 333–379, Institute for Creation Research, El Cajon, California, and Creation Research Society, St. Joseph, Missouri, 2000.

Ivanchik, A., P. Petitjean, E. Rodriguez, and D. Varshalovich, Does the proton-to-electron mass ratio $\mu = m_p/m_e$ vary in the course of cosmological evolution?, *Astrophysics and Space Science, 283*, 583–588, 2003.

Ji, X., A QCD analysis of the mass structure of the nucleon, *Physical Review Letters, 74*, 1071–1074, 1995.

Joyce, D. D., Compact 8-manifolds with holonomy *Spin*(7), *Inventiones Mathematicae, 123*, 507–552, 1996a.

Joyce, D. D., Compact Riemannian 7-manifolds with holonomy G_2. I, *Journal of Differential Geometry, 43*(2), 291–328, 1996b.

Joyce, D. D., Compact Riemannian 7-manifolds with holonomy G_2. II, *Journal of Differential Geometry, 43*(2), 329–375, 1996c.

Kane, G. L., Experimental evidence for more dimensions reported, *Physics Today, 51*(5), 13–15, 1998.

Kaplunovsky, V. S., One-loop threshold effects in string unification, *Nuclear Physics B, 307*, 145–156, 1988.

Kaplunovsky, V. S., Erratum, *Nuclear Physics B, 382*, 436, 1992.

Kimberly, D., and J. Magueijo, *Physics Letters B, 584*, 8–15, 2004.

Kirsten, T., Geochemical double beta decay experiments, in *Science Underground (Los Alamos 1982)*, edited by M. M. Nieto, W. C. Haxton, C. M. Hoffman, E. W. Kolb, V. D. Sandberg, and J. W. Toevs, pp. 396–410, American Institute of Physics, New York, 1983.

Kirsten, T., W. Gentner, and O. A. Schaeffer, Massenspektrometrischer Nachweis von $\beta\beta$-Zerfallsprodukten, *Zeitschrift für Physik, 202*, 273–292, 1967.

Kirsten, T., and H. W. Müller, Observation of ^{82}Se double beta decay in selenium ores, *Earth and Planetary Science Letters, 6*, 271–274, 1969.

Kirsten, T., E. Heusser, D. Kaether, J. Oehm, E. Pernicka, and H. Richter, New geochemical double beta decay measurements on various selenium ores and remarks concerning tellurium isotopes, in *Nuclear Beta Decays and Neutrino*, edited by T. Kotani, H. Ejiri, and E. Takasugi, pp. 81–92, Proceedings of the International Symposium, Osaka, Japan, June 1986, World Scientific, Singapore, 1986.

Kirsten, T., O. W. Schaeffer, E. Norton, and R. W. Stoenner, Experimental evidence for the double-beta decay of Te^{130}, *Physical Review Letters, 20*(23), 136–139, 1968.

Konopinski, E. J., Beta-decay, *Reviews of Modern Physics, 15*, 209–245, 1943.

Konopinski, E. J., and G. E. Uhlenbeck, On the Fermi theory of beta-radioactivity, *Physical Review, 48*, 7–12, 1935.

Konopinski, E. J., and G. E. Uhlenbeck, On the Fermi theory of beta-radioactivity. II. The "forbidden" spectra, *Physical Review, 60*, 308–320, 1941.

Levi, B. G., Two-neutrino double beta-decay seen; neutrinoless decay sought, *Physics Today, 40*(12), 19–22, 1987.

Levine, I., *et al.* (TOPAZ Collaboration), Measurement of the electromagnetic coupling at large momentum transfer, *Physical Review Letters, 78*,

424–427 ,1997.

Lin, W.J., O.K. Manuel, G.L. Cumming, D. Krstic, and R.I. Thorpe, Geochemically measured half-lives of ^{82}Se and ^{130}Te, *Nuclear Physics A, 481*, 477–483, 1988.

Linde, A.D., Phase transitions in gauge theories and cosmology, *Reports on Progress in Physics, 42*, 389–437, 1979.

Linde, A.D., The inflationary universe, *Reports on Progress in Physics, 47*, 925–986, 1984.

Linde, A.D., *The Inflationary Universe*, Addison Wesley, Reading, Massachusetts, 1997.

Liss, T.M., and P.L. Tipton, The discovery of the top quark, *Scientific American, 277*(3), 54–59, 1997.

Lykken, J.D., Weak scale superstrings, *Physical Review D, 54*, 3693–3697, 1996.

Malyshev, V.I., V.G. Melkov, A.L. Yakubovich, Z.A. Sokolova, L.V. Sumin, M.B. Shiryayeva, M.Ye. Kotsen, Yu.P. Salmin, V.I. Kharlamov, V.V. Dunayev, and L.I. Manuilova, Tests of the theory of possible shifts of the U^{235}/U^{238} ratio in nature, *Doklady, Earth Sciences Section, 223*(1–6), 212–214, 1977.

Manuel, O.K., Geochemical measurements of double-beta decay, in *Nuclear Beta Decays and Neutrino*, edited by T. Kotani, H. Ejiri, and E. Takasugi, pp. 71–80, Proceedings of the International Symposium, Osaka, Japan, June 1986, World Scientific, Singapore, 1986.

Manuel, O.K., Geochemical measurements of double-beta decay, *Journal of Physics G, Nuclear and Particle Physics, 17*, S221–S229, 1991.

Marti, K., and S.V.S. Murty, Double beta-decay half-life of ^{82}Se, *Physics Letters B, 163*, 71–74, 1985.

Murty, S.V.S., and K. Marti, Nucleogenic noble gas components in the Cape York iron meteorite, *Geochimica et Cosmochimica Acta, 51*, 163–172, 1987.

Nash, C., and S. Sen, *Topology and Geometry for Physicists*, Academic Press, New York, 1983.

Nath, P., and R. Arnowitt, Matter parity, intermediate scale breaking, and $\sin^2\theta_W$ in Calabi-Yau Superstring models, *Physical Review Letters, 62*, 1437–1440, 1989a.

Nath, P., and R. Arnowitt, Symmetry breaking in three-generation Calabi-Yau manifolds, *Physical Review D, 39*, 2006–2012, 1989b.

Nath, P., and M. Yamaguchi, Effects of extra space-time dimensions on the Fermi constant, *Physical Review D, 60*(11), 116004-1 to 116004-4, 1999.

Nelson, P., Naturalness in theoretical physics, *American Scientist, 73*, 60–67, 1985

Page, D. N., The importance of the anthropic principle, *The World and I*, August 1987, pp. 392–397, 1987.

Parrington, J. R., H. D. Knox, S. L. Breneman, E. M. Baum, and F. Feiner, *Chart of the Nuclides*, fifteenth edition, Knolls Atomic Power Laboratory, 1996.

Pierronne, M., and L. Marquez, On the complex energy eigenvalue theory of alpha decay, *Zeitschrift für Physik A, 286*, 19–25, 1978.

Pontryagin, L. S., *Foundations of Combinatorial Topology*, Dover, New York, 1999.

Potekhin, A. Y, A. V. Ivanchik, D. A. Lanzetta, K. M. Baldwin, G. M. Williger, and R. F. Carswell, Testing cosmological variability of the proton-to-electron mass ratio using the spectrum of PKS 0528-250, *Astrophysical Journal, 505*(2), 523–528, 1998.

Preston, M. A., The theory of alpha-radioactivity, *Physical Review, 71*, 865–877, 1947.

Quigg, C., Top-ology, *Physics Today, 50*(5), 20–26, 1997.

Randall, L., and C. Csaki, The doublet-triplet splitting problem and higgses as pseudo-goldstone bosons, *hep-ph/9508208*, also in *Particles, Strings, and Cosmology*, edited by J. Bagger, World Scientific, Singapore, 1996.

Renton, P., Has the Higgs boson been discovered?, *Nature, 428*, 141–144, 2004.

Rourke, C., and I. Stewart, Poincaré's perplexing problem, *New Scientist, 112* (4 September), 41–45, 1986.

Rubin, M. A., and D. B. Roth, Temperature effects in five-dimensional Kaluza-Klein theory, *Nuclear Physics B, 226*, 444–454, 1983.

Sastry, K. S. R., On the third forbidden beta-decay of [87]Rb, *Physics Letters B, 28*(7), 462–464, 1969.

Schwinger, J., On gauge invariance and vacuum polarization, *Physical Review, 82*, 664–679, 1951.

Shankar, R., *Principles of Quantum Mechanics*, second edition, Plenum, New York, 1994.

Shiu, G., and S.-H.H. Tye, TeV scale superstring and extra dimensions, *Physical Review D, 58*, 106007-1 to 106007-13, 1998.

Shlyakhter, A.I., A direct test of the constancy of the fundamental nuclear constants, *Nature, 264*, 340, 1976.

Snelling, A.A., Radiohalos, in *Radioisotopes and the Age of the Earth: A Young-Earth Creationist Research Initiative*, edited by L. Vardiman, A.A. Snelling, and E.F. Chaffin, pp. 381–468, Institute for Creation Research, El Cajon, California, and Creation Research Society, St. Joseph, Missouri, 2000.

Snelling, A.A., The relevance of Rb-Sr, Sm-Nd and Pb-Pb isotope systematics to elucidation of the genesis and history of recent andesite flows at Mt Ngauruhoe, New Zealand, and the implications for radioisotopic dating, in *Proceedings of the Fifth International Conference on Creationism*, edited by R.L. Ivey, Jr., pp. 285–303, Creation Science Fellowship, Pittsburgh, Pennsylvania, 2003a.

Snelling, A.A., Whole-rock K-Ar model and isochron, and Rb-Sr, Sm-Nd and Pb-Pb isochron, "dating" of the Somerset Dam Layered Mafic Intrusion, Australia, in *Proceedings of the Fifth International Conference on Creationism*, edited by R.L. Ivey, Jr., pp. 305–324, Creation Science Fellowship, Pittsburgh, Pennsylvania, 2003b.

Snelling, A.A., Fission tracks in zircons: evidence for abundant nuclear decay, in *Radioisotopes and the Age of the Earth: Results of a Young-Earth Creationist Research Initiative*, edited by L. Vardiman, A.A. Snelling, and E.F. Chaffin, pp. 209–324, Institute for Creation Research, El Cajon, California, and Creation Research Society, Chino Valley, Arizona, 2005a.

Snelling, A.A., Isochron discordances and the role of inheritance and mixing of radioisotopes in the mantle and crust, in *Radioisotopes and the Age of the Earth: Results of a Young-Earth Creationist Research Initiative*, edited by L. Vardiman, A.A. Snelling, and E.F. Chaffin, pp. 393–524, Institute for Creation Research, El Cajon, California, and Creation Research Society, Chino Valley, Arizona, 2005b.

Snelling, A.A., S.A. Austin, and W.A. Hoesch, Radioisotopes in the diabase sill (Upper Precambrian) at Bass Rapids, Grand Canyon, Arizona:

an application and test of the isochron dating method, in *Proceedings of the Fifth International Conference on Creationism*, edited by R. L. Ivey, Jr., pp. 269–284, Creation Science Fellowship, Pittsburgh, Pennsylvania, 2003.

Srinivasan, B., E. C. Alexander, Jr., R. D. Beaty, D. E. Sinclair, and O. K. Manuel, Double beta decay of ^{82}Se, *Economic Geology, 68*, 252–257, 1973.

Srinivasan, B., E. C. Alexander, Jr., and O. K. Manuel, ^{130}Te-^{130}Xe age determinations of tellurium minerals, *Economic Geology, 67*, 592–596, 1972.

Strominger, A., and E. Witten, New manifolds for superstring compactification, *Communications in Mathematical Physics, 101*, 341–361, 1985.

Taylor, J., Gauge theories in particle physics, in *The New Physics*, edited by P. Davies, pp. 458–480, Cambridge University Press, New York, 1989.

Thomson, J. J., On the electric and magnetic effects produced by the motion of electrified bodies, *Philosophical Magazine, 11*, 229–249, 1881.

't Hooft, G., Naturalness, chiral symmetry, and spontaneous chiral symmetry breaking, in *Recent Developments in Gauge Theories*, edited by G. 't Hooft, C. Itzykson, A. Jaffe, H. Lehman, P. K. Mitter, I. M. Singer, and R. Stora, pp. 135–137, Plenum Press, New York and London, 1980.

Thurber, D. L., Anomalous U^{234}/U^{238} in nature, *Journal of Geophysical Research, 67*, 4518–4520, 1962.

Thurston, W. P., *Three-Dimensional Geometry and Topology*, Princeton University Press, Princeton, New Jersey, 1997.

Thurston, W. P., Orbifolds, in *The Geometry and Topology of Three-Manifolds*, www.msri.org/publications/books/gt3m, accessed 26 March 2004, 2002.

van Ritbergen, T., and R. G. Stuart, Complete 2-Loop quantum electrodynamic contributions to the muon lifetime in the Fermi model, *Physical Review Letters, 82*, 488–491, 1999.

Veneziano, G., The myth of the beginning of time, *Scientific American, 290*(5), 54–65, 2004.

Warburton, E. K., J. A. Becker, B. A. Brown, and D. J. Millener, First-forbidden beta decay near A-40, *Annals of Physics, 187*, 471–501, 1988.

Weber, T. A., C. L. Hammer, and V. S. Zidell, Resonances and analyticity of scattering wave function for square-well type potentials, *American Journal of Physics, 50*(9), 839–845, 1982.

Weinberg, S., Supersymmetry at ordinary energies: masses and conservation laws, *Physical Review D, 26*(1), 287–302, 1982.

Weinberg, S., Charges from extra dimensions, *Physics Letters B, 125*(4), 265–269, 1983a.

Weinberg, S., Overview of theoretical prospects for understanding the values of fundamental constants, *Philosophical Transactions of the Royal Society of London, Series A, Mathematical and Physical Sciences, 310,* 249–252, 1983b.

Wildermuth, K., and W. McClure, *Cluster Representations of Nuclei*, Springer Tracts in Modern Physics No. 41, Springer-Verlag, New York, 1966.

Wilkinson, D. H., Symmetries and nuclei, in *Nuclear Physics with Heavy Ions and Mesons*, edited by R. Balian, M. Rho, and G. Ripka, pp. 877–1017, North Holland, 1978.

Witten, E., Search for a realistic Kaluza-Klein theory, *Nuclear Physics B, 186,* 412–428, 1981.

Witten, E., Some properties of O(32) superstrings, *Physics Letters B, 149,* 351–356, 1984.

Witten, E., Strong coupling expansion of Calabi-Yau compactification, *Nuclear Physics B, 471,* 135–158, 1996.

Witten, E., Deconstruction, G_2 holonomy, and doublet-triplet splitting, *hep-th/0201018,* 2002.

586

Chapter 8

^{14}C Evidence for a Recent Global Flood and a Young Earth

John R. Baumgardner, Ph.D.*

Abstract. A remarkable discovery made over the past twenty-five years is that organic samples from every level in the Phanerozoic portion of the geological record, when tested by highly sensitive accelerator mass spectrometer (AMS) methods, display significant and reproducible amounts of ^{14}C. Because the lifetime of ^{14}C is so brief, these AMS measurements pose an obvious challenge to the standard geological timescale that assigns millions to hundreds of million of years to this part of the rock record. With a half-life of 5730 years, ^{14}C decays to levels undetectable by any currently available technique after only 100,000 years (17.5 half-lives). After one million years (175 half-lives), the amount of ^{14}C remaining is only 3×10^{-53} of the initial ^{14}C concentration—so vanishingly small as to exclude even a single ^{14}C atom in a beginning mass of ^{14}C equal to the mass of the earth itself. However, in samples with uniformitarian ages between one and 500 million years, the peer-reviewed radiocarbon literature documents scores of examples of ^{14}C/C ratios in the range 0.1–0.5 percent of the modern ^{14}C/C ratio. The lower limit of this range is a factor of ten above the detection threshold of most AMS laboratories in the world. Another noteworthy observation is that the ^{14}C/C ratio of these samples appears to be uncorrelated with their position in the geological record. RATE's own measurement of ^{14}C levels in ten coal samples using one of the world's best AMS laboratories strongly confirms both this reported range in ^{14}C/C ratio and the lack of dependence of this ratio on position in the rock record. In terms of ^{14}C age, if one makes the assumption, as is normally done, that the

---

* *Astrogeophysics Department, Institute for Creation Research, Santee, California*

^{14}C/C ratio in these fossilized organisms when they died was close to that of today's atmosphere, the range in ^{14}C/C ratio of 0.1–0.5 percent of the modern value corresponds to ^{14}C ages between 44,000 and 57,000 years. A straightforward but startling inference from these AMS data is that all but the very youngest fossil material in the geological record was buried contemporaneously only thousands of years ago in what must have been a major global cataclysm. The simultaneous destruction of so much life implies, however, that dramatically more total carbon (now in the form of coal, oil, and oil shale) had to be present in the earth's biosphere prior to this cataclysmic event. In this case using today's atmospheric ^{14}C/C ratio as the initial ^{14}C/C ratio for this fossil material almost certainly would not be a proper assumption. Using a lower, more realistic estimate for the biospheric ^{14}C/C ratio prior to this cataclysm reduces the actual ^{14}C age by roughly a factor of ten from about 50,000 years to a value of about 5000 years. This latter age estimate, of course, is consistent with the Biblical account of a global Flood that destroyed most of the life on the planet, both plants and animals, in a single brief cataclysm some four to five millennia ago. Finally, our ^{14}C RATE project has measured ^{14}C/C ratios above the AMS threshold in diamonds from a variety of locations. Although more confirmation is needed to justify a strong claim in this regard, these measurements appear to limit the age of the physical earth itself to the range of thousands (as opposed to billions) of years.

1. Introduction

The presence of detectable ^{14}C in fossils that, according to the uniformitarian timescale, should be entirely ^{14}C-dead has been reported from the earliest days of radiocarbon dating. *Whitelaw* [1970], for example, surveyed all the dates reported in the journal *Radiocarbon* up to 1970 and commented that for the more than 15,000 samples reported, "All such matter is found datable within 50,000 years as published." The samples included coal, oil, natural gas, and other allegedly very ancient material. The reason these anomalies were not taken seriously is because the earlier β-decay counting technique that counted actual ^{14}C decay events had difficulty distinguishing genuine low intrinsic levels of ¹⁴C in the samples from background counts due to cosmic rays. The low ¹⁴C levels measured in samples that, according to their location in the geological record, ought to have been ¹⁴C-dead were therefore simply attributed to the cosmic ray background. This β-counting method was used exclusively until the advent of the accelerator mass spectrometer (AMS) method in the early 1980s. The AMS method, because it counts ¹⁴C atoms directly instead of counting ¹⁴C decay events, does not have this complication of spurious counts due to cosmic rays. In retrospect, in light of the presence of ¹⁴C in AMS measurements at levels significantly above the AMS detection threshold in samples from throughout the Phanerozoic record, it is almost certain that many of the β-counting analyses were indeed recording intrinsic ¹⁴C.

In the late 1990s *Snelling* [1997, 1998, 1999, 2000a, b] applied the highly sensitive AMS technology to fossilized wood derived from Tertiary, Mesozoic, and upper Paleozoic strata having conventional uniformitarian ages ranging from 40 to 250 million years. A reputable commercial laboratory analyzed all the samples, while a specialist laboratory at a major research institute ran several duplicates. In all cases these labs obtained ¹⁴C levels notably above the AMS detection threshold. Values ranged from 7.58±1.11 percent of the modern atmospheric ¹⁴C/C ratio (commonly referred to as *percent modern carbon*, or pMC) for a lower Jurassic sample to 0.38±0.04 pMC for a middle Tertiary sample. This range in ¹⁴C/C ratio implies radiocarbon ages of between 20,700±1200 and 44,700±950 years, respectively, provided one assumes the modern atmospheric ¹⁴C/C ratio existed when these trees were alive. Given the short ¹⁴C half-life, the presence of *any* intrinsic ¹⁴C in these wood samples represents, of course, a profound challenge to the uniformitarian timescale. Such ¹⁴C limits the age of this wood to mere thousands of years, whereas the conventional timescale posits ages from tens to hundreds of millions of years.

Giem [2001] published an article in which he tabulated about seventy AMS measurements published between 1984 and 1998 in the standard radiocarbon literature reporting significant levels of ¹⁴C in organic material that, according to the conventional uniformitarian timescale, should be entirely ¹⁴C dead. Giem documented that organic samples from every portion of the Phanerozoic record display detectable amounts of ^{14}C well above the AMS threshold. For the measurements considered most reliable, these ^{14}C/C ratios appear to fall in the range 0.1–0.5 percent of the modern ^{14}C/C ratio (pMC). He argued that instrument error could be eliminated as an explanation on experimental grounds. He further showed contamination of the ^{14}C-bearing fossil material *in situ* was unlikely, but theoretically possible, and was a testable hypothesis. While contamination during sample preparation was a genuine problem, the literature showed it could be reduced to low levels by proper laboratory procedures. He concluded the ^{14}C detected in these samples most likely originates from the organisms themselves from which the samples are derived. Moreover, because most fossil carbon seems to have roughly the same ^{14}C/C ratio, he deemed it a clear logical possibility that all these fossil organisms had lived together on earth at the same time.

Although all the projects originally identified as part of the RATE initiative involved long half-life radioisotopes, because of the mounting evidence for genuine intrinsic ^{14}C in organic samples throughout the Phanerozoic record (that is, the part of the geological record containing evidence for multicellular life), the RATE group decided in 2001 to add a project to investigate ^{14}C in materials from the portion of the rock record conventionally dated Tertiary and older. One of the priorities of this new project was to undertake AMS analyses on a carefully selected set of samples to attempt to verify the ^{14}C levels reported in the radiocarbon literature for samples that should be ^{14}C-dead according to the uniformitarian timescale. We decided that coal samples from the U. S. Department of Energy Coal Sample Bank maintained at Pennsylvania State University would be an excellent choice for this study, particularly because of the rigorous and uniform quality control involved with their collection, processing, and storage. As will be described in more detail later, the AMS analyses of these samples confirmed both the range of ^{14}C levels that had been reported for Phanerozoic fossil material and the uniformity of this range with respect to depth in the geological record [*Baumgardner et al.*, 2003].

2. Description of the AMS Method

Before we discuss the AMS measurements, let us first review some of the basic features of the AMS technique itself. Briefly, the first step in the AMS method is conversion of the carbon in the sample to CO_2, either by combustion with oxygen or, in the case of carbonates, dissolution in acid. The CO_2 is then reduced to graphite as a spot on an aluminum target that in turn is placed inside the vacuum environment of the AMS system. Within the AMS system, a beam of high-energy cesium ions converts some of the graphite on the target to C^- ions, which in turn are formed into a tight beam at kilovolt energies. This beam of C^- ions is then accelerated to MeV energies and in the process converted to mostly C^{3+} ions. These C^{3+} ions are in turn separated by mass in a strong 90° bending magnet, with the lighter ^{12}C atoms bent more than the ^{13}C atoms, and the ^{13}C atoms more than the ^{14}C atoms. The ^{14}C atoms, the only ones with the proper angular trajectory, are counted in a special detector chamber. The objective is to measure the ratio of ^{14}C to ^{12}C atoms in as precise a fashion as possible. Figure 1 shows the principal components in the Vienna Environmental Research Accelerator, a typical modern AMS facility.

The detection limit for the best modern AMS facilities is about one ^{14}C atom for every 10^{17} C atoms, or an absolute $^{14}C/C$ ratio of 10^{-17}. A more representative limit is a factor of ten larger, or an absolute $^{14}C/C$ ratio of 10^{-16}. Since the modern $^{14}C/C$ ratio in living things is about 10^{-12}, the current AMS technology can reliably measure ratios as low as about 10^{-4} times (0.01%) the modern ratio (0.01 pMC). If one makes the uniformitarian assumption that the modern atmospheric $^{14}C/C$ ratio has prevailed more or less unchanged into the indefinite past, 0.01 pMC implies an age of 75,000 years.

3. AMS ^{14}C Levels in Samples Conventionally Dated as Older than 100,000 Years

Over the past 20 years the primary radiocarbon journals, *Radiocarbon* and *Nuclear Instruments and Methods in Physics Research B,* have

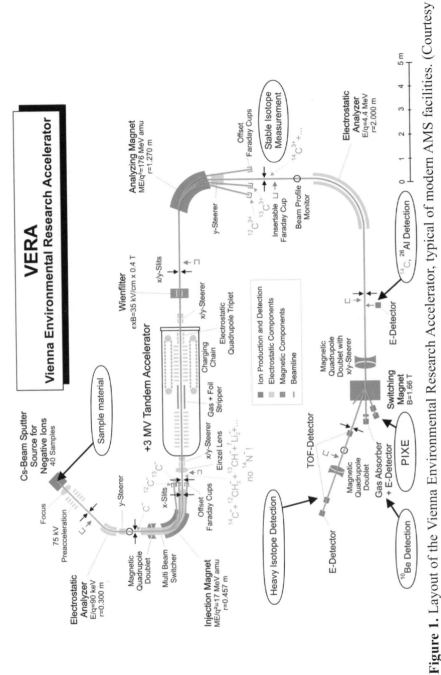

Figure 1. Layout of the Vienna Environmental Research Accelerator, typical of modern AMS facilities. (Courtesy of W. Kutschera, VERA.)

published a significant number of articles reporting AMS measurements made on samples that, based on their conventional geological age, should be ¹⁴C dead. These measurements were performed in several different laboratories around the world. Many were made in an attempt to understand and isolate the source or sources of the unexpected ¹⁴C that always seemed to be present.

Despite the fact that the conventional uniformitarian age for the samples in question was well beyond 100,000 years (in most cases it was tens to hundreds of millions of years), it is helpful nonetheless to be able to translate the results presented in these papers back and forth between a measured ¹⁴C/C ratio and the corresponding ¹⁴C "age." This translation is simple when one makes the usual uniformitarian assumption of a nearly constant ¹⁴C/C level in the atmosphere as one goes backward in time. The conversion is then given by the formula, $pMC = 100 \times 2^{-t/5730}$, where t is the time in years. Applying this formula, one obtains values of 0.79 pMC for $t = 40,000$ years, 0.24 pMC for $t = 50,000$ years, 0.070 pMC for 60,000 years, 0.011 pMC for 75,000 years, and .001 pMC for 95,000 years, as shown in graphical form in Figure 2.

However, as we will show later, if all the organisms represented in the fossil record were alive simultaneously prior to a massive catastrophe that generated the portion of the geological record that now contains their remains, then the amount of total carbon in the biosphere interacting with the atmosphere was dramatically larger prior to the cataclysm. If the source of the ¹⁴C in the system was the same as today, namely, conversion of ¹⁴N atoms to ¹⁴C atoms by cosmic ray generated neutrons in the atmosphere, it is reasonable that the total amount of ¹⁴C in the biosphere could be similar to what it is today. In that case the biospheric ¹⁴C/C ratio would have been much different (that is, smaller), and the simple formula given above would no longer apply. If applied, it would yield ages that were much larger than actual.

Let us now consider the AMS measurements that have been reported over the past 20 years for organic samples that, given their position in the geological record, should have absolutely no intrinsic ¹⁴C. Table 1 contains most of Giem's [2001] data, plus data from several more recent papers. Included in the list are a number of samples from the Precambrian, that is, what we consider non-organic pre-Flood settings. Most of the graphite samples with $^{14}C/C$ values below 0.05 pMC are in this category. Note that ^{14}C levels are reported as $^{14}C/C$ ratios in percent modern carbon (pMC). Figure 2 can be applied to translate $^{14}C/C$ ratios into corresponding conventional radiocarbon ages.

To provide a more visual picture of the distribution of the $^{14}C/C$ ratios presented in Table 1 we show the same data in histogram format in Figure 3. We have separated the source material into three categories:

(1) those (mostly graphites) that are likely from Precambrian geological settings,

(2) those that are likely from Phanerozoic geological settings, and

(3) those (mostly marbles) whose affinity is uncertain.

We show categories (1) and (2) in Figure 3(a) and 3(b), respectively, and ignore for these purposes samples in category (3). Some caution is in order with respect to the nature of comparison implicit in Table 1

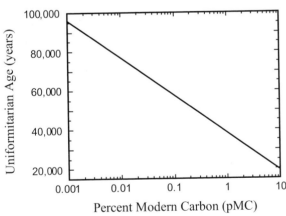

Figure 2. Uniformitarian age as a function of $^{14}C/C$ ratio, in percent modern carbon. The uniformitarian approach for interpreting the ^{14}C data assumes a nearly constant atmospheric $^{14}C/C$ ratio, extrapolated into the indefinite past. It does not account for the possibility of a recent global catastrophe that removed a large quantity of carbon from the global inventory and caused the present atmospheric $^{14}C/C$ ratio to be much higher than it was before the cataclysm.

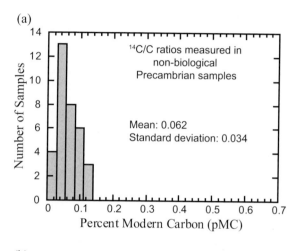

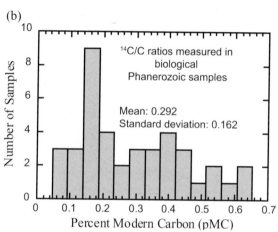

Figure 3. Distribution of ¹⁴C values for (a) non-biogenic Precambrian samples, and (b) biogenic Phanerozoic samples, from Table 1. Given their position in the geological record, all these samples should contain no detectable ¹⁴C according to the standard geological timescale.

and Figure 3. In some cases the reported values have a "background" correction, typically on the order of 0.07 pMC, subtracted from the raw measured values, while in other cases such a correction has not been made. In most cases, the graphite results do not include such "background" corrections since they are usually intended themselves to serve as procedural blanks. Therefore, Figure 3 is to be understood

Table 1. AMS measurements on samples conventionally deemed older than 100 ka.

Item	^{14}C/C (pMC) (±1 SD)	Material	Reference
1	0.71±?*	Marble	*Aerts-Bijma et al.* [1997]
2	0.65±0.04	Shell	*Beukens* [1990]
3	0.61±0.12	Foraminifera	*Arnold et al.* [1987]
4	0.60±0.04	Commercial graphite	*Schmidt et al.* [1987]
5	0.58±0.09	Foraminifera (*Pyrgo murrhina*)	*Nadeau et al.* [2001]
6	0.54±0.04	Calcite	*Beukens* [1990]
7	0.52±.20	Shell (*Spisula subtruncata*)	*Nadeau et al.* [2001]
8	0.52±0.04	Whale bone	*Jull et al.* [1986]
9	0.51±0.08	Marble	*Gulliksen and Thomsen* [1992]
10	0.5±0.1	Wood, 60 ka	*Gillespie and Hedges* [1984]
11	0.46±0.03	Wood	*Beukens* [1990]
12	0.46±0.03	Wood	*Vogel et al.* [1987]
13	0.44±0.13	Anthracite	*Vogel et al.* [1987]
14	0.42±0.03	Anthracite	*Grootes et al.* [1986]
15	0.401±0.084	Foraminifera (untreated)	*Schleicher et al.* [1998]
16	0.40±0.07	Shell (*Turitella communis*)	*Nadeau et al.* [2001]
17	0.383±0.045	Wood (charred)	*Snelling* [1997]
18	0.358±0.033	Anthracite	*Beukens et al.* [1992]
19	0.35±0.03	Shell (*Varicorbula gibba*)	*Nadeau et al.* [2001]
20	0.342±0.037	Wood	*Beukens et al.* [1992]
21	0.34±0.11	Recycled graphite	*Arnold et al.* [1987]
22	0.32±0.06	Foraminifera	*Gulliksen and Thomsen* [1992]
23	0.3±?	Coke	*Terrasi et al.* [1990]
24	0.3±?	Coal	*Schleicher et al.* [1998]
25	0.26±0.02	Marble	*Schmidt et al.* [1987]
26	0.2334±0.061	Carbon powder	*McNichol et al.* [1995]
27	0.23±0.04	Foraminifera (mixed species avg)	*Nadeau et al.* [2001]
28	0.211±0.018	Fossil wood	*Beukens* [1990]
29	0.21±0.02	Marble	*Schmidt et al.* [1987]
30	0.21±0.06	CO_2	*Grootes et al.* [1986]
31	0.20–0.35* (range)	Anthracite	*Aerts-Bijma et al.* [1997]
32	0.20±0.04	Shell (*Ostrea edulis*)	*Nadeau et al.* [2001]
33	0.20±0.04	Shell (*Pecten opercularis*)	*Nadeau et al.* [2001]
34	0.2±0.1*	Calcite	*Donahue et al.* [1997]
35	0.198±0.060	Carbon powder	*McNichol et al.* [1995]
36	0.18±0.05 (range?)	Marble	*Van der Borg et al.* [1997]
37	0.18±0.03	Whale bone	*Gulliksen and Thomsen* [1992]
38	0.18±0.03	Calcite	*Gulliksen and Thomsen* [1992]
39	0.18±0.01**	Anthracite	*Nelson et al.* [1986]
40	0.18±?	Recycled graphite	*Van der Borg et al.* [1997]
41	0.17±0.03	Natural gas	*Gulliksen and Thomsen* [1992]
42	0.166±0.008	Foraminifera (treated)	*Schleicher et al.* [1998]
43	0.162±?	Wood	*Kirner et al.* [1997]
44	0.16±0.03	Wood	*Gulliksen and Thomsen* [1992]
45	0.154±?**	Anthracite coal	*Schmidt et al.* [1987]

Item	^{14}C/C (pMC) (±1 SD)	Material	Reference
46	0.152±0.025	Wood	*Beukens* [1990]
47	0.142±0.023	Anthracite	*Vogel et al.* [1987]
48	0.142±0.028	CaC$_2$ from coal	*Gurfinkel* [1987]
49	0.14±0.02	Marble	*Schleicher et al.* [1998]
50	0.13±0.03	Shell (*Mytilus edulis*)	*Nadeau et al.* [2001]
51	0.130±0.009	Graphite	*Gurfinkel* [1987]
52	0.128±0.056	Graphite	*Vogel et al.* [1987]
53	0.125±0.060	Calcite	*Vogel et al.* [1987]
54	0.12±0.03	Foraminifera (*N. pachyderma*)	*Nadeau et al.* [2001]
55	0.112±0.057	Bituminous coal	*Kitagawa et al.* [1993]
56	0.1±0.01	Graphite (NBS)	*Donahue et al.* [1990]
57	0.1±0.05	Petroleum, cracked	*Gillespie & Hedges* [1984]
58	0.098±0.009*	Marble	*Schleicher et al.* [1998]
59	0.092±0.006	Wood	*Kirner et al.* [1995]
60	0.09–0.18* (range)	Graphite powder	*Aerts-Bijma et al.* [1997]
61	0.09–0.13* (range)	Fossil CO$_2$ gas	*Aerts-Bijma et al.* [1997]
62	0.089±0.017	Graphite	*Arnold et al.* [1987]
63	0.081±0.019	Anthracite	*Beukens* [1992]
64	0.08±?	Natural Graphite	*Donahue et al.* [1990]
65	0.080±0.028	Carrarra marble	*Nadeau et al.* [2001]
66	0.077±0.005	Natural Gas	*Beukens* [1992]
67	0.076±0.009	Marble	*Beukens* [1992]
68	0.074±0.014	Graphite powder	*Kirner et al.* [1995]
69	0.07±?	Graphite	*Kretschmer et al.* [1998]
70	0.068±0.028	Calcite (Icelandic double spar)	*Nadeau et al.* [2001]
71	0.068±0.009	Graphite (fresh surface)	*Schmidt et al.* [1987]
72	0.06–0.11 (range)	Graphite (200 Ma)	*Nakai et al.* [1984]
73	0.056±?	Wood (selected data)	*Kirner et al.* [1997]
74	0.05±0.01	Carbon	*Wild et al.* [1998]
75	0.05±?	Carbon-12 (mass spectrometer)	*Schmidt, et al.* [1987]
76	0.045–0.012 (-0.06)	Graphite	*Grootes et al.* [1986]
77	0.04±?*	Graphite rod	*Aerts-Bijma et al.* [1997]
78	0.04±0.01	Graphite (Finland)	*Bonani et al.* [1986]
79	0.04±0.02	Graphite	*Van der Borg et al.* [1997]
80	0.04±0.02	Graphite (Ceylon)	*Bird et al.* [1999]
81	0.036±0.005	Graphite (air)	*Schmidt et al.* [1987]
82	0.033±0.013	Graphite	*Kirner et al.* [1995]
83	0.03±0.015	Carbon powder	*Schleicher et al.* [1998]
84	0.030±0.007	Graphite (air redone)	*Schmidt et al.* [1987]
85	0.029±0.006	Graphite (argon redone)	*Schmidt et al.* [1987]
86	0.029±0.010	Graphite (fresh surface)	*Schmidt et al.* [1987]
87	0.02±?	Carbon powder	*Pearson et al.* [1998]
88	0.019±0.009	Graphite	*Nadeau et al.* [2001]
89	0.019±0.004	Graphite (argon)	*Schmidt et al.* [1987]
90	0.014±0.010	CaC$_2$ (technical grade)	*Beukens* [1993]

*Estimated from graph **Lowest value of multiple dates

only as a low precision means for gaining a bit more insight into these AMS results.

We draw several observations from this comparison, imprecise as it may be. First, the set of samples with Phanerozoic affinity display a mean value significantly different from those without such affinity. In terms of the standard geological timescale, all these samples should be equally ^{14}C dead. The samples with Phanerozoic affinity display an unambiguously higher mean than those without such affinity, 0.29 versus 0.06 pMC. A second observation is that the variation in ^{14}C content for the Phanerozoic samples is large. Although a peak in the distribution occurs at about 0.2 pMC, the mean value is near 0.3 pMC with a standard deviation of 0.16 pMC. This large spread in ^{14}C content invites an explanation. A third observation, although weaker that the first two, is that the distribution of values for Precambrian material displays a peak offset from zero. This may provide a hint that the carbon not cycled through Phanerozoic living organisms—in many cases locked away in Precambrian geological settings—may nevertheless contain a low level of intrinsic ^{14}C.

4. Coping with Paradigm Conflict

How do the various ^{14}C laboratories around the world deal with the reality that they measure significant amounts of ^{14}C, distinguishably above the detection threshold of their instruments, in samples that should be ^{14}C dead according to the standard geological timescale? A good example can be found in a recent paper by *Nadeau et al.* [2001] entitled, "Carbonate ^{14}C background: does it have multiple personalities?" The authors are with the Leibniz Laboratory at Christian-Albrechts University in Kiel, Germany. Many of the samples they analyze are shells and foraminifera tests from sediment cores. It would be very useful to them if they could extend the range for which they could date such biological carbonate material from roughly 40,000 years ago (according to their uniformitarian assumptions), corresponding to about 1 pMC, toward the 0.002 pMC limit of their AMS instrument, corresponding to about 90,000 years in terms of uniformitarian assumptions. The reason they are presently stuck at this 40,000 year barrier is that they consistently and reproducibly measure ^{14}C levels approaching 1 pMC in shells and foraminifera from depths in the record where, according to the standard geological timescale, there should be no detectable ^{14}C.

Their paper reports detailed studies they have carried out to attempt to understand the source of this ^{14}C. They investigated shells from a late Pleistocene coring site in northwestern Germany dated by U/Th methods at 120,000 years. The mean ^{14}C levels measured in the shells of six different species of mussels and snails varied from 0.1 to 0.5 pMC. In the case of one species, *Spisula subtruncata*, measurements were made on both the outside and inside of the shell of a single individual specimen. The average ^{14}C value for the outside of the shell was 0.3 pMC, while for the inside it was 0.67 pMC. At face value, this suggests the ^{14}C/C ratio more than doubled during the lifetime of this organism. Most of their foraminifera were from a Pleistocene core from the tropical Atlantic off the northwest coast of Africa, dated at 455,000 years. The foraminifera from this core showed a range of ^{14}C values from 0.16 to 0.4 pMC with an average, taken over 115 separate measurements, of 0.23 pMC. A benthic species of foraminifera from another core, chosen because of its thick shell and smooth surface in the hope its "contamination" would be lower, actually had a higher average ^{14}C level of 0.58 pMC.

The authors then performed a number of experiments involving more aggressive pre-treatment of the samples to attempt to remove contamination. These included progressive stepwise acid hydrolization of the carbonate samples to CO_2 gas and ^{14}C measurement of each of four separate gas fractions. They found a detectable amount of surface contamination was present in the first fraction collected, but it was not large enough to make the result from the final gas fraction significantly different from the average value. They also leached samples in hydrochloric acid for two hours and cracked open the foraminifera shells to remove secondary carbonate from inside, but these procedures did not significantly alter the measured ^{14}C values.

The authors summarize their findings in the abstract of their paper as follows:

> The results ... show a species-specific contamination that reproduces over several individual shells and foraminifera from several sediment cores. Different cleaning attempts have proven ineffective, and even stronger measures such as progressive hydrolization or leaching of the samples prior to routine preparation, did not give any indication of the source of contamination.

In their conclusion they state:

> The apparent ages of biogenic samples seem species related and can be reproduced measuring different individuals for larger shells or even different sediment cores for foraminifera. Although tests showed some surface contamination, it was not possible to reach lower ^{14}C levels through cleaning, indicating the contamination to be intrinsic to the sample.

They continue:

> So far, no theory explaining the results has survived all the tests. No connection between surface structure and apparent ages could be established.

The measurements reported in this paper obviously represent serious anomalies relative to what should be expected in the uniformitarian framework. There is a clear conflict between the measured levels of ^{14}C in these samples and the dates assigned to the geological setting by other radioisotope methods. The measured ^{14}C levels, however, are distinguishably above instrument threshold as well as any identifiable sample processing contamination. Moreover, the striking difference in ^{14}C levels among species co-existing in the same physical sample violates the assumption that organisms living together in the same environment should share a common ^{14}C/C ratio. The position the authors take in the face of these conflicts is that this ^{14}C, which should not be present according to their framework, represents "contamination" for which they currently have no explanation. On the other hand, in terms of the framework of a young earth and a recent global Flood, these measurements provide important clues these organisms are much younger than the standard geological timescale would lead one to suspect.

This same approach of treating measurable and reproducible ^{14}C values in samples that ought to be ¹⁴C dead, given their position in the geological record, as "contamination" is found throughout the current literature. *Bird et al.* [1999], for example, freely acknowledge "contamination" in old samples leads to a "radiocarbon barrier":

Detecting sample contamination and verifying the reliability of the ages produced also becomes more difficult as the age of the sample increases. In practice this means that many laboratories will only quote ¹⁴C ages to about 40 ka BP (thousands of ¹⁴C years before present), with ages greater than this generally considered to be "infinite", or indistinguishable from procedural blanks. The so-called "radiocarbon barrier" and the difficulty of ensuring that ages are reliable at <1% modern carbon levels has limited research in many disciplines.

This statement is in the context of a high precision AMS facility the authors use, capable of measuring ¹⁴C levels in the range of <<0.01 pMC.

In their paper they describe a strategy for eliminating various types of genuine contamination commonly associated with charcoal samples. A main component of this strategy is a stepped combustion procedure in which the sample is oxidized to CO_2 in a stepwise manner, at temperatures of 330°C, 630°C, and 850°C, with the resulting CO_2 fractions analyzed separately using AMS. Oxidation of most of any surficial contamination generally occurs at the lowest temperature, and the ¹⁴C level of the highest temperature fraction is generally considered the one representing the least contaminated portion of the sample. The variation among the three fractions is considered a general indicator of the overall degree of contamination. They apply this approach to analysis of charcoal from one of the early sites of human occupation in Australia.

Included in their paper is considerable discussion of what is known as a "procedural blank," or a sample that represents effectively infinite ¹⁴C age. For this they use what they refer to as "radiocarbon-dead" graphite from Ceylon. They apply their stepped combustion procedure, using only the highest temperature fraction, on fourteen such graphite samples to get a composite value of 0.04±0.02 pMC for this background material. The quoted precision is ± one standard deviation. They note that a special pre-treatment they use for charcoal samples, applied to four of the fourteen samples, yielded results indistinguishable from the other ten graphite samples that had no pre-treatment. They further note that sample size variation between 0.1 and 2.2 mg among the fourteen samples also made no difference in the results. From this they acknowledge, "the few ^{14}C atoms observed may already be present in the Ceylon graphite itself." Indeed, they offer no explanation for the fact that this graphite displays ^{14}C levels well above the detection threshold of their AMS system other than it might be inherent to the graphite itself.

Measuring notable levels of ^{14}C in samples intended as procedural blanks or "background" samples is a phenomenon that has persisted from the earliest days of AMS down to the present time. For example, *Vogel et al.* [1987] describe their thorough investigation of the potential sources and their various contributions to the ^{14}C background in their AMS system. The material they used for the blank in their study was anthracite coal from a deep mine in Pennsylvania. An important part of their investigation was variation of the sample size of the blank by a factor of 2000, from 10 μg to 20 mg. They found that samples 500 μg and larger displayed a ^{14}C concentration of 0.44 ± 0.13 pMC, independent of sample size, implying this ^{14}C was intrinsic to the anthracite material itself. For samples smaller than 500 μg, the measured ^{14}C could be explained in terms of this intrinsic ^{14}C, plus contamination by a constant amount of modern carbon that seemed to be present regardless of sample size. After many careful experiments, the authors concluded that the main source of this latter contamination was atmospheric CO_2 adsorbed within the porous Vicor glass used to encapsulate the coal sample in its combustion to CO_2 at 900°C. Another source of smaller magnitude was CO_2 and CO adsorbed on the walls of the graphitization apparatus retained from reduction of earlier samples. It was found that filling the apparatus with water vapor at low pressure and then evacuating the apparatus before the next graphitization mostly eliminated this memory effect. Relative to these two sources, measurements showed that storage and handling of the samples, contamination of the copper oxide used in combustion, and contamination of the iron oxide powder used in the graphitization were effectively negligible. And when the sample size was greater than 500 μg, the intrinsic ^{14}C in the coal swamped all the sources of real ^{14}C contamination. Rather than deal with the issue of the nature of the ^{14}C intrinsic to the anthracite itself, the authors merely refer to it as "contamination of the sample *in situ*," "not [to be] discussed further."

As it became widely appreciated that many high carbon samples, which ought to be ^{14}C dead given their position in the geological record, had in fact ^{14}C levels substantially above AMS machine thresholds, the approach was simply to search for specific materials to use as procedural blanks that had as low a ^{14}C background level as possible. For example, *Beukens* [1990], at the IsoTrace Laboratory at the University of Toronto, describes measurements on two samples that, from his experience at that time, displayed exceptionally low background ^{14}C levels. He reports 0.077 ± 0.005 pMC from a sample of industrial CO_2 obtained by combustion of natural gas and 0.076 ± 0.009 pMC from Italian Carrara marble. Previously for his blank material he had used an optical grade calcite (Iceland spar) for which he measured a ^{14}C level of $0.13–0.15$ pMC. He emphasizes that the pre-treatment, combustion, and hydrolysis techniques applied to these new samples were identical to those normally applied to samples submitted for analysis to his laboratory, and these techniques had not changed appreciably in the previous five years. He states:

> The lower ^{14}C levels in these [more recent] measurements should therefore be attributed entirely to the lower intrinsic ^{14}C contamination of these samples and not to changes in sample preparation or analysis techniques.

Note that he indeed considers the ^{14}C in all these materials to be "intrinsic," but he has to call it "contamination." In his search for even better procedural blanks, he tested two standard blank materials, a calcite and an anthracite coal, used by the Geological Survey of Canada in their β-decay counting ^{14}C laboratory. These yielded ^{14}C levels of 0.54 ± 0.04 pMC for the calcite and 0.36 ± 0.03 pMC for the coal. Beukens noted with moderate alarm that the background corrections being made by many decay-counting radiocarbon dating facilities that had not checked the intrinsic ^{14}C content of their procedural blanks by

AMS methods were probably quoting ages systematically older than the actual ages. His AMS analysis of the samples from the Geological Survey of Canada "clearly shows these samples are not ^{14}C-free," since these levels were markedly higher than those from his own natural gas and marble blanks.

AMS analyses reveal carbon from fossil remains of living organisms, regardless of their position in the geological record, consistently contains ^{14}C levels well in excess of the AMS machine threshold, even when extreme pre-treatment methods are applied. Experiments in which the sample size is varied by large factors seem to demonstrate in a convincing manner that the ^{14}C is intrinsic to the fossil material and not a result of handling or pre-treatment. These conclusions continue to be confirmed in the very latest peer-reviewed papers. Moreover, even non-organic carbon samples appear consistently to yield ^{14}C levels well above machine threshold. Graphite samples formed under metamorphic and reducing conditions in Precambrian limestone environments commonly display ^{14}C values on the order of 0.05 pMC. Most AMS laboratories are now using such Precambrian graphite for their procedural blanks. A good question is what possibly could be the source of the ^{14}C in this Precambrian material? We conclude that one possibility is that this ^{14}C is primordial. Finding ^{14}C in diamond formed in the earth's mantle, as we will describe later, provides support for such a possibility. Establishing that non-organic carbon from the mantle and from Precambrian crustal settings consistently contains inherent ^{14}C well above the AMS detection threshold hints that the earth itself might be less than 100,000 years old, which, of course, is orders of magnitude younger than the 4.56 Ga currently believed by the uniformitarian community.

5. Results of RATE Study of ^{14}C in Coal

Table 2 summarizes the results from ten coal samples prepared by our RATE team and analyzed by one of the foremost AMS laboratories in the world. These measurements were performed using the laboratory's "high precision" procedures which involved four runs on each sample, the

Table 2. Results of AMS ¹⁴C analysis of ten RATE coal samples. The reported values shown in the last column are the measured values minus the laboratory's standard background of 0.077±0.005.

Sample	Coal Seam Name	State	County	Geological Interval	¹⁴C/C (pMC)
DECS-1	Bottom	Texas	Freestone	Eocene	0.30±0.03
DECS-11	Beulah	North Dakota	Mercer	Eocene	0.20±0.02
DECS-25	Pust	Montana	Richland	Eocene	0.27±0.02
DECS-15	Lower Sunnyside	Utah	Carbon	Cretaceous	0.35±0.03
DECS-16	Blind Canyon	Utah	Emery	Cretaceous	0.10±0.03
DECS-28	Green	Arizona	Navajo	Cretaceous	0.18±0.02
DECS-18	Kentucky #9	Kentucky	Union	Pennsylvanian	0.46±0.03
DECS-21	Lykens Valley #2	Pennsylvania	Columbia	Pennsylvanian	0.13±0.02
DECS-23	Pittsburgh	Pennsylvania	Washington	Pennsylvanian	0.19±0.02
DECS-24	Illinois #6	Illinois	Macoupin	Pennsylvanian	0.29±0.03

results of which were combined as a weighted average and then reduced by 0.077±0.005 pMC to account for a "standard background" of contamination believed by the laboratory to be introduced by sample processing. This standard background value is obtained by measuring the ¹⁴C in a purified natural gas. Subtraction of this background value is justified by the laboratory under the assumption that the ¹⁴C in the natural gas analyses must somehow represent contamination. Figure 4 displays these AMS results in histogram format.

5.1 Details of RATE Coal Sample Selection and Analysis

The ten samples in Table 2 were obtained from the U. S. Department of Energy Coal Sample Bank maintained at Pennsylvania State University. The coals in this bank are intended to be representative of the economically important coalfields of the United States. The original samples were collected in 180 kg quantities from recently exposed areas of active mines, where they were placed in 115 liter steel drums with high-density gaskets and purged with argon. As soon as feasible after

J. R. Baumgardner

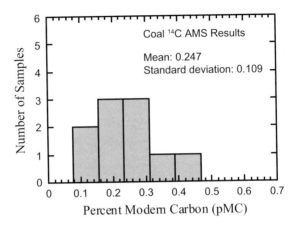

Figure 4. Histogram representation of AMS ^{14}C analysis of ten coal samples undertaken by the RATE ^{14}C research project.

collection, these large samples were processed to obtain representative 300 g samples with 0.85 mm particle size (20 mesh). These smaller 300 g samples were sealed under argon in foil multi-laminate bags and have since been kept in refrigerated storage at 3°C. We selected ten of the thirty-three coals available with an effort to obtain good representation geographically as well as with respect to depth in the geological record. Our ten samples include three Eocene, three Cretaceous, and four Pennsylvanian coals.

The ^{14}C analysis at the AMS laboratory we selected involves processing the coal samples to make graphite targets, and then counting the relative numbers of atoms from the different C isotopes in the accelerator mass spectrometer system. Sample processing consists of three steps: combustion, acetylene synthesis, and graphitization. The coal samples are first combusted to CO_2 and then converted to acetylene using a lithium carbide synthesis process. The acetylene is then dissociated in a high voltage AC electrical discharge to produce a circular disk of graphite on spherical aluminum pellets that represent the targets for the AMS system. Four separate targets are produced for each sample. Every target is analyzed in a separate AMS run with two modern carbon standards (NBS I oxalic acid). Each target is then analyzed on sixteen different spots (organized on two concentric circles). The advantage of this procedure over a single high precision measurement is that a variance check (typically a T-test) can be performed for the sixteen spots on each target. If an individual target fails this variance test, it is rejected. While this has advantages for any kind of sample, it is particularly useful for samples with very low ¹⁴C levels because they are especially sensitive to contamination. While great care is taken to prevent target contamination after the graphitization step, it nevertheless can happen. Any contaminated spot or any contaminated target would bias the average. This variance test attempts to identify and eliminate this source of error.

The background standard of this AMS laboratory is CO_2 from purified natural gas that provides their background level of 0.077±0.005 pMC. This same laboratory obtains values of 0.076±0.009 pMC and 0.071±0.009 pMC, respectively, for Carrara marble (IAEA Standard Radiocarbon Reference Material C1) and optical-grade calcite from Iceland spar. They claim this is one of the lowest background levels quoted among AMS labs, and they attribute this low background to their special graphitization technique. They emphasize backgrounds this low cannot be realized with any statistical significance through only one or two measurements, but many measurements are required to obtain a robust determination.

Table 3 gives the measurements in pMC from the four separate targets for our ten coal samples. The numbers in parentheses are the % errors, calculated from the ¹⁴C count rate of the sample and the two NBS standards, and from the transmission of errors in the ¹²C and ¹³C current measurements of the sample and two standards. The composite results in Table 2 represent the weighted averages of these numbers in Table 3 and the subtraction of a standard background of 0.077±0.005 pMC.

The laboratory has carefully studied the sources of error within its AMS hardware, and regular tests are performed to ensure these remain small. According to these studies, errors in the spectrometer are very low and usually below the detection limit since the spectrometer is energy dispersive and identifies the ion species by energy loss. The detector electronic noise, the mass spectrometric interferences

Table 3. Detailed AMS ^{14}C measurements for ten RATE coal samples in pMC.

Sample	Target 1	Target 2	Target 3	Target 4
DECS-1	0.398 (12.0%)	0.355 (13.2%)	0.346 (15.1%)	0.346 (15.1%)
DECS-11	0.237 (18.2%)	0.303 (14.8%)	0.292 (17.8%)	0.294 (17.2%)
DECS-25	0.342 (13.3%)	0.359 (15.3%)	0.352 (14.2%)	0.328 (14.8%)
DECS-15	0.416 (13.1%)	0.465 (12.2%)	0.467 (12.2%)	0.377 (13.6%)
DECS-16	0.184 (25.0%)	0.233 (21.8%)	0.141 (38.4%)	0.163 (34.0%)
DECS-28	0.203 (18.3%)	0.379 (14.5%)	0.204 (21.2%)	0.204 (21.2%)
DECS-18	0.533 (11.8%)	0.539 (11.4%)	0.492 (11.6%)	0.589 (10.0%)
DECS-21	0.183 (22.0%)	0.194 (20.0%)	0.230 (18.2%)	0.250 (18.0%)
DECS-23	0.225 (18.1%)	0.266 (13.8%)	0.246 (18.7%)	0.349 (13.2%)
DECS-24	0.334 (19.7%)	0.462 (17.5%)	0.444 (13.4%)	0.252 (25.8%)

(the E/q and mE/q^2 ambiguities), and the cross contamination all contribute less than 0.0004 pMC to the background. Ion source contamination as a result of previous samples (ion source memory) is a finite contribution because 50–80% of all sputtered C atoms are not extracted as C ions and are therefore dumped into the ion source region. To limit this ion source memory effect, the ion source is cleaned every two weeks and critical parts are thrown away. This keeps the ion source contamination at approximately 0.0025 pMC for the duration of a two-week run. Regular spot checks of these contributions are performed with a zone-refined, reactor-grade graphite sample (measuring ^{14}C/^{12}C ratios) and blank aluminum target pellets (measuring ^{14}C only).

The laboratory claims most of their quoted system background arises from sample processing. This processing involves combustion (or hydrolysis in the case of carbonate samples), acetylene synthesis, and graphitization. Yet careful and repeated analysis of their methods over more than fifteen years have convinced them that very little contamination is associated with the combustion or hydrolysis procedures, and almost none with their electrical dissociation graphitization process. By elimination they conclude that the acetylene synthesis must contribute almost all of the system background. But they provide little definitive evidence it actually does. Our assessment from the information we have is that the system background value they apply is derived from the ¹⁴C levels they measure in their background standards. They admit that most of the ¹⁴C measured in these standards is intrinsic ¹⁴C. The values we report in Table 2 and Figure 4 nevertheless include the laboratory's subtraction of their standard background. In any case, the measured ¹⁴C/C values are notably above their background value.

6. Results of RATE Measurements of ¹⁴C in Diamond

Given the apparent presence of ¹⁴C at levels well above the AMS threshold in a variety of carbon-bearing materials from the Precambrian portion of the geological record (Table 1 and Figure 3), our RATE team realized that testing for the presence of ¹⁴C in samples of natural diamond would be an important step in either establishing or refuting the premise that ¹⁴C exists at detectable levels in all terrestrial carbon. Natural diamond is a good candidate because it requires high pressure for its formation—pressures realizable only at depths greater than 100 km inside the earth. Diamonds that today are found at or near the earth's surface are generally believed by the uniformitarian community to have been formed in the mantle between one and three billion years ago, and in most cases brought to the surface in the more recent past by violent eruptive events through conduits known as kimberlite pipes. Diamond, creation's hardest substance, is extremely resistant to contamination via chemical exchange with the external environment. Finding ¹⁴C in natural diamond at levels well above the AMS threshold would support the thesis that even carbon that has been locked away from exchange with the atmosphere since early in the earth's history nevertheless contains detectable levels of ¹⁴C. Because of ¹⁴C's short half-life, such a finding would argue that carbon and probably the entire physical earth as well must have a recent origin, unless somehow ¹⁴C can be produced at such levels *in situ* and in the recent past.

The RATE team therefore included a diamond sample along with the ten coal samples in the set of samples sent to the AMS laboratory whose procedures were described in the preceding section. Our sample consisted of about 50 mg of sub-millimeter diamond chips obtained by shattering a diamond from the Kimberley district in South Africa in a sapphire mortar and pestle. Because of the laboratory's lack of experience in oxidizing diamond, it required several attempts before they were successful. They therefore reported their analysis results for the diamond sample several months after those for the ten coal samples. These results came too late to be included in our paper that appeared in the Proceedings volume of the Fifth International Conference on Creationism [*Baumgardner et al.*, 2003], but they were included in the oral presentation at that conference. The ^{14}C/C value for the diamond, which as in the case for the coal samples was a composite number based on four separate AMS runs, was 0.096 ± 0.026 pMC, where the precision represents $\pm1\sigma$, or 68.3% confidence limits. This number, unlike the coal results presented above, does not have the laboratory's standard background of 0.077 ± 0.005 pMC subtracted from it. The reason for reporting the uncorrected measurement here is to be able more clearly to compare it directly with the laboratory's standard background value. From a statistical standpoint, the result for this diamond overlapped, in terms of its confidence limits, the value obtained from a much larger number of runs on the purified natural gas the laboratory uses as its background standard. The fact that the diamond displayed a comparable ^{14}C/C value as the natural gas background standard, however, was consistent with our working hypothesis that all carbon in the earth contains a detectable and reproducible (using the AMS technique) level of ^{14}C. Note that these levels exceed the measurement threshold of <0.01 pMC for the AMS hardware itself by about a factor of ten.

This result from the initial diamond sample encouraged us to obtain and analyze additional diamond samples to either confirm or reject our preliminary conclusion with a higher statistical level of confidence. In September 2003 we acquired several diamonds from two De Beers mines in Botswana. Three of these diamonds are shown in Figure 5. Four such diamonds were crushed to small chips and sent to the same AMS laboratory for analysis. The results from these diamonds, plus one from a placer deposit in the Kankan district of Guinea in West Africa, plus the initial South African diamond, are displayed in Table 4. The ^{14}C/C values for these six diamonds cluster tightly about the

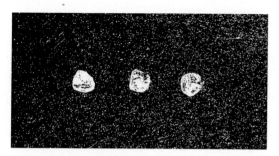

Figure 5. Photo of three diamonds from the Orapa mine, Botswana, from the set analyzed in this study. Weight of each is approximately 0.20 carats, or 40 mg. The average diameter is about 2.5 mm.

mean value of 0.12±0.01 pMC. From a statistical standpoint, this mean value is consistent with an identical ¹⁴C/C ratio in all six of the diamonds. With the larger number of diamond analyses, there was now a clear statistical separation between the mean diamond value and the laboratory's background value of 0.08 pMC obtained by repeated runs on a sample of purified natural gas. The laboratory concurred with this conclusion. We note that by using the usual uniformitarian assumptions for converting a ¹⁴C/C value into an age (which obviously do not apply since these diamonds almost certainly have not experienced any recent exchange of their carbon atoms with those in the atmosphere), one gets a uniformitarian age from this mean ¹⁴C/C ratio of 55,700 years.

Table 4. AMS ¹⁴C results for six African diamonds. The AMS laboratory's high precision procedure was used, but no standard background correction has been applied.

Sample ID	Geological Setting	Country	¹⁴C/C (pMC)
Kimberley-1	kimberlite pipe (Kimberley)	South Africa	0.10±0.03
Orapa-A	kimberlite pipe (Orapa mine)	Botswana	0.14±0.03
Orapa-F	kimberlite pipe (Orapa mine)	Botswana	0.11±0.03
Letlhakane-1	kimberlite pipe (Letlhakane mine)	Botswana	0.12±0.03
Letlhakane-3	kimberlite pipe (Letlhakane mine)	Botswana	0.15±0.02
Kankan	alluvial deposit	Guinea	0.11±0.03

These results motivated us in early 2004 to obtain additional diamonds, this time from alluvial deposits in Namibia in southwest Africa. Each of these six diamonds was crushed to powder and divided into two samples each of approximately 25 mg size. The six pairs of samples were analyzed by the same AMS laboratory that had performed the earlier coal and diamond ^{14}C analyses, applying their high precision method that involved four independent measurements on each sample. Results for these additional six diamonds are displayed in Table 5. The values in the table represent the average of the eight analyses for each diamond as provided by the laboratory, without their standard background correction of 0.08 pMC subtracted away.

Whereas there was little statistical variation in ^{14}C/C levels among the first six diamond samples, this latter set of samples showed a wide spread in their levels, from a smallest value of 0.12 pMC to a largest value of 0.39 pMC. The latter is five times larger than the standard background and higher than all but two of the ten RATE coal samples. What might be the explanation for the dramatic difference in ^{14}C statistics between the first set of six diamonds and the second set? One possible contributor could be the difference in geological setting. Whereas five of the first six diamonds were from deep mines in volcanic kimberlite pipes, all of the second set of diamonds had resided near the earth's surface in water-deposited alluvium, probably for most of the time since they were explosively erupted from subcrustal depths inside the earth.

Table 5. AMS ^{14}C results for six alluvial diamonds from Namibia. The AMS laboratory's high precision procedure was used, but no standard background correction has been applied.

Sample ID	Geological Setting	Country	[14]C/C (pMC)
NMBclr1	alluvial deposit	Namibia	0.39±0.02
NMBclr2	alluvial deposit	Namibia	0.25±0.02
NMBclr3	alluvial deposit	Namibia	0.21±0.03
NMByel1	alluvial deposit	Namibia	0.17±0.02
NMByel2	alluvial deposit	Namibia	0.12±0.02
NMBbrn2	alluvial deposit	Namibia	0.15±0.02

Prior to the time we received the results from the Namibian diamond samples, our working hypothesis on the origin of the ¹⁴C in the diamonds was that it likely represented primordial ¹⁴C formed during the creation of the earth itself. But with these newer results that showed such large ¹⁴C variation from one diamond to the next, we began to explore the alternative possibility that much of the ¹⁴C in these diamonds might have been produced recently, but *in situ*, from a very large flux of thermal neutrons. Two other RATE projects were providing noteworthy evidence that hundreds of millions of years worth of nuclear decay of U has occurred in crustal rocks of the earth within the last few thousand years [*Humphreys et al.*, 2003; *Snelling and Armitage*, 2003; *Humphreys*, 2005; *Snelling*, 2005]. In today's world, α-particles emitted by U and its unstable daughter products interact with lighter elements abundant in crustal rocks such as Si, O, Al, and Mg to generate readily detectable levels of thermal neutrons [*Zito et al.*, 1980]. Episodes of accelerated nuclear decay in the recent past of the sort suggested by our other RATE studies would have generated extreme neutron fluxes throughout the continental crust. As we show in the next section, the ¹⁴C levels generated in turn by such episodes of high neutron flux appear to be of the right order of magnitude to account for the substantial variations in ¹⁴C/C ratio we observe in our diamonds.

In summary, diamond, the material that ought to be the ultimate "standard background" because of its extreme resistance to external contamination, displayed a ¹⁴C/C ratio above the laboratory's standard background for each of the twelve samples analyzed. Table 6 displays the measurements shown in Tables 4 and 5 but with the laboratory's standard background subtracted away. Presented in this manner the diamond results can be compared directly with those for the ten coal samples shown in Table 2. Although the ¹⁴C/C ratios shown in Table 6 are small when the standard background is subtracted away, and in some cases are smaller than the confidence interval of the measurements from which they are derived, they nevertheless are all positive, that is, greater than the laboratory's standard background value. If one averages the values in Table 6 of the five diamonds from kimberlite mines to get better statistics, one obtains the value 0.04 pMC. Doing the same for the

Table 6. AMS ^{14}C results for the twelve diamonds listed in Tables 4 and 5, but with the laboratory's standard background correction applied.

Sample ID	Geological Setting	Country	[14]C/C (pMC)
Kimberley-1	kimberlite pipe (Kimberley)	South Africa	0.02 ± 0.03
Orapa-A	kimberlite pipe (Orapa mine)	Botswana	0.01 ± 0.03
Orapa-F	kimberlite pipe (Orapa mine)	Botswana	0.03 ± 0.03
Letlhakane-1	kimberlite pipe (Letlhakane mine)	Botswana	0.04 ± 0.03
Letlhakane-3	kimberlite pipe (Letlhakane mine)	Botswana	0.07 ± 0.02
Kankan	alluvial deposit	Guinea	0.03 ± 0.03
NMBclr1	alluvial deposit	Namibia	0.31 ± 0.02
NMBclr2	alluvial deposit	Namibia	0.17 ± 0.02
NMBclr3	alluvial deposit	Namibia	0.13 ± 0.03
NMByel1	alluvial deposit	Namibia	0.09 ± 0.02
NMByel2	alluvial deposit	Namibia	0.04 ± 0.02
NMBbrn2	alluvial deposit	Namibia	0.07 ± 0.02

seven alluvial samples, one obtains 0.12 pMC. These data suggest, at least from a statistical standpoint, that ^{14}C exists in these diamonds to a high degree of certainty, as astonishing as that may seem.

7. Quantifying *in situ* [14]C Generation in Crustal Environments

Let us now attempt to quantify the levels of ^{14}C that one might expect to be generated in crustal environments today by subsurface neutrons. *Zito et al.* [1980], in a paper entitled "Possible subsurface production of C-14," identify two primary reactions by which subsurface neutrons can generate ^{14}C in the context of buried organic materials such as coal and also diamonds. The first is a thermal neutron interacting with a ^{14}N atom to produce a ^{14}C atom plus a proton. This reaction, of course, is the one by which most of the ^{14}C in today's world is produced, involving thermalized cosmic ray generated neutrons converting atmospheric ^{14}N atoms into [14]C. Thermal neutrons are produced in crustal rocks, however, primarily by the interactions of α-particles generated by U and Th decay with common isotopes of O, Al, Mg, and Si that are abundant in crustal minerals. Nitrogen-14 occurs at modest levels in most organic materials and also exists at low levels as an impurity in diamonds. The second reaction that conceivably might be important is that of a thermal neutron interacting with a ^{13}C atom to produce a ^{14}C atom plus a γ-ray. About one percent of C atoms, including those in diamond, are ^{13}C. However, because the cross-section for this second reaction with ^{13}C is some 2,000 times smaller than that of the first reaction involving ^{14}N [*Stehn et al.*, 1964], it is probable that in most circumstances this second reaction can be ignored relative to the first. In any case, the following analysis applies to both.

Reliable measurements exist for the volume production rate Q of thermal neutrons currently being generated by radioactive decay processes in various crustal environments, including granite in which moderately high levels of radioactivity are common. In addition, the mean neutron lifetime τ_n and mean velocity v of such thermal neutrons are well known. The subsurface thermal neutron flux Φ in neutrons per unit area per unit time is simply the product of these three quantities, that is, $\Phi = Q\tau_n v$ [*Beckurts and Wirtz*, 1964; *Glasstone and Sesonske*, 1967]. Using 2200 m/sec for the most probable velocity of thermal neutrons at 20°C [*Beckurts and Wirtz*, 1964], 10^{-3} sec for the measured lifetime of thermal neutrons in dry rock [*Humphreys et al.*, 1983] (it is even shorter if any water is present), and 3.3×10^7 thermal neutrons/ m^3/yr as a maximum observed value for the thermal neutron volume production rate in granite in deep mine environments [*Kuhn et al.*, 1984], we obtain an upper bound for the thermal neutron flux Φ in crustal granite of 7.3×10^7 neutrons/m^2/yr.

The volume rate of ^{14}C production in turn is the product of the volume density of ^{14}N atoms, the thermal neutron cross section σ, and the thermal neutron flux Φ. If we seek the steady state ^{14}C/C ratio in which the rate of ^{14}C production equals the rate of ^{14}C decay and normalize by the number of C atoms per unit volume, we get the relation $(^{14}C/C)_{abs} = {}^{14}N/C\ \sigma\Phi\tau_b$, where τ_b is the lifetime of ^{14}C. The measured thermal neutron cross section for this reaction is 1.8 barns $= 1.8 \times 10^{-28}$ m^2 [*Stehn et al.*, 1964], and τ_b for ^{14}C is $5730/\ln 2 = 8267$ years. If we assume a ^{14}N concentration of 0.1% $=0.001$ or 1000 ppm, which is well above the 200 ppm average for peridotitic diamonds and 300 ppm average for eclogitic diamonds [*Dienes et al.*, 1993; *Cartigny*, 2005], we obtain an absolute steady state $^{14}C/C$ ratio of 1.1×10^{-19}. If we then convert this to percent modern carbon (pMC) by dividing by the modern $^{14}C/C$ ratio of 1.2×10^{-12} and multiplying by 100, we get the steady state value $^{14}C/C = 9 \times 10^{-6}$ pMC. This is more than 13,000 times smaller than the mean value of 0.12 ± 0.01 pMC we measured for our first six diamond samples and is far below the AMS detection threshold. We therefore conclude that *in situ* production of ^{14}C by thermal neutrons at presently observed levels is unable, by several orders of magnitude, to account for the ^{14}C levels we measure in our diamond samples. On the other hand, a recent episode of accelerated nuclear decay corresponding to, say, 500 million years worth of U decay, would generate on the order of $5 \times 10^8/\tau_b$ times the steady state $^{14}C/C$ ratio, or 6×10^4 times 9×10^{-6} pMC, or 0.5 pMC, which is close to what we measured in our diamond samples. Moreover, given that the local concentration of U in crustal rocks as well as the N concentration in organic materials are both highly variable, it is not implausible that much if not most of the ^{14}C variability observed in C samples that ought to be ^{14}C dead can be accounted for in this manner also.

8. Major Features of the Geological Record Challenge Uniformitarian Belief

Carbon-14 measurements that yield uniformitarian ages of 40,000–60,000 years for organic samples such as coal with uniformitarian ages of 40–350 million years provided by long half-life isotope methods applied to the surrounding host rocks, not to mention the notable ^{14}C levels in diamonds with uniformitarian ages exceeding a billion years, represent an obvious inconsistency among radioisotope dating techniques. Our hypothesis is that the source of the discrepancy is the interpretational framework that underlies the long half-life methods. We are convinced the proposition, promulgated 180 years ago by Charles Lyell, that the present is the key to the past, simply is not valid. Hence the standard practice, employed all these years by earth scientists and others, of extrapolating the processes and rates observed in today's world into the indefinite past leads to unsound conclusions. As authors of this book we are convinced that there is abundant observational evidence in the geological record that the earth has experienced a global tectonic catastrophe of immense magnitude, one that generated most of the Phanerozoic geological record. Indeed, we are persuaded it is no longer possible successfully to defend the claim that geological processes and rates observable today can account for the majority of the Phanerozoic sedimentary record. To us the evidence is persuasive that global scale processes operating at rates much higher than any observable on earth today are responsible for this geological change (for example, *Austin et al.* [1994] *Baumgardner* [1994a, b, 2003]). Not only are the ¹⁴C data at odds with the standard geological timescale, but the general character of the sedimentary and tectonic record is as well. We realize for many such a view of the geological data is new, or at least controversial. For those new to this possibility we urge reading of some of our papers on this topic. We are convinced that not only do the observations strongly support this interpretation of the geological record, but a theoretical framework also now exists to explain it [*Baumgardner*, 1994a, b, 2003]. Our approach for making sense of these ¹⁴C data, therefore, is to do so in the light of a major discontinuity in earth history in its not so distant past, an event we correlate with the Flood described in the Bible and in many other ancient documents.

9. What Was the ¹⁴C/C Ratio in the Biosphere Before the Flood Cataclysm?

With a date for the Biblical Flood derived from the Masoretic Hebrew text of only about 4500 years ago, which is less than the ¹⁴C half-life, one would expect that ¹⁴C in plants and animals buried in this cataclysm to be detectable today. What sorts of ¹⁴C/C values might we expect to find today in organic remains of plants and animals that perished during this global event which rapidly formed the Cambrian to middle-upper Cenozoic part of the Phanerozoic geological record? Such a cataclysm would have buried a huge amount of C from living organisms to form today's coal, oil, and oil shale, probably most of the natural gas, and some fraction of today's fossiliferous limestone.

Estimates for the amount of C in this inventory are typically several hundred times greater than what resides in the biosphere today [*Brown*, 1979; *Morton*, 1984; *Scharpenseel and Becker-Heidmann*, 1992; *Giem*, 2001]. These studies indicate the biosphere just prior to the cataclysm would have had, conservatively, 300–700 times the total C relative to our present world. Living plants and animals would have contained most of this biospheric C, with only a tiny fraction of the total resident in the atmosphere. The vast majority of this C would have been ^{12}C and ^{13}C, since even in today's world, only about one C atom in a trillion is ^{14}C.

To estimate the pre-Flood $^{14}C/C$ ratio we of course require an estimate for the amount of ^{14}C. As a starting point we might assume the total amount, that is, the total number of atoms, of ^{14}C was similar to what exists in today's world. If that were the case, and this ^{14}C were distributed uniformly throughout the biosphere, and the total amount of biospheric C were, for example, 500 times that of today's world, the resulting $^{14}C/C$ ratio would be 1/500 of today's level, or about 0.2 pMC. This follows from the fact that 500 times more C in the biosphere would dilute the available ^{14}C and cause the biospheric $^{14}C/C$ ratio to be 500 times smaller than today. But this guess of 0.2 pMC is very soft because of the large uncertainly in knowing the total amount of ^{14}C in the pre-Flood world. The short span of time of less than 2000 years between Creation and the Flood, according to the Masoretic text, would mean generation of ^{14}C by cosmic rays in the atmosphere would fall far short of creating the amount of ^{14}C we observe in today's world, even with today's magnetic field strength. A stronger magnetic field would have provided more effective deflection of charged cosmic ray particles and even less ^{14}C generation in the atmosphere. On the other hand, there may well have been some significant amount of ^{14}C generated at Creation as a consequence of the large amount of nuclear disintegration of elements like U and the resulting neutron interactions with ^{14}N. As our other RATE projects document, large amounts of U daughter elements indeed exist today in the earth's earliest rocks. Our present conjecture is that the total mass of ^{14}C in the pre-Flood world was likely not much greater than that of our present world. This then implies a pre-Flood ¹⁴C/C ratio of about 0.2 pMC. Again, we emphasize this estimate is very soft. Accounting for the ¹⁴C decay over the span of 4500 years since the Flood catastrophe reduces the pre-Flood level by a factor of 0.6, so that organisms with 0.2 pMC ¹⁴C 4500 years ago would display a level of 0.12 pMC today. This is a level that can be measured by the AMS technique. Indeed, many of our samples and many of those reported in the radiocarbon literature for samples with uniformitarian ages greater than 100,000 years are in this range.

We note, however, that the amount of ¹⁴C potentially generated *in situ* from an episode of accelerated nuclear decay during the Flood catastrophe, as outlined in a preceding section, can be of comparable or even larger amplitude as that just discussed for the ¹⁴C that existed in the tissues of the pre-Flood organisms. Therefore, as a tentative working explanation of the available measurements, we favor a model that includes both these sources for the observed ¹⁴C. In this working model, the pre-Flood ¹⁴C component would provide a low, more or less uniform, contribution to the total ¹⁴C/C ratio of perhaps 0.05–0.1 pMC. The *in situ* component, on the other hand, would be much more variable and depend on the local U concentration and the amount of N in the sample. Its contribution could be in the range from zero to, perhaps, 1 pMC. The complexity and uncertainties in this working model, however, in no way detract from the reality that the documented levels of ¹⁴C in materials throughout the Phanerozoic record represent a genuine and as yet unresolved difficulty for the uniformitarian framework.

In the context of this section on the pre-Flood ¹⁴C/C ratio, it is useful to note that it is necessary for the ¹⁴C/C ratio to have increased dramatically and rapidly, by a factor on the order of 500, to reach its present value after the cataclysm. The means by which this could have occurred has long been a difficulty for the young-earth Creation/global Flood framework. However, the presence of high levels of crustal neutrons arising from accelerated nuclear decay during the Flood would have converted substantial amounts of crustal N to ¹⁴C, most of which would have been oxidized to CO_2 and eventually escape to the atmosphere. The notable ¹⁴C variations among separate species dwelling in a common Pleistocene environment as well as the striking ¹⁴C differences within the shell of a single specimen, as reported by *Nadeau et al.* [2001] and summarized earlier in Section 4 of this chapter, support the notion that large spatial and temporal variations in the $^{14}C/C$ ratio did indeed exist during the interval immediately following the cataclysm.

10. Effect of an Accelerated Decay Episode on ^{14}C Decay

As already mentioned other RATE projects are building a case for episodes of accelerated nuclear decay accompanying the creation of the earth as well as the Genesis Flood [*Humphreys*, 2005; *Snelling*, 2005]. Evidence from this research suggests that several billions of years worth of cumulative decay at today's rates occurred for isotopes such as ^{238}U during the creation of the physical earth and that a significant amount of such decay likewise took place during the Flood cataclysm. An important issue then arises as to how an episode of accelerated decay during the Flood might have affected a short half-life isotope like ^{14}C. The surprising levels of ^{14}C in fossil material from organisms that were alive before the cataclysm suggests that perhaps only a modest amount of accelerated ^{14}C decay took place during the cataclysm itself, an amount insufficient to eliminate the ^{14}C that existed in these organisms prior to the cataclysm. Accordingly, we here offer the tentative hypothesis that, whatever the physics was describing the decay acceleration, it did not operate in so simple a manner as to reduce temporarily the effective half-lives of all radioisotopes by the same factor. Had this simple description of the process been the case, then all radioisotopes would have experienced a fractional amount of accelerated decay given by $2^{-\alpha t/\tau_{is}}$, where t is the time over which the accelerated decay occurred, τ_{is} is the present half-life of a given radioisotope, and α is the dimensionless acceleration factor. A value of α large enough to produce 500 million years worth of decay in ^{87}Rb with a half-life of 48.8 billion years, for example, would entirely annihilate any ^{14}C that might have been present before the accelerated decay episode occurred. Note that the half-life of ^{87}Rb is 8.5 million times larger than the ^{14}C half-life of 5730 years.

Snelling et al. [2003] and *Austin* [2005], in studies of the K-Ar, Rb-Sr, U-Pb, and Sm-Nd systematics of a Precambrian diabase sill in the

Grand Canyon, provide documentation that the amount of decay for these isotopes does not obey the simple formula of the preceding paragraph. Deviation from this formula is reflected in the discordant isochron dates for this single rock unit. For example, ^{147}Sm yielded a mineral isochron age of 1379±140 Ma while ^{238}U/^{235}U decay yielded a Pb-Pb whole-rock isochron age of 1250±130 Ma. Each decays by α-emission, and ^{147}Sm has a greater half-life than either ^{238}U or ^{235}U. Similarly, of the β-emitters, ^{87}Rb, with the longer half-life yielded a whole-rock isochron age of 1055±46 Ma and a mineral isochron age of 1060±24 Ma, compared to a K-Ar whole-rock isochron age of 841.5±164 Ma. The trend in these data is that the shorter the half-life, both for α- and β-emitters, the less is the amount of decay in terms of elapsed time at today's rates. Carbon-14 is a β-emitter. If one extrapolates the fractional decrease in isochron age, assuming this decrease to scale directly with half-life, obtained for the two β-emitters ^{87}Rb and ^{40}K in this diabase sill to the case of ^{14}C, one obtains an amount of ^{14}C decay of only 3860 years at today's rate. In terms of cumulative radioisotope decay, this Precambrian diabase sill displays about twice the radioisotope age of the earliest Flood rocks. Hence this scaling, speculative as it may be, suggests only about 2000 years worth of accelerated ^{14}C decay occurred during the Flood. This amount of decay represents $1 - 2^{-2000/5730} \sim 20\%$ reduction in ^{14}C as a result of accelerated decay. This is well within the uncertainties in the ^{14}C/C ratio we considered in connection with the pre-Flood world, so it has little impact on the larger issues discussed in this chapter.

11. Discussion

The initial vision that high precision AMS methods should make it possible to extend ^{14}C dating of organic materials back as far as 90,000 years has not been realized. The reason seems to be clear—few, if any, organic samples can be found containing so little ^{14}C! The diverse set of samples studied includes many that uniformitarians presume to be millions, even hundreds of millions, of years old. At face value, these ^{14}C AMS determinations suggest—entirely apart from any consideration of a Flood catastrophe—that life has existed on earth for less than 90,000 years. Although repeated analyses over the past two decades have continued to confirm that ^{14}C is an intrinsic component of the sample material being tested, such ^{14}C is still referred to as "contamination" if it is derived from any part of the geological record deemed older than about 100,000 years. To admit otherwise would call into question the uniformitarian framework. For the creationist, however, this body of data represents obvious support for the recent creation of life on earth. Significantly, the research and data underpinning the conclusion that ^{14}C exists in fossil material from all portions of the Phanerozoic record are already established in the standard peer-reviewed literature. Moreover, the work has been performed largely by uniformitarians who hold no bias whatever in favor of this outcome. The evidence is now so compelling that additional AMS determinations on samples from deep within the Phanerozoic record can make the case only marginally stronger than it already is.

Indeed, the AMS results for our ten coal samples, as summarized in Table 2 and Figure 4, fall nicely within the range for similar analyses reported in the radiocarbon literature, as presented in Table 1 and Figure 3(b). Not only are the mean values of the two data sets almost the same, but the variances are also similar. Moreover, when we average the results from our coal samples over a geological interval, we obtain mean values of 0.26 pMC for Eocene, 0.21 pMC for Cretaceous, and 0.27 pMC for Pennsylvanian—remarkably similar to one another. These results, limited as they are, indicate little difference in ^{14}C level as a function of position in the Phanerozoic portion of the geological record. This is consistent with the young-earth view that the entire fossil record up to somewhere within the middle-upper Cenozoic is the product of a single recent global catastrophe. On the other hand, an explanation for the notable spread in the ^{14}C ratios among the ten samples of Table 2 was at first not obvious to us. However, as we calculated the levels of ^{14}C that would be generated by thermal neutrons in the crust as a consequence of an episode of accelerated nuclear decay during the Flood, we realized that such an *in situ* source of ^{14}C possibly is of sufficient magnitude to account for the observed variation, given the large variations in N content and local U concentration.

If through further study we are able to find a reliable means to resolve the fraction of the total ^{14}C that is due to *in situ* generation from that which was present in the material before the accelerated decay episode, we can potentially, using ^{14}C, place strong constraints on the age of the earth itself. Establishing, for example, that diamonds contain a component of their ^{14}C that cannot be accounted for by *in situ* generation would, because of the short ^{14}C half-life, limit the age of the earth to mere thousands of years instead of the uniformitarian billions. A nearly constant ^{14}C/C ratio in diamonds characterized by low N levels could imply, for example, their ^{14}C is primordial and not from *in situ* generation. Already documented in the radiocarbon literature are inorganic materials such as Iceland spar that display consistent and reproducible levels of [14]C. These could be analyzed further for their N content and, if sufficiently low, would add support to the case that a low level of ^{14}C, on the order of 0.005–0.1 pMC, is still present from the earth's earliest history. This would be significant evidence for a young earth. We therefore believe a research effort focused on these issues deserves continued earnest support.

12. Conclusions

The careful investigations performed by scores of researchers in more than a dozen AMS facilities in several countries over the past twenty years in an attempt to identify and eliminate sources of contamination in AMS ^{14}C analyses have, as a by-product, served to establish beyond any reasonable doubt the existence of intrinsic ^{14}C in remains of living organisms from all portions of the Phanerozoic record. Such samples, with "ages" from 1–500 Ma as determined by other radioisotope methods applied to their geological context, consistently display ^{14}C levels that are well above the AMS machine threshold, reliably reproducible, and typically in the range of 0.1–0.5 pMC. Such levels of intrinsic ^{14}C represent an obvious difficulty for uniformitarianism. After one million years, corresponding to 174.5 ^{14}C half-lives, the fraction of original ^{14}C remaining is 3×10^{-53}. Yet a mass of ^{14}C equal to the entire mass of the earth (6×10^{24} kg) contains only about 3×10^{50} [14]C atoms.

Under uniformitarian assumptions, not a single atom of ^{14}C formed one million years ago anywhere in or on the earth should conceivably still exist. The clear inconsistency between the ages implied by the AMS-determined ^{14}C/C ratios and the corresponding rock ages provided by [238]U, [87]Rb, and [40]K techniques can no longer be treated merely as a yet to be understood anomaly by the specialists, for the time being to be explained away as "[14]C contamination," and therefore ignored by rest of the scientific world. Inconsistency of this magnitude demands substantive explanation. Our explanation is that the assumption of time-invariant nuclear decay rates is almost certainly not correct and is, in fact, the root of this inconsistency. Our other RATE research projects (for example, *Humphreys* [2005] and *Snelling* [2005]) lend strong support to this conclusion. Put simply, the evidence of ^{14}C throughout the Phanerozoic part of the geological record argues the half billion years of time uniformitarians assign to this portion of earth history was instead a much briefer interval. Moreover, the relatively narrow range of ^{14}C/C ratios suggests all Phanerozoic fossil organisms prior to somewhere in the middle to upper Cenozoic were contemporaries and perished almost simultaneously in the not so distant past. Finally, we note the presence of detectable levels of ^{14}C in natural diamonds, formed deep within the earth during its early history, hints the age of the planet itself may likewise be constrained by the brief life span of [14]C. We therefore conclude the ^{14}C data provide noteworthy support for a recent global Flood and a young earth.

Acknowledgments

I would like to thank Paul Giem for the helpful input that prompted our team to initiate this project. I thank Andrew Snelling for his pioneering vision in applying the AMS method to wood samples from deep within the geological record well prior to the RATE effort and for the extra confidence his results provided during the initial stages of this project. I thank Steve Austin for his preparation of the ten RATE coal samples and Luis Morales for his preparation of the diamonds for AMS analysis. I thank Russ Humphreys for the derivation of the rate of ^{14}C production in subsurface crustal environments due to thermal neutrons arising from nuclear decay processes as presented in Section 7 of this chapter. I thank several anonymous reviewers for their careful reviews of the chapter and for the considerable improvement these reviews afforded. I also express heartfelt appreciation to the RATE donors who provided the financial means to undertake the AMS analyses of the coal and diamond samples.

References

Aerts-Bijma, A. T., H. A. J. Meijer, and J. van der Plicht, AMS sample handling in Groningen, *Nuclear Instruments and Methods in Physics Research B, 123*, 221–225, 1997.

Arnold, M., E. Bard, P. Maurice, and J. C. Duplessy, ¹⁴C dating with the Gif-sur-Yvette Tandetron accelerator: status report, *Nuclear Instruments and Methods in Physics Research B, 29*, 120–123, 1987.

Austin, S. A., Do radioisotope clocks need repair? Testing the assumptions of isochron dating using K-Ar, Rb-Sr, Sm-Nd, and Pb-Pb isotopes, in *Radioisotopes and the Age of the Earth: Results of a Young-Earth Creationist Research Initiative*, edited by L. Vardiman, A. A. Snelling, and E. F. Chaffin, pp. 325–392, Institute for Creation Research, El Cajon, California, and Creation Research Society, Chino Valley, Arizona, 2005.

Austin, S. A., J. R. Baumgardner, D. R. Humphreys, A. A. Snelling, L. Vardiman, and K. P. Wise, Catastrophic plate tectonics: a global flood model of earth history, in *Proceedings of the Third International Conference on Creationism*, edited by R. E. Walsh, pp. 609–621, Creation Science Fellowship, Pittsburgh, Pennsylvania, 1994.

Baumgardner, J. R., Computer modeling of the large-scale tectonics associated with the Genesis Flood, in *Proceedings of the Third International Conference on Creationism*, edited by R. E. Walsh, pp. 49–62, Creation Science Fellowship, Pittsburgh, Pennsylvania, 1994a.

Baumgardner, J. R., Runaway subduction as the driving mechanism for the Genesis Flood, in *Proceedings of the Third International Conference on Creationism*, edited by R. E. Walsh, pp. 63–75, Creation Science Fellowship, Pittsburgh, Pennsylvania, 1994b.

Baumgardner, J. R., Distribution of radioactive isotopes in the earth, in *Radioisotopes and the Age of the Earth: A Young-Earth Creationist Research Initiative*, edited by L. Vardiman, A. A. Snelling, and E. F. Chaffin, pp. 49–94, Institute for Creation Research, El Cajon, California, and Creation Research Society, St. Joseph, Missouri, 2000.

Baumgardner, J. R., Catastrophic plate tectonics: the physics behind the Genesis Flood, in *Proceedings of the Fifth International Conference on Creationism*, edited by R. L. Ivey, Jr., pp. 113–126, Creation Science Fellowship, Pittsburgh, Pennsylvania, 2003.

Baumgardner, J. R., A. A. Snelling, D. R. Humphreys, and S. A. Austin, Measurable ^{14}C in fossilized organic materials: confirming the young earth Creation-Flood model, in *Proceedings of the Fifth International Conference on Creationism*, edited by R. L. Ivey, Jr., pp. 127–142, Creation Science Fellowship, Pittsburgh, Pennsylvania, 2003.

Beckurts, K. H., and K. Wirtz, *Neutron Physics*, Springer-Verlag, New York, p. 100, 1964.

Beukens, R. P., High-precision intercomparison at IsoTrace, *Radiocarbon, 32*, 335–339, 1990.

Beukens, R. P., Radiocarbon accelerator mass spectrometry: background, precision, and accuracy, in *Radiocarbon After Four Decades: An Interdisciplinary Perspective*, edited by R. E. Taylor, A. Long, and R. S. Kra, pp. 230–239, Springer-Verlag, New York, 1992.

Beukens, R. P., Radiocarbon accelerator mass spectrometry: background and contamination, *Nuclear Instruments and Methods in Physics Research B, 79*, 620–623, 1993.

Beukens, R. P., D. M. Gurfinkel, and H. W. Lee, Progress at the IsoTrace radiocarbon facility, *Radiocarbon, 28*, 229–236, 1992.

Bird, M. I., L. K. Ayliffe, L. K. Fifield, C. S. M. Turney, R. G. Cresswell, T. T. Barrows, and B. David, Radiocarbon dating of "old" charcoal using a wet oxidation, stepped-combustion procedure, *Radiocarbon, 41*(2), 127–140, 1999.

Bonani, G., H.-J. Hofmann, E. Morenzoni, M. Nessi, M. Suter, and W. Wölfli, The ETH/SIN dating facility: a status report, *Radiocarbon, 28*, 246–255, 1986.

Brown, R. H., The interpretation of C-14 dates, *Origins, 6*, 30–44, 1979.

Cartigny, P., Stable isotopes and the origin of diamond, *Elements, 1,* 79–84, 2005.

Dienes, P., J. W. Harris, and J. J. Gurney, Depth-related carbon isotope and nitrogen concentration variability in the mantle below the Orapa kimberlite, Botswana, Africa, *Geochimica et Cosmochimica Acta, 57,* 2781–2796, 1993.

Donahue, D. J., A. J. T. Jull, and L. J. Toolin, Radiocarbon measurements at the University of Arizona AMS Facility, *Nuclear Instruments and Methods in Physics Research B, 52,* 224–228, 1990.

Donahue, D. J., A. J. T. Jull, and T. H. Zabel, Results of radioisotope measurements at the NSF-University of Arizona tandem accelerator mass spectrometer facility, *Nuclear Instruments and Methods in Physics Research B, 5,* 162–166, 1984.

Donahue, D. J., J. W. Beck, D. Biddulph, G. S. Burr, C. Courtney, P. E. Damon, A. L. Hatheway, L. Hewitt, A. J. T. Jull, T. Lange, N. Lifton, R. Maddock, L. R. McHargue, J. M. O'Malley, and L. J. Toolin, Status of the NSF-Arizona AMS Laboratory, *Nuclear Instruments and Methods in Physics Research B, 123,* 51–56, 1997.

Giem, P., Carbon-14 content of fossil carbon, *Origins, 51,* 6–30, 2001.

Gillespie, R., and R. E. M. Hedges, Laboratory contamination in radiocarbon accelerator mass spectrometry, *Nuclear Instruments and Methods in Physics Research B, 5,* 294–296, 1984.

Glasstone, S., and A. Sesonske, *Nuclear Reactor Engineering,* Van Nostrand Reinhold, New York, p. 72, 1967.

Grootes, P. M., M. Stuiver, G. W. Farwell, D. D. Leach, and F. H. Schmidt, Radiocarbon dating with the University of Washington accelerator mass spectrometry system, *Radiocarbon, 28,* 237–245, 1986.

Gulliksen, S., and M. S. Thomsen, Estimation of background contamination levels for gas counting and AMS target preparation in Trondheim, *Radiocarbon, 34,* 312–317, 1992.

Gurfinkel, D. M., An assessment of laboratory contamination at the IsoTrace radiocarbon facility, *Radiocarbon, 29,* 335–346, 1987.

Humphreys, D. R., Young helium diffusion age of zircons supports accelerated nuclear decay, in *Radioisotopes and the Age of the Earth: Results of a Young-Earth Creationist Research Initiative,* edited by L. Vardiman, A. A.

Snelling, and E. F. Chaffin, pp. 25–100, Institute for Creation Research, El Cajon, California, and the Creation Research Society, Chino Valley, Arizona, 2005.

Humphreys, D. R., R. W. Barnard, H. M. Bivens, D. H. Jensen, W. A. Stephenson, and J. H. Weinlein, Uranium logging with prompt fission neutrons, *International Journal of Applied Radiation and Isotopes, 34*(1), 262–268, 1983 (see Figure 3, p. 262).

Humphreys, D. R., J. R. Baumgardner, S. A. Austin, and A. A. Snelling, Helium diffusion rates support accelerated nuclear decay, in *Proceedings of the Fifth International Conference on Creationism*, edited by R. L. Ivey, Jr., pp. 175–196, Creation Science Fellowship, Pittsburgh, Pennsylvania, 2003.

Jull, A. J. T., D. J. Donahue, A. L. Hatheway, T. W. Linick, and L. J. Toolin, Production of graphite targets by deposition from CO/H_2 for precision accelerator ^{14}C measurements, *Radiocarbon, 28*, 191–197, 1986.

Kirner, D. L., R. E. Taylor, and J. R. Southon, Reduction in backgrounds of microsamples for AMS ^{14}C dating, *Radiocarbon, 37*, 697–704, 1995.

Kirner, D. L., R. Burky, R. E. Taylor, and J. R. Southon, Radiocarbon dating organic residues at the microgram level, *Nuclear Instruments and Methods in Physics Research B, 123*, 214–217, 1997.

Kitagawa, H., T. Masuzawa, T. Makamura, and E. Matsumoto, A batch preparation method for graphite targets with low background for AMS ^{14}C measurements, *Radiocarbon, 35*, 295–300, 1993.

Kretschmer, W., G. Anton, M. Benz, S. Blasche, E. Erler, E. Finckh, L. Fischer, H. Kerscher, A. Kotva, M. Klein, M. Leigart, and G. Morgenroth, The Erlangen AMS facility and its applications in ^{14}C sediment and bone dating, *Radiocarbon, 40*, 231–238, 1998.

Kuhn, M. W., S. N. Davis, and H. W. Bentley, Measurements of thermal neutrons in the subsurface, *Geophysical Research Letters, 11*(6), 607–610, 1984. (The value of 33 neutrons/cm^3/yr is the largest observed at depths greater than 800 m.)

McNichol, A. P., A. R. Gagnon, E. A. Osborne, D. L. Hutton, K. F. Von Reden, and R. J. Schneider, Improvements in procedural blanks at NOSAMS: reflections of improvements in sample preparation and accelerator operation, *Radiocarbon, 37*, 683–691, 1995.

Morton, G. R., The carbon problem, *Creation Research Society Quarterly*, *20*, 212–219, 1984.

Nadeau, M.-J., P. M. Grootes, A. Voelker, F. Bruhn, A. Duhr, and A. Oriwall, Carbonate ¹⁴C background: does it have multiple personalities?, *Radiocarbon*, *43(*2A), 169–176, 2001.

Nakai, N., T. Nakamura, M. Kimura, T. Sakase, S. Sato, and A. Sakai, Accelerator mass spectroscopy of ¹⁴C at Nagoya University, *Nuclear Instruments and Methods in Physics Research B*, *5*, 171–174, 1984.

Nelson, D. E., J. S. Vogel, J. R. Southon, and T. A. Brown, Accelerator radiocarbon dating at SFU, *Radiocarbon*, *28*, 215–222, 1986.

Pearson, A., A. P. McNichol, R. J. Schneider, and C. F. Von Reden, Microscale AMS ¹⁴C measurements at NOSAMS, *Radiocarbon*, *40*, 61–75, 1998.

Scharpenseel, H. W., and P. Becker-Heidmann, Twenty-five years of radiocarbon dating soils: paradigm of erring and learning, *Radiocarbon*, *34*, 541–549, 1992.

Schleicher, M., P. M. Grootes, M.-J. Nadeau, and A. Schoon, The carbonate ¹⁴C background and its components at the Leibniz AMS facility, *Radiocarbon*, *40*, 85–93, 1998.

Schmidt, F. H., D. R. Balsley, and D. D. Leach, Early expectations of AMS: greater ages and tiny fractions. One failure?—one success, *Nuclear Instruments and Methods in Physics Research B*, *29*, 97–99, 1987.

Snelling, A. A., Radioactive "dating" in conflict! Fossil wood in ancient lava flow yields radiocarbon, *Creation Ex Nihilo*, *20*(1), 24-27, 1997.

Snelling, A. A., Stumping old-age dogma: radiocarbon in an "ancient" fossil tree stump casts doubt on traditional rock/fossil dating, *Creation Ex Nihilo*, *20*(4), 48–51, 1998.

Snelling, A. A., Dating dilemma: fossil wood in ancient sandstone, *Creation Ex Nihilo*, *21*(3), 39–41, 1999.

Snelling, A. A., Geological conflict: young radiocarbon date for ancient fossil wood challenges fossil dating, *Creation Ex Nihilo*, *22*(2), 44–47, 2000a.

Snelling, A. A., Conflicting "ages" of Tertiary basalt and contained fossilized wood, Crinum, central Queensland, Australia, *Creation Ex Nihilo Technical Journal*, *14*(2), 99–122, 2000b.

Snelling, A. A., Radiohalos in granites: evidence for accelerated nuclear decay, in *Radioisotopes and the Age of the Earth: Results of a Young-Earth*

Creationist Research Initiative, edited by L. Vardiman, A. A. Snelling, and E. F. Chaffin, pp. 101–207, Institute for Creation Research, El Cajon, California, and Creation Research Society, Chino Valley, Arizona, 2005.

Snelling, A. A., and M. H. Armitage, Radiohalos—a tale of three granitic plutons, in *Proceedings of the Fifth International Conference on Creationism*, edited by R. L. Ivey, Jr., pp. 243–268, Creation Science Fellowship, Pittsburgh, Pennsylvania, 2003.

Snelling, A. A, S. A. Austin, and W. A. Hoesch, Radioisotopes in the diabase sill (Upper Precambrian) at Bass Rapids, Grand Canyon, Arizona: an application and test of the isochron dating method, in *Proceedings of the Fifth International Conference on Creationism*, edited by R. L. Ivey, Jr., pp. 269–284, Creation Science Fellowship, Pittsburgh, Pennsylvania, 2003.

Stehn, J. R., M. D. Goldberg, B. A. Magurno, and R. Wiener-Chasman, *Neutron Cross Sections, Vol. I, Z = 1 to 20*, second edition, Supplement No. 2, BNL 325, Brookhaven National Laboratory, p. 7-14-1, 1964.

Terrasi, F., L. Campajola, A. Brondi, M. Cipriano, A. D'Onofrio, E. Fioretto, M. Romano, C. Azzi, F. Bella, and C. Tuniz, AMS at the TTT-3 tandem accelerator in Naples, *Nuclear Instruments and Methods in Physics Research B, 52*, 259–262, 1990.

Van der Borg, K., C. Alderliesten, A. F. M. de Jong, A. van den Brink, A. P. de Haas, H. J. H. Kersemaekers, and J. E. M. J. Raaymakers, Precision and mass fractionation in ^{14}C analysis with AMS, *Nuclear Instruments and Methods in Physics Research B, 123*, 97–101, 1997.

Vogel, J. S., D. E. Nelson, and J. R. Southon, ^{14}C background levels in an accelerator mass spectrometry system, *Radiocarbon, 29*, 323–333, 1987.

Whitelaw, R. L., Time, life, and history in the light of 15,000 radiocarbon dates, *Creation Research Society Quarterly, 7*(1), 56–71, 1970.

Wild, E., R. Golser, P. Hille, W. Kutschera, A. Priller, S. Puchegger, W. Rom, and P. Steier, First ^{14}C results for archaeological and forensic studies at the Vienna environmental research accelerator, *Radiocarbon, 40*, 273–281, 1998.

Zito, R., D. J. Donahue, S. N. Davis, H. W. Bentley, and P. Fritz, Possible subsurface production of carbon-14, *Geophysical Research Letters, 7*(4), 235–238, 1980.

Chapter 9

Statistical Determination of Genre in Biblical Hebrew: Evidence for an Historical Reading of Genesis 1:1–2:3

Steven W. Boyd, Ph.D.*

Abstract. It is axiomatic that a Biblical text cannot be properly interpreted unless its genre is known. This is particularly true for poetry *vis-à-vis* prose. The goal of this study was to determine the genre of Genesis 1:1–2:3 and to explore the hermeneutical implications of this finding. To accomplish this task it was necessary to develop a method to rigorously distinguish Biblical Hebrew poetry from narrative, in general. But the task was formidable, because Biblical authors left us no hermeneutical treatises, labeled their texts inconsistently (and these refer to content rather than form) and did not even have a word for poetry. Moreover, our best manuscripts attest a unique "brick-upon-brick" stichography only for old poetry. Perforce, Hebraists have turned to study the texts themselves to discover an objective and accurate method for distinguishing these genres. Subjective descriptions of each abound, but the nature of these genres is that the characteristics of each blur into the characteristics of the other: major features of one are not absent from the other. An alternative approach therefore was undertaken to address this problem: a statistical analysis of countable linguistic features. Two populations were identified using the descriptive methods well documented in the literature. A stratified random sample from each population was generated and the finite verb distribution for each was determined. Side-by-side scatter plots of the ratio of preterites to total finite verbs for each text in the narrative sample *vis-à-vis* those in the poetry sample revealed that this ratio varies with genre to the extent that it could have the inferential capacity to classify texts. To determine if this was the case, the null hypothesis H_0, that a logistic regression model

* *Associate Professor of Bible, The Master's College, Santa Clarita, California*

derived from the relative frequency of preterites observed in the joint-sample classifies texts according to genre no better than chance classification, was tested against the alternative hypothesis H_1, that the model classifies texts better. This null hypothesis was rejected with $p < .0001$. In addition, the model was found to reduce the number of classification errors in the sample by more than 96% when compared to random classification. When extended to the population level, it was found that our logistic regression model based on relative frequency of preterites yields a superb protocol (between 85.5 and 95.5% reduction in the number of classification errors) for categorizing texts as narrative or poetry at a 95% confidence level. The logistic regression model calculates the probability that a text is a narrative. For Genesis 1:1–2:3, this probability is between 0.999942 and 0.999987 at a 99.5% confidence level. Thus, we conclude with statistical certainty that this text is narrative, not poetry. It is therefore statistically indefensible to argue that this text is poetry. The hermeneutical implication of this finding is that this text should be read as other historical narratives, whose authors evinced supererogatory concern with the past and staunchly upheld the historicity of their accounts even to the point of challenging their contemporaries to prove or disprove their documented historical references.

1. Introduction

What kind of text is Genesis 1:1–2:3? To answer this question it is necessary to address a longstanding *desideratum* of Biblical Hebrew studies: a method to objectively and accurately determine the genre[†] of texts.[1] In particular, the most pressing and prevalent task is distinguishing poetry from prose. As *Berlin* [2003, p. 2097] has recently said,

> The identification of biblical poetry and the definition of what constitutes poetry in the Bible has been a vexed issue since early post-biblical times.

1.1 The Importance of this Task

Few if any scholars would doubt the significance of establishing the

---

[†] See the Glossary (p. 725, after the Appendices and Endnotes) for definitions of selected terms.

genre of texts as a prerequisite to correctly interpreting them. *Wendland* [1994, p. 386] remarks:

> ... what are the features that mark a text as being 'poetic' as distinct from 'prosaic' in nature? The distinction between prose and poetry is important, for it affects how the process of interpreting a given text is carried out, for example, more or less literally, or with greater or lesser emphasis on formal patterning.[2]

But how severe are the philological and hermeneutical repercussions for genre misidentification?

In a *Hi and Lois* comic strip from a number of years ago, baby Trixie is listening to Hi and Lois having a conversation, which is full of figures of speech: "hot news," "bumped into," "knocking down doors," "ran into," "hit me up for a loan" and "my boss chewed me out." Insensible to such metaphors she imagines her parents involved in a chain of violent encounters [*Browne*, 1989]. Her utterly erroneous interpretation is more than just humorous and illustrative. When applied to Biblical hermeneutics, it poignantly teaches us that genre misidentification of Biblical texts will lead to equally fatuous misunderstanding—but, with far more serious consequences.

Consider the following two texts: Psalm 98:8: "The rivers will clap their hands. In unison the mountains will sing for joy" and 2 Kings 24:10–17:

> At that time the servants of Nebuchadnezzar the king of Babylon came up to Jerusalem and the city was besieged ... and Jehoiachin king of Judah came out to the king of Babylon ... [Nebuchadnezzar] carried off all the treasures of ... And the king of Babylon made Mattaniah, Jehoiachin's uncle, king in his place.

How should these texts be read? Doubtless, the first text is not suggesting that rivers and trees literally clap their hands. Such an absurdity signals the reader that the words of the text comprise the vehicle of a metaphor and, therefore, that the genre of the text is poetry.

On the other hand, the second text is clearly asserting that the Babylonians actually executed a prolonged siege of Jerusalem. Its genre is narrative. Even without the independent corroboration of the

Babylonian Chronicle, the reader knows what the Biblical text is saying, whether he assents to its historicity or not.

What if the first text were read as narrative instead of poetry? What if the historical account of the surrender of Jerusalem in 597 BC, which is recorded in 2 Kings 24:10–17, were read as if it were non-literal? What if the reader were to look for some non-existent tenor of a vehicle, which plainly reports reality? Obviously, to read a text counter to its genre would lead to aberrant philology and tortured hermeneutics.

As important as it is to distinguish poetry from prose for texts in general, it is even more important for Genesis 1:1–2:3 in particular, because there is nothing less at stake than our understanding of the fundamental text of the Bible.

Is Genesis 1:1–2:3 an historical narrative (with the plain sense of its words corresponding to reality and the sequence of events portrayed correlating with real time) or an extended poetic metaphor?

Answering this question will determine how Genesis 1:1–2:3 *should* be read.

1.2 Overview of this Chapter

Section 2 examines two important interpretive issues: the major approaches, which have been advocated for reading Genesis 1:1–2:3, and the interrelationships among author, readers and text, which must be understood to properly interpret a text. Subsequent to this, Section 3 briefly surveys and evaluates qualitative approaches to distinguishing Biblical poetry from narrative. Then, the bulk of this chapter (Sections 4–5) presents the method and results of a quantitative approach to determining the genre of texts: a statistical model, which accurately classifies texts as poetry or prose. After this general *desideratum* is accomplished, this model is applied—in Section 6—to Genesis 1:1–2:3, in particular, in order to answer the crucial question: is this text narrative or poetry? Section 7 explores the hermeneutical implications of this determination. And Section 8 contains the conclusions of the study. Acknowledgments follow. The back matter comprises four Appendices, Endnotes, Glossary and References.

2. Interpretive Issues

2.1 Three Approaches to Reading Genesis 1:1–2:3

How *should* we read Genesis 1:1–2:3? Note that I said *should*, not *can*. There are three *possible* approaches to reading and interpreting this text:

(1) reading it as an extended poetic metaphor, which communicates truth but the plain sense of its words does not correspond to reality;

(2) reading it as a narrative, which purports to be the truth when in fact it is in error;

(3) reading it as a narrative, which accurately portrays reality.[3]

In approach number 1 this text is read as an extended poetic metaphor, (rather than as an historical narrative), which teaches a truth, but its words do not have their normal meanings and the sequence of events portrayed in it should not be correlated with real time. But is this approach linguistically defensible? First we will briefly consider the morphology, syntax and vocabulary of this text.

Its grammar differs little from other narrative texts. The morphological sequences found in this text are well represented in historical narrative texts but not in poetic texts.[4] Moreover, its vocabulary is neither rare nor obscure. Taken at face value its meaning also appears to be clear. In fact, advocates of this approach often acknowledge the plain sense of the text[5]—God created the world in six 24-hour days—but at the same time insist that this cannot be what the text means.[6]

In addition its plain sense does not appear to be absurd or contradictory to the rest of the Bible—the normal diagnostics for detecting metaphor. For example, it is obvious that the phrase, "YHWH is my rock," is the vehicle of a metaphor, because its plain sense is both absurd—since the LORD is not actually a rock—and contradictory—because He is a spirit.

Why then is a straightforward historical interpretation rejected? Two lines of arguments have been advanced: textual and extra-textual. As far as the first is concerned three objections have been offered against an historical reading of the text.[7] The first objection offered is that an historical reading stems from a misunderstanding of the nature of narrative; that the correct understanding is that the text tells a story, which is to be separated from the events it portrays and communicates a message, which is also distinct from actual history.

Waltke [2004], drawing on *Sternberg* [1985], presents this objection. Although, it is true that Sternberg separates the narrative from the events, he *vehemently opposes* the idea that the *Biblical author* separated them:

> Suppose the Creation narrative elicited from the audience the challenge "But the Babylonians tell a different story" .... Would the biblical narrator shrug his shoulders as any self-respecting novelist would do? *One inclined to answer in the affirmative would have to make fictional sense of all the overwhelming evidence to the contrary; and I do not see how even a confirmed anachronist would go about it with any show of reason. This way madness lies—and I mean interpretive, teleological as well as theological madness* [*Sternberg*, 1985, p. 32; emphasis mine].

Moreover, Sternberg's main thesis is that the genius of Old Testament narrative is that the historiographical, literary and theological (what he calls "ideological") aspects of the text are not only in balance but dependent on one another in a non-mutually exclusive nexus [*Sternberg*, 1985, pp. 1–57].[8]

The second objection is that the text exhibits temporal incoherence. Anachrony elsewhere in the Scriptures is adduced as evidence: in the Gospels (between pericopes), Genesis 11:1–9 being a flashback, and the order of the plagues in Psalm 105 differing from the account in Exodus. But all but the last of these occur between narratives, not within them. Psalm 105 (and Psalms 78 and 106) represent a special case, in which narrative clauses are juxtaposed in poetic bicolons.

Or, it is alleged that structure for theological purpose can nuance temporality. The structure of the account of the fourth day of Creation is given as an example. Although it is true that this account is in the form of an elaborate palistrophic structure, which defines the exact role of the sun, moon and stars as "rulers," this does not preclude the account referring to actual events.

Or it is asserted that a literal reading would contradict later texts[9] and scientific paradigms: that too many events happened on day six for it to be an ordinary 24-hour day; that light could not precede the creation of the Sun, etc. However, these are just opinions. In short, other texts (Biblical or otherwise) and non-textual considerations are given priority over the text itself in interpreting it.

Finally, the third objection is that there are anthropomorphisms in Genesis 1:1–2:3. But, the Biblical narratives are replete with anthropomorphisms: in the patriarchal narratives, in Exodus, in Joshua, in Judges, in Samuel, in Kings, in Daniel, in Ezra, in Nehemiah and in Chronicles. We certainly would not question the historicity of these texts because of attested anthropomorphisms.

The second line of argument—and by far the main reason—that an historical reading of Genesis 1:1–2:3 is rejected is actually extra-textual: such a reading advances a theory of origins at variance with the reigning scientific theory (whatever is the current incarnation of evolution).

Approach number 1 often is manifested when the text is read through the lens of science (a naturalistic interpretation of empirical data is made to trump the plain reading of the text) or when the text is read as if it were meant to be a scientific treatise. In an effort to make the Biblical text comply with a certain set of conclusions drawn from empirical evidence, approach number 1 is adopted for this text. It is asserted that a literal hermeneutic would introduce contradictions with the findings of science, which has presented supposedly irrefragable proof that the earth is billions of years old.[10] Consequently, the text is interpreted in such a way so as not to contradict these findings. The reason: to save the integrity of the truth of the text. The result: words are assigned meanings, which are deracinated from their immediate literary context and stripped of their plain sense. It is a noble undertaking to defend the truth of the text. But is it linguistically defensible to read *this* text as a poem?

Neither approach number 2 (Genesis 1:1–2:3 is an erroneous narrative) nor approach 3 (Genesis 1:1–2:3 is an accurate historical narrative) has the findings of science as its hermeneutical starting point. In both of these approaches *this* text is read as a narrative. But they differ regarding its historicity. In approach number 2 the historicity of the text is rejected. In approach number 3 the historicity of the text is affirmed. Proponents of approach number 2 adopt a literal approach to the text, reading the text as a narrative—most Hebraists recognize a narrative when they see one—but at the same time denying its historicity.[11] They adamantly insist that the author believed in the truth of what he was saying, but just as adamantly do not accept the account as factual, adducing putative contradictions with empirical "evidence" to support this position.

On the other hand, in approach number 3, Genesis 1:1–2:3 is read as an historical narrative, which portrays real events. Why read this text as an historical narrative? First of all it is the plain reading of the text. Second, it is the reading that comes from the *text*, not from external considerations. The *text* is the starting point of interpretation. The *text* is the standard, to which the conclusions drawn from empirical evidence must conform. Third, Genesis 1:1–2:3 is linked thematically and lexically to the rest of Genesis and by extension to the rest of the grand narrative recounted in Exodus 1:1–2 Kings 25:30 (which I understand to be an historical narrative).

When the Biblical Creation account in Genesis 1:1–2:3 is read as an ordinary narrative text, albeit, with extraordinary content, it is clear what the author is asserting: eternal God created space, time, matter, the earth, the atmosphere, the oceans, the continents, plants and trees, the sun, moon and stars, aquatic creatures, flying creatures, land animals and man and woman in one week, in that order. Furthermore, if the Flood account (Genesis 6:5–9:29) is read in the same way, we must conclude that that same author is asserting that the earth originally created was inundated with a catastrophic deluge of such proportions that the earth was returned to the empty featureless water globe (its initial state when God created it). Based on this approach to these texts, the only tenable view for the age of the earth is that it is young.

This series of conclusions drawn by the reader is predicated on the hermeneutical approach that the Biblical Creation account (Genesis 1:1–2:3) and the Flood account (Genesis 6:5–9:29) should be read as other historical narratives are read—that these texts relate a sequence of events in which narrative time corresponds to real time and in which words have a range of meaning refined by a hierarchy of contexts, starting with the text under examination. Underlying this approach is the assumption that these texts are historical narratives.

Three approaches—which one is correct? How did the author of this text *intend* for his text to be read?[12]

2.2 Understanding Texts: The Relationship of Author and Readers

The last paragraph raises an issue that has been hotly debated in literary circles: is it possible to discover the intent of an author? Or is this a quixotic quest, doomed to failure? Since the middle of the twentieth century hermeneutical theory has questioned and in some cases rejected the concept of auctorial intent. *Wimsatt and Beardsley* [1976, p. 1] stated in their now classic essay "The Intentional Fallacy":

> The design or intention of the author is neither available nor desirable as a standard for judging the success of a work of literary art.[13]

It is argued that we cannot know an author's intent, because it was in the mind of the author, a place inaccessible to us.

Although it is true that we cannot know what was in the mind of an author, this does not imply that we cannot know his intent, because evidence of his intent is found in an accessible place, his text. His mind is reflected in his text. In fact, proponents of a relatively new field of text linguistic studies, pragmatics,[14] maintain that textual meaning is author based.

For example, building on the seminal work of *Halpern* [1988], *Winther-Nielsen* [2002] asserts that an author of a text intended to *communicate* something to his readers.[15] So readers are *not* free—contra reader criticism, deconstructionism and post-modernism—to interpret a text any way they choose. Moreover, *Winther-Nielsen* [2002, p. 67] argues that texts are *coherent,* that authors of texts wrote their texts aware of the contexts of their first readers. As he so memorably states: "words are anchored in worlds by the will of the writer".

In clarifying the concept of coherence *Winther-Nielsen* [2002, p. 68] writes:

The coherence principle first of all explains how *meaning in a contextual sense* is solidly anchored in situations without being completely relative or polyvalent [Winther-Nielsen's italics].

So, the author guides his readers by means of sometimes subtle, sometimes obvious cues how he wants them to read his text. Citing *Tomlin et al.* [1997], *Winther-Nielsen* [2002, p. 69; emphasis mine] states:

> Instead the speaker (or author) becomes the architect of his text who guides his listener (or reader) in construing a *conceptual representation* of events and ideas. The speaker (author) as the architect and the hearer (reader) as constructor must both construe a coherent text through their integration of knowledge and management of information. The hearer (reader) makes pragmatic implicatures from the contextual situation and builds cognitive inferences from the text and the world knowledge he shares with the speaker (author).

In other words, the author shaped his text commensurate with the particular historical, cultural, linguistic and ideological context he had in common with his original readers.

We might picture the production of a text as in Figure 1. The author looks at an event (1) and then at his original readers (2) in order to produce his text (3).

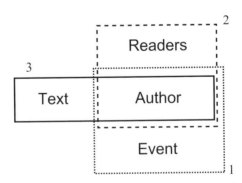

Figure 1. Production of a text by an author.

Our task of interpretation as modern readers is more difficult than that of the original readers: we do not have the advantage of living in the context(s) in which the text was written. What was intuitive for them, we must deduce. How can we know what was the *conceptual representation* of the author and original readers, since the author has not given us a separate treatise on this subject?[16] *Winter-Nielsen* [2002, p. 69, note 51] quotes *Tomlin et al.* [1997, p. 104; emphasis mine] again in this regard:

> Morpho-syntactic cues reveal the memorial and attentional characteristics of the speakers (author's) *conceptual representation* and direct those of the listener (reader) to conform to the speaker's (author's) conceptual representation.

In other words, a Biblical author has left his stamp on his work in the language itself. The result is that the author—either inadvertently or deliberately—has placed sufficient cues in his text so that it can be interpreted correctly.

Although the author did not provide a separate hermeneutical treatise comprising these cues, modern readers can deduce them by detecting, assembling and cogently analyzing the clues in the text. Readers are not free to apply arbitrary criteria to the interpretive process.[17] As *Winther-Nielsen* [2002, p. 61] says:

> Readers of literary texts are tied to authors by many mutual assumptions that 'constrain how the meaning of texts are defined'.[18]

Halpern [1988, p. 9] states that the reader must "accurately construe the author's intent." So, readers must be guided by the clues offered by the intratextual, intertextual and extratextual contexts of a text.

Thus, texts provide readers clues as to how they should be read. I submit that *whether an author wanted his readers to treat his text as an extended poetic metaphor, which communicates a theological message, or as a historical narrative, which relates both an accurate account of the event and a powerful theological message [Sternberg, 1985],[19] must have been part of his* **conceptual representation** *and fairly obvious to his original readers.* Did he want his readers to believe in the plain meaning of his words or in some derived message disconnected from his words? The text itself will answer the question: should we read this text as an extended metaphorical poem? Or should we read it as an historical narrative?

3. Problems of a Qualitative Approach

3.1 Problems with External Indicators

The task of finding external indicators, which rigorously distinguish poetry from prose, is a daunting one from the outset for at least five reasons. First, there is no word for poetry in Biblical Hebrew. The words "poetry," "poet," and "poem" come from the Greek verb ποιειν *poiein*, "to do" or "to make." There is no corresponding derivation in Biblical Hebrew.

Second, the nature of Hebrew poetry—in contrast to Greek poetry—was not clarified by its contemporaries: there is no extant treatise on Hebrew poetry from the period in which it was written.

Third, Biblical authors did not consistently label their texts—whether it was because they had no category called poetry or because they knew it would be obvious to their readers is a moot point—nor did the Dead Sea Scrolls copyists, nor did the Masoretic scholars responsible for our best Hebrew texts.

Some poems are marked in the text: Exodus 15; Deuteronomy 32; Judges 5; 2 Samuel 1:19–27; 22; Isaiah 5:1–7; Song of Solomon and a dozen or so psalms. Each text says that it is either a שִׁירָה *šîrāʰ* "song" (Exodus 15:1; Deuteronomy 31:30; 2 Samuel 22:1; Song of Solomon) or a קִינָה *qînāʰ* "dirge" (2 Samuel 1:17–27), that someone sang it (Judges 4:24) or both that it was a song and someone sang it (Exodus 15:1; Isaiah 5:1–7).

But not all poems are so marked. Large poetic sections in the Prophets are not marked—for example in Isaiah. Moreover, the marking most likely refers to content rather than form.

Fourth, terms which describe poetic compositions, such as psalms, are used inconsistently and refer to content rather than form. For example, in Psalms, the words מִזְמוֹר *mizmôr* "praise composition" and שִׁיר *šîr* or שִׁירָה *šîrāʰ* "song," occur in superscriptions, but refer to content not form. In addition, not all psalms are so marked. Only 57 have the first term: 35 psalms have the second term only Psalm 18 has the third. Another example is the word מָשָׁל *māšāl* applied to the aphorisms in the

Book of Proverbs. This term refers to the frequent comparisons between abstract principles and concrete observations made in the book.

This leads us to the fifth reason: the extant manuscripts and codices provide no reliable guidance to the reader. This would seem to be surprising at first because, the fact that the four poems Exodus 15, Deuteronomy 32, Judges 5 and 2 Samuel 22 have a distinct stichography in the oldest codices, the Aleppo Codex (A) and the Leningrad Codex (L), could suggest that the copyists had poetic sensibilities.

The Leningrad Codex is the oldest complete extant codex of the Hebrew Bible.[20] In his managing editor's introduction to this codex, *Beck* [1998, p. 11; also note 6] writes concerning the Song of the Sea (Exodus 15):

> This poem, laid out in poetic stichs, is one of our earliest examples of prosody in the Bible. It offers numerous clues as to just what was considered poetry in the early traditions that ultimately informed the Bible.

He is speaking of the codex's "brick upon brick" textual arrangement of Exodus 15 and Judges 5 and the bicolon layout of Deuteronomy 32 and 2 Samuel 22.[21] Is his assessment correct or were the copyists indicating something else?

It is true that these four texts are laid out differently in L, but so are plainly non-poetic lists in Joshua 12:9–24; 1 Samuel 6:17; and Esther 9:7–9. Moreover, other poems in the Torah, both major and minor, are given the default, three-column format: Adam's words to Eve (Genesis 2:23); the cruel poem of Lamech to his wives (Genesis 4:23–24); Jacob's final blessings upon his sons (Genesis 49); the oracles of Balaam (Numbers 23–24); and even the final blessing of Moses (Deuteronomy 33).

The same three-column format is also found in the Prophets, in portions that by all other indications are poetry. In the Former Prophets the Song of Hannah (1 Samuel 2:1–10) and the Song of the Bow (2 Samuel 1:19–27) are clearly poems, but are not marked by the "brick upon brick" stichography. And inexplicably, not a single poetic text in the Latter Prophets and the Writings is so marked!

In addition, in L, the texts of the books distinguished by a separate accentuation system, Job, Proverbs and Psalms, have a two-column format, but the text is not laid out in poetic bicolons, instead it is continuous from column one to column two—like a newspaper. But again great poetic texts in the Prophets and the Writings do not have this arrangement! In fact, these texts are written in the same three column format as narrative texts!

All of these inconsistencies in the stichography suggest that its purpose was not to indicate genre.[22]

3.2 Problems with Internal Indicators: Parallelism

Since there is no consistent external means of identifying Biblical Hebrew poetry, attempts to clarify the nature of poetry are reduced to an examination of the poetry itself. Here also there is endless debate and no consensus. There are those who say that prose and poetry do not differ in kind but rather in degree. *Wendland* [1994, p. 386] states:

> However, as in much of art, so also in literary discourse, it is not so much a matter of either-or as it is more-or-less.

Although parallelism (phonological, morphological, syntactic, the infrequent lexical, semantic, and merely formal) is the main structural feature of Biblical Hebrew poetry—in particular the poetic line—not all would agree that it rigorously distinguishes poetry from prose. *Kugel* [1981]—who calls parallelism a "seconding sequence"—argues that this feature occurs in both poetry and prose (albeit, I would argue, blatantly and almost always in the former and more subtly and rarely in the latter).[23]

The problem of a qualitative approach is clearly illustrated in *Kugel's* [1981, pp. 59–62] *tour de force* presentation of the case for "seconding sequences" occurring *outside* the traditional poetic texts. He argues that such texts as "and the LORD visited Sarah as He said. And the LORD did for Sarah as He had spoken" (Genesis 21:1), "God has made me laugh. All who hear will laugh at me" (Genesis 21:6) and "do not stretch out your hand against the boy. Do not do anything to him" (Genesis 22:12) exhibit parallelism. Who could argue? Particularly in the first and third examples the second sentence does little to advance the story line, but rather reiterates and restates what was said in the first. His other examples, however, are not as convincing: narrative passages are artificially laid out in a bicolon structure, which he imposes on the text. After imposing this structure on the text of Exodus 2:1–7, he compares it with Psalm 106:29–34. He maintains that the structure is the same for both. But this psalm and Psalms 78 and 105 are rather unique in the Psalms: they are historical psalms with parallel narrative clauses.

Alonzo-Schökel [1966, pp. 56–57] concludes on the issue of the distinction between the two genres:

> It is no more possible to draw a clear division between the characteristics of poetic style and prose than between "poetic" vocabulary and "prosaic" vocabulary. ... stylistic devices ... by their frequency and their force, are a sign of poetic language. Meeting them in prose, we feel an unexpected poetic resonance.[24]

Although *Berlin* [2003, p. 2097] concurs that both are elevated discourse she also so aptly states, "... at a certain point quantitative difference becomes qualitative difference."

I will give *Kugel* [1981, p. 83] the last word. He quips about Alonzo-Schökel's remark:

> Yet one is moved to wonder precisely how much 'unexpected poetic resonance' is required before prose drifts into poetry.

Observations of qualitative differences of the texts themselves are helpful but not decisive. Merely because parallelism is attested in both genres—but all would admit—in disparate frequencies—does not imply that the frequency of occurrence of parallelism is not a statistically significant variable with respect to the two populations of poetic texts and prose texts. Nor does it obviate a careful statistical analysis of this feature if its frequency could be quantified. Such an undertaking, however, is steeped with difficulty, primarily the difficulty of distinguishing deliberate parallelism from accidental parallelism.

Since parallelism can be lexical, semantic, morphological, syntactical, phonological or even just formal, at issue is whether the author intended for his readers to notice it or not. Accidental morphological and phonological parallelism can occur because of the inflectional constraints of the Hebrew language. So, how can we know if an alleged parallelism of one of these two types is accidental or intentional? It is too subjective. And what of lexical and semantic parallelism? With a limited repertoire of verbs of motion, speaking, cognition, and perception, should the repetition of these be construed as parallelism? Another issue connected with parallelism is that in some cases the apparent parallelism may not be an author imposed structure at all, but rather may result from the structure of the events.[25] A case in point is the literary framework of Genesis 1:1–2:3, the bilateral structure of which stems from the events it portrays.[26] On the other hand, lexical parallelism does punctuate this account at strategic places.[27]

3.3 Problems with Internal Indicators: Other Features

Since parallelism eludes easy definition, identification and, most significantly, enumeration, we must look elsewhere for quantifiable features of the two genres, to find the essential quantum that distinguishes poetry from prose in the Hebrew Bible, or even if they are distinguishable.

Let us briefly survey, therefore, other qualitative but unquantifiable differences between the two genres, which have been adduced in the literature.

Milton [1644], in his famous dictum, in which he contrasts classic poetry to classic rhetoric, described the former, "as being less subtle and fine, but more simple, sensuous and passionate."

Muilenburg [1975, col. 671] states "the most characteristic features of Biblical poetry are action, imagery, simplicity, vigor, and concreteness."

Lichtenstein [1984] astutely discusses the linearity of prose *vis-à-vis* the non-linearity of poetry as he contrasts the prose version of the crossing of the Red Sea and the subsequent destruction of the Egyptian chariotry (Exodus 14) with the poetic version of the same (Exodus 15). His remarks serve to clarify the difference between the two genres: it is not the poet's intention to relate a complete story from beginning to end or to put events in the correct order. In fact, the Song of the Sea starts with the last event mentioned in the prose version, "Horse and rider he cast into the sea." The historical sequence of events is irrelevant.

Even the inclusion of cogent details of the story is not important. What is important, what is the key is "the creation of an indelible image" and reflection and retrospection on the same. *Lichtenstein* [1984, p. 113] talks about the "subjective reactions of the poet himself ... evocative word choice [and] ... well calculated juxtapositions."[28] Furthermore, he argues that these are not characteristic of prose. As cogent as his observations are, how can these differences be quantified?

Cotter [1992, pp. 6, 10–17, 34–41] discusses four rubrics in regard to how poetry differs from prose: its function is different; it uses language in a different way; it is atypically "highly organized, patterned and unified"; and it must be read differently. As to the characteristics of poetry, he adds to "enhanced unity of meaning and form" the following, which others have overlooked or at least not specifically mentioned: "violence committed on ordinary speech," "vastidity of deception" (expanded ambiguity), and "strangeness in the foreground" (multiplied atypicalities)."

Weiss [1984, p. 241] brilliantly expostulates on the unique function of poetry:

> The nature of poetry is that it does not so much *represent* the real world as *reflect* it, in the mirror of the internal and external senses; its language alone is what touches the mind and emotions. The poetic word appeals directly to the senses by a) its sound and rhythm, its conformity to its context—in short, its musicality; or b) its evocative power—its capacity to summon memories and associations which create harmony or disharmony between sound and sense [Weiss's italics].

Finally, *Wendland* [1994] offers the following list of the stylistic features of poetry: balanced lineation, condensation, figuration, intensification, transposition, phonoesthetic appeal, dramatization, lexical distinction, accentual uniqueness, and strophic structuration.[29]

My own list of the poetics (how the poetry does what it does) of Biblical Hebrew poetry comprises opacity (the sound of the words and arrangement of the words contributes to the meaning), atypical philology (phonologically, morphologically, syntactically, and lexically), extraordinary isometry, balanced lineation (parallelism), vivid metaphors, interlocutory shifts,[30] and pronounced brevity. In short, they are highly structured semantic sculptures.[31]

But as helpful as these descriptions are, they are not easily, if at all, quantifiable.

I will conclude this all too brief survey with the oft quoted, recondite remarks of *Jacobson* [1960, p. 358] on poetry: the poetic function "projects the principle of equivalence from the axis of selection into the axis of combination." *Cotter's* [1992] abstruse explanation is: "poetry creates equivalences between items that are normally only contiguous."[32] Jacobson is referring to the placement of a second (or even third) set of equivalences (synonyms) next to the first part of a poetic line, as in the bicolon, Psalm 15:1: יְהוָה מִי־יָגוּר בְּאָהֳלֶךָ מִי־יִשְׁכֹּן בְּהַר קָדְשֶׁךָ. The first colon reads, *YHWH, mî yāḡûr bᵊᵓohᵒlekā* "LORD, who may sojourn in your tent?" In the second colon the poet uses the semantic equivalents, שׁכן *škn* "dwell (in a tent)" in place of גּוּר *gûr* "sojourn" and הַר *har* "mountain" for אֹהֶל *ōhel* "tent." And קֹדֶשׁ *qōḏeš* "holiness" compensates for the ellipsis of *YHWH* from the second colon. The effect is that the paradigmatic is mapped onto the syntagmatic. As astute as this observation is, it is hardly quantifiable!

3.4 Observations on How Prose Differs from Poetry

Narrative differs from poetry in that it tells a story, with a plot and characters. *Scholes and Klaus* [1971, pp. 17–19], in their analysis of words and their relationship to literary forms, describe the difference:

> A story uses words to develop a view of character and situation through the report of the story-teller to the reader. Its essential quality is narration.

On the other hand, they say of poetry:

> The poem in its purest form uses words to express feelings addressed by a speaker talking or thinking to him/her -self rather than to the reader. Its essential quality is ... meditation.

In their analysis they make "plots and characters" the *y*-axis and "poetic" the *x*-axis and place them in opposing quadrants: story (narration) in the II quadrant and poem (meditation) in the IV quadrant.

Narratives in general are characterized by an attention to setting, plot, characterization and point of view.[33] Biblical Hebrew narratives (contra

Biblical Hebrew poetry) exhibit four elements: a narrator (point of view), characters, plot and setting; thus, supporting the above distinctions made by *Scholes and Klaus* [1971]. The narrator, his characters, the plot and time and space are interrelated. *Fokkelman* [1999] discusses all four.[34]

Narratives have a narrator, who usually writes in the third person (the first person sections of Jeremiah, Daniel, and Nehemiah are exceptions). The narrator is omniscient, able to tell us of details about the moment of the creation of the universe (Genesis 1:1); to tell us the thoughts of his characters; and even to tell us if his characters are speaking the truth. He is selective and presents his story with great skill. For the most part he is quite laconic in his presentation: he rarely includes unnecessary details.

Also according to *Fokkelman* [1999], every Biblical narrative has a "hero." He defines a "hero" as the subject of a quest, which he undertakes "in order to solve or cancel the problem or deficit presented at the outset" of the story. But there are different kinds of "heroes." Some heroes are more heroic than others—like Joshua, Caleb, and David (before his sin with Bathsheba). Some are more goat than hero—can we really call Samson a hero? And some, so-called heroes, are scoundrels—or at least—not very admirable. Abraham was decidedly un-heroic when he passed off his wife as his sister in order to save himself. In pursuit of the patriarchal blessing, Jacob stooped to deceiving his own father, Isaac. Even though Rebecca, Isaac's wife and Jacob's mother suggested, assisted and enabled the prevarication, we cannot exonerate Jacob, who followed through with the charade. And what of Joseph? At what point in his story is he clearly unambiguously admirable? These caveats notwithstanding, we can identify the main character in a Biblical narrative.

The third element is plot. Plot is arguably the most important: inclusions of details are driven by the plot.[35] The reader is drawn to the action. The characters encounter a situation that involves some kind of suspense building to a climax and then to a final resolution.[36] And the action unfolds in an evolving setting, the fourth element. The "hero" and his supporting cast march through time and space. The sequence of events is important. Sometimes the characters march in place. Time speeds up, slows, stops or even goes backwards—but only for a short time. Shortly, the inexorable sequence resumes. Time is linear in narrative. Not so in poetry.

4. Statistical Study: Exploratory Phase

The discussion above shows that characteristic features of poetry are also found in narrative. The converse is also true: characteristic features of narrative are also present in poetry. We conclude that qualitative descriptions of poetry and prose—although helpful in identifying their genre—do not rigorously distinguish them. We turn instead therefore to examine countable features of texts, which admit a statistical analysis.

As argued above, parallelism is not easily quantifiable, and, therefore, this most prevalent linguistic feature of Biblical Hebrew poetry cannot be used to distinguish prose from poetry. But Biblical Hebrew has other linguistic features, which are easily counted, measurable characteristics, such as morphological distribution, word order, and clause length.[37]

4.1 The Distribution of Finite Verbs in Biblical Hebrew

Although it would be ideal to look at all of these features, morphological distribution was the easiest to determine and, what is more, preliminary tests indicated that prose and poetry evince strikingly different distributions with respect to this countable feature. The specific morphological distribution chosen was the distribution of finite verbs, verbs inflected for person (1st—I, we; 2nd—you; 3rd—he, she, they) as well as gender (masculine and feminine) and number (singular and plural).[38]

The distribution of finite verbs should be ideal for ascertaining if a text is a narrative. Since narratives are characterized by an attention to setting, plot, characterization, and point of view (narrator)—with plot as arguably the most important—we need to find a countable linguistic feature, which reflects the action of characters unfolding in time.

Finite verbs carry the main action. The other verb forms in Biblical

Hebrew do not. Infinitive constructs provide the setting, often marking a circumstantial clause. Volitives (jussives, imperatives, and cohortatives) indicate what one individual wants the action of himself (singular cohortative) or others (jussive, imperative, and plural cohortative) to be, but it is not that action. Infinitive absolutes modify finite verbs. Participles are used attributively, substantively, or predicatively (as verbs). When they are used this last way they do not indicate the main action.

There are four finite verb forms in Biblical Hebrew (see Glossary, p. 725): the preterite *(wayyiqtol)*, the imperfect *(yiqtol)*, the perfect *(qatal)* and the waw-perfect *(wᵊqatal)*. Rarely, the preterite occurs without the initial waw patach (or qamets) before the prefix (such as in the last two verbs of Psalm 8:6) and, therefore, could be misconstrued as an imperfect, but for the most part it is a sequential past tense.[39] Of all finite verbs the distribution of preterites within the finite verbs should most clearly mark whether a passage is tracking events through time.

The imperfect can be a present/future, general present or modal when the action is ongoing or anticipated or it can express habitual action when the action is in the past.

Preterites with prefixed waw-consecutives must come first in a sentence. If another syntactic element is fronted (it comes first in the sentence instead of the verb to indicate a contrast), the verb cannot be a preterite, but will usually be a perfect. The perfect is normally a non-sequential past tense, although word order constraints demand that it be used in a sequential sense if an explicit subject precedes what would otherwise be a preterite.

The waw-perfect is perforce clause initial and is used to express habitual action in the past and sequential action in the future. It continues the force of the verbs that precede it. It is often found in procedural literature, such as the instructions for assembling the tabernacle (Exodus 25–31).

4.2 Statistical Study: Two Questions

The statistical portion of this study asks two pertinent questions.

The *first* question is: is the finite verb distribution identical across genres (poetry versus narrative)? And the *second* is: if it is not, can the distribution in a given text be used to determine its genre? To test the feasibility of the study, fourteen texts of each type— narrative and poetry—were analyzed. No statistically valid conclusions could be drawn from this part of the study, because the texts were selected rather than from a random sample.

4.2.1 Texts Selected

Texts acknowledged to be either narratives or poems were chosen. The narrative texts included in the analysis were: the Joseph Story (Genesis 37–50), Joshua's conquest of the Promised Land (Joshua 5–8), the Samson pericopes (Judges 13–16), the Ark narrative (1 Samuel 5:1–7:1), the Books of Ruth, Esther, and Nehemiah, the Court History of David (2 Samuel 11–20), the Ministry of Elijah (1 Kings 17–19), Hezekiah and Sennacherib, Jehoiakim burning the scroll of Jeremiah (Jeremiah 36), the Fall of Jerusalem (2 Kings 25), and the entire books of Kings and Chronicles.

For the poetic texts both old Hebrew poetry [Jacob blessing his sons (Genesis 49), the Song of the Sea (Exodus 15), the Oracles of Balaam (Numbers 23—24), the Song of Moses (Deuteronomy 32), the Jael Poem (Judges 5), the Prayer of Hannah (1 Samuel 2:1–10), and the dialogues and monologues of Job], and later Hebrew poetry [David's Song (2 Samuel 22), the prayer of Jonah (Jonah 2:2–10), Isaiah 1—35, Minor Prophets, Psalms, Proverbs, and Lamentations] were included in the sample tested.

4.2.2 Methodology

The Westminster Theological Morphological database in *BibleWorks 5.0* was used to determine the finite verb counts (FV) for each text[40] and then the following were computed: preterites/FV, imperfects/FV, perfects/FV, imperfects/(preterites+imperfects), and preterites/(preterites+imperfects).

4.2.3 Meritorious Results

Reported in this section are the results of the exploratory phase, which proved the merit of pursuing the confirmatory analysis upon a random sample of texts but were not reproduced in that portion of the study,

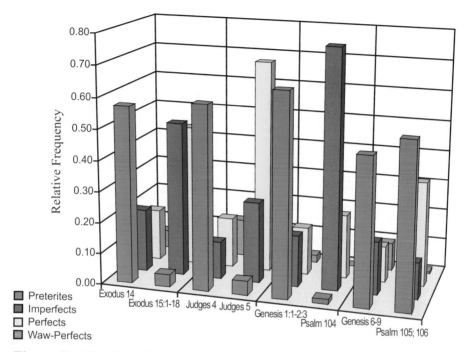

Figure 2. 3-D plot of paired-texts data, showing contrasting finite verb distribution for narrative and poetic versions of the same event.

and in addition, were significant in their own right: paired-texts data plotted in 3-D bar graphs (Figure 2) and cluster analysis (Figure 3). The rest of the results of the exploratory phase can be found in Appendix A: the relative frequency of finite verbs for each genre (displayed in contrasting 3-D bar graphs), scatter plots of relative frequencies of finite verb types, and two kinds of inferential modeling.

The 3-D bar graph of the paired-texts data plot (Figure 2) contrasts the distributions of finite verbs for narrative and poetic versions of the same event. The following texts were contrasted: Exodus 14 (the narrative account of the crossing of the Red Sea) with Exodus 15:1–18 (the poetic version of the same event, "The Song of the Sea"); Judges 4 (the narrative account of Barak and Deborah defeating Jabin the king of the Canaanites and his general Sisera by divine intervention at the Kishon and Jael's subsequent killing of the

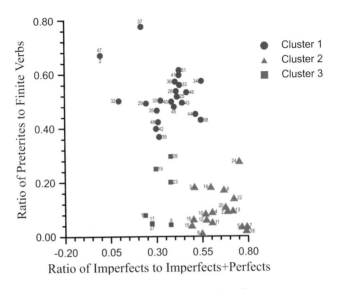

Figure 3. Cluster analysis plot.

cowardly Sisera) with Judges 5 (called "the Song of Deborah," which is the poetic version of the account, which focuses on what Jael did and the frustrated expectations of Sisera's mother). For the sake of comparison the distributions of Genesis 1:1–2:3, Psalm 104 (a poetic account of Creation), Genesis 6–9 (the Flood account), and two historical psalms, Psalms 105 and 106, were plotted on the same graph. Again green dominates in historical narrative; red and yellow in poetry. For these texts therefore narrative has a larger relative number of preterites than poetry.

Because each text in a pair portrays the same event, only a few differences can account for the disparate finite verb distributions: different authors, different times of composition, and different genres. The confirmatory phase of the present study will show that genre was the decisive factor.

To ascertain if there were groupings in the data a cluster analysis was performed on the selected texts.[41] The variables used in clustering were the ratio of preterites to finite verbs, and the ratio of imperfects to imperfects plus perfects. Significantly, the software grouped the data in clusters corresponding to the genre even though the actual classification (narrative or poetry) was not used in this analysis.

As the plot in Figure 3 shows, three groups were found. Cluster 1, which is in the upper half of the plot (the solid blue circles), corresponds with the narrative sections. The intriguing part is that the part of the graph corresponding to the poetry sections is broken into two clusters, clusters 2 and 3, one with lower values of imperfects/ (imperfects+perfects) and one with higher values. Only one narrative section was not put in cluster 1. However, the Genesis 1:1–2:3 section was placed with cluster 1.

4.2.4 Exploratory Phase: Preliminary Conclusions and Caveats

The results, which are described in Section 4.2.3 and Appendix A, showed that finite verb distribution varies so much with genre that it could likely serve to distinguish genre. In particular, the ratio of preterites to finite verbs would best classify texts as narrative or poetry.

But to be statistically valid our study must examine either the entire population or a random sample of that population. Moreover, we do not know how *rigorously* this ratio distinguishes genre. We turn, therefore, to discuss the confirmatory phase of the study.

5. Statistical Study: Confirmatory Phase

This was the heart of the statistical part of the study. And for this reason the following procedures and results (some in brief; others in great detail) are covered in this section: the identification of the two populations, statement of the null hypothesis tested and the alternative hypothesis, acquisition of the random sample, visualization of the data, the theory of logistic regression, description of inferential models, classification of texts by the chosen model, statistical analysis of the classification accuracy of our model, and the logistic curve results.

5.1 Identifying Each Population

It was necessary to identify the complete population of each genre, but not to analyze all these texts. A random sample from each population ensured the statistical validity of the study.[42] Also to guarantee statistical validity a necessary condition for the inclusion of a text was that the finite verb count not be too low. Thirty was the lower limit for the study. Consequently, short contiguous narratives were grouped together and psalms were grouped by author (if indicated in the superscription), type, collections, and so forth. Another thing avoided was widely divergent text sizes. Long texts, therefore, were subdivided into smaller units.

How can Biblical Hebrew narratives be identified? In addition to what was said in Section 3.4 above, Biblical Hebrew narratives—just as narratives in any other literature—tell a story, with a setting, the time and place in which the events of the story unfold; character(s), the person or persons who do and say things in the story or have things done or said to them; and the plot. Plot involves two movements. The first is a movement from a situation in which the characters are in equilibrium with one another to one where the characters are no longer in equilibrium. They encounter a situation that places them in danger or introduces an unrealized expectation. This last situation is unstable and demands resolution. This resolution is the second movement: the characters move to a new equilibrium. Linguistically, narratives are characterized by lexical transparency, normal syntax, and literal language.

Biblical Hebrew poetry also is not difficult to identify. First of all (as discussed in Section 3.1 above), in the oldest complete manuscript of the Hebrew Bible, the Leningrad Codex B19a, a few texts are laid out as verse: the Song of the Sea, the Balaam Oracles, the Song and Blessing of Moses, the Song of Deborah, the Song of David (2 Samuel 22), the Final Words of David (2 Samuel 23) and Psalms 119 and 136. Second, poetry has a different poetics from narrative [see Sections 3.2 and 3.3 above]. Third, poetry differs from narrative in its intended effects. The Biblical poet wants his readers to see, hear, smell, feel, and taste what he is experiencing. He is seeking to evoke his readers' emotions and experiences. He does this by creating vivid unforgettable images, which resonate with his readers.

By applying the criteria discussed above the two populations were identified—295 narrative texts and 227 poetic texts.

5.2 The Null Hypothesis

To determine the inferential potential of the ratio of preterites to finite verbs the null hypothesis H_0 and the alternative H_1 were put forth as follows:

H_0: All logistic regression classification models, in which the relative frequency of preterites is the only independent variable, classify texts according to genre no better than random classification.

This is tested against the alternative hypothesis:

H_1: There is a classification model that classifies texts by genre better than random classification.

5.3 The Random Sample

In order to ensure that texts from all periods and from all three parts of the Hebrew Bible (Torah, Prophets, and Writings) were included in the analysis, a stratified random sample was generated. Also, this sample included extra texts to replace any primary texts rejected for violating any of the conditions stated above.

The breakdown of the narrative text in the sample is: Torah (15 out of 87, 2 extra); Former Prophets (21 out of 138, 3 extra); Latter Prophets (2 out of 11, 2 extra); and Writings (10 out of 59, 2 extra). The breakdown of the poetic texts in the sample is: Torah (3 out of 13, 2 extra); Former Prophets (3 out of 12, 2 extra); Latter Prophets (23 out of 104, 3 extra); and Writings (22 out of 98, 3 extra).

5.4 Visualizing the Data

Again *BibleWorks 5.0* was used to count the verbs for each text. The data is tabulated in Appendix B in Tables B1–B8.

3-D bar graphs and scatter plots visually present the data. 3-D bar graphs display the relative frequency of finite verbs. For the 3-D bar graphs (Figures 4–5) the colors for the relative frequencies of preterites, imperfects, perfects and waw-perfects are green, red, yellow, and blue, respectively (going back into the page on the y-axes). The passages

Steven W. Boyd

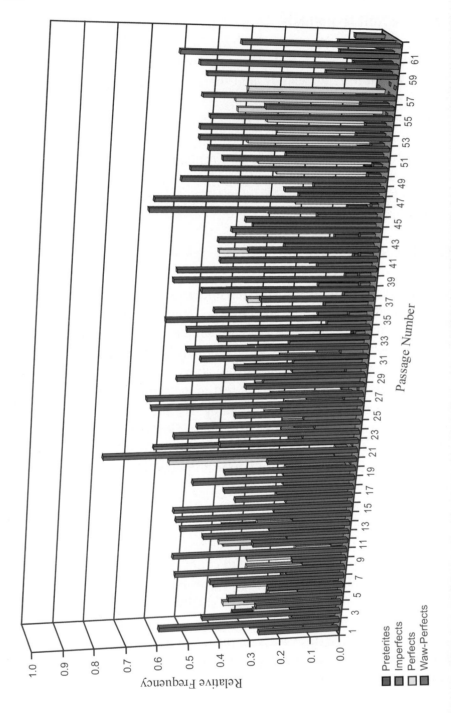

Figure 4 (left). 3-D bar graph of finite verb distribution in narrative. The Biblical passages that are represented by the numbers on the x-axis are found in Tables B1–B4 in Appendix B.

tested are numbered along the x-axes and the relative frequencies of each finite verb are plotted on the z-axes. As can be seen in Figure 4, the dominant color for narrative texts is green, which corresponds to a dominance of preterites; whereas the prominent colors for poetic texts (Figure 5) are red and yellow, which corresponds to a dominance of imperfects and perfects.

These graphs show that the finite verb distribution of narrative texts drastically differs from that of poetic texts. But this difference must be quantified. Scatter plots helped do this. Not only do they provide an additional way of visualizing the data, but they validated the track we followed in our analysis.

In both scatter plots (Figures 6 and 7) the relative frequency of preterites for each passage is plotted on the x-axis, but the variables plotted on the y-axes differ. In Figure 6 the y-coordinate is the relative frequency of imperfects for each passage; whereas in Figure 7 the y-coordinate is the relative frequency of perfects. For both plots, poetic passages are indicated by red squares and narratives by green diamonds. Also the paired-texts data, which is presented as a 3-D bar graph in Figure 2, is plotted in Figures 6 and 7.

These plots show that finite verb distribution clusters texts by genre. In addition, the paired-texts data are correctly grouped.

Each scatter plot (Figures 6 and 7) also shows that the separation of the sample clusters is greatest along the x-axis, which is the ratio of preterites to finite verbs for each Biblical passage. This confirmed the impression garnered during the exploratory phase, that this ratio was the most significant for our study, and prompted the question: is the median of the distribution of relative frequency of preterites for narrative the same as that for poetry?

In an effort to answer this question and to provide a graphic display of the results, the narrative texts and poetic texts from the samples were plotted side by side (Figure 8) with the passages on the x-axis and the relative frequency of preterites for each passage on the y-axis.

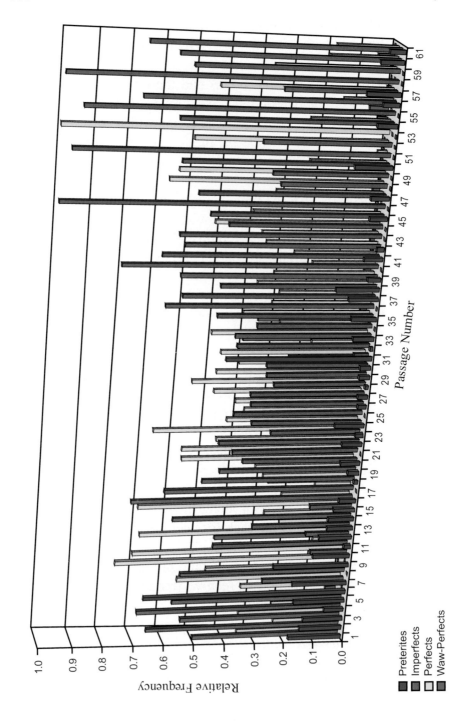

Figure 5 (left). 3-D bar graph of finite verb distribution in poetry. The Biblical passages that are represented by the numbers on the *x*-axis are found in Tables B5–B8 in Appendix B.

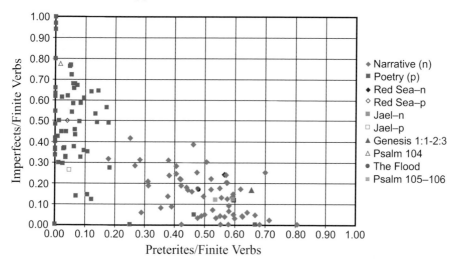

Figure 6. Scatter plot showing the ratio of preterites to finite verbs on the *x*-axis and the ratio of imperfects to finite verbs on the *y*-axis.

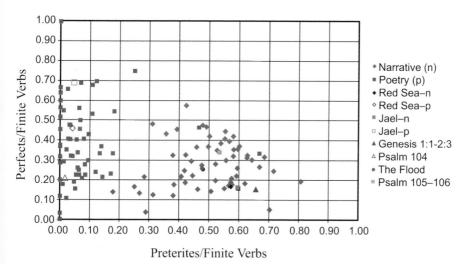

Figure 7. Scatter plot showing the ratio of preterites to finite verbs on the *x*-axis and the ratio of perfects to finite verbs on the *y*-axis.

As in Figures 6 and 7, green diamonds represent the narrative passages; red squares—poetry, and—for the sake of comparison—the solid blue triangle represents Genesis 1:1–2:3. In addition, the blue horizontal line through each sample is the median for that sample.

Looking at Figure 8, the above question, "is the median of the distribution of relative frequency of preterites for narrative the same as that for poetry?" is easily answered. It is quite obvious that the medians differ dramatically.

The data presented in the bar graphs (Figures 4 and 5), finite verbs scatter plots (Figures 6 and 7), side-by-side preterite distribution plot (Figure 8), and histograms (not shown) indicated that narrative and poetry have distinctly different finite verb distributions—in particular, the relative frequency of preterites. In fact, this difference was so stark, that it appeared that the proper inferential model could exploit it, in order to classify texts of unknown genre.

Moreover, the exploratory phase of the study showed us that logistic regression would be the best way to model the data to use it to categorize texts[43]—Genesis 1:1–2:3 in particular.

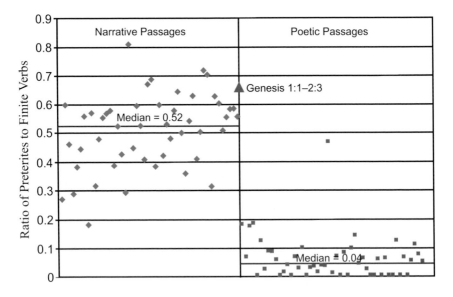

Figure 8. Side-by-side plot of the distribution of the relative frequency of preterites in narrative *vis-à-vis* poetry.

5.5 Inferential Study: Logistic Regression Modeling

5.5.1 Theory

In general, logistic regression is used when there are only two possibilities for the dependent variable, but the independent variable(s) is (are) multivalued.[44] Moreover, it is common to assign two possible values to this dummy dependent variable: either 0 or 1.

Although logistic regression does not have as many stringent conditions as ordinary least squares regression, it has a few: linearity of the log of the odds, non-additivity, non-multicollinearity, and sampling adequacy.[45] (See Section 5.5.2 for the relevance of these to our study.)

There are three types of logistic models. We were interested in the classification type of model, which can be used to categorize data into two populations according to the values of the independent variable(s) for the data.[46]

In logistic regression a linear model of the logarithm of the odds ($P/(1-P)$) is produced in terms of certain independent variables so that

$$\log (P/(1-P)) = A + \sum_i B_i X_i \qquad (1)$$

where P is the probability of the dummy being 1, the Xs are independent variables, and the intercept A and the coefficients B_i are derived by the maximum log-likelihood estimation (MLE) method from the actual dichotomous data.[47]

We then use the right hand side of equation (1) to predict values of P outside the sample.

Logistic regression has a way of measuring the goodness of fit of a model, the substantive significance of a model, the classification accuracy of a model, and the statistical significance of this accuracy level as follows.

• **Goodness of fit.** The "model chi-square" statistic is a measure of how well a model fits the data. The "model chi-square" statistic, G_M, which is defined as $-2[\mathrm{LL}(A) - \mathrm{LL}(A, B_1, B_2, \ldots B_k)]$, where k is the number of independent variables represented by a model, is computed to test the null hypothesis that a model does not fit the data any better than the model with all B_is = 0 and LL(...) is the log likelihood function. This statistic follows a chi-square distribution with k degrees of freedom. A good model will be significant at the .05 level or better.[48]

• **Substantive significance of the model.** The pseudo-R^2 statistic is a measure of the substantive significance of a logistic regression model. That is, how much does the model reduce the variation from that in the zero coefficients model? A preferred pseudo-R^2 statistic is R_L^2, which is defined as G_M/D_0, where D_0 is the zero coefficients model, LL(A), R_L^2 ranges from 0 for a poor model to 1 for a perfect model.[49]

• **Classification accuracy.** The issue at stake for a classification model—and therefore the most important for us—is how well does the model classify texts from observed categories into those categories? The classification accuracy is usually presented in the form of a 2×2 table, which shows the actual number of texts in each category versus the number classified by the model.

Building on *Menard* [2002, pp. 28–40], if we define a statistic τ_p as *the proportional change in the number of errors for a classification model like ours*, then

$$\tau_P = (E_0 - E_m)/E_0 \qquad (2)$$

where E_0 is the expected number of errors without the model, and E_m is the number of errors with the model.

Menard [2002, pp. 28–40] argues that τ_p is the best option for analyzing classification accuracy. Since τ_p measures how much the model reduces error, it is a measure of substantive significance.[50] If τ_p is positive, the model classifies texts better than a "chance" classification. On the other hand, if the ratio is negative, the model is a poorer classifier.

• **Statistical significance of classification accuracy.** To determine the statistical significance of a model as a classifier (the statistical significance of τ_p), we can employ the binomial statistic

$$d = \left(P_0 - P_m \right)/ \sqrt{P_0 \left(1 - P_0 \right) N} \qquad (3)$$

where N is the total sampling and P_0 and P_m are the proportion misclassified ($P_0 = E_0/N$, $P_m = E_m/N$), to test the null hypothesis that the proportion incorrectly classified by a model is no lower than the proportion that would be incorrectly classified by chance classification [*Menard*, 2002, p. 34].

5.5.2 Descriptions of Models

We used logistic regression to categorize texts as narrative or poetry based on the finite verb distribution in each text. A model's goodness of fit to the data (borrowing the term of *Menard* [2002]) and exactness in classifying texts of known genre will determine how accurately it can identify the genre of texts of unknown genre. The results will be in the form of a probability (P) that a given text is a narrative.

Brief mention is made below of the model's goodness of fit, but a model's exactness in classifying texts is the focus of our study and therefore two complete sections below (Sections 5.5.3 and 5.5.4) are devoted to it. First, however, we will look at the models tested.

In our study the dependent, dummy variable was *NARRATIVE*, which can have only two possible values: 1 if it is a narrative; 0 if it is not. In other words, there were only two possibilities in the texts analyzed, narratives and non-narratives (poetry). The independent variables, the X_is represented the ratios among the finite verbs for each text. The model might consider only one ratio, for example, preterites to finite verbs, or preterites to preterites plus imperfects, or imperfects to imperfects plus perfects, and so forth. Or the model might consider a combination of ratios.

For the sake of completeness, three different models were considered, each represented by a different ratio:

- X_1 = preterites/total finite verbs
- X_2 = preterites/(preterites + imperfects)
- X_3 = perfects/(imperfects + perfects)

These ratios were considered alone and together in a logistic regression that estimates the probability that a passage is a narrative given the values of X_1, X_2, and X_3 for the 97 narrative and poetry passages with known genres.

Of all the models considered, X_2 had the highest statistical significance for a one variable model, but misclassified three passages. On the other hand, the model using X_1—although it had a slightly lower statistical significance than the X_2 model—only misclassified two passages.

Because our purpose was to determine the classification accuracy of the model, we chose the model that had the lowest number of misclassifications: the model using X_1, the relative frequency of preterites. The fact that this model had the fewest misclassifications confirmed our analysis up to this point: the ratio of preterites to finite verbs—as Figures 4–8 indicate—varied the most with genre. It also had the advantage of being a simpler model than a two or three independent variable model; reducing, thereby, the chances of overfitting (explaining noise instead of signal) and eliminating any possibility of additivity or multicollinearity in the independent variables. Finally, it made the most sense in light of Hebrew grammar.

The detailed output of the statistics program *NCSS* can be found in Tables C1 and C2 in Appendix C. A summary is presented here.

For Model 1—the model with one independent variable X_1 (hereafter model 1 will be referred to as "our model" and X_1 will be referred as X)—the statistics generated take into consideration the number of finite verbs in each passage. This weighting effectively gave less influence to the smaller passages in estimating the logistic regression curves.

Because our model has only one independent variable, X, the log likelihood equation has only the intercept, A, and one coefficient, B.

The description of our model is as follows: the intercept, $A = -5.6562$; $B = 24.7276$. Thus our model for predicting P is

$$\log (P/(1-P)) = -5.6562 + 24.7276\, X \qquad (4)$$

where X is the relative frequency of preterites. Note that because our model has only one independent variable the right hand side of this equation is a simple straight line, $y = mx + b$.

Our primary concern in this study was: how good a classifier is our model? Consequently, goodness of fit was an ancillary issue, but the interested reader can find the calculations in Appendix C, Section C2.

5.5.3 Classification of Texts

The "Percent Correct Predictions" which is a widely accepted measure of the overall performance of the model. Classification of the texts using the model was done by the usual procedure: if the predicted probability (*P*) is greater than or equal to 0.5, then *NARRATIVE* equals 1; if *P* is less than 0.5, *NARRATIVE* equals zero.

The probability that a text with a given ratio of preterites to finite verbs is a narrative is its logistic score. Solving for *P* in equation (4), we obtain the following:

$$P = 1/(1+e^{\,(5.6562\,-\,24.7276X)}) \tag{5}$$

where *X* is the ratio of preterites to finite verbs for each text and *e* is 2.7183, the base of the natural logarithm.

The plot of all of these *P*s is the logistic regression curve (in blue) seen in Figure 9. The poetry texts are depicted by solid red squares (as in the scatter plots in Figures 6–8) and the narrative texts are solid green diamonds (same as scatter plots in Figures 6–8). And for the sake of comparison, the score of Genesis 1:1–2:3 is plotted as well.

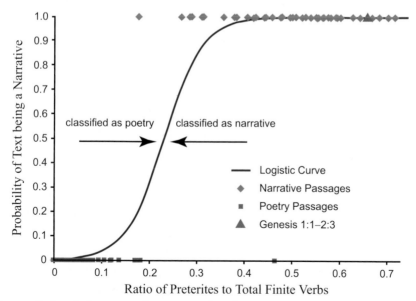

Figure 9. Logistic regression curve showing the probability a passage is a narrative based on the ratio of preterites to finite verbs.

Classification was done in the following way. For our model, $P=0.5$ corresponds to $X=0.2287$. Thus, if $X<0.2287$, then the text is classified as poetry; if $X>0.2287$, then it is classified as narrative. The labeled arrows in Figure 9 depict this classification convention. The results of this classification procedure are in Table 1.

Table 1. Classification table (by passage).

Actual Genre	Classified by Model		Total
	Poetry	Narrative	
Poetry	48	1	49
Narrative	1	47	48
Total	49	48	97

Table 1 depicts in color how accurately our model identified the genre of texts of known genre. Wherever the color at the top of a column matches the row color, the model correctly classified the text. Wherever the color does not match, the model incorrectly classified the texts. The percent correctly classified, therefore, was 97.94.

Of the 97 sample narrative and poetry passages, only two were misclassified: Ezekiel 19 was classified as narrative and Exodus 33 was classified as poetry. These misclassifications inform us about the quality of our model and about the nature of Biblical Hebrew narrative. Our model caught an incorrect analysis of Ezekiel 19 but was tripped up by Exodus 33, a narrative that largely recounts habitual action.

On the one hand, our model misclassified Ezekiel 19, because it was incorrectly included in the poetry population from which the random sample was drawn. Ezekiel 19 was assigned to the poetry population, because it has an elaborate, extended metaphor: two of the last four kings of Judah are portrayed as lions. Jehoahaz (third son of Josiah) and Jehoiachin (grandson of Josiah), whom Neco II of Egypt and Nebuchadnezzar II of Babylon deposed, deported to Egypt and Babylon respectively, and replaced with puppet kings, are pictured as lion cubs, reared by a lioness (Judah). They became young lions. They learned to hunt and became man-eaters. The nations heard about them, trapped them in pits, and brought them to Egypt and Babylon by hooks.

This is highly symbolic language. Most of the specifics of the text did not happen: kings are not lions, no lioness reared them, and they were not caught in a pit. But, they were taken off by hooks into captivity to Egypt and Babylon.

The identification of kings and kingdoms with animals (or trees) reminds us of portions of Daniel, Zechariah, other passages in Ezekiel and even the vine imagery in Isaiah 5:1–7. Ezekiel 19 therefore belongs to neither genre tested: it is neither historical narrative nor poetry but rather, apocalyptic.

On the other hand, our model misclassified Exodus 33, because of the finite verb distribution in this text: there are more waw-perfects (29) than preterites (14). Statistical analysis suggests a high negative correlation between the number of waw-perfects and preterites in narrative texts. The statistical analysis of this correlation is determined by the Pierson r correlation test, which yields a value of -0.71 with $p < 0.0001$. This is to be expected, since the former is found mostly in future sequential usage and the latter in past sequential usage. (See Appendix C, Section C3 for details of the correlation analysis.)

But the reason for the dominance of waw-perfect in this text is that the waw-perfect also can indicate habitual action in the past—and both of these uses are manifested in this text. The text opens with three future uses of the form: "I will send," "I will drive out" and, the threat, "If for a moment I would go up (construed by a modalistic imperfect) in your midst, I would consume you." This is followed by fourteen habitual usages (verses 7–11), telling the reader how Moses would customarily talk with YHWH at the tent of meeting and what the people customarily did. The passage concludes with twelve sequential future uses of the form, in which YHWH communicated to Moses His intentions and what Moses should do.

5.5.4 Statistical Analysis of Classification Accuracy

In order to determine how accurately our model classifies texts we need to compare it with a random model that classifies texts by genre, which is subject to the constraint that the number of texts classified as narrative is the same as the number of narrative texts and similarly with poetry.

With this constraint in mind, let us define $p_{narrative}$ as the "chance" probability of classifying a passage as narrative, p_{poetry} as the "chance" probability of classifying a passage as poetry, $n_{narrative}$ as the number of narrative texts in the sample, n_{poetry} as the number of poetic texts in the sample, and n_{total} is the total number of texts in the sample. Then

$$p_{narrative} = n_{narrative}/(n_{narrative} + n_{poetry}) \qquad (6a)$$

and

$$p_{poetry} = n_{poetry}/(n_{narrative} + n_{poetry}) \qquad (6b)$$

The expected number of errors without the model (E_0) is the expected errors for a "chance" classification model, which is the number of poetry texts misclassified as narrative plus the number of narrative texts misclassified as poetry.[51] Thus

$$E_0 = n_{poetry}p_{narrative} + n_{narrative}p_{poetry} \qquad (7)$$

This easily simplifies to

$$E_0 = 2n_{narrative}n_{poetry}/(n_{narrative} + n_{poetry}) \qquad (8)$$

Computing this for our sample we get

$$E_0 = 48.4948 \qquad (9)$$

This value will be the same for all samples with 48 narrative texts and 49 poetic texts.

We will use the "binomial statistic" d [equation (3)] to test the null hypothesis H_0.

Let S be the set of all random samples with 48 narrative and 49 poetry texts, which can be taken from the two populations of 295 narrative and 227 poetic texts. Now apply our model to each of these samples and compute d for each of these.

We can write equation (3) in terms of expected errors as follows:

$$d = (E_0 - E_m)/E_0 \sqrt{(N - E_0)/NE_0} \tag{10}$$

Since the expected errors depends only on the number of narrative texts and poetic texts in the sample, which is the same for all samples, d for each sample will vary only with the number of classification errors made by our model when it is applied to a sample.

The set of all these ds will approximate a normal distribution with mean 0 and standard deviation 1.

Based on equation (10), if H_0 is true, the number of classification errors of our model must equal or exceed the number of classification errors of the random model. Or in other words, the average of all the ds must be ≤ 0.

But using equation (10) to compute d for our sample, we get

$$d = 9.4421 \tag{11}$$

This is more than nine standard deviations above the expected mean if H_0 is true. The probability of randomly selecting a sample from our joint population of narrative and poetry texts with a standard deviation this far from the expected mean is <0.0001. We reject therefore the null hypothesis H_0 and at the same time accept the alternative hypothesis H_1. Our model therefore classifies texts better than a "chance" model ($p < 0.0001$). But we want to know how much better.

Recall that τ_P (the proportional change in the number of errors for a classification model like ours) is

$$\tau_P = (E_0 - E_m)/E_0 \tag{12}$$

where E_m is the number of errors using our model.

In our case $\tau_P = (48.4948 - 2)/48.4948 = 0.9588$. This means that for the texts in our sample, our model reduces classification error by almost 96%. We must now estimate our model's classification accuracy for the entire population of 522 texts.

To extend the results for one random sample (comprised of 48 narrative texts taken from the population of all narrative texts and 49 poetic texts taken from the population of all poetic texts) to the entire joint population, we will determine a 95% confidence interval for the average τ_p for all the samples in population S. Let T denote the set of all these possible τ_ps.

As with the ds, the expected number of errors depends only on the number of narrative texts and poetic texts in the sample, which is the same for all samples. Consequently—as with the ds—τ_p for each sample will vary only with the number of classification errors made by our model when it is applied to a sample.

Since τ_p is a measure of the proportional change in the number of errors obtained by using our model, μ_T (the mean of all the possible τ_ps) will be a measure of how accurately on the average our model classifies texts. For our sample we computed τ_p as 0.9588.

When we solve for τ_p in terms of d we get

$$\tau_P = d\sqrt{(N - E_0)/NE_0} \tag{13}$$

Since N and E_0 are the same for all samples, $\sqrt{(N - E_0)/(NE_0)}$ is a constant $= 0.1015$; and thus, T has a binomial distribution like the ds.

To compute a confidence interval for τ_p the statistics program SAS was used to calculate the following exact 95% confidence interval for P_m, the proportion misclassified by our model:

$$0.0025 \le P_m \le 0.0725 \tag{14}$$

Of course for our random sample, $P_m = 0.0206$.

We can now easily compute a confidence interval for τ_p. Multiplying by the number of texts in the sample we get a confidence interval for E_m:

$$0.2425 \le E_m \le 7.0325 \tag{15}$$

Now if we substitute in equation (12) these values and the value of E_0 we arrive at the desired confidence interval:

$$0.8550 \leq \mu_T \leq 0.9950 \qquad (16)$$

That is, we are 95% certain that the average τ_P is between 0.8550 and 0.9950. In other words our model is an excellent classifier of texts.

5.5.5 The Logistic Curve: Determining Genre from the Ratio of Preterites to Finite Verbs

The logistic curve in Figure 9 was derived from one sample. Again we need to extend these results to the level of the total population. We need to see the band of logistic curves, which could be produced by all the possible samples from the total population of texts. Such a plot is found in Figure 10.

In Figure 10 the light blue lines mark the outer edges of this band. All possible logistic curves derived from the ratio of preterites to finite verbs for the joint-population of 522 texts lie inside the band edges. Moreover, the vertical distance between the band edges for a given value of X is a confidence interval for the probability that a text with that X will be a narrative.

Since the sample texts used to develop the logistic regression model were either poetry or narrative, their actual probabilities were 0 and 1, respectively. Thus, the poetic texts (the red squares) are plotted at $P=0$ (the x-axis); whereas, the narrative texts (the green diamonds) are plotted at $P=1$. The x-coordinate for each square or diamond corresponds to the observed ratio of preterites to finite verbs for that text (its X value).

We can use the logistic regression curve band to classify texts with undetermined genre as follows: if a text lies on the curve to the left of the left edge of the band, we classify it as poetry; if it lies on the curve to the right of the right edge of the band, we classify it as narrative.

Texts with undetermined genre, which lie close to the horizontal line $P=0.5$ are in "no man's land." The slope of the curve is steepest at this point, the confidence interval is the greatest and candidly genre identification is uncertain. But far away from these lines, where the

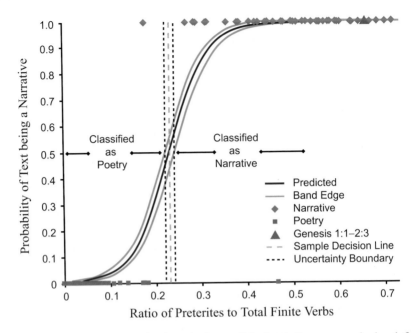

Figure 10. Plot showing the band of possible logistic curves derived from random samples from the total population of texts. The vertical distance between the light blue lines at a given ratio of preterites to finite verbs is a 99.5% confidence interval for the probability that a text with that ratio is a narrative.

curve is flattening out and approaching its asymptotes, $P=0$ and $P=1$, genre identification is almost certain, because the confidence interval becomes miniscule and virtually indistinguishable from our model curve.

The only area of uncertain classification is the box around the orange dashed decision line for the sample bounded by the black dotted vertical lines going through the points where the edges of the band intersect $P=0.5$, at $X=0.22$ and 0.24. This box is surprisingly narrow. In fact, this logistic regression band for the joint population of texts categorizes the sample texts identically to the logistic curve for the sample texts (Figure 9 and dark blue line in Figure 10), because none of the sample texts fall within the box.

6. Statistical Study: Conclusions

We undertook this study to determine the genre of Genesis 1:1–2:3—to put the conclusions drawn on the firm footing of statistical analysis (a quantitative approach) instead of the more tentative basis of subjective description (a qualitative approach)—and to explore the hermeneutical implications of our findings.

Rejection of the null hypothesis H_0 (that our model does not classify texts according to genre any better than random classification) at an extremely statistically significant level ($p < 0.0001$) and average τ_p between 0.855 and 0.955 ($\alpha = 0.05$), means that our model representing the ratios of preterites to finite verbs is an excellent classifier of texts according to genre.

In addition with R_L^2 more than 88% ($p < 0.0001$) our model fits the data like a glove (see Appendix C, Section C2).

Our model therefore proves itself to be highly substantively significant in model fit and classification accuracy.

Because Genesis 1:1–2:3 was not part of the random sample, which we modeled using logistic regression, it has not been identified as poetry or narrative. As a result, the solid yellow triangle (same as scatter plots) in Figure 10, which represents this text, is neither at $P = 0$ or $P = 1$. Instead, it is within the band of logistic regression curves.

Figure 10 shows that Genesis 1:1–2:3 is far to the right of the area of uncertain classification—in fact, very close to the asymptote $P = 1$. There is no doubt therefore that our model classifies Genesis 1:1–2:3 as narrative. But what is the probability?

With X equal to 0.654762, the vertical interval for this text (the range of probabilities for the text being a narrative) is

$$0.999942 \leq P \leq 0.999987 \tag{17}$$

at a 99.5% confidence level.

The nature of statistics is that all results are stated in terms of probabilities. So strictly speaking, we can say that with two choices for the genre of Genesis 1:1–2:3 (poetry or narrative), this text is narrative, not poetry, with a very high degree of probability. Or to put the results in scientific terms: the text is a narrative with statistical certainty. In other words, it is statistically indefensible to argue that this text is poetry.

A distinctive of our model is that a text actually classifies itself. By its ratio of preterites to finite verbs, it identifies itself as narrative or poetry. We argued at the beginning of this study (Section 2.2) that the text itself would do this: tell us how we should read it. We have come—by way of a lengthy statistical analysis—to a conclusion, which would have been obvious to the original readers: Genesis 1:1–2:3 is a narrative.

Another thing that would have been obvious to them is how this narrative should be read. We turn now therefore to explore the hermeneutical implications of our findings thus far to complete our study.

7. Interpretive Implications

The primary implication of the virtual certainty that Genesis 1:1–2:3 is a narrative is that it should be read as other Hebrew narratives are intended to be read. This prompts us to ask the question: how did Biblical authors intend their narratives to be read? To answer this question we must investigate the Biblical authors' perspective toward the events they related and how they presented their material. We pose therefore a second question: did Biblical authors believe that they were referring to real events?[52]

Answering the last question, *Halpern* [1988, p. 3] states:

The ancient Israelite historians . . . had authentic antiquarian intentions. *They meant to furnish fair and accurate representations of Israelite antiquity* . . . [they meant to] communicate information about specific phenomena outside the text, in the text . . . [the reader of this history is also involved in a communicative process by] determining what data its author meant the reader to extract .

Brueggemann [1997] also addresses this issue in his **Theology of the Old Testament**, which he builds on Israel's speech about YHWH: "Israel's speech about YHWH is characteristically situated historically."[53] But it is *Sternberg* [1985, p. 31], who drives the point home:

So does the Bible belong to the historical or fictional genre? … Of course *the narrative is historiographic*, inevitably so considering its teleology and incredibly so considering its time and environment. *Everything points in that direction.* … it addresses a people *defined in terms of their past* and *commanded to keep its memory alive*—which ordinance, judging by the *numerous retrospects performed by biblical characters* within the drama itself, they religiously observed. … The Bible is even the first to anticipate the appeal to the surviving record of the past that characterizes modern history-telling. Such relics abound on the narrative surface itself, appearing as facts to be interpreted and brought into pattern.

The following discussion comprises fifteen proofs that the authors of Biblical narratives believed that they were portraying real historical events. The first four pertain to perspectives and the next eleven to presentation and rhetoric.[54] In brief, these are: (1) God's people are defined in terms of their past; (2) God's people are commanded to keep the memory of their past alive; (3) God's people engage in retrospection on their past; (4) the remembrance of the past devolves on the present and determines the future; (5) customs are elucidated; (6) ancient names and current sayings are traced back to their origins; (7) monuments and pronouncements are assigned a concrete reason as well as a slot in history; (8) historical footnotes are sprinkled throughout the text; (9) written records used as sources are cited; (10) precise chronological reference points are supplied; (11) genealogies are given; (12) observations of cultic days and seasons are called acts of commemoration; (13) prophetic utterances are recalled and related to events in the narrative; (14) "time" words challenge ancient readers to validate historical claims made in the text; and (15) historical "trajectories" link different portions of the text and widely separate historical periods.

These fifteen are discussed in the numbered sections below. The illustrative examples in the discussions are supplemented by many more examples (with table notes) in Tables D1–D8 in Appendix D.

(1) God's people are defined in terms of their past. No matter where we dip into the narratives of the Old Testament, we encounter the past of the authors' characters as an integral part of the narrative.

Abraham is noted for having left his past and launching out into an uncertain future. YHWH made promises to Israel based on the promises He had made to the patriarchs. This is particularly evident in Exodus 6:2–8.[55] Seven "I wills," *bring out, deliver, redeem, take, be, take in,* and *give,* prospects for Israel's future, are inexorably linked to four verbs referring to YHWH's promises made in Israel's past: *I appeared* (ראה) to Abraham, to Isaac, and to Jacob as El Shaddai, but by name YWWH I was *not known* (ידע) to them, *I established* my covenant with them to give to them the land of their sojourning in which they were sojourning, to the land which *I lifted up* my hand to give to Abraham, to Isaac, and to Jacob. In addition, there are two verbs that immediately affect Israel's present: *I have heard* (שמע) their cry and *I have remembered* (זכר) my covenant.[56]

We cannot help but notice that Israel's past is an expanding past as we move *ad seriatim* through the Hebrew Bible. In other words, by the time of the events recorded in Joshua, Israel had been miraculously delivered from the "house of bondage," crossed the Yam Suph, the Egyptian chariotry had been crushed under the returning waters, the covenant stipulations articulated, agreed upon and the covenant ratified, the same covenant violated by worshiping the golden calf, the wilderness wanderings completed, Balaam's plot thwarted and himself executed, and the entire adult generation (with the exception of Caleb and Joshua), who witnessed all of this past, had died. Even Aaron and Moses had died.

Or even farther along in the Bible—for example, by the time of 2 Kings 17—the period of judges had occurred, Samuel had anointed Israel's first two kings, David had reigned and was the exemplar for the kings of Judah, Solomon had built the temple, the kingdom had divided, Elijah had successfully challenged Baalism, Jehu had trampled Jezebel, and Shalmaneser V had conquered Samaria. And so it goes. The narrative constantly refers to this ever accreting past.

(2) God's people are commanded to keep the memory of the past alive. There are three types of examples, evincing this perspective: questions from sons, commands to inculcate the past to the next generation, and commands to remember. Examples of type one begin,

"When your son/s says/asks you/their fathers what is the significance of …" (Exodus 12:26; Deuteronomy 6:20; Joshua 4:6, 21). The hypothetical question is followed by the answer (rather extensive in some cases) to be given to the questioner. And the anticipation is that not only the present generation—when they are old enough—but future generations will ask this question and their fathers must respond appropriately.

The second type involves commands to teach principles to the next generation. The parade example of such a command is Deuteronomy 6:7, "Repeat them to your children … ." A second, very illustrative example occurs in Deuteronomy 26:1–10. Within this text, the specifics of the first fruit presentation, is a review of Israel's past, which the presenter was required to recite. The perspective of the author of the text is that these recitals would occur in the future ("when you enter into the land, which YHWH your God is about to give to you as an inheritance and you possess it … "), which would look back on what YHWH had already accomplished in the author's time and what He had yet to accomplish by the author's time but would have accomplished by the time of these recitals. According to the text, after the Israelite put the first fruits in a basket and traveled to the location of the central sanctuary, he was to give two recitals: the first to the officiating priest before the offering is made, "I am telling YHWH your God today that I have come into the land which YHWH swore to our fathers to give to them," and the second "before YHWH your God" was a sweeping first person narrative of the past, which included the Patriarchal period, the Egyptian sojourn, the oppression in Egypt, the Exodus and allusions to the plagues, allusion to the conquest, and a description of the land, "a land flowing with milk and honey." A final example, although in poetry instead of narrative, is found in Judges 5:10–11, "Those who ride on tawny she-asses, who sit on carpets, who walk on the road, muse. To the sound of musicians, among the water drawers, there let them recount the righteous deeds of YHWH." In this case the people of God were enjoined to relate the story of Jael's, Deborah's and Baraq's victory over Sisera and Jabin.

The third type is introduced by זכר (zkr) "remember." Particularly notable are isolated infinitive absolutes of this root. At the Exodus:

"Remember this day that you came out of Egypt out of the house of slaves, because by a strong hand YHWH has brought you out from here, so that which is leavened must not be eaten" (Exodus 13:3). In a warning about leprosy: "Remember what YHWH your God did to Miriam ..." (Deuteronomy 24:9). Concerning Amalek's unconscionable attack on the rear of Israel's column: "Remember what Amalek did to you on the way when you came out of Egypt ... how he 'tailed' you, the weak ones in your rear, while you were faint and weary, he did not fear God. When YHWH your God has given you rest from all your surrounding enemies in the land, which the YHWH your God is going to give to you as an inheritance to possess, you must blot out the memory of Amalek from under heaven. Do not forget" (Deuteronomy 25:17–19). Also we find regular imperatives, such as in Micah 6:5: "Please, remember, my people, what Balak king of Moab purposed and what Balaam the son of Beor answered him from Shittim to Gilgal in order to know the righteous deeds of YHWH." As a final example consider this reminder to the people before the conquest: "Remember the word that Moses the servant of YHWH commanded you: YHWH your God is about to give you rest and to give you this land" (Joshua 1:13).

(3) **The Bible contains numerous retrospections on the past.** The Bible is replete with historical reviews of the past, which are theological reflections, often for the purpose of ameliorating behavior. These are found in the Torah, the Prophets and the Writings. For examples see Appendix D, Table D1.

(4) **The remembrance of the past devolves on the present and determines the future.** Often accompanying a review of the past is an exhortation to learn from the past, the strongest being warnings not to follow the trail of perfidy blazed by their fathers. Although discussed above under different rubrics, four additional texts invite comment: Deuteronomy 4, Joshua 24:1–13, Hosea 12:4–7, and Psalm 78. The first of these texts is the last part of the historical prologue preceding the restating of the Decalogue. Moses reminded the people assembled to hear his final addresses of the crucial historical reference points of the Baal Peor incident and the Sinai Theophany, what they should have learned from them and the consequences of not acting upon this

knowledge.

The covenant renewal ceremony (Joshua 24:1–13) included an extensive historical review, going all the way back to the patriarchs' former worship of idols in their country of origin. This speech contains twenty 1cs [first person common singular] verbs, which detail YWHW's past actions for the people (who are mostly referred to in the 2mp [second person masculine plural]).

Although brief, the historical reference in Hosea 12:4–7 to Jacob is telling. Hosea, an eighth century BC prophet, appealed to the example of the transformation of Jacob, which had been effected when he had wrestled with the angel of YHWH to enjoin the people of the Northern Kingdom of Israel to undergo a similar transformation: to return to their God and to wait for God continually.

Finally, there is the extraordinary text of Psalm 78:1–8:

> … Testimony arose in Jacob and instruction He placed in Israel, which He commanded our fathers to make known to their children, in order that a later generation, sons who would be born, would arise and relate (them) to their sons, in order that they might place their confidence in God and not forget the deeds of God and His commandments they would guard, so that they would not be like their fathers, a refractory and rebellious generation, which did not establish its heart and whose spirit was not firm in God.

The rest of this psalm is a review of the rebellions of Israel. The psalmist drew on his past in his time in order to mold the future.

(5) Customs are elucidated. Authors would have had little reason to elucidate customs if they were not convinced of their historicity. The first to be discussed pertains to a dietary exclusion, which was originated to memorialize when Jacob wrestled with God and the latter dislocated his hip with a touch. For this reason, the text says, the children of Israel do not eat the portion of animals, which is in the same location as Jacob's injury, until this day (Genesis 32:26, 32–33). This obviously challenged the ancient reader to test what the author had said.

A second custom elucidated involved the removal of a sandal, which meant that a kinsman redeemer had refused to engage in levirate marriage, that is, a brother's duty to raise up a seed for his heirless, deceased brother, by marrying his widow (Deuteronomy 25:5–10). The custom is elucidated in Ruth 4:7 as a clarification to the reader, whom the author thought was unfamiliar with the custom (this is the only report of levirate practice in the Old Testament). The custom is introduced with the phrase, "This was (the way) previously in Israel concerning redemption and exchange, to confirm any word: a man would draw off his sandal." The word "previously" suggests that the custom was not practiced in the author's day—a fact that the author deems important for his readers to know (Ruth 4:8).

The third custom is discussed in 1 Samuel 30. David, upon returning to Ziklag, discovered that a band of Amalekites had raided and kidnapped his family. He and his 600 men immediately set off after the miscreants. Arriving at the Wadi Besor, 200 of his men were too exhausted to continue on. Four hundred continued with David. After slaughtering all but 400 of the Amalekites (who had escaped on camels) and rescuing his family, David returned to the 200 who had remained behind and shared the booty with them against the protests of some of the 400. After this, David's pronouncement became statute and custom in Israel, which was still in effect in the author's time.

(6) Ancient names and current sayings are traced back to their origins. A Biblical author frequently explained how a place had received its name by appealing to the historical context in which the naming had occurred. Often this name persisted in the author's day. It is clear that the author expected that his readers would be interested in the explanation of the origin of names current in their day, almost as if he was tacitly asking his readers the question, "Would you like to know how so and so received its name?" And then, anticipating a "Yes, we would" answer, he supplied the information. The following texts explained the origins of names.[57] Also historical tracings of the origins of sayings are attested. Examples are in Appendix D, Table D2.

(7) Monuments and pronouncements are assigned a concrete reason as well as a slot in history. Biblical authors frequently explained the purposes for the placement of monuments, which often involved the naming of these monuments. Four of these stand out: the dual naming of Gilead—Laban gave it an Aramaic name—Jacob, its Hebrew name

(Genesis 31:44–54); the monuments created to mark the crossing of the Jordan (Joshua 4:1–9); the cairn erected over the corpses of Achan and his family (Joshua 7:25–26); and how Caleb obtained his inheritance (Joshua 14:6–14).

In the second and third of these the author virtually challenged his ancient readers to prove him wrong. This is significant in at least two ways. First of all, he would not have issued the challenge if he knew that it was not true. Second, because the pile must have existed in the author's day and rocks used for building can be dislodged through earth tremors—the account of the events cannot extensively post-date the events themselves.

In the fourth account there is an unstated allusion to the promise YHWH had made to Caleb, which is recorded in Numbers 14:24.

Biblical authors also explained why things were the way they were in their day. Three examples of this will suffice. The first concerns Israel; the other two do not, and, in fact, take place outside of the land of Israel. All three accounts move us to ask the question how did the author know this? The first, although it involves Israel is about a non-Israelite, Rahab. The author anticipated and supplied the answer to the question: how did a non-Israelite former prostitute end up living in their midst (Joshua 6:25)?

The second pertains to the lands and crops of the Egyptian people. According to Genesis 47:13–22, the people had exhausted their resources, money and animals, yet the famine persisted and they needed food. Out of desperation they offered themselves and their lands in exchange for food. Joseph, Pharaoh's vizier, agreed. All their land became Pharaoh's and they became his slaves—but this did not apply to the Egyptian priests and their land; they received an "allowance" of grain directly from the royal granaries and, therefore, did not have to sell their land, nor did they have to give the crown one-fifth of their crop like the rest of the people. The information about these exemptions is supplied by the author as an historical note. And the author tells us that that was the way it was in his day.

The third story is in 1 Samuel 5. After the Philistines defeated Israel at the Battle of Aphek, captured the Ark of the Covenant and brought it to Ashdod, they—being staunch adherents to the Ancient Near Eastern syllogism that my army cannot defeat your army until my god defeats your god—positioned the Ark next to the statue of Dagon, to proclaim his victory over YHWH. But when they entered the temple of Dagon the next day, Dagon had fallen over in such a way that he appeared to be prostrating himself to YHWH. The Ashdodites dutifully replaced him back on his pedestal on the dais, unaware that their actions mocked the putative deity of Dagon, who had supposedly defeated YHWH, but was incapable of even righting himself! The next day Dagon had fallen in the same posture again and in addition his decapitated head and his two severed hands had fallen onto his dais. This time the Ashdodites did not attempt to right Dagon. Dagon was desecrated, his dais cursed and, perhaps, he was even considered dead.[58] Even his priests dared not tread on his dais. A situation that the author tells us obtained also in his day. The narrative continues: YHWH ravaged Philistia with plagues and compelled its rulers and people to acknowledge His sovereignty, which—the author has told us—Dagon had already done.

(8) Historical footnotes are sprinkled throughout the text. In most cases, narrative details are not superfluous.[59] On occasion, however, the reason the author included a piece of information escapes us— meaning that we cannot ascertain how it impinges on the development of the narrative. Information supplied does not qualify as either gaps or blanks.[60] It is not a matter of a lack of knowledge but a surplus. This is historical information supplied for the benefit of the interested reader. Examples of these are found in Appendix D, Table D3.

(9) Written records used as sources are cited. Not surprisingly, there are references made to the Book of the Law of Moses (Joshua 8:31; 23:6; 2 Kings 14:6; Nehemiah 8:1), the Book of Moses (2 Chronicles 35:12; Ezra 6:18), the Book of the Law of God (Joshua 24:26), the Book of the Law (Joshua 8:34), the Book of the Law of YHWH (2 Chronicles 17:9) and the Book of the Covenant (2 Kings 23:21).[61] Additional sources are in Appendix D, Table D4.

(10) Precise chronological reference points are supplied. The Bible begins with an account locked into time. A prominent feature of the Creation Account in Genesis 1:1–2:3 is the steady sequence of six days (explicitly marked off by the phrase "evening was; morning was: X day," after God's creative acts on the first six days). Table D5 in Appendix D lists events dated to specific chronological reference points.

(11) Genealogies are given. This preoccupation with the progenitors of the past is not gratuitous. It serves at least three historiographical purposes. Alone or often intertwined with narrative—with narrative imbedded in genealogies or genealogies imbedded in narrative— genealogies *structure* history, *survey* history and *support* history. In addition to structuring the Book of Genesis and the first nine chapters of 1 Chronicles, genealogies can *structure* history (meaning event sequence). Examples of all three uses of genealogies are found in Appendix D, Table D6.

(12) The observation of cultic days and seasons are called acts of commemoration. The appointed times for Israel were Sabbaths (to remind them that YHWH is Creator [Exodus 20:8–11] and Deliverer [Deuteronomy 5:15]), new moons and the three annual feasts. See Table D7 in Appendix D for specifics.

(13) Past prophetic utterances are recalled. With this rubric and the two that follow the polarity of the Biblical time line is established and aligned with a largely continuous narrative from Genesis 1:1 through Nehemiah 13:31. We begin by looking at the time line in two directions. The first direction is an orientation toward the prophet's future. When reporting declarations about the future, the Biblical authors often explicitly linked prophetic statements to particular contexts. When an author from a later time and farther along in the canon mentioned a fulfillment of a prophetic pronouncement, he makes us focus on the second direction, an orientation toward the past (both his and that of his characters), in particular the context, which provoked the initial utterance. Four noteworthy examples are Joshua's curse on the rebuilding of Jericho (pronouncement [Joshua 6:26]; fulfillment announced [1 Kings 16:34]); the removal of Eli's line from the priesthood (pronouncement [1 Samuel 2:31]; fulfillment announced [1 Kings 2:27]); the proclamation of an anonymous man of God that a king named Josiah would desecrate Jeroboam's altar at Bethel and the account of the former's death and burial (pronouncement [1 Kings 13]; fulfillment announced and discovery of the man of God's tomb [2 Kings 23]); and the captivity would last 70 years (pronouncement [Jeremiah 25: 11–12]; promises claimed on the basis of this pronouncement [Daniel 9:2]).

(14) "Time words" explicitly indicate testable temporal continuity or discontinuity. With this rubric we continue our examination of the polarity of the Biblical time line, moving to a consideration of a very interesting characteristic of the text. Biblical authors could have told their stories without making any connections to their present. And thus their texts would only have been unverifiable tales—riveting, to be sure—but of little historical interest. But the fact of the matter is that the Biblical authors did just the opposite: they deliberately anchored their stories to testable and therefore falsifiable claims.[62] In fact, their express statements linking the past to their present or severing the present from the past was a risky business if they did not know their facts! They were challenging their contemporary readers to disprove their claims.

Two classes of temporal markers are attested, which link at least two separate times, the author's present and his past: the group of time words, which indicate temporal continuity with the past, and those which mark discontinuity with the past. Table D8 in Appendix D comprises a selection of the first class.

The second class of temporal markers indicates discontinuity.[63] By using these markers a Biblical author was stating that the present names, customs, sayings and situations, which were familiar to his readers, were different in the past. Although not verifiable, the very mention of these differences enforces the historical nature of the account. As I mentioned above, why would the author go to the trouble of concocting an elaborate past, which would only tangentially engage his readers? If there were only a few of these it would be one thing. But in fact, there are many—all covered in the discussions above.

(15) Historical trajectories occur. Certain people, statements, and ideas are projected with such great force in the Pentateuch that their trace is found through large expanses of text and time. Outside of the promises made to the Patriarchs, which are discussed above, we will look at the following fascinating trajectories: the journey of Joseph's bones, the enigma of Balaam, YHWH's dogged pursuit of the Amalekites, and the checkered history of Moab and Ammon. We begin at the deathbed of Joseph.

Recognizing that he was to die soon, Joseph asserted to his family that God would intervene on their behalf and bring them up from Egypt and into the land, which He swore to Abraham, to Isaac and to Jacob (Genesis 50:24). Moreover, repeating his assertion and even strengthening it "God will surely intervene," in an act of faith reminiscent of his father's, Joseph charged his family to not leave his bones in Egypt (Genesis 50:25). Nevertheless, the Book of Genesis ends with Joseph embalmed in a sarcophagus in Egypt.

We do not hear the slightest rattle of his bones during the hundreds of years of Egyptian sojourn and oppression, nor do we hear anything during the years of the plagues in Egypt. But suddenly they are clanking quite loudly at the Exodus:

> Moses took the bones of Joseph with him, because he had clearly made the children of Israel take an oath, 'God will surely intervene for you, then you will bring out my bones from this place with you' (Exodus 13:19).

Again there was silence: the skeleton was back in the "closet." And there it quietly hung until the children of Israel buried it back in the land:

> And the bones of Joseph, which the children of Israel had brought up form the land of Egypt, they buried in the portion of the field, which Jacob had purchased from Hamor, the father of Shechem for one hundred qeshita (Joshua 24:32).

The burial of Joseph's bones marks a closure in the narrative. Joseph was the first son of Jacob to leave the land and with his burial he was the final son to return.

We now turn to a much less noble character, Balaam. Outside of the contiguous narrative in Numbers 22–24, Balaam is presented as a despicable character. But the Biblical authors persistently mention his name, what he did, what YHWH did in response, and what happened to him. It seems that Balaam made an impact. He is mentioned as late as Nehemiah 13:2 and even in the last book of the New Testament![64]

Balaam tried to curse Israel in order to receive a handsome remuneration from King Balak of Moab. YHWH would not let him curse Israel but turned his attempted cursing into blessing. But Balaam did not give up his fee that easily. He figured out another way to frustrate Israel: lure them into idolatry. This he was able to do at a place synonymous with idolatry, Baal Peor (Numbers 25). YHWH ordered 12,000 Israelites into battle against the Midianites because of the Baal Peor incident. The final enemy casualty mentioned in the battle report was Balaam: "And they also killed Balaam, the son of Beor, with a sword" (Numbers 31:1–8). Moses mentioned Balaam again: his effort to curse Israel and YHWH's interdiction of these efforts (Deuteronomy 23:4–5). Joshua mentioned Balaam's execution (Joshua 13:22) and YHWH transforming the seer's curses (Joshua 24:9–10). Even the prophet Micah pointed out YHWH's righteous deed in delivering the people from Balaam's first efforts (Micah 6:5).

Amalek, flawed in his pedigree (the grandson of Esau and Adah, a Hittite, and born of a concubine [Genesis 36:2, 12]), fathered the Amalekites, a people deemed even more despicable than Balaam. They were desert marauders from the outset. These bandits cowardly descended on the rear of Israel's column coming out of Egypt, and sealed their own doom. YHWH pronounced national extermination upon them, a sentence which He never rescinded for the group as a whole and individual Amalekites fared no better.

The trajectory of the Amalekites is clear. After assaulting Israel during the Exodus (Exodus 17), they and the Canaanites routed the presumptuous Israelites, who tried to enter the land after YHWH pronounced judgment upon them (Numbers 14:45). Moses mentioned them immediately before Israel entered the Land, reminding the people to exterminate them as soon as they were settled in the Land (Deuteronomy 25:17–19). During the period of the judges, the Amalekites joined with the Ammonites and the Moabites under the leadership of Eglon, the king of Moab to oppress Israel (Judges 3:13). Also, Gideon faced and defeated a coalition of Midianites and Amalekites, who had been ravaging the land (Judges 6:3, 33; 7:12). Near the end of this period YHWH reminded the people that He had given them victory over a number of oppressors—including the Amalekites (Judges 10:11–12). Saul, Israel's first king, fought against the Amalekites (1 Samuel 14:47–48). But Saul did not eliminate the Amalekite threat even though he was charged to do so. In his infamous encounter with the Amalekites, he spared their king and their best animals (1 Samuel 15:1–33; 28:18). David, his successor, regularly raided among the Amalekites from Ziklag (1 Samuel 27:8) and had a serious encounter with the Amalekites at about the same time that Saul was fighting the Philistines. On this occasion, he slaughtered most of the Amalekite bandits who had kidnapped his family, but 400 escaped into the desert on camels (1 Samuel 30:1–18). Moreover, David ordered the execution of an Amalekite who claimed to have killed a mortally wounded Saul at the latter's request (2 Samuel 1:1–16). Those Amalekites who escaped from David on camels apparently made their way to Mount Seir, because they were later supplanted by the Simeonites (1 Chronicles 4:43). This was the end of the Amalekites. Their trajectory parallels the history of Israel, from the patriarchal period, through the Exodus, wilderness years, period of the judges, and the reigns of Saul and David.

Finally, we will trace back to the Patriarchal Period the checkered history of Moab and Ammon, in which later texts refer to incidents reported in earlier texts, forming the links of a chain, which goes back to the origin of these peoples. The author of Chronicles has the latest mention of Moab and the Sons of Ammon. He looks back to the time in which Jehoshaphat—pleading for YHWH to deliver Judah from an invading horde, which included Moabites and Ammonites—made the following biting observation:

> So now as far as the Sons of Ammon, Moab and Mount Seir are comcerned, among whom you would not allow Israel to enter, when they came from Egypt, with the result that they turned aside from them and did not destroy them, they would recompense us by coming and driving us from your possession, which you caused us to possess (2 Chronicles 20:10–11).

The original records of these divine prohibitions are found in Deuteronomy 2:9, 19. Concerning Moab, YHWH said:

> Do not harm Moab and do not stir up strife for battle against them, because I have not given you any of his land a possession; because to the sons of Lot

I have given Ar as a possession (Deuteronomy 2:9). YHWH's almost identical prohibition regarding Ammon is in Deuteronomy 2:1. These texts look back to the time just before the Children of Israel arrived at the Plains of Moab. Having defeated the Canaanites and Amalekites, Israel was eager to fight the Moabites and Ammonites, but YHWH forbad it, explaining that they were sons of Lot. This is of course takes us back to the story told in Genesis 19: the story of Lot and his daughters. His daughters made their father drunk on two successive nights. In his inebriated state he impregnated each of his daughters. Their sons by their father were the progenitors of the Moabites and the Ammonites.

The chain is complete. It extends back from the days of the author of Chronicles to the time of Jehoshaphat; from his time to the days before the Conquest; from the days before the Conquest to the Patriarchal Period.

8. Conclusions

Although lacking the mathematical rigor of the statistical study, which rejected the null hypothesis H_0 (a classification model derived from the distribution of the relative frequency of preterites classifies texts no better than random results) and accepted the alternative hypothesis H_1 (a classification model derived from this distribution classifies texts better than random results), which computed that the proportion of error reduction using the model is between 85.5 and 95.5 percent with a 95% confidence interval, and which determined that the probability that Genesis 1:1–2:3 is narrative is between 0.999942 and 0.999987 at a 99.5% confidence level, the weight of evidence (summarized in Section 7 and Appendix D) is so overwhelming that we must acknowledge that Biblical authors believed that they were recounting real events. We must therefore call their work history.[65]

The combination of the statistical and Biblical arguments is the "evidence" to which the subtitle of this chapter, "evidence for an historical reading of Genesis 1:1–2:3," refers.

Since Genesis 1:1–2:3 has the same genre as historical narrative texts and is linked lexically and thematically to these texts it *should* be read as these texts are read: as a realistic portrayal of the events.

Sailhamer [1992, p. 13] explains what "realistic portrayal of the events" means:

> A biblical narrative text takes the raw material of language and shapes it into a version of the world of empirical *reality*. Its essential linguistic structures are adapted to conform to events in *real* life. The constraints that shape *real* life (for example, the limitations of time and space and perspective) are the constraints to which historical narrative texts must strive to conform in their imitation of *real* life ... Events and characters are put before the reader as happening just as they happen in *real* life. The reader looks at the events in the narrative in much the same way as he or she would look at events in *real* life. They happen in the text before one's eyes (emphasis mine).

How then *should* we read Genesis 1:1–2:3 in light of the fact that it is an historical narrative? Answer: as a realistic portrayal of the Creation of the universe. So again we have come—this time by means of a lengthy accumulation of evidence—to a conclusion, which would have been obvious to the original readers of this text.

Now as modern readers we are faced with a choice: to believe or not believe that it happened the way the author described. *Should* we as readers believe what the authors wrote? If we are faithful to their presentation we should. These historians do not allow us to be dispassionate observers of the past as we read their texts. They *compel us* to believe the past they portray. But *will* we believe *this* text?

Sternberg [1985, pp. 32–34] forcefully argues:

> Were the narrative written or read as fiction, then God would turn from the lord of history into a creature of the imagination, with the most disastrous results. The shape of time, the rationale of monotheism, the foundations of conduct, the national sense of identity, the very right to the land of Israel and the hope of deliverance to come: all hang in the generic balance. Hence, the Bible's determination to sanctify and compel literal belief in the past. It claims not just the status of history but ... of *the* [author's italics] history, the one and only truth that, like God himself, brooks no rival .... *if as seekers for the truth, professional or amateur, we can take or leave the*

truth claim of inspiration, then as readers we must simply take it—just like any other biblical premise or convention, from the existence of God to the sense borne by specific words—*or else invent our own text* [last emphasis mine].
Will we believe this text? The answer: we must.

9. Acknowledgments

My sincere gratitude to Dr. Roger Longbotham, Senior Statistician at Amazon.com, my main statistical consultant, who advised me on theory, assumptions, tests, results and conclusions and generated the random sample, suggested and tested the models, and created all the logistic curves.

Also my deep appreciation to Dr. David Neu, Emeritus Professor of Mathematics and Retired Chairman of the Mathematics Department at Westmont College, for his extensive input on my statistical analysis.

My heartfelt thanks to the faculty, administration, staff and students of The Master's College—principally to Dr. Tom Halstead, Chairman of Biblical Studies, and my colleagues in the department, the faculty of the Science and Mathematics Department, and Dr. John Hotchkiss, Chairman of the English Department. I particularly want to recognize the support of Dr. John MacArthur, President, Dr. Richard Mayhue, Senior Vice President and Provost, and Dr. John Hughes, Academic Vice-President.

I also want to thank Dr. William Barrick, Professor of Old Testament and Director of Th.D. Studies at The Master's Seminary (TMS), for his thorough copy-editing, and Dr. Trevor Craigen, Associate Professor of Theology at TMS, for carefully reading the whole.

Of course, I gratefully acknowledge all connected with the RATE project: the donors, the entire ICR organization, the scientists of the RATE team—but especially Dr. Larry Vardiman for his leadership of the team and careful editorial supervision of my chapter.

But I direct my most profound gratitude toward my Creator and Savior. To Him be the glory. Isaiah 40:25–26.

Appendix A: Additional Results of the Exploratory Phase

A.1 Texts Selected

I picked texts acknowledged to be either narratives or poems. The narrative texts included in the analysis and plotted according to the following numbers in Figure A1 were: (1) the Joseph Story (Genesis 37–50), (2) Joshua's conquest of the Promised Land (Joshua 5–8),

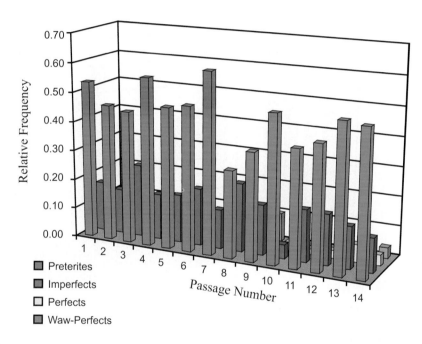

Figure A1. 3-D bar graph of the finite verb distribution in selected narrative texts. The numbers on the *x*-axis represent the following narrative passages: (1) the Joseph Story (Genesis 37–50), (2) Joshua's conquest of the Promised Land (Joshua 5–8), (3) the Samson pericopes (Judges 13–16), (4) the Ark narrative (1 Samuel 5:1–7:1), (5) Ruth, (6) Esther, (7) Nehemiah, (8) the Court History of David (2 Samuel 11–20), (9) the Ministry of Elijah (2 Kings 17–19), (10) Hezekiah and Sennacherib; (11) Jehoiakim burning the scroll of Jeremiah (Jeremiah 36), (12) the Fall of Jerusalem (2 Kings 25), (13) Kings, and (14) Chronicles.

(3) the Samson pericopes (Judges 13–16), (4) the Ark narrative (1 Samuel 5:1–7:1), (5) Ruth, (6) Esther, (7) Nehemiah, (8) the Court History of David (2 Samuel 11–20), (9) the Ministry of Elijah (1 Kings 17–19), (10) Hezekiah and Sennacherib; (11) Jehoiakim burning the scroll of Jeremiah (Jeremiah 36), (12) the Fall of Jerusalem (2 Kings 25), (13) Kings, and (14) Chronicles.

The poetic texts I chose are plotted in Figure A2 as follows: (1) Jacob blessing his sons (Genesis 49), (2) The Song of the Sea (Exodus 15),

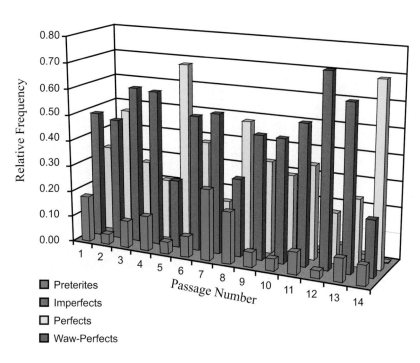

Figure A2. 3-D bar graph of the finite verb distribution in selected poetic texts. The numbers on the *x*-axis represent the following poetic passages: (1) Jacob blessing his sons (Genesis 49), (2) The Song of the Sea (Exodus 15), (3) The Oracles of Balaam (Numbers 23–24), (4) The Song of Moses (Deuteronomy 32), (5) The Jael Poem (Judges 5), (6) The Prayer of Hannah (1 Samuel 2:1–10), (7) David's Song (2 Samuel 22), (8) the prayer of Jonah (Jonah 2:2–10), (9) Isaiah 1–35, (10) Minor Prophets, (11) Psalms, (12) Proverbs, (13) the dialogues and monologues of Job, and (14) Lamentations.

(3) The Oracles of Balaam (Numbers 23–24), (4) The Song of Moses (Deuteronomy 32), (5) The Jael Poem (Judges 5), (6) The Prayer of Hannah (1 Samuel 2:1–10), (7) David's Song (2 Samuel 22), (8) the prayer of Jonah (Jonah 2:2–10), (9) Isaiah 1–35, (10) Minor Prophets, (11) Psalms, (12) Proverbs, (13) the dialogues and monologues of Job, and (14) Lamentations.

A.2 3-D Bar Graphs of Relative Frequency

The relative frequencies plotted in Figures A1 and A2 (green for preterites, red for imperfects, yellow for perfects and blue for waw-perfects) show green dominates in narrative, red and yellow in poetry, indicating that the relative number of preterites is not just significant but decisive.

A.3 Scatter Plots

Simple x-y scatter plots confirm the visual impression of the 3-D bar graphs. In the first x-y plot (Figure A3) the ratio of preterites to finite verbs is plotted on the x-axis and the ratio of imperfects to finite verbs is plotted on the y-axis, with the ratios for both genres appearing on the same graph. The points for each genre were colorized and given distinct shapes to manifest any clustering, with green diamonds for narrative and red squares for poetry. In addition, the eight texts that are compared and contrasted in Figure 2 were included: Red Sea texts are marked by large blue diamonds (solid for narrative, outline for poetry); Baraq-Deborah-Jael texts by large blue squares (solid for narrative, outline for poetry): Creation texts by blue triangles (solid for Genesis 1:1–2:3, outline for Psalm 104); the Flood text by a solid magenta circle and Psalms 105–106 are indicated by a solid orange square. The second x-y plot (Figure A4) was done in exactly the same way but with the ratio of perfects to finite verbs on the y-axis. In both x-y plots clustering is clearly evident, although the clusters are more defined for the "imperfect" data. Moreover, the paired texts from Figure 2 are clearly clustered by genre.

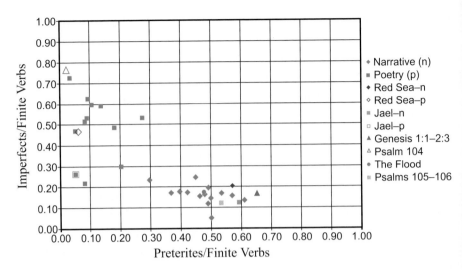

Figure A3. Scatter plot for selected texts, with preterites/(finite verbs) on the *x*-axis and imperfects/(finite verbs) on the *y*-axis. Clustering by genre is evident in both selected texts and paired texts.

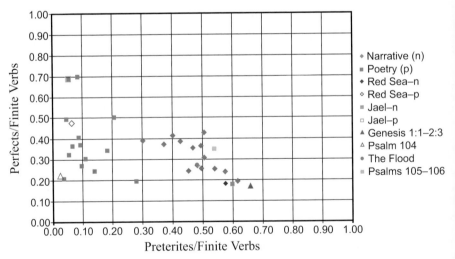

Figure A4. Scatter plot for selected texts, with preterites/(finite verbs) on the *x*-axis and perfects/(finite verbs) on the *y*-axis. Clustering by genre is evident in both selected texts and paired texts.

A.4 Inferential Modeling

Given the distinctly different distribution of finite verbs in narrative and poetry two inferential analyses were tested to determine if one or both could identify the genre of a text with unknown genre by its finite verb distribution. The two tested were discriminant analysis and logistic regression.[66]

A.4.1 Discriminant Analysis

The first method tested was discriminant analysis. The necessary condition for this inferential approach is that independent variables have a joint multivariate normal distribution. In other words, each independent variable must have Gaussian distributions for both narrative and poetry.

Since the discriminant analysis only included one independent variable, the percent of preterites among finite verbs, we only needed to check the normality of that distribution. Histograms of the distribution of the percent of preterites among finite verbs for the narrative passages show that this distribution is normal. Moreover, several other tests for normality were conducted and all failed to reject the null hypothesis that the distribution is normal.

On the other hand, for the poetic passages the distribution of the percent of preterites among finite verbs for poetic texts is not normal. Several other tests for normality were conducted and most rejected the null hypothesis that the distribution is normal.

Even though this model discriminated well between the two groups of texts, because the *joint* multivariate distribution is not normal, we chose to model the data by the second method, logistic regression.

A.4.2 Logistic Regression

The second method tested was logistic regression. Logistic regression is discussed in detail in Section 5.5 above. In brief, it was ideal for our study because with only two possibilities for the dependent variable, narrative or poetry, the data is patently non-linear, and, therefore, does not yield easily—if at all—to an ordinary least squares analysis.

Also, logistic regression does not require our data to form a normal distribution—it does not, nor does it assume homoscedasticity (variance is independent of the mean).[67]

The model produces a flattened S-shaped curve, which is relatively flat at the origin, climbs (steeply or gradually, depending on the general distribution of the data), and eventually flattens out at $y=1$ (see Figure 9).

Appendix B: Data for Confirmatory Phase

The data for narrative is in Tables B1–B4; the data for poetry is in Tables B5–B8.

Table B1. Finite verb counts for narrative: Torah

| | Text | Verb Counts | | | | | | | [ ]/Total Finite Verbs | | | |
		Total Verbs	Preterites	Imperfects	Perfects	Waw-Perfects	Total Finite Verbs	Total Non-Finite Verbs	Preterites	Imperfects	Perfects	Waw-Perfects
1	Genesis 17	70	16	17	8	19	60	10	0.27	0.28	0.13	0.32
2	Genesis 21	113	57	14	25	0	96	17	0.59	0.15	0.26	0.00
3	Genesis 31	193	70	24	56	3	153	40	0.46	0.16	0.37	0.02
4	Exodus 3	99	21	23	16	14	74	25	0.28	0.31	0.22	0.19
5	Exodus 7:14–25	52	14	5	12	6	37	15	0.38	0.14	0.32	0.16
6	Exodus 11	32	6	10	4	4	24	8	0.25	0.42	0.17	0.17
7	Exodus 15:22–16:36	166	52	21	35	10	118	48	0.44	0.18	0.30	0.08
8	Exodus 32	156	65	15	35	2	117	39	0.56	0.13	0.30	0.02
9	Exodus 33	103	14	25	11	29	79	24	0.18	0.32	0.14	0.37
10	Exodus 39	79	30	2	21	0	53	26	0.57	0.04	0.40	0.00
11	Numbers 10:11–34	42	10	6	4	12	32	10	0.31	0.19	0.13	0.38
12	Numbers 12	52	19	10	11	0	40	12	0.48	0.25	0.28	0.00
13	Numbers 20:1–21:9	147	66	21	19	14	120	27	0.55	0.18	0.16	0.12
14	Numbers 21:10–14, 15, 21–27, 31–35	56	26	11	8	1	46	10	0.57	0.24	0.17	0.02
15	Numbers 22	185	77	27	28	2	134	51	0.57	0.20	0.21	0.01
16	Exodus 7:1–13	43	13	8	6	7	34	9	0.38	0.24	0.18	0.21
17	Exodus 18	89	29	15	13	12	69	20	0.42	0.22	0.19	0.17

Table B2. Finite verb counts for narrative: Former Prophets

	Text	Total Verbs	Preterites	Imperfects	Perfects	Waw-Perfects	Total Finite Verbs	Total Non-Finite Verbs	Preterites	Imperfects	Perfects	Waw-Perfects
		Verb Counts					[ ]/Total Finite Verbs					
18	Joshua 7	122	50	21	19	6	96	26	0.52	0.22	0.20	0.06
19	Joshua 13:8–33	28	11	0	15	0	26	2	0.42	0.00	0.58	0.00
20	Joshua 15	60	15	3	2	32	52	8	0.29	0.06	0.04	0.62
21	Judges 3:8–31	90	58	0	14	0	72	18	0.81	0.00	0.19	0.00
22	Judges 4	76	24	9	12	9	54	22	0.44	0.17	0.22	0.17
23	Judges 11–12	222	104	23	39	10	176	46	0.59	0.13	0.22	0.06
24	1 Samuel 3	98	37	12	20	2	71	27	0.52	0.17	0.28	0.03
25	1 Samuel 27	47	15	9	8	5	37	10	0.41	0.24	0.22	0.14
26	2 Samuel 4	58	30	2	12	1	45	13	0.67	0.04	0.27	0.02
27	2 Samuel 8:1–18	56	28	0	13	0	41	15	0.68	0.00	0.32	0.00
28	2 Samuel 15:13–37	104	22	18	7	11	58	46	0.38	0.31	0.12	0.19
29	2 Samuel 23:8–39	52	25	2	15	0	42	10	0.60	0.05	0.36	0.00
30	1 Kings 1:1–2:12	256	84	44	50	23	201	55	0.42	0.22	0.25	0.11
31	1 Kings 6	79	30	4	20	3	57	22	0.53	0.07	0.35	0.05
32	1 Kings 10:14–29	35	12	5	4	0	21	14	0.57	0.24	0.19	0.00
33	1 Kings 15:25–16:20	93	32	2	32	1	67	26	0.48	0.03	0.48	0.01
34	1 Kings 17	97	42	9	13	9	73	24	0.58	0.12	0.18	0.12
35	2 Kings 16	66	34	3	16	0	53	13	0.64	0.06	0.30	0.00
36	2 Kings 17	165	66	18	49	0	133	32	0.50	0.14	0.37	0.00
37	1 Kings 21	94	27	6	33	10	76	18	0.36	0.08	0.43	0.13
38	2 Kings 25	78	35	2	25	3	65	13	0.54	0.03	0.38	0.05
39	2 Kings 13	99	52	3	27	1	83	16	0.63	0.04	0.33	0.01
40	2 Samuel 24	108	47	13	14	2	76	32	0.62	0.17	0.18	0.03
41	1 Kings 22:29–50	69	24	2	23	0	49	20	0.49	0.04	0.47	0.00

Table B3. Finite verb counts for narrative: Latter Prophets

	Text	Total Verbs	Preterites	Imperfects	Perfects	Waw-Perfects	Total Finite Verbs	Total Non-Finite Verbs	Preterites	Imperfects	Perfects	Waw-Perfects
		Verb Counts					[ ]/Total Finite Verbs					
42	Jeremiah 32:1–15	55	13	9	7	3	32	23	0.41	0.28	0.22	0.09
43	Jeremiah 52 (same event reported in 2 Kings 25)	75	32	3	27	2	64	11	0.50	0.05	0.42	0.03
44	Amos 10–15	23	6	5	2	0	13	10	0.46	0.38	0.15	0.00
45	Jeremiah 26	104	27	12	21	4	64	40	0.42	0.19	0.33	0.06

Table B4. Finite verb counts for narrative: Writings

		Verb Counts						[ ]/Total Finite Verbs			
	Text	Total Verbs	Preterites	Imperfects	Perfects	Waw-Perfects	Total Finite Verbs	Total Non-Finite Verbs	Preterites	Imperfects	Perfects	Waw-Perfects
46	1 Chronicles 10	62	35	1	12	1	49	13	0.71	0.02	0.24	0.02
47	1 Chronicles 11:1–9	29	14	5	1	0	20	9	0.70	0.25	0.05	0.00
48	1 Chronicles 12	66	9	6	14	0	29	37	0.31	0.21	0.48	0.00
49	2 Chronicles 13	66	30	2	15	1	48	18	0.63	0.04	0.31	0.02
50	2 Chronicles 16	53	21	1	13	0	35	18	0.60	0.03	0.37	0.00
51	2 Chronicles 18:1–27	122	42	25	12	4	83	39	0.51	0.30	0.14	0.05
52	2 Chronicles 21	61	27	2	20	0	49	12	0.55	0.04	0.41	0.00
53	2 Chronicles 23:16–24:27	127	58	9	32	1	100	27	0.58	0.09	0.32	0.01
54	2 Chronicles 31	60	18	2	11	0	31	29	0.58	0.06	0.35	0.00
55	2 Chronicles 36:1–21	67	26	0	21	0	47	20	0.55	0.00	0.45	0.00
56	2 Chronicles 12	61	18	4	21	3	46	15	0.39	0.09	0.46	0.07
57	2 Chronicles 26–27	106	40	0	29	0	69	37	0.58	0.00	0.42	0.00
58	Exodus 14	116	48	17	14	5	84	32	0.57	0.20	0.17	0.06
59	Judges 4	96	44	9	12	9	74	22	0.59	0.12	0.16	0.12
60	Genesis 1:1–2:3	111	55	14	13	2	84	27	0.65	0.17	0.15	0.02
61	The Flood	250	94	34	51	18	197	53	0.48	0.17	0.26	0.09

Table B5. Finite verb counts for poetry: Torah

		Verb Counts						[ ]/Total Finite Verbs			
	Text	Total Verbs	Preterites	Imperfects	Perfects	Waw-Perfects	Total Finite Verbs	Total Non-Finite Verbs	Preterites	Imperfects	Perfects	Waw-Perfects
1	Genesis 49:2–27	64	8	22	15	0	45	19	0.18	0.49	0.33	0.00
2	Numbers 23:7–10	18	2	9	3	0	14	4	0.14	0.64	0.21	0.00
3	Numbers 24:3–9	23	2	8	5	0	15	8	0.13	0.53	0.33	0.00
4	Genesis 2:23, etc.	41	2	21	7	1	31	10	0.06	0.68	0.23	0.03
5	Deuteronomy 32	155	20	66	27	4	117	38	0.17	0.56	0.23	0.03

Each table is structured as follows: column 1 is the text number; column 2 lists the texts; columns 3–9 are the verb counts for each text (column 3—total verbs, column 4—preterites, column 5—imperfects, column 6—perfects, column 7—waw-perfects, column 8—total finite

Table B6. Finite verb counts for poetry: Former Prophets

	Text	Verb Counts							[ ]/Total Finite Verbs			
		Total Verbs	Preterites	Imperfects	Perfects	Waw-Perfects	Total Finite Verbs	Total Non-Finite Verbs	Preterites	Imperfects	Perfects	Waw-Perfects
6	1 Samuel 15:22–23	7	2	0	1	0	3	4	0.67	0.00	0.33	0.00
7	2 Samuel 1:19–27; 3:33b–34	30	4	6	12	0	22	8	0.18	0.27	0.55	0.00
8	2 Samuel 23:1b–7	17	0	6	5	0	11	6	0.00	0.55	0.45	0.00
9	Judges 14:14b	6	1	0	3	0	4	2	0.25	0.00	0.75	0.00
10	2 Kings 19:20b–28	42	4	4	23	2	33	9	0.12	0.12	0.70	0.06

Table B7. Finite verb counts for poetry: Latter Prophets

	Text	Verb Counts							[ ]/Total Finite Verbs			
		Total Verbs	Preterites	Imperfects	Perfects	Waw-Perfects	Total Finite Verbs	Total Non-Finite Verbs	Preterites	Imperfects	Perfects	Waw-Perfects
11	Isaiah 11:1–9, 12–12:6	66	1	21	5	20	47	19	0.02	0.45	0.11	0.43
12	Isaiah 21:1–15	65	3	4	19	2	28	37	0.11	0.14	0.68	0.07
13	Isaiah 29:1–24	111	6	23	16	26	71	40	0.08	0.32	0.23	0.37
14	Isaiah 30:1–18	70	3	21	10	2	36	34	0.08	0.58	0.28	0.06
15	Isaiah 37:22b–29	37	2	4	20	3	29	8	0.07	0.14	0.69	0.10
16	Isaiah 41:1–29	120	5	67	21	0	93	27	0.05	0.72	0.23	0.00
17	Isaiah 60:1–22	80	0	37	7	16	60	20	0.00	0.62	0.12	0.27
18	Isaiah 65:1–25	109	1	41	24	16	82	27	0.01	0.50	0.29	0.20
19	Isaiah 66:1–16, 22–23	83	2	25	18	11	56	27	0.04	0.45	0.32	0.20
20	Jeremiah 4:5–8, 13–18	42	1	6	9	0	16	26	0.06	0.38	0.56	0.00
21	Jeremiah 4:19–31	53	0	16	22	1	39	14	0.00	0.41	0.56	0.03
22	Jeremiah 10:2b–25	69	3	21	21	1	46	23	0.07	0.46	0.46	0.02
23	Jeremiah 12:1–13	55	1	12	27	1	41	14	0.02	0.29	0.66	0.02
24	Jeremiah 20:7–18	60	4	15	18	5	42	18	0.10	0.36	0.43	0.12
25	Jeremiah 21:12b–14; 22:6b–7, 10; 13–17, 18b–23, 28–30	88	0	20	18	10	48	40	0.00	0.42	0.38	0.21
26	Jeremiah 31:2–22, 23b, 29b, 35–37	116	2	27	30	15	74	42	0.03	0.36	0.41	0.20
27	Jeremiah 46:3–28	105	2	24	31	8	65	40	0.03	0.37	0.48	0.12
28	Jeremiah 47:2–7; 48:1b–20, 28–33, 40–47	145	1	27	50	13	91	54	0.01	0.30	0.55	0.14
29	Jeremiah 50:2, 11–16, 21–27, 31–32, 35–38, 41–43	93	2	19	28	10	59	34	0.03	0.32	0.47	0.17
30	Jeremiah 51:25–58	131	3	29	36	21	89	42	0.03	0.33	0.40	0.24
31	Ezekiel 19:2b–14	50	20	2	20	1	43	7	0.47	0.05	0.47	0.02
32	Micah 3:1–5:15	152	1	48	20	44	113	39	0.01	0.42	0.18	0.39
33	Nahum 1:2–15	47	2	13	15	0	30	17	0.07	0.43	0.50	0.00
34	Isaiah 18:1–19:15	74	0	18	14	17	49	25	0.00	0.37	0.29	0.35
35	Isaiah 50:1–51:23	162	8	50	41	2	101	61	0.08	0.50	0.41	0.02
36	Isaiah 44:1–8, 21–28	68	0	27	13	1	41	27	0.00	0.66	0.32	0.02

Table B8. Finite verb counts for poetry: Writings

	Text	Total Verbs	Preterites	Imperfects	Perfects	Waw-Perfects	Total Finite Verbs	Total Non-Finite Verbs	Preterites	Imperfects	Perfects	Waw-Perfects
		Verb Counts					**[ ]/Total Finite Verbs**					
37	Job:16–17	81	7	45	22	0	74	7	0.09	0.61	0.30	0.00
38	Job 19	73	9	32	24	0	65	8	0.14	0.49	0.37	0.00
39	Job 23–24	107	4	60	31	2	97	10	0.04	0.62	0.32	0.02
40	Job 25	8	0	4	1	0	5	3	0.00	0.80	0.20	0.00
41	Job 38:2–40:2	158	8	91	35	0	134	24	0.06	0.68	0.26	0.00
42	Psalms [David: Mizmor: Praise]	446	7	196	113	4	320	126	0.02	0.61	0.35	0.01
43	Psalms [David: Tephillah]	40	0	12	7	0	19	21	0.00	0.63	0.37	0.00
44	Psalms [David: Shir, Mizmor: Lament]	99	0	29	31	0	60	39	0.00	0.48	0.52	0.00
45	Psalms [David: Maskil: Lament]	106	4	39	29	0	72	34	0.06	0.54	0.40	0.00
46	Psalms [David: Tehillah]	37	0	23	0	0	23	14	0.00	1.00	0.00	0.00
47	Psalms [David: NDIS: Lament]	318	11	109	63	4	187	131	0.06	0.58	0.34	0.02
48	Psalms [Sons of Korah: Mizmor, Song, Maskil]	45	0	11	22	0	33	12	0.00	0.33	0.67	0.00
49	Psalms [Asaph: Maskil: Lament]	55	0	13	23	0	36	19	0.00	0.36	0.64	0.00
50	Psalms [Asaph: NDIS: Wisdom]	38	3	16	6	0	25	13	0.12	0.64	0.24	0.00
51	Psalms [Solomon: Praise]	42	0	32	1	0	33	9	0.00	0.97	0.03	0.00
52	Psalms [Anonymous: Mizmor]	21	0	4	6	0	10	11	0.00	0.40	0.60	0.00
53	Psalms [Anonymous: Mizmor, Todah]	8	0	0	1	0	1	7	0.00	0.00	1.00	0.00
54	Proverbs 1:20–33	39	2	21	8	1	32	7	0.06	0.66	0.25	0.03
55	Proverbs 2:1–11	20	0	16	0	1	17	3	0.00	0.94	0.00	0.06
56	Proverbs 4:1–27	72	2	30	6	1	39	33	0.05	0.77	0.15	0.03
57	Lamentations 3	120	11	36	55	1	103	17	0.11	0.35	0.53	0.01
58	2 Chronicles 6:41–42	5	0	3	0	0	3	2	0.00	1.00	0.00	0.00
59	Solomon [Wisdom]	16	0	5	3	0	8	8	0.00	0.63	0.38	0.00
60	Job 4–5	112	6	55	17	4	82	30	0.07	0.67	0.21	0.05
62	Exodus 15:1–18	64	2	25	23	0	50	14	0.04	0.50	0.46	0.00
63	Judges 5	103	3	17	45	0	65	38	0.05	0.26	0.69	0.00
64	Psalm 104	84	1	48	13	0	62	22	0.02	0.77	0.21	0.00
65	Psalm 105; 106	207	77	17	49	1	144	63	0.53	0.12	0.34	0.01

verbs [sum of columns 4–7], column 9—total non-finite verbs); and columns 10–13 are the relative frequencies of each finite verb type with respect to the total number of finite verbs (column 10—of preterites [bright green highlight for narrative; dark orange for poetry], column

11—of imperfects, column 12—of perfects, and column 13—of waw-perfects). The texts marked in pale yellow are the extra texts analyzed to account for any non-compliance with the conditions of the statistical tests (sample size, etc.) in the primary texts.

Appendix C: Details of Statistical Analysis

C.1 Logistic Regression Model Summary Statistics—Weighted

Table C1. Parameter estimation section

Variable	Regression Coefficient	Standard Error	Chi-Square $\beta=0$	Probability Level	Last R^2
Intercept	-5.685615	0.1806291	990.79	0.000000	0.131845
X_1	24.72761	0.8122928	926.70	0.000000	0.124378

Table C2. Model summary section

R^2	Degrees of Freedom	Chi-Square	Probability
0.550457	1	7988.52	0.000000

C.2 Goodness of Fit Calculations

To determine the goodness of fit of our model, the null hypothesis that our model did not fit the data any better than the model with all the coefficients equal to 0 was tested by calculating the model chi-square statistic, G_M, as follows:

$$G_M = -2[LL(A) - LL(A, B_I)] \tag{C1}$$

where $LL(A)$ is the log likelihood for the zero coefficients model and $LL(A, B_I)$ is the log likelihood for our model. For our model this statistic follows a chi-square distribution with 1 degree of freedom.

The model chi-square of our model is 7988.52, with 1 degree of freedom. We rejected therefore this null hypothesis at the extremely significant level of $p < 0.0001$.

The rejection of this null hypothesis at such an extremely significant statistical level means that our model fits the data better than a zero coefficients model at a very high level of probability. But it is possible that even an extremely statistically significant model may not be substantively significant, because large sample size could inflate the model chi-square statistic. It is necessary, therefore, to calculate our model's *substantive* significance.

According to *Menard* [2002, pp. 24–27] the question is: how much does our model reduce the proportional reduction in the absolute value of the log likelihood measure in comparison with the zero coefficients model? This is R_L^2, which is defined as G_M/D_o, where both G_M and D_o depend on the model.

For our model, $D_o = 9042.753$. Thus, $R_L^2 = 0.8834$. This corresponds to an 88.34% variation reduction.

C.3 Correlation Analysis of Preterites with Waw-Perfects

A graphic picture of the negative correlation is seen in Figure C1, in which the coordinates of each green oval are the relative frequencies of preterites and waw-perfects for each narrative text as follows: the x-coordinate is the relative frequency of preterites, and the y-coordinate is the relative frequency of waw-perfects. The oval the farthest to the left represents Exodus 33.

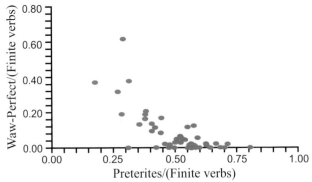

Figure C1. Scatter plot with preterites/(finite verbs) on the x-axis and waw-perfects/(finite verbs) on the y-axis, which shows the negative correlation of these verb frequencies in narrative. The oval farthest to the left represents Exodus 33.

Appendix D: Historiographical Tables

Table D1. Retrospections on the past

Portion of Canon	Texts
Torah	Deuteronomy 1:6—3:29
Former Prophets	Judges 1:1–3:6; 1 Samuel 12:7–11; 2 Samuel 11:19–21[a]; 2 Kings 17:7–18
Latter Prophets	Jeremiah 2:2–13; 7[b]; Ezekiel 16; 20; 23
Writings	Psalms 105[c] and 106; Daniel 9; and Nehemiah 9:6–35

[a] This retrospection is in a narrative clearly not driven by aetiological concerns. Joab anticipated that David might question his judgment in sending his troops so close to the wall of Rabbah, and might remind him that Abimelek had died at the hands of a woman because he had stood too close to a wall (an incident, which is recorded in Judges 9:52–54).

[b] This is Jeremiah's Temple Speech, in which he excoriated rather than extolled the people, disabusing them of the false notion that the presence of the temple ensured the inviolability of Jerusalem by reminding them what had happened to the holy sanctuary at Shiloh because of their ancestors' sins.

[c] Psalms 105:5–10 the nation was commanded more than a millennium after the patriarchs lived, "Remember His miraculous works, which He did, and His wonders and the judgments of His mouth, seed of Abraham, His servant, sons of Jacob, His chosen ones. He is YHWH our God. His judgments are in all the earth. He remembered His covenant in perpetuity, commanded a word for a thousand generations, which He cut with Abraham, His oath to Isaac, caused it to stand as a statute for Jacob, for Israel a perpetual covenant: 'To you I will give the land of as the territory of your inheritance.'" Following this is an historical review from the Patriarchal Period until the Exodus. This review is largely positive in nature. Not so the retrospect in Psalm 106, which stresses the unfaithfulness of Israel in stark contrast to the continued faithfulness of YHWH, starting with the Exodus and ending with the exile.

Table D2. Origins of names and sayings

Categories	Texts
Origins of names (general)	Genesis 4:17; 11:9; 19:22; 25:30; 26:26–33; 28:17–19[a]; 33:17; Deuteronomy 3:14; Judges 10:4; Joshua 5:9; 7:26; Judges 1:26; 6:24; 15:19; 18:12; 2 Samuel 6:8; 1 Chronicles 13:11; 2 Samuel 18:18; 1 Kings 9:13; 2 Kings 14:7
Naming in Numbers[b]	Taberah "burning" (11:1–3), Qibrot Hattaavah "graves of craving" (11:4–34), Meribah "place of the contention" (20:1–13) and Hormah[c] "destruction" (21:1–3)
Renaming foretold	Isaiah 62:14 (2×); Jeremiah 7:32
Origins of sayings[d]	Genesis 10:9; 22:14; Numbers 21:13–15[e]; 1 Samuel 9:9; Jeremiah 16:14

ª This story does not have the usual עַל כֵּן, "therefore" which identifies this category.

ᵇ The first is in Numbers 11:1–3, a brief account of the first time after Sinai that the people complained to YHWH, which gives us the sequence for all such episodes recorded in the book: the people came to a place, which had the name to be explained; they grumbled, murmured or even rebelled against Moses because of some perceived deprivation (usually food or water); YHWH heard their complaining and swiftly sent judgment; they cried out; Moses interceded to YHWH on their behalf; the judgment desisted; and the place was named so as to remind people what had happened there.

ᶜ Hormah is mentioned before the account of its naming, as the site of an Israelite defeat following the rebellion at Kadesh Barnea (Numbers 14:4–45). Its actual naming happened near the end of the wilderness years—nearly forty years later.

ᵈ These were identified by the phrase "it is said" (יֵאָמֵר or אָמַר).

ᵉ In this case the author traced back a phrase from the Book of the Wars of YHWH—an apparently extant source in the author's day, otherwise why would he even have mentioned it—to the locations in which Israel had camped.

Table D3. Historical footnotes.

Categories	Texts
Information about persons, apparently irrelevant to the plot of the story: information about the former inhabitants of regions and even more remote, what peoples outside of Israel called other people.	1 Chronicles 4:40–43; Deuteronomy 2:9–23; 2 Samuel 4:3
Former place names. The author gives us former names of places or former status.ª The author supplied his readers with this information, which he did not expect them to know. This implies that these locations did not have these names or statuses in the author's day. Usually, the author employed, in his narrative, the current name known to his readers, but felt compelled for some reason to give the old name as well. On other occasions, an author used the older name in his narrative and put the more recent name in—as it were—a footnote.	Hazor was formerly the capital city of the kingdoms, which Joshua defeated in his northern campaign (Joshua 11:10). Hebron was formerly called Qiryat Arba (Joshua 14:15; Judges 1:10). The old name of Debir was Qiryat Sepher (Joshua 15:15; Judges 1:11). The previous name of Bethel was Luz (Genesis 28:19; Judges 1:23). Laish was the former name of the city of Dan (Judges 18:29). Finally, "Sarah died in Qiryat Arba (it is Hebron) in the Land of Canaan" (Genesis 23:2)
Miscellaneous. Sometimes the *raison d'être* for the note is evident, but other times the connection is not so clear.	We are told of the words of a song sung in the wilderness when water was discovered (Numbers 21:17–18).ᵇ We are informed of the lyrics of Heshbon's previous victory chant over the Moabites (Numbers 21:26–30). Arcane information is supplied in 1 Chronicles 4:21–23

ª The key to finding these is the term לִפְנִים "formerly."

ᵇ Why is this information given to us? It does not move the narrative forward nor is it necessary information to understand the narrative. It is just an historical footnote attesting to the eyewitness account of the events.

Table D4. Sources cited.

Sources	Texts
Unknown[a]	Exodus 17:14
The Book of the Torah	Deuteronomy 28:61
The Book of the Wars of YHWH	Numbers 21:14
The Book of Yasher[b]	Joshua 10:13; 2 Samuel 1:18
The Book of the Words of Solomon	1 Kings 11:41
The Book of the Chronicles of the Kings of Israel[c]	1 Kings 14:19; 15:31; 16:5, 14, 20, 27; 22:39; 2 Kings 1:18; 10:34; 13:8, 12; 14:15, 28; 15:11, 15, 21, 26, 31: 2 Chronicles 33:18
The Book of the Chronicles of the Kings of Judah[d]	1 Kings 14:29; 15:7, 15:23; 22:45; 2 Kings 8:23; 12:19; 14:18; 15:6, 36; 16:19; 20:20; 21:17, 25; 23:28; 24:5
The Book of the Kings of Judah and Israel[e]	2 Chronicles 16:11; 25:26; 28:26; 32:32
The Chronicles of David the King	1 Chronicles 27:24
The Chronicles of Samuel the Seer	1 Chronicles 29:29
The Chronicles of Nathan the Prophet	1 Chronicles 29:29
The Chronicles of Gad the Seer	1 Chronicles 29:29
The History of Nathan the Prophet	2 Chronicles 9:29
The Prophecy of Ahijah the Shilonite	2 Chronicles 9:29
The Visions of Iddo the Seer	2 Chronicles 9:29
The Chronicles of Shemaiah the Prophet and Iddo the Seer	2 Chronicles 12:15
The Chronicles of Jehu, the son of Hanani	(2 Chronicles 20:34)[f]

[a] Amalek's atrocity against Israel was to be recorded in a book (unnamed) (Exodus 17:14).
[b] In this context "Yasher" ‏ישר‎ "upright" or "straight," refers to either the heroes of the nation or a strict chronological account, respectively. Or it might refer to both.
[c] The Book of the Chronicles of the Kings of Israel cannot be the canonical Book of Chronicles (C) for four reasons: (1) Because it was a source for The Book of Kings, it must antedate that book, which is known to antedate the Book of Chronicles. C can be dated both linguistically and in terms of its content. The Hebrew of C is known as Late Biblical Hebrew (LBH). Its grammar, vocabulary and orthography is markedly different from earlier Hebrew. (2) Its content demands a late date. Statements referring to the exile as being in the past appear in C (1 Chronicles 9:1) and the decree of Cyrus to repatriate the nation appears in C; thus, making it late. (3) C cites the Book of the Chronicles of the Kings of Israel as a source in 2 Chronicles 33:18. So they cannot be the same book. (4) The author of C (Ezra, according to Baba Bathra 14b, but his identity does not affect the following argument) had a particular perspective of the monarchy *vis-à-vis* that of Samuel and Kings: temple instead of throne and priest instead of prophet. Consequently, because of its aberrant worship of the Northern Kingdom, he almost entirely excluded its history from his account. As a result it could not have served as the source of Kings.
[d] The Book of the Chronicles of the Kings of Judah cannot be the canonical Book of Chronicles (C) for some of the same reasons that The Book of the Chronicles of the Kings of Israel cannot be C. See reasons (1) and (2) in note c above.
[e] This is the canonical Book of Kings, which the Book of Chronicles uses as a source. Thrice "Judah" and "Israel" are reversed (2 Chronicles 27:7; 35:27; 36:8). Two times it is cited as the Book of the Kings of Israel (1 Chronicles 9:1; 20:34). And once as the Book of Kings (2 Chronicles 24:27).
[f] This text records the interesting detail that this chronicle has been incorporated into the Book of Kings.

Table D5. Chronological reference points.

Reference Point	Correlation	Texts
Age of antediluvians	Birth of sons	Genesis 4; 5; 11
Year of Noah's life	Beginning and end of the Flood	Genesis 7:6, 11; 8:13–14
Narrator mentions age of Abraham; Isaac; Joseph; Moses, Aaron; Joshua, Caleb; Eli; Ishbosheth; Mephibosheth; David; Barzillai and Hezron	Various significant events	Genesis 12:4, 16:16, 17:1, 24; 21:5, 25:20, 26; 37:2; 41:46; Exodus 7:7; Joshua 24:29; Judges 2:8; 1 Samuel 4:15; 2 Samuel 2:10; 4:4; 5:4; 19:33; 1 Chronicles 2:21
Own age mentioned: Abraham (he also mentions Sarah's)	Impossibility of Sarah and him having a child	Genesis 17:17
Jacob	As reply to Pharaoh's query	Genesis 47:8–10
Moses	Transfer of leadership to Joshua	Deuteronomy 31:2
Caleb	Ages when he spied out the land and conquered his territory	Joshua 14:7, 10
Barzillai	His speech to David	2 Samuel 19:36
The date of the Exodus[a]	The death of Aaron; Temple building begun	Numbers 33:38; 1 Kings 6:1
The death of Uzziah	Isaiah's vision of YHWH	Isaiah 6:1
The days of Ahaz	Rezin and Pekah's attack on Jerusalem	Isaiah 7:1
The death of Ahaz	An oracle concerning Philistia	Isaiah 14:28
Sennacherib's attack on Ashdod	YHWH's instructions to Isaiah	Isaiah 20:1
Fourteenth year of Hezekiah's reign	Sennacherib's invasion of Judah	Isaiah 36:1
Jehoiachin's exile to Babylon	Ezekiel's vision of God's glory	Ezekiel 1:1–3
	call be a watchman	Ezekiel 3:16
	corruption at the Temple vision	Ezekiel 8:1
	discourse with elders	Ezekiel 20:1
	second siege of Jerusalem	Ezekiel 24:1
	judgment pronounced on Tyre	Ezekiel 26:1
	Fall of Jerusalem	Ezekiel 33:21
	the new temple vision	Ezekiel 40:1
	six prophecies concerning Egypt	Ezekiel 29:1, 17; 30:20; 31:1; 32:1, 17; 33:21
The second year of Darius I of Persia (521–486 BC)	Haggai's first message (1st day of the sixth month)[b]	Haggai 1:1
	Haggai's second message (24th day of the sixth month)	Haggai 1:15
	Haggai's third message (21st day of the seventh month)	Haggai 2:1
	Haggai's fourth message (24th day of the ninth month)	Haggai 2:10, 20
Age at death	The antediluvians; Terah; Sarah; Abraham Ishmael; Isaac; Joseph; Aaron; Moses and Jehoiadah	Genesis 5; 11:32; 23:1; 25:8; 25:17; 35:28; 50:26; Numbers 33:39; Deuteronomy 34:7; 2 Chronicles 24:15

Table D5. (continued)

Reference Point	Correlation	Texts
Reigns of kings during the divided monarchy	With his counterpart in the other kingdom[c] Prophets ministry: Isaiah to Uzziah, Jotham, Ahaz and Hezekiah; Hosea to Israel in this same time period; Micah to Judah; Jeremiah from the thirteenth year of Josiah's reign until the end of the eleventh year of Zedekiah, which was in the fifth month; Zephaniah to Josiah; Amos to Uzziah and Jeroboam II	Isaiah 1:1, 7:1; Hosea 1:1; Micah 1:1; Jeremiah 1:2–3; Zephaniah 1:1; Amos 1:1
The end of the Flood	Lifespan of Noah; nations dispersed; birth of sons;	Genesis 9:28; 10:1, 32; 11:10
Earthquake	The commencement of Amos' ministry	Amos 1:1

[a] "At the end of 430 years, on that very day, all the armies of YHWH came out of the land of Egypt (Exodus 12:41)."

[b] Haggai preached his messages in a fifteen week period, during the second year of Darius I of Persia (521–486 BC). Each message is precisely dated to the day, month and year of Darius's reign.

[c] Synchronisms between the kings of Judah and Israel are given for every king of the divided kingdom. Kings of Judah began their reign in a certain year of the continuing reign of the King of Israel and vice-versa. For example, Asa of Judah began to reign over Judah during the twentieth year of Jeroboam's reign over Israel (1 Kings 15:3). Similarly, Baasha of Israel began his reign over Israel in the twenty-third year of Asa's reign over Judah. Also the age at succession is given.

Table D6. Function of genealogies.

Relationship to History	Examples	Texts
Structure	Antediluvians[a]	Genesis 4–5; 11
	The Flood; patriarchal narratives[b]	Genesis 6–9; 12–50; Ruth 4:18[c]
Survey	Narrative has commentary roled	1 Chronicles 1–9[d]
Support[e]	Esau[f]	
	Aaron	
	Perez[g]	Genesis 49:10; Ruth 4:18
	Ezra[h]	Ezra 7:1–10

[a] Mini-narratives are imbedded in these genealogies, with the result that each genealogical report is a comment on history. The reports on Adam, Enoch, Lamech, and Noah stand out because they depart from the formulaic elements found in the other reports. For instance, Noah's report includes the entire Flood account and its aftermath before it closes with the formulaic account of his death (9:29). The first nine verses in chapter 11 are a flash back, explaining how the different languages emerged. This is followed by the genealogy of Shem, in which the longevity of the men in the list is considerably reduced from those of chapter 5 and the ominous words, "and he died" are missing.

[b] Although the toledot provide the structure, the narratives are the main thing. In chapters twelve through to thirty-five a sequence of chapter-length narratives encapsulates the life of each of the Patriarchs. Chapters thirty-seven through to fifty are altogether different, which tell one story: the unfolding of YHWH's sovereign plan to remove the family of Jacob from the corrupting influence of the Canaanites and ensconce them in Egypt and to cause Joseph and Judah to emerge as leaders of the family transitioning to nationhood.

[c] Not only does the presence of genealogies structure history but so also their absence and atavistic re-emergence. A case in point is the recrudescence of the phrase וְאֵלֶּה תּוֹלְדוֹת "these are the generations" in Ruth 4:18 as a continuation of the genealogy of the Patriarchs. Curiously, the link is made back to the Patriarchs with no mention of the Egyptian hiatus. The latter is treated as an historical parenthesis; not part of the Patriarchal promises trajectory. But with the people back in the Land, the path to fulfillment of the promises YHWH made to the Patriarchs is again made clear.

[d] The Book of Chronicles begins with the barest of lists, only names, matching those in Genesis 5 but stripped of even the schematized formula of that chapter. The genealogies of Japheth, Ham, and Shem follow. Then the bald list resumes, concluding with Abraham and his first two sons, but in reverse order: Isaac then Ishmael. Introduced by אֵלֶּה תֹּלְדֹתָם "these are their generations" (similar to Genesis 25:19), a segmented genealogy of Ishmael is given. The progeny of Abraham's third wife—called here his concubine—is given without the introductory אֵלֶּה תּוֹלְדוֹת. These thirty-three verses sweep through thousands of years of history. In contrast, the chronicler devoted twenty chapters (1 Chronicles 10–29) to the forty and one-half years of the reign of David!

[e] Infrequently, a genealogy precedes the unfolding of an account. The brief genealogy in Genesis 22:20–23 serves to enigmatically introduce the one whom Isaac will marry. But most often genealogies follow rather than adumbrate words or deeds.

[f] The genealogy of Esau, whose descendants were kings before Jacob's (36:31), showed that YHWH was already fulfilling his promise to Abraham that kings would come from him and Sarah (17:6, 16), because although Esau was rejected, he was still a descendant of Abraham. Another example of how genealogies comment on history is how the reporting of the chosen line (Isaac and Jacob) differs from the rejected lines (Ishmael and Esau): the former is presented in a linear genealogy (only one descendant indicated per generation); the latter—in a truncated segmented genealogy (siblings are listed). Also, the genealogy of the one rejected always precedes that of the one chosen.

[g] This genealogy, found at the end of the Ruth, establishes the legitimacy of the reign of David, at least as far as his lineage was concerned. Just before his death, Jacob pronounced the following somewhat enigmatic but nevertheless quite significant words concerning Judah's destiny, "the scepter shall not depart from Judah nor a lawgiver from between his feet until Shiloh comes (Genesis 49:10)." It meant that the monarchy would eventually immovably lodge in the tribe of Judah. In other words, kings of Israel eventually would only come from Judah. The passage in Ruth 4:18 linked David to Judah through Perez.

[h] The reality of the exile and the first return, in which the temple was rebuilt, made it imperative that the religious pedigrees of the leaders of subsequent repatriations be clearly stated. Ezra did so, tracing his line back to Aaron. Thereby, Ezra proved to his people that he could lead them in worship and, in no uncertain terms, asserted his God-given authority to demand their obedience to his dictates.

Table D7. Commemorative days and feasts.

Memorial Aspects	Passover/Unleavened Bread	Weeks	Booths/Ingathering
At its inauguration[a]	Exodus 12:14		
Practiced in perpetuity[b]	Exodus 12:17, 24–25, 42		Leviticus 23:41
Catechetical purpose	Exodus 12:26–27[c]		Leviticus 23:43[d]
Enshrined in the Law[e]	Exodus 23:14–17; 34:18; Leviticus 23:4–8; Numbers 28:16–29:40; Deuteronomy 16:1–17	Exodus 23:16; 34:22; Leviticus 23:15–21; Deuteronomy 16:10	Exodus 34:22; Leviticus 23:34–42; Deuteronomy16:12–15
Penalty for disobedience	Numbers 9:13		
Provisions for impurity	Numbers 9:6–12[f]; 2 Chronicles 30:17–20[g]		
Historical attestations	Numbers 9:5; Joshua 5:10–11; 2 Chronicles 30:1–27; 2 Kings 23:21–23; Ezra 6:19–22		Ezra 3:4

[a] The feasts of Passover/Unleavened Bread and Booths were called זִכָּרוֹן "memorial" at their inception. In fact the Passover service was instituted before YHWH's historical act of striking the Egyptian firstborn.

[b] So that the people would never forget.

[c] For both them and their progeny (both "sons" and "generations" occur). Also they were commanded to explain the significance of the Passover service when their sons would ask.

[d] "… in order that your generations may know …"

[e] Three times a year all men were required to come the feasts (Exodus 23:14, 17; 34:23–34; Deuteronomy 16:16; 1 Kings. 9:25; 2 Chronicles 8:13).

[f] The celebration of these was deemed so essential that provision was made for celebrating them one month later if compromise in ritual purity precluded their timely celebration.

[g] Hezekiah's Passover was a second-month Passover. There were some who were still ritually impure at this time. But a special dispensation was made for them to celebrate anyway without any negative repercussions.

Table D8. Temporal continuity.

Claim	Texts
Unprecedented phenomenon of the fiery hail to come[a]	Exodus 9:18
The severity of the locust plague to come	Exodus 10:6
Ai was still in ruins	Joshua 8:28
The corpse of its king was still buried under the same pile of rocks, which Joshua had heaped on him	Joshua 8:29
The Hivites were still a servant class of "hewers of wood" and "drawers of water" in Israel	Joshua 9:27
The Geshurites were still living among the Israelites as an unconquered, unassimilated people	Joshua 13:13
The Jebusites were still living among the Israelites[b]	Joshua 15:63
The Canaanites were living in Gezer among the Ephraimites as forced laborers	Joshua 16:10
The deposition of the Ark of the Covenant	1 Samuel 6:18
Ziklag still belonged to the kings of Judah[c]	1 Samuel 27:6
The Ark was placed in the temple, with its long axis in line with that of the temple's long axis[d]	1 Kings 8:8
Solomon had incorporated all foreign enclaves into a greater Israel	1 Kings 9:20–21
Israel had seceded from Judah, forming the Northern Kingdom of Israel	1 Kings 12:19
Water miraculously purified by Elisha was still potable	2 Kings 2:22
Moab had broken away from Judah	2 Kings 8:22
Rezin, the king of Aram had forcibly removed the Judahites from Eilat and subsequently, the city had been occupied by the Edomites[e]	2 Kings 16:6

NOTE: A number of these have pointed out above under other rubrics. The most common phrase is עַד הַיּוֹם הַזֶּה "until this day." A special case of this class are those accounts which also include the phrase לְמִן הַיּוֹם "since the day" or its equivalent, because it suggests an uninterrupted continuity; whereas, the more common "until this day," allows for a break in continuity as long as it was re-established by the author's time. As a result, the special case would be "easier" for a reader, who was a contemporary of the author, to falsify.

[a] In this and the next statement Moses claimed knowledge of Egyptian history.

[b] The Jebusite presence in what would become Jerusalem is also mentioned in Judges 1:21.

[c] The complicating factor in the Books of Samuel is the death of Samuel, reported in (1 Samuel 25:1). Following the chronology of the author of 1 Samuel, Samuel's death occurred before David sought refuge with the Philistines and was given Ziklag. Consequently, Samuel, could only have been the author of 1 Samuel up to chapter twenty-four. Tradition has suggested—and it is likely—that one of the royal prophets, Gad or Nathan, finished the book and authored 2 Samuel. Yet it is doubtful that either of these prophets would have penned the words that Ziklag belonged to the kings of Judah. This sounds like a statement made later, reflecting on the history of the Davidic dynasty.

[d] I deduce this because the text says that the Ark's poles were visible from the holy place not from the courtyard. Of course only priests could verify that the poles were visible when they were serving in the holy place. We are told that they were not visible from outside the holy place. Because the Inner Sanctum was a square, if the poles extended beyond the confines of the Inner Sanctum they had to protrude either to the sides—and thus would have been visible—but the text says they were not—or to the front and back—and thus been visible only to the priests—which they were. Assuming that the poles were parallel to the long axis of the Ark, implies then that the Ark was oriented in an east-west direction.

[e] The only difference in the readings is *daleth* versus *resh*. Since, in the history of the Hebrew language *daleth* has resembled *resh* in all periods, paleographical considerations cannot resolve the textual problem. Nevertheless, Edomites—rather than Arameans—is the preferred reading based upon the context, since the author described Tiglath Pileser III's destruction of Aram in the next paragraph in the text.

Endnotes

1. Of course this is a general *desideratum* for literature, as *Hirsch* [1976, p. 36] cogently argues: The probability that I am right in the way I educe implications depends upon my familiarity with the type of meaning I consider. That is the reason, of course, that the genre concept is so important in textual study. By classifying the text as belonging to a particular genre, the interpreter, automatically posits a general horizon for its meaning. The genre provides a sense of the whole, a notion of typical meaning components.

2. *Wendland*'s [1994] article, "Genre criticism and the Psalms," is a précis of his monograph, *Comparative Discourse Analysis and the Translation of Psalm 22 in Chichewa a Bantu Language of South-Central Africa* [1993].

3. In discussing the characteristics of historical narratives, *Sailhamer* [1992, pp. 12–14] emphasizes the reality of their portrayal of events. No less than eighteen times he refers to the word "real" and its cognates in his discussion of Biblical historical narrative. He uses the phrases "realistic manner," real world" [7×], "realistic picture," "mimic the real world," "reproduce the real world," "depictions of reality," "empirical reality," and "real life" [6×] to describe Biblical narratives.

4. I ran searches of the most basic morphological sequences according to the main categories in *BibleWorks 5.0*, involving verbs, nouns, pronouns, prepositions, articles, accusative markers, and other particles. Giving a different point of view, Dr. Andrew Bowling (in a private communication) maintains that some preterites in Genesis 1:1–2:3 have a summary function, which is somewhat rare for preterites.

5. Note the following quotes from *Archer* [1974, p. 181]:
   From a superficial reading of Genesis 1, the impression received is that the entire creative process took place in six twenty-four-hour days;
   and *Ross* [1999, p. 113]:
   The steady march of days, day one, day two, day three, etc.—strongly suggests a sequential, chronological account. The sanctification of the

seventh day, and its enshrinement in the Decalogue as rooted in the seven-day creation, only strengthens this impression.

6. *Bradley and Olsen* [1984, p. 287; emphasis mine] state:

   In the sections that follow, we shall assume Genesis 1 deals with real time-space events and seek to interpret the Genesis 1 account of origins in the most general way possible. The goal is to first define *the latitude of permissible interpretation* of the biblical account of origins.

   In a response to them, which supports their old earth understanding of Genesis 1:1–2:3, *Archer* [1984, p. 332] says:

   The realization that the six stages of Genesis 1 do not represent calendar days leaves the Christian geologist free to draw tentative conclusions from his data.

   Snoke [1998, pp. 5–8]states:

   [People] will say, 'But you have come up with this just because you want the Bible to agree with science.' I freely confess to this charge .... The question which lies before us is therefore, 'Is it ever legitimate to prefer a "possible" interpretation over a simpler, "obvious" interpretation, based on our experience?'.

   Ross [1999, pp. 113–114]says:

   Nevertheless, first impressions, and even considered second impressions, are not always accurate; reasons can arise which lead one to reject a seemingly obvious and well-supported view in favor of an alternative, perhaps a more subtle alternative.

7. *Archer* [1974, 1984], *Chisholm* [2003], and *Waltke* [2004] have all offered some or all of the three objections.

8. *Merrill* [2003, p. 78] comments about the historical dimension of the Old Testament:

   Its character as sacred history—a notion that must never be ignored—does not in anyway diminish its value as a source of 'ordinary' historical information.

9. This is *Archer*'s [1984, p. 329] concern. He maintains that reading Genesis 1:1–2:3 as if all the events occurred in one week would contradict Genesis 2:4ff.:

   Entirely apart from any findings of modern science or challenges of contemporary scientism, the twenty-four hour theory was never correct and should never have been believed—except by those who are bent on proving the presence of genuine contradictions in Scripture.

10. The previous chapters in this book strongly militate against this bold assertion and the putative proofs of deep time. *Austin* [2005], *Chaffin* [2005], and *Snelling* [2005a, b, c] have successfully challenged the underlying assumptions of radiometric dating to the point of invalidating the procedure. And in addition, the findings by *Humphreys* [2005] on He retention in zircons, and the discovery by *Baumgardner* [2005] of ^{14}C in coals and diamonds, offer new alternative geochronometers, which yield dates of thousands rather than millions or billions of years.

11. *Speiser*'s [1964, p. 8] comments on Genesis 1 are typical of this group:

    What we have here is not primarily a description of events or a reflection of unique experience. Rather, we are given the barest sequence of facts resulting from the fiat of the supreme and absolute master of the universe.

    Sarna [1966, pp. 9–10], after discussing the Babylonian creation account, Enuma Elish, contrasts Genesis 1:1–2:3 to it and other extra-Biblical versions of Creation:

    Genesis is but a prologue of the historical drama that unfolds in the ensuing pages of the Bible.

    Furthermore:

    The outstanding peculiarity of the biblical account is the complete absence of mythology in the classic pagan sense of the term.

    Finally:

    Nowhere is the non-mythological outlook better illustrated than in the Genesis narrative. The Hebrew account is matchless in its solemn and majestic simplicity.

12. How to interpret texts is a major debate in literary circles. For a history of the discussion see *Weiss* [1984, pp. 1–73].

13. Originally published in *Sewanee Review 54* (summer 1946). *Wimsatt* [1976, p. 136] in his essay "Genesis: a fallacy revisited" emended this quote to:

    The design or intention of the author is neither available nor desirable as a standard for judging *either the meaning or* the success of a work of literary art (emphasis mine).

The original essay, Wimsatt's second essay, *Hirsch*'s [1976] rejoinders, and clarifications on both sides of the debate are in *Newton-De Molina* [1976]; *Vanhoozer* [1998] shows how the post-Hirschian hermeneutics of Fish and Derrida have taken away the author, the text and the reader.

14. Pragmatics is a hermeneutical approach in which texts are treated as linguistic utterances, which were given in a particular context. *Winther-Nielsen* [2002] cites *Mey*'s [1993], *Schiffrin*'s [1994], *Green*'s [1996], and *Blum-Kulka*'s [1997] definitions of this discipline. He also explains how it evolved from the work of *Austin* [1975] and *Grice* [1957]. The former investigated how *"To do things with words"* and the latter studied how listeners interpret meaning in context. *Searle* [1969] built his speech act theory on these studies: words not only convey information (locutionary function), but also intend to motivate the listener to do something (the illocutionary function). *Mey* [1993] advanced two principles. Three emphases come out of this theoretical base: the determination of meaning in relation to the total context, an extention of grammar to the discourse level, and a consideration of the "collaboration in interaction" of speaker (author) and listener (reader). See the discussion in *Winther-Nielsen* [2002, pp. 53–58].

15. *Winther-Nielsen* [2002] discusses the two principles of pragmatics, which are advanced by *Mey* [1993]: the communication principle and the coherence principle, on pages 55–56. See the references he cites there. *Groom* [2003] lists and interacts with the "seven standards of textuality" proposed by *Beaugrande and Dressler* [1992]: cohesion (regular sentence level grammar, texts have to make sense), coherence (meaning is extracted from a text by an interaction of text with its context), intentionality (authors want to communicate to their readers and do it to the best of their ability), acceptability (the reader expects a text to be cohesive, coherent, is meant to tell him something and meant to motivate him to do something), informativity (a reader expects a text to contain a reasonable amount of new information),

situationality (a text is conveyed depending on the reading situation of its readers), and intertexuality (earlier texts, which are quoted or alluded to, inform the present text). For her discussion see *Groom* [2003, pp. 131–138].

16. Unlike Greek literature, in particular, Greek poetry, the Hebrews did not leave us a treatise on how to interpret their poetry.

17. *Winther-Nielsen* [2002, p. 61; note 33] critiques *Mey*'s [1993, p. 281] contention that "the ways textual and dialogical constraints are manipulated depend entirely on the contemporary conditions."

18. *Winther-Nielsen* [2002] is quoting *Gibbs* [1994].

19. *Sternberg*, in his magnum opus, *The Poetics of Biblical Narrative: Ideological Literature and the Drama of Reading* [1985], discusses three issues that are germane to this study: (1) that in the Bible there is a non-contradictory balance between its three characteristics: it is a literary masterpiece, it purports to be reporting historical events, and it is giving a clear ideological message; (2) that it is easy to under-read the Bible but almost impossible to counter-read the Bible. In other words, many times readers do not pick up all the subtleties of the text, but the theological message is clear; (3) the Biblical authors believed that they were writing real history. See Section 7 of the present study for an extended discussion of the historiographical aspects of the Old Testament.

20. See *Dotan*'s excellent foreword to *Biblica Hebraica Leningradensia* [2001, pp. vii–x], in which he discusses the relative merits of the two extant Ben Asher texts: The Aleppo Codex and the Leningrad Codex.

21. "Brick upon brick" refers to an arrangement of the lines of text, in which one line is divided into three textual blocks, the next line is divided into two blocks, the third line is divided into three again, and so forth down the page. The resulting page resembles a brick wall, with the blocks of text as the bricks and the spaces between the blocks as the mortar.

22. Perhaps it was meant to honor the authors of these texts, Moses, Samuel, and David. But in the final analysis the reason escapes us. We can conclude, however, that the copyists do not clearly evidence

poetic sensibilities.

23. *Kugel* [1981, p. 52] argues that parallelism is not the intention of the Biblical authors, but rather it is a seconding sequence: "Biblical lines are parallelistic not because B is meant to be a parallel of A, but because B typically supports A, carries it further, backs it up, completes it, goes beyond it."

24. Cited and translated by *Kugel* [1981, p. 83]. Emphasis is his, not *Alonzo-Schökel*'s.

25. *Cotter* [2003, p. xxix] comments that putative "structures" in narrative are often not the intention of the author of the text but are the creation of the interpreter.

26. In Genesis 1:1–2:3 the events that occurred on days four, five, and six correspond with those on days one, two, and three, respectively; thus, forming a bilateral structure as follows: days one and four concern light; days two and five concern the skies and the seas; and days three and six concern the dry land.

27. Genesis 1:27, a tricolon which marks the zenith of God's Creation, the Creation of man, contains a three-fold use of בּרא, "create."

28. *Lichtenstein* [1984] examines the what, how, and why of Biblical Hebrew poetry, commencing with Moses' words to Aaron after YHWH immolated his sons and ending by disabusing us of the idea that poetry was Israel's most sublime medium only for expressing their most sublime thoughts. He points out that Lamech boasted to his wives of murdering a young man—certainly not a noble idea! Most instructive is his treatment of the poetic passages which follow narrative accounts of the same event.

29. The one paragraph definitions in *Wendland*'s [1993] chapter are considerably shortened from those in his monograph. In the latter he furnishes examples and provides extensive discussion of each category.

30. This term refers to the type of directional shifts in the communication nexus of the psalmist, the reader/listener and YHWH, such as are found in Psalm 23, in which the psalmist refers to YHWH in the third person in verses 1–3 (while talking to his reader/listener), in the second person in verses 4–5 (while the reader "listens in") and

back to the third person in verse 6 (he returns to talking to the reader about YHWH). In grammar, the change of persons is called enallage. In rhetoric, such diversion of speech is called apostrophe.

31. Adapted from *Brogan*'s [1993] discussion of sound and meaning; Brogan cites *Wimsatt* [1976] in this regard:

> Poetry approximates the sensuous condition of paint and music not by being less verbal, less characteristic of verbal expression, but actually by being more than usually verbal, by being hyper-verbal.

32. Jacobson's definitions of the poetic function are discussed by *Cotter* [1992, pp. 12–20].

33. I want to thank Kirk Lowery, the Director of the Hebrew Institute at Westminster Theological Seminary (East) and manager of the WTT (Westminster Theological Biblia Hebraica Stuttgartensia Hebrew Old Testament, fourth edition) and WTM (Westminster Theological Hebrew Old Testament Morphology) databases for his illuminating interaction with me on the characteristics of narrative and poetry. Standard treatments of Old Testament narratives abound: *Alter* [1981], *Berlin* [1983], *Sternberg* [1985], *Bar-Ephrat* [1989], and *Ska* [1990]. All have provided thoughtful treatments on the characteristics of Hebrew narrative; but *Sternberg*'s [1985] volume is magisterial. Fokkelman's works are listed in *Fokkelman* [1999]. *Gunn and Fewell* [1993] have an extensive bibliography on Hebrew narrative studies.

34. *Fokkelman* [1999, pp. 73–111] discusses the four characteristics of narrative suggested here under six headings: narrator, action, plot, quest, hero, and time and space. He further clarifies that hero is meant in a narratological sense, not necessarily in a moral sense.

35. *Fokkelman* [1999, 75–78; esp. p. 78] discusses the author's selection principle for inclusion of details: "His criterion for selection is the plot. . . . The biblical narrator only uses details if they are functional to his plot."

36. *Cotter* [2003] defines plot as

> the pattern of events in a narrative. Classically, these events are seen as linked by a chain of causality, such that the beginning of the story is some moment that is not caused by what precedes, the middle is caused

by what precedes and causes what follows, and the end is that which is caused by what precedes but which causes nothing else.

Further, that "a plot has several moments that describe an arc of tension." These movements are *exposition* (scene and characters introduced, no action), *inciting moment* (initiates the conflict between characters), *rising action* (or complication, the events that move the characters to the climax or crucial point of the story), *falling action* (or resolution, one of the characters emerges triumphant) and *conclusion* (resolution of the conflict). He also gives a simplified version for Genesis 1:1–2:3: exposition (1:1–2), development (1:3–30), turning point (1:31), and conclusion (2:1–3) [2003, xxvii]. *Sailhamer* [1992, p. 25] includes the following in his description of the general structure of historical narratives: introduction, conclusion, sequence, disjuncture, repetition, deletion, description, and dialogue.

37. *Geller* [1993, p. 509] comments on Hebrew poetry:

An essential empirical fact is the general symmetry in clause length displayed in most passages which, on other grounds, might reasonably be termed "poetic."

On the other hand, referring to narrative he says:

By contrast, in books like Genesis or Judges, mainly narrative in content, clause length seems to be random.

38. Statistical analysis of the Hebrew Bible has been used to address higher critical issues, such as the unity of Isaiah. Recently, *Polak* [1998] has used a statistical analysis of finite verb to non-finite verb ratios to determine the relative chronology of Biblical texts; *Weil* [1974] uses the ratio [(total verbs)–particles]/(total words) to determine discourse type (what we are calling genre type) in the Pentateuch and the three major prophets. According to *Weil* [1974], poetry has a positive ratio; narrative a negative. *Forbes* [1992] discusses the conditions that must prevail for a statistical analysis of the Bible to be valid. Also he evaluates *Weil*'s studies and defends his and *Andersen*'s [1986] study of orthography in the Hebrew Bible.

39. These particular verbs can be identified as preterites because the

3ms [third person masculine singular] suffix on a preterite differs from that on an imperfect: וֹה versus וֹ, respectively. Although, this distinction is a "hard and fast" rule in Ugaritic, it is not certain that it is in Biblical Hebrew. In the Hebrew weak verbs, the forms are distinguishable. Such is not the case with strong verbs. Without pronominal suffixes, the forms for strong verbs are indistinguishable and context must decide. This is the only aspect of the debate concerning the preterite, which could impact this study. But the number of hidden preterites is quite small and does not significantly affect the conclusions of this study. Issues concerning the function of the preterite and even what it should be called do not impact this study. The nature of the Hebrew verbal system is an ongoing topic of study, with a huge literature and many unsettled issues. Fundamentally, the question is whether finite verbs mark tense, aspect or a blend of the two. *Goldfajn* [1998] argues that finite verbs mark tense. Although there is also debate on the preterite, most Hebraists would recognize it as the "backbone" of Hebrew narrative, or as *Walsh* [2001, pp. 155–172] puts it, "the main narrative line." Other verb forms, perfect and imperfect, are "off-line." See his discussion of narrative sequences (in which he surveys the various constructions and perforce, the alternative verb forms, which obtain when there are breaks in the main narrative sequence) and the bibliography cited there; Dr. Andrew Bowling has pointed out in a private communication that there are preterites in Genesis 1:1–2:3 that have a summary function and that this is somewhat rare for preterites, but this does not affect the statistical study because it depends only on the number of preterites—not their function.

40. The command line syntax in *BibleWorks 5.0* was *\<root>@v(erb) <stem(?)> <w(preterite)/ i(imperfect)/ p(perfect)/ q(waw-perfect)>

41. Dr. Roger Longbotham, Senior Statistician for Amazon.com, the statistical consultant for this study, performed this analysis and generated the plot.

42. Longbotham generated the random sample from the 295 narrative texts and 227 poetic texts.

43. *Pampel* [2000, pp. 1–18] and *Long* [1997] thoroughly explain the appropriateness of binary logistic regression for dichotomous categorical dependent variables and the rationale for the shape of the logistic curve. In brief, logistic regression (a non-linear regression method) was employed, because our data violates the following conditions for ordinary least squares: the data does not form a normal distribution; with only two values for *NARRATIVE*, but a range of values for X_i, the relationship between these variables is patently non-linear; our data is discreet and because our independent variables are relative frequencies, our independent variables are neither continuous nor unbound; and with categorical dependent variable (like ours), the distribution is heteroscedastic. *Long* [1997] shows that if the distribution for categorical dependent variables has a mean μ, its variance will be $\mu(1-\mu)$. In terms of the independent variables, $\mu = XB$, where X is the independent variables matrix and B is the coefficients matrix. The variance, therefore is $XB(1-XB)$. Thus, the variance is dependent on the independent variables, which is a violation of homoscedasticity. Moreover, for a Bernoulli distribution like ours, variance depends on the mean, which depends on the genre of the text [*Longbotham*, personal communication].

44. The theory of logistic regression is discussed in the following works among others: *Hosmer and Lemeshow* [1989], *Darlington* [1990], *Nagelkerke* [1991], *DeMaris* [1992], *Kleinbaum* [1994], *Rice* [1994], *Raftery* [1995], *Long* [1997], *Estrella* [1998], *Fox* [2000], *Pampel* [2000], and *Menard* [2002].

45. *Menard* [2002, pp. 67–91] discusses the conditions that must be met in order to use logistic regression. As far as sampling adequacy is concerned, no consensus has been reached. See *Long* [1997] for some discussion.

46. *Menard* [2002, pp. 28–29] describes the differences among prediction, classification, and selection models.

47. MLE is an iterative algorithm initiated with a best guess and run until there is convergence (no change in the coefficients for the next iteration). The theory of MLE is thoroughly discussed by *Long*

[1997, pp. 52–60].

48. *Menard* [2002, pp. 17–22] explains how to use the model chi-square statistic to determine the statistical significance of the model.

49. *Menard* [2002] discusses the definition and significance of R_L^2 and why he prefers it to other pseudo-R^2 on pp. 24–27.

50. *Ibid*, p. 28. The expected errors without the model depends on whether the model is a prediction, classification or selection model.

51. See *Menard* [2002, p. 40] for the expected errors without the model for classification type models.

52. *Sternberg* [1985, p. 25] clarifies the difference between this question and the question: did the events really happen? He states:

History-writing is not a record of fact—of what 'really happened'—but a discourse that claims to be a record of fact.

Howard [2003, pp. 26–29] differentiates the three meanings of "history": event (the facts), account of the event (the record of the facts, historiography), and the study of this account.

53. *Brueggemann* [1997, p. 118, n. 3] builds his *Old Testament Theology* on the statements in the text about God. He differentiates between the authors believing that they were writing about real events and that the events actually happened.

54. I adopted Rubrics 1–12 from [*Sternberg*, 1985, 31, 41] and adduced numerous texts to support his ideas. Rubrics 13–15 are original.

55. *Martens* [1998] sees four major Old Testament themes flowing out of this passage: YHWH delivers His people, He will make them His people and He will be their God, they will know Him and He will give them the Land.

56. These verbs are prominent in Exodus, occurring first in Exodus 2:24–25, along with ראה "see" and ידע "know." The last verb is especially important in that one of YHWH's primary purposes for the Exodus event was that Israel, Egypt, but, particularly, Pharaoh, would know that He is YHWH. Recall that Pharaoh said, "Who is YHWH? I do not know YHWH" (Exodus 5:3). He, thereby, "threw down the gauntlet," challenging YHWH to a duel of will and word, which he lost.

57. These were identified by noting naming formulas using קָרָא.
58. Decapitation and severed hands proved that an enemy was dead. For other examples in the Bible see Judges 7:25; 8:6; 1 Samuel 17:54; 31:9; and 2 Samuel 4:2.
59. Narratological studies argue—and for the most part—correctly that inclusion of details are plot driven.
60. "Gaps" are information, which we do not have but need to know in order to fully understand a narrative. They result from the deliberate withholding of this information, which is later supplied. "Blanks" are information, which we do not have, nor do we need, and is not supplied later. See *Sternberg*'s [1985, pp. 186–229] insightful discussion of this issue.
61. Strictly speaking, this is the only citation of the book found by Hilkiah the priest, when he was ordered to clean up the temple precincts and in the process found the book. The book is also referred to (but not cited) as The Book of the Law (2 Kings 22:8, 11) and the Book of the Law of YHWH (2 Chronicles 34:14, 15).
62. Contra Biblical historians who maintain that Biblical narratives depict a "'fictive world,' entire in itself and referring only to itself" and "Its (the Bible's) integrity must not be compromised by seeking to relate it to anything outside itself" (*Grisanti* [2004, p. 167] citing *Provan* [1995, p. 6]), Biblical authors "break frame" by breaking away from the narrative flow to directly address their contemporary readers, in a supererogatory effort to relate the history they are narrating to their time.
63. The most important word in the second type is לְפָנִים "previously."
64. 2 Peter 2:15; Revelation 2:14.
65. *Halpern* [1988, p. 8] speaks to this issue:
    We call a narrative a history based on its author's perceived intentions in writing, the author's *claim* that the account is accurate in its particulars, the author's sincerity (Halpern's italics).
66. These two analyses were suggested and performed by Longbotham.
67. The problems with a linear fit for categorical data are discussed in *Long* [1997, pp. 38–40].

Glossary

aetiology   A narrative which explains the name origin of persons, places, objects or customs.

anthropomorphism   God's attributes and actions, described in human terms.

apocalyptic   Highly symbolic literature.

bicolon   The bilateral structure of most lines of Biblical Hebrew (BH) poetry.

clause length   The number of words/accentual units from the beginning of a verse to its major disjunctive accent or from there to its end. The major bisecting accents are ʾaṭnaḥ and ʿole wᵉyored (only in Psalms, Job and Proverbs). q.v. *Yeivin* [1980].

codex   A very early handwritten book; not a scroll.

discriminant analysis   q.v. *The Oxford Dictionary of Statistical Terms (ODST)* [*Dodge*, 2003].

finite verbs   BH verbs which are inflected for person, gender and number.

genre   The type of literature. q.v. endnote 1; *New Princeton Encyclopedia of Poetry and Poetics (NPEPP)*.

hermeneutics   The science of interpreting texts.

heteroscedasticity   The variance of the error for a dependent variable is not the same for a given *x*, which precludes using linear regression to model the data. q.v. in *ODST*.

historicity   A history accurately portrays real events.

historiography   The method of reporting and writing history.

homoscedasticity   The variance of the error for a dependent variable is the same for a given *x*. q.v. in *ODST*.

imperfect   The BH verb form *yiqtol* in which person, gender, and number are marked by prefixes and suffixes. It indicates imperfective, progressive or durative aspect of present, future, general present, and habitual past and modal (may, might, should, could, must, etc.). q.v. *Biblical Hebrew Reference Grammar (BHRG)* § 19.3.

isometry   The parity of the number of words, accentual units, syllables or even letters on each side of the major bifurcating cessura (usually the major disjunctive accent) in a BH poetic line. q.v. *Geller* [1993] in *NPEPP*.

lexicography   The study of word meaning. q.v. *Zgusta* [1971].

logistic regression (LR)   A non-linear regression model, based on the log of the odds ($P/(1-P)$), where P is the probability of the occurrence of an event. LR is ideal for categorical data—when there are only limited (in our case, two) values for the dependent variable. q.v in *ODST*.

morphology   A study of the transformations of individual words (the specific forms of a lexical item) which convey the major grammatical information of a language: person, gender, number, tense, aspect, and mood.

multicollinearity   One independent variable is dependent on another.

parallelism   In BH, semantic and/or lexical and/or morphological and/or syntactical and/or phonological and/or merely formal echoing of parts or all of the first part of a poetic line in the second part of the line. q.v. *Anchor Bible Dictionary*.

perfect   The BH verb form *qatal* in which person, gender, and number are marked by suffixes only. It indicates punctiliar or constative aspect of present (only stative verbs), past or antierior past. q.v. *BHRG* § 19.2.

philology   "The love of words" is the study of the phonology, morphology (q.v.), syntax (q.v.), and lexicography (q.v.) of a text—a prerequisite to interpretation.

preterite   The BH verb form *wayyiqtol* in which person, gender, and number are marked by prefixes and suffixes. Perforce, it is a main clause initial form. It indicates past action, forming the main story line of a narrative. q.v. *BHRG* § 21.2.

prosody   "The study of ... structures of sound patterning in verse: chiefly, meter, rhyme and stanza .... the study of those extensions, compressions, and intensifications of meaning of which bound speech becomes capable by increase in formal structure." q.v. in *NPEPP*, pp. 982–983; *Geller* [1993] in *NPEPP*; "Prosody" in *Encyclopedia Judaica,* cols. 1200–1202.

stichography   The layout of a literary text on a page.

syntax   Each sentence is an example of a typical specific structure, and each word is an example of a specific type of word. Syntax endeavors to ask how specific words are combined into specific sentences. From Rabin's תחביר לשון המקרא [1963].

tenor   The complex of meanings conveyed by a metaphor. For example, יהוה צוּרִי, "YHWH is my rock" (Psalm 19:15), means that YHWH is strong, steadfast, dependable, etc.

vehicle   The actual words of a metaphor. For example, יהוה צוּרִי, "YHWH is my rock" (Psalm 19:15).

waw-perfect   The BH verb form wᵊ*qatal* in which person, gender, and number are marked by suffixes only. Perforce, it is a main clause initial form. It sequentially maintains the force of the previous verb. The wᵊ*qatal* form is a sequential future if it follows an imperfect referring to the future. It is a habitual past if it follows an imperfect used in a text referring to the past. And it is a sequential command if it follows an imperative. q.v. *BHRG* § 21.3.

word order   The sequence of the main sentence constituents: the subject (S), verb (V), and the (direct) object (O). English is predominantly an SVO language: "God created man." BH narrative, on the other hand, is predominantly VSO (OSV in the right to left order of the language): וַיִּבְרָא אֱלֹהִים אֶת־הָאָדָם, "Created God man" (Genesis 1:27).

References

Alonzo-Schökel, L., Poésie hébraique, in *Dictionnaire de le Bible, Supplément 42,* edited by H. Cazelles, pp. 56–57, Letouzey et Ané, Paris, 1966–.

Alter, R., *The Art of Biblical Narrative,* Basic Books, New York, 1981.

Alter, R., *The Art of Biblical Poetry,* Basic Books, New York, 1985.

Andersen, F. I., and A. D. Forbes, *Spelling in the Hebrew Bible,* Biblical Institute Press, Rome, 1986.

Archer, G. L., A response to the trustworthiness of Scripture in areas related to natural science, in *Hermeneutics, Inerrancy and the Bible (Papers from the ICBI Summit II),* edited by E. D. Radmacher and R. D. Preus, pp. 321–334, Zondervan, Grand Rapids, 1984.

Archer, G. L., *A Survey of Old Testament Introduction,* Moody Press, Chicago, 1974.

Austin, J. L., *How to Do Things with Words,* second edition, Harvard University Press, Cambridge, Massachusetts, 1975.

Austin, S., Do radioisotope clocks need repair? Testing the assumptions of isochron dating using K-Ar, Rb-Sr, Sm-Nd, and Pb-Pb isotope pairs, in *Radioisotopes and the Age of the Earth: Results of a Young-Earth Creationist Research Initiative,* edited by L. Vardiman, A. A. Snelling, and E. F. Chaffin, pp. 325–392, Institute for Creation Research, El Cajon, California, and Creation Research Society, Chino Valley, Arizona, 2005.

Bar-Ephrat, Sh., Narrative art in the Bible, *Journal for the Study of the Old Testament Supplement Series, 70,* Bible and Literature Series, 17, Almond Press, Sheffield, 1989.

Baumgardner, J. R., ^{14}C evidence for a recent global Flood and a young earth, in *Radioisotopes and the Age of the Earth: Results of a Young-Earth Creationist Research Initiative,* edited by L. Vardiman, A. A. Snelling, and E. F. Chaffin, pp. 587–630, Institute for Creation Research, El Cajon, California, and Creation Research Society, Chino Valley, Arizona, 2005.

Beaugrande, R. de, and W. Dressler, *Introduction to Text Linguistics,* Longman, London, 1992.

Beck, A., Introduction to the Leningrad codex, in *The Leningrad Codex: A Facsimile Edition,* Eerdmans Publishing Company, Grand Rapids, and Brill Academic Publishers, Leiden, 1998.

Berlin, A., *Poetics and Interpretation of Biblical Narrative,* Bible and Literature Series, 9, Almond Press, Sheffield, 1983.

Berlin, A., Reading Biblical poetry, in *The Jewish Study Bible,* edited by A. Berlin and M. Z. Brettler, pp. 2097–2104, Oxford University Press, Oxford, 2003.

Berlin, A., Parallelism, *The Anchor Bible Dictionary,* vol. 5, pp. 155–162, 1992.

Blum-Kulka, S., in *Discourse as Social Interaction,* Discourse Studies, vol. 2, edited by T. A. van Dijk, pp. 38–63, Sage, London, 1997.

Bradley, W., and R. Olsen, The trustworthiness of Scripture in areas related to natural science, in *Hermeneutics, Inerrancy and the Bible (Papers from the ICBI Summit II),* edited by E.D. Radmacher and R.D. Preus, pp. 285–317, Zondervan, Grand Rapids, 1984.

Brogan, T. V. F., Poetry, in *The New Princeton Encyclopedia of Poetry and Poetics,* edited by A. Preminger and T. V. F. Brogan, pp. 938–942, MSF Books, New York, 1993.

Browne, D., *Hi and Lois,* in *Cincinnati Enquirer* (Cincinnati, Ohio), 9 April, 1989 (Color Comics Supplement), King Features Syndicate, 1989.

Brueggemann, W., *Theology of the Old Testament: Testimony, Dispute, Advocacy,* Augsburg Fortress, Minneapolis, 1997.

Chaffin, E. F., Accelerated decay: theoretical considerations, in *Radioisotopes and the Age of the Earth: Results of a Young-Earth Creationist Research Initiative,* edited by L. Vardiman, A. A. Snelling, and E. F. Chaffin, pp. 525–585, Institute for Creation Research, El Cajon, California, and Creation Research Society, Chino Valley, Arizona, 2005.

Chisholm, R. B., History or story? The literary dimensions in narrative texts, in *Giving the Sense: Understanding and Using Old Testament Historical Texts,* edited by D. M. Howard and M. A. Grisanti, pp. 54–73, Kregel Publications, Grand Rapids, Michigan, 2003.

Cotter, D., *A Study of Job 4–5 in the Light of Contemporary Literary Theory,* Society of Biblical Literature Dissertation Series, 124, Scholars Press, Atlanta, 1992.

Cotter, D., *Genesis,* Berit Olam: Studies in Hebrew Narrative and Poetry, The Liturgical Press, Collegeville, Minneapolis, 2003.

Darlington, R. B., *Regression and Linear Models,* McGraw-Hill, New York, 1990.

DeMaris, A., *Logit Modeling: Practical Applications,* Quantitative Applications in the Social Sciences, No. 106, Sage Publications, Thousand Oaks, California, 1992.

Dodge, Y. (editor), *The Oxford Dictionary of Statistical Terms,* Oxford University Press, Oxford, 2003.

Dotan, A., Foreword, in *Biblia Hebraica Leningradensia,* Hendrickson Publishers, Peabody, Massachusetts, 2001.

Estrella, A., A new measure of fit for equations with dichotomous dependent variables, *Journal of Business and Economic Statistics, 16*(2), 198–205, 1998.

Fokkelman, J. P., *Reading Biblical Narrative: An Introductory Guide*, John Knox Press, Louisville, 1999.

Forbes, D., Statistical research on the Bible, *The Anchor Bible Dictionary*, vol. 6, pp. 185–206, 1992.

Fox, J., *Multiple and Generalized Nonparametric Regression*, Quantitative Applications in the Social Sciences Series, No. 131, Sage Publications, Thousand Oaks, California, 2000.

Geller, S. A., Hebrew prosody and poetics, in *The New Princeton Encyclopedia of Poetry and Poetics*, edited by A. Preminger and T. V. F. Brogan, pp. 509–511, MSF Books, New York, 1993.

Gibbs, R. W., *The Poetics of The Mind: Figurative Thought, Language and Understanding*, Cambridge University Press, Cambridge and New York, 1994.

Goldfajn, T., *Word Order and Time in Biblical Hebrew Narrative*, The Clarendon Press, Oxford, 1998.

Green, G. M., *Pragmatics and Natural Language Understanding*, second edition, Erlbaum, Mahwah, New Jersey, 1996.

Grice, H. P., Meaning, *Philosophical Review, 66*, 377–388, 1957.

Grisanti, M., Old Testament poetry as a vehicle for historiography, *Bibliotheca Sacra, 161* (April–June), 163–178, 2004.

Groom, S. A., *Linguistic Analysis of Biblical Hebrew*, Paternoster Press, 2003.

Gunn, D. M., and D. N. Fewell, *Narrative in the Hebrew Bible*, Oxford University Press, Oxford, 1993.

Halpern, B., *The First Historians: The Hebrew Bible and History*, Harper and Row, San Francisco, 1988.

Hirsch, E. D., Objective interpretation, in *On Literary Intention: Critical Essays*, edited by D. Newton De-Molina, pp. 26–54, University Press, Edinburgh, 1976.

Hosmer, D., and S. Lemeshow, *Applied Logistic Regression*, John Wiley & Sons, New York, 1989.

Howard, D. M., History as history: the search for meaning, in *Giving the Sense: Understanding and Using Old Testament Historical Texts*, edited by D. M. Howard and M. A. Grisanti, pp. 25–53, Kregel Publications, Grand Rapids, Michigan, 2003.

Humphreys, D. R., Young helium diffusion age of zircons supports accelerated nuclear decay, in *Radioisotopes and the Age of the Earth: Results of a Young-Earth Creationist Research Initiative*, edited by L. Vardiman, A. A. Snelling, and E. F. Chaffin, pp. 25–100, Institute for Creation Research, El Cajon, California, and Creation Research Society, Chino Valley, Arizona, 2005.

Jacobson, R., Closing statement: linguistics and poetics, in *Style in Language*, edited by T. A. Sebeok, pp. 350–377, Technology Press of MIT, New York, 1960.

Kleinbaum, D. G., *Logistic Regression: A Self-Learning Text*, Springer-Verlag, New York, 1994.

Kugel, J., *The Idea of Biblical Poetry: Parallelism and its History*, Yale University Press, New Haven and London, 1981.

Lichtenstein, M., Biblical poetry, in *Back to the Sources: Reading the Classic Jewish Texts*, edited by Barry Holz, pp. 105–127, Summit Books, New York, 1984.

Long, J. S., *Regression Models for Categorical and Limited Dependent Variables*, Advanced Quantitative Techniques in the Social Sciences Series, 7, Sage Publications, Thousand Oaks, California, 1997.

Martens, E. A., *God's Design: A Focus on Old Testament Theology*, third edition, Bibal Press, N. Richland Hills, Texas, 1998.

Menard, S., *Applied Logistic Regression Analysis*, second edition, Quantitative Applications in the Social Sciences, No. 106, Sage Publications, Thousand Oaks, California, 2002.

Merrill, E., Archaeology and Biblical history: its uses and abuses, in *Giving the Sense: Understanding and Using Old Testament Historical Text*, edited by D. M. Howard and M. A. Grisanti, pp. 74–96, Kregel Publications, Grand Rapids, Michigan, 2003.

Mey, J., *Pragmatics: An Introduction*, Blackwell, Oxford, United Kingdom, and Cambridge, Massachusetts, 1993.

Milton, J., *Of Education*, 1644.

Muilenburg, J., Poetry, in *Encyclopedia Judaica*, vol. 13, cols. 670–681.

Nagelkerke, N. J. D., A note on a general definition of the coefficient of determination, *Biometrika, 78*(3), 691–692, 1991.

Newton-De Molina, D. (editor), *On Literary Intention: Critical Essays*,

University Press, Edinburgh, 1976.

Pampel, F. C., *Logistic Regression: A Primer*, Quantitative Applications in the Social Sciences, No. 132, Sage Publications, Thousand Oaks, California, 2000.

Polak, F. H., The oral and the written: syntax, stylistics and the development of Biblical prose narrative, *Journal of the Ancient Near Eastern Society of Columbia University, 26*, 59–105, 1998.

Provan, I. W., *1 and 2 Kings,* New International Bible Commentary, Hendrickson, Peabody, Massachusetts, 1995.

Rabin, H., תחביר לשון המקרא, edited according to the notes of S. Shekolnekov, second edition, Student Union of Hebrew University, Jerusalem, 1963.

Raftery, A. E., Bayesian model selection in social research, in *Sociological Methodology 1995*, edited by P. V. Marsden, pp. 111–163, Tavistock, London, 1995.

Rice, J. C., Logistic regression: an introduction, in *Advances in Social Science Methodology*, vol. 3, edited by B. Thompson, pp. 191–245, JAI Press, Greenwich, Connecticut, 1994.

Ross, M., The framework hypothesis: an interpretation of Genesis 1:1–2:3, in *Did God Create in Six Days?*, edited by J. A. Pipa and D. W. Hall, pp. 113–130, Southern Presbyterian Press, Oak Ridge, Tennessee, 1999.

Sailhamer, J., *The Pentateuch as Narrative: A Biblical Theological Commentary,* Zondervan Publishing House, Grand Rapids, Michigan, 1992.

Sarna, N., *Understanding Genesis*, Schocken Books, New York, 1966.

Schiffrin, D., *Approaches to Discourse,* Blackwell, Oxford, United Kingdom, and Cambridge, Massachusetts, 1994

Scholes, R., and C. Klaus, *Elements of Drama*, Oxford University Press, New York, 1971.

Searle, J. R., *Speech Acts,* Cambridge University Press, London, 1969.

Ska, J. L., *"Our Fathers Have Told Us": Introduction to the Analysis of Hebrew Narratives*, Subsidia Biblica, 13, Pontifical Biblical Institute, Rome, 1990.

Snelling, A. A., Radiohalos in granites: evidence for accelerated nuclear decay, in *Radioisotopes and the Age of the Earth: Results of a Young-Earth Creationist Research Initiative*, edited by L. Vardiman, A. A. Snelling, and E. F. Chaffin, pp. 101–207, Institute for Creation Research, El Cajon, California, and Creation Research Society, Chino Valley, Arizona, 2005a.

Snelling, A. A., Fission tracks in zircons: evidence for abundant nuclear decay, in *Radioisotopes and the Age of the Earth: Results of a Young-Earth Creationist Research Initiative*, edited by L. Vardiman, A. A. Snelling, and E. F. Chaffin, pp. 209–324, Institute for Creation Research, El Cajon, California, and Creation Research Society, Chino Valley, Arizona, 2005b.

Snelling, A. A.., Isochron discordances and the role of inheritance and mixing of radioisotopes in the mantle and crust, in *Radioisotopes and the Age of the Earth: Results of a Young-Earth Creationist Research Initiative*, edited by L. Vardiman, A. A. Snelling, and E. F. Chaffin, pp. 393–524, Institute for Creation Research, El Cajon, California, and Creation Research Society, Chino Valley, Arizona, 2005c.

Snoke, D., *A Biblical Case for an Old Earth,* Interdisciplinary Biblical Research Institute, Hatfield, Pennsylvania, 1998.

Speiser, E. A., *Genesis,* Anchor Bible Commentary, Doubleday and Co., Inc., Garden City, New York, 1964.

Sternberg, M., *The Poetics of Biblical Narrative: Ideological Literature and the Drama of Reading,* Indiana University Press, Bloomington, 1985.

Tomlin, R. S., L. Forrest, M. M. Pu, and M. H. Kim, Discourse semantics, in *Discourse as Structure and Process*, Discourse Studies, vol. 1, edited by T. A. van Dijk, pp. 63–111, Sage, London, 1997.

Vanhoozer, K., *Is there a Meaning in this Text?: The Bible, the Reader, and the Morality of Literary Knowledge*, Zondervan, Grand Rapids, Michigan, 1998.

van der Merwe, C. H. J., J. Naudé, and J. H. Kroeze, *A Biblical Hebrew Reference Grammar*, Biblical languages: Hebrew 3, Sheffield Academic Press, Sheffield, 1999.

Walsh, J., *Style and Structure in Biblical Hebrew Narrative,* The Liturgical Press, Collegeville, Minnesota, 2001.

Waltke, B., Literary form of Genesis 1:1–2:4a, Unpublished paper presented at Dallas Theological Seminary, 2004.

Watson, W. G., Classical Hebrew poetry: a guide to its techniques, *Journal for the Study of the Old Testament Supplement Series, 26,* Almond Press, Sheffield, 1984.

Weil, G. E., Bible hébraique et targum araméen, in *Informatique et Philologie*, edited by P. Frajolet, pp. 5–39, Le Chasnay, 1974.

Weiss, M., *The Bible from Within: The Method of Total Interpretation*, The Magnes Press, Jerusalem, 1984.

Wendland, E., *Comparative Discourse Analysis and the Translation of Psalm 22 in Chichewa a Bantu Language of South-Central Africa*, Studies in the Bible and Early Christianity, 13, The Edwin Mellen Press, Lewiston, New York, 1993.

Wendland, E., Genre criticism and the Psalms, in *Biblical Hebrew and Discourse Analysis*, edited by R. D. Bergen, Summer Institute of Linguistics, 1994.

Wimsatt, W. K., Genesis: a fallacy revisited, in *On Literary Intention: Critical Essays*, edited by D. Newton-De Molina, pp. 116–138, Edinburgh University Press, Edinburgh, 1976.

Wimsatt, W. K., and M. C. Beardsley, The intentional fallacy, in *On Literary Intention: Critical Essays*, edited by D. Newton-De Molina, pp. 1–13, Edinburgh University Press, Edinburgh, 1976.

Winther-Nielsen, N., Fact, fiction and language use: can modern pragmatics improve on Halpern's case for history in Judges?, in *Windows into Old Testament History: Evidence, Argument, and the Crisis of "Biblical Israel,"* edited by V. P. Long et al., pp. 44–81, Wm. B. Eerdmans Publishing Co., Grand Rapids, Michigan, 2002.

Yeivin, I., *Introduction to the Tiberian Masorah*, Society of Biblical Literature Masoretic Studies, 5, translated and edited by E. J. Revell, Scholars Press, 1980.

Zgusta, L., *Manual of Lexicography*. Academia Publishing House of the Czechoslovak Academy of Sciences, Prague, Mouton, The Hague, 1971.

Chapter 10

Summary of Evidence for a Young Earth from the RATE Project

Larry Vardiman, Ph.D.[1]
Steven A. Austin, Ph.D.[2]
John R. Baumgardner, Ph.D.[3]
Steven W. Boyd, Ph.D.[4]
Eugene F. Chaffin, Ph.D.[5]
Donald B. DeYoung, Ph.D.[6]
D. Russell Humphreys, Ph.D.[7]
Andrew A. Snelling, Ph.D.[8]

Abstract. This chapter summarizes the technical results of the RATE Project and evaluates the significance of the overall project. The main purpose of the RATE Project was to investigate radioisotopic processes and rock-dating methods to determine why the conventional model for the age of the earth is not consistent with a young-earth time frame. The RATE team offers a scientific alternative favoring the thousands-of-years scenario for the age of the earth rather than simply critiquing the conventional billions-of-years scenario. The major result of the project is that nuclear decay processes appear to have been accelerated during brief periods in earth history. Some of the discussion addresses unresolved problems and objections that will likely be raised by critics.

[1] Atmospheric Scientist, Institute for Creation Research, California
[2] Geologist, Institute for Creation Research, California
[3] Geophysicist, Institute for Creation Research, California
[4] Hebraist, The Master's College, California
[5] Physicist, Bob Jones University, South Carolina
[6] Physicist, Grace College and Seminary, Indiana
[7] Physicist, Institute for Creation Research, California
[8] Geologist, Institute for Creation Research, California

1. Background

When the RATE group began its investigation of radioisotopes and the age of the earth in 1997 it sought to resolve the conflict between the billions-of-years time frame of the conventional scientific community and the thousands-of-years time frame of the literal Biblical community. Each member of the team recognized that this conflict was a major problem that needed resolution. However, there was no initial agreement on how to approach this issue.

A few in the RATE group believed that the most likely solution lay in studying the rates at which radioactive decay had occurred in the past. If this approach were to be successful it meant that for the earth to be young the decay of parent isotopes and the production of daughter isotopes would have occurred at rates many orders of magnitude greater than they are currently estimated to be. Until the start of RATE few investigators had seriously entertained periods of extremely high rates of decay during earth history.

The concept of so-called *accelerated decay* would be highly controversial and not easily accepted by the scientific community or the public at large without strong supporting evidence. It also meant that global, catastrophic events, possibly even cosmic events, operating at scales and speeds far beyond anything observed today, had occurred during the history of the earth, if the earth is young. Until recently it had not been demonstrated in the laboratory that the rate of nuclear decay could be changed by more than a few tenths of a percent even under extreme temperature, pressure, and chemical conditions [*Bosch et al.*, 1996]. So, the basic hypothesis of this minority view within the RATE group called for supernatural intervention by God to accelerate the decay rate at one or more periods within the mass-space-time continuum of earth history. This suggestion would be highly unpopular in the scientific community. Any reference to supernatural intervention is strictly taboo according to the conventional definition of the scientific method today. Even scientists who are Christians often react negatively to such explanations.

During the first phase of the RATE project when the literature review was occurring and the research design was being developed, two other basic hypotheses were considered. Although these two hypotheses also had their ultimate source in supernatural action by the Creator, they were thought to have occurred at the very beginning of time or during the early Creation events of the Creation week. Subsequent processes which occurred following the initial supernatural creation by God could be studied by conventional scientific methods and would not be as controversial. The alternative hypotheses were considered in parallel with accelerated decay until the first RATE book was published. They were:

- large initial concentrations of daughter isotopes in the mantle which were mixed into the crust on Day 3 of Creation week, and
- large concentrations of daughter elements produced during Creation week which were later mixed into the crust by the Genesis Flood.

By the time the first book was published by the RATE group [*Vardiman et al.*, 2000] the majority of the RATE group had decided that accelerated decay would be the primary research hypothesis, but that the other two concepts should be investigated as well. In fact, the final explanations offered by this study are actually a combination of all three hypotheses. Accelerated decay during several periods of earth history became the primary hypothesis because of the strong physical evidence the RATE group had accumulated that a large amount of nuclear decay had indeed occurred in the rocks themselves after their initial creation. This evidence suggested that most of the decay occurred during Creation week events, but also that a large amount must have taken place during the Genesis Flood. The RATE group considered the possibility that a substantial amount of decay might have occurred during the Judgment in the Garden of Eden, but then it was concluded that the implied levels of radiation and heating would have been so highly destructive to biology at that point in earth history as to render this possibility unlikely. The evidence for these conclusions comes from the physical presence of fission tracks, radiohalos, and residual He in rocks that contain U and other radioactive elements to be discussed shortly. Most creationists who had previously addressed these issues did not fully appreciate the evidences for radioactive decay beyond the chemical presence of the daughter isotopes themselves. Most believed that the large quantity of daughter isotopes observed today was primarily God's doing during Creation, that is, the concentration of daughter isotopes was non-zero when time began. If this were in fact the case, then the problem could be solved simply by resetting the radioisotope clocks to account for this initial inventory of daughter isotopes. However, the physical evidence argues otherwise.

There are many independent lines of evidence that large quantities of daughter isotopes were formed since Creation and even since the beginning of the Flood! These findings and assertions are major departures from the previously-held understanding in creation science. They not only force creationists to discover a much more complex scenario for the decay of radioisotopes than has been considered in the past, but they also require us to link such an explanation to serious Biblical and scientific constraints. Either accelerated radioactive decay accounts for the large daughter isotope residues in a short period of time, or a large amount of decay occurred at conventional rates and the earth is old. The RATE group now believes that an old-earth concept can be refuted on Biblical as well as scientific grounds, and also offers a plausible explanation of how and when large quantities of nuclear decay occurred in a young-earth time frame.

Before launching into a summary of the technical results, however, a brief discussion needs to be given about why the young-earth time frame is supported by the Bible. The support for this viewpoint is fully presented in several sources such as **The Genesis Flood** [*Whitcomb and Morris*, 1961], **Scientific Creationism** [*Morris*, 1974], **The Genesis Record** [*Morris*, 1976], **The Young Earth** [*Morris*, 1994], and **Footprints in the Ash** [*Morris and Austin*, 2003]. A few of the arguments are:

• the Biblical text requires the days of Creation to be literal, 24-hour days;

• the genealogies from Creation to Christ listed in the Bible indicate earth's history to be thousands, not billions, of years; and

• many geological and geophysical processes argue for an age of the earth of thousands, not billions, of years.

This raises the question as to why the Bible should be taken literally when it deals with the age of the earth? It should be said at the outset that there are places in Scripture where some passages are intended to be taken figuratively or allegorically. In general, however, the RATE group takes the position that a passage should be taken literally unless there is clear evidence from the context that it is intended to be taken figuratively. For example, if a passage is poetic or it appears that the author intends for it to be an allegory, then more care should be taken during interpretation. Even in such allegorical passages, however, there may still be useful historical content. The RATE project reports on the historicity of Genesis 1:1–2:3 not only from radioisotope evidence, but also from internal grammatical evidence in the Hebrew text of the Bible.

2. Results from RATE

2.1 Helium Diffusion

The RATE group believes it has uncovered evidence that focuses the spotlight on the primary source of the discrepancy between the billions-of-years time frame of the conventional scientific community and the thousands-of-years time frame of the literal Biblical community. Dr. D. Russell Humphreys conducted a series of experiments and developed the supporting theory during the RATE project that allowed two independent clocks to be simultaneously compared [*Humphreys*, 2005]. One clock is based on the decay of a parent isotope (^{238}U) and the production of its two daughter products (^{206}Pb and ^{4}He). The other clock is based on the diffusion of ^{4}He from zircon where the daughter products appear. Because ^{4}He is produced as ^{238}U is transformed to ^{206}Pb and is a simultaneous daughter product, the diffusion of ^{4}He out of the zircon is tightly coupled to the radioactive decay process. Dr. Humphreys was aware that surprisingly large quantities of ^{4}He had been measured in zircons taken from a drill core extracted near the Jemez volcanic caldera, Fenton Lake, New Mexico, from Precambrian granodiorite [*Humphreys*, 2000]. Given the previously known diffusivities of ^{4}He in other minerals, nobody expected to find much ^{4}He remaining in the zircon if the time period was 1.5 billion years since the rock crystallized. The high concentrations of ^{4}He, however, suggested that the zircons are very young, that the time period for the production of ^{4}He must have been short and the nuclear decay process must therefore have been accelerated. A photomicrograph of a zircon grain from the core used in the study is shown in Figure 1. Helium diffusion measurements were used to develop an independent clock to test the assumptions underlying the standard U-Pb radioisotope dating method.

Dr. Humphreys arranged for the rate of diffusion of He through zircon to be measured as a function of temperature in a laboratory well known for its He diffusion studies. Interestingly, although done for other materials, the measurement of He diffusion in zircon had never been unambiguously reported prior to the RATE project. Dr. Humphreys calculated the diffusion rates required to retain the observed amount of He still present in the zircons in the Precambrian granodiorite as a function of temperature. He calculated the diffusivity for a Creation model time of 6000 years and compared it with the diffusivity which would be necessary for the escape of the same amount of He for an

Figure 1. SEM photomicrograph of a zircon crystal containing ^{238}U, ^{206}Pb, and ^{4}He extracted from the Jemez granodiorite, Fenton Lake, New Mexico. Length scale in the lower right-hand corner is 30 μm. Photo courtesy of Mark H. Armitage.

evolution model time of 1.5 billion years (an age based on the measured amount of Pb present, but assuming today's rate of U decay to Pb). Figure 2 shows the results of these measurements and calculations plotted as the logarithm of diffusivity versus temperature. Temperature is plotted on the horizontal axis in a manner which permits theoretical relationships to appear as straight lines and produces an Arrhenius

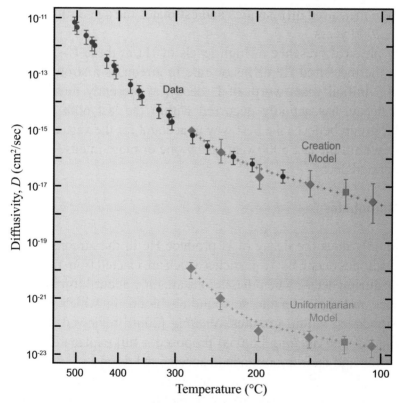

Figure 2. Comparison of diffusivity between Creation and uniformitarian models in zircon as a function of temperature. The upper dashed line shows the theoretical diffusivity needed for the Creation model of 6000 years. The lower dashed line shows the theoretical diffusivity needed for the uniformitarian model of 1.5 billion years. The red diamonds are calculated values of diffusivity using measured He concentrations and temperatures from *Gentry et al.* [1982], and the blue dots and green diamonds are from *Humphreys* [2005] for the same Jemez granodiorite.

diagram. Diffusivity is a measure of the rate at which He escapes from zircons. The Creation and uniformitarian models differ by a factor of about 100,000. The actual laboratory measurements of He diffusion through zircon fall on the Creation model line, well within the error bars. This is highly significant, because the method quantifies the disparity in the standard radioisotope and He diffusion methods for estimating the ages of rocks. The Creation model is more consistent with the measured diffusivities and estimates the age of the rock to be 6000±2000 years.

The physical presence of high levels of He in these U-rich zircons, given the measured He diffusion rate in zircon, is a strong argument that 1.5 billion years worth of U decay, at presently measured rates of U decay, has actually occurred within the last 6000 years. The RATE group believes the best way to account for the vast amount of U decay within the last 6000 years is by one or more intense episodes of accelerated decay.

2.2 Radiohalos

Not only does the decay of U produce He in the zircons where the radioisotopes occur, but α-particles which are ejected from the nucleii of atoms during decay, when the zircons are only about 1 μm in diameter, produce radiohalos in the surrounding biotite in which the zircons are embedded within granites. *Snelling* [2000] reviewed research on radiohalos, and *Snelling* [2005a] proposed a full explanation for their formation and their importance to accelerated decay.

The high-velocity α-particles produced by the decay of U cause damage to the crystal structure of the biotite outside the zircons as they race outward from a radioactive zircon. Alpha-particles are ionized and contain two protons and two neutrons. They become He atoms when they have decelerated greatly and captured two electrons to form a neutral atom. Many of the α-particles exit the zircon crystals and collide with the stationary atoms in the biotite surrounding the radioactive centers, producing discolored spherical shells of damage. Biotite occurs in thin sheets which can, with care, be peeled away to reveal the discolored rings. By inspecting the sheets as they are removed several at a time, the sheet containing the largest diameter ring of discoloration and the radioactive center simultaneously can be located. The radius of discoloration and the number of rings can be used to identify the radioactive isotope which formed the radiohalo. Each radioisotope produces α-particles with distinctive energy levels which, in turn, reach different penetration distances in the crystal as they decelerate. Many millions of α-particles are required to form a ring which is intense enough to be seen under a microscope.

Figure 3 shows photomicrographs of ^{210}Po and ^{218}Po radiohalos (concentric circles near arrows). Polonium-210 releases α-particles with a single energy level creating a single ring surrounding a radiocenter. Polonium-218 releases α-particles to form ^{214}Po which releases α-particles at a different energy level to form ^{210}Po which in turn releases α-particles at a third energy level, creating a total of three rings. See *Snelling* [2000] for more details on radiohalo production by various radioisotopes.

The significance of Po radiohalos to the age-of-the-earth argument lies in their formation conditions and short half-lives. Three isotopes of radioactive Po occur within the ^{238}U decay chain—all with short half-lives. Polonium-210 has the longest half-life of 138 days. This means that whenever Po is formed it exists only for a brief time, on the order of only months, for the longest-lived isotope. Yet, radiohalos can only be formed in solid crystalline rock (such as granite) at temperatures below the annealing temperature of 150°C. The rings of discoloration can form only after the granitic magma has cooled to form solid mineral crystals. Radiohalos can be retained in the rock crystals only if the temperature remains below the annealing temperature. This means that conventional scenarios in which granite is slowly cooled from high-temperature liquid magma over hundreds of thousands or millions of years cannot form Po radiohalos. Yet, such radiohalos are commonly observed in granites all over the earth. Dark U radiohalos require at least 100 million years worth of decay to form and also to supply enough Po isotopes to generate Po radiohalos. But unless the U decay is accelerated, the supply of the Po isotopes will be too

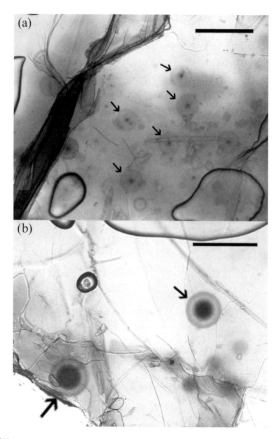

Figure 3. (a) ^{210}Po radiohalos. (b) ^{218}Po radiohalos. Length scale in the upper right-hand corner of each figure is 60 µm. Photos courtesy of Mark H. Armitage.

meager to produce the radiohalos. In other words, a lot of Po has to be produced very rapidly. Otherwise, there won't be enough Po to form the Po radiocenters. But at the same time the granites have to cool rapidly so that the rapid supply of a lot of Po isotopes is occurring at or below the annealing temperature of 150°C. Therefore, the cooling of granites and the formation of radiohalos must be rapid and decay rates must be accelerated. So, the rapid formation of granites and Po radiohalos are a strong argument for a young earth.

Gentry [1988], who first interpreted Po radiohalos as a unique signature for instantaneous, recent Creation by God, believes that radiohalos occur only in Creation week granites. However, *Snelling* [2005a] reports on a survey of radiohalos in granites from many selected locations, some of which provide evidence that they were also formed in mountain-building episodes during and immediately following the Genesis Flood (see Figure 4). Note that the frequency of occurrence of radiohalos is relatively low for rocks conventionally older than 600 Ma and younger than 65 Ma. But, for rocks conventionally dated between 65 Ma and 600 Ma, which the RATE group believes are likely to be Genesis Flood rocks, the occurrence of radiohalos is often high.

The RATE team does not believe this interpretation detracts from God's supernatural intervention in the formation of radiohalos, because God was as intimately involved in the processes of the Genesis Flood as

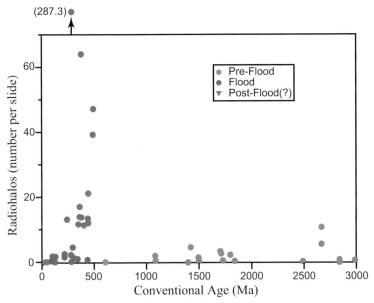

Figure 4. Plot of radiohalo occurrence in granites versus conventional age for three categories of granites—pre-Flood, Flood, and post-Flood(?). Arbitrary designations of pre-Flood were assigned to granites conventionally dated as 600 Ma or older, post-Flood(?) to granites 65 Ma or younger, and Flood for granites between 65 Ma and 600 Ma.

He was in Creation. However, the formation of Po radiohalos in granites associated with the Genesis Flood seems to require more explanation about the need to separate Po from U, and the possible mechanism because of the constraints of temperature and cooling rates.

Dr. Snelling proposes that radiohalos were formed only during catastrophic hydrothermal events when the rate of radioisotope decay was simultaneously accelerated. He found that Po radiohalos are associated with the occurrence of U radiohalos, and with the relative positions of the radiohalos in cleavages and near cracks and other lattice imperfections. Polonium radiohalos occur in greater frequency when U radiohalos are present upflow of the locations where the Po radiocenters can form and produce the Po radiohalos. Because Po is formed in a decay chain by the process of U turning to Pb, Po radiohalos appear to have been produced in an environment in which hot fluids were transporting and depositing intermediate radioisotopes at opportune sites within the crystals of biotite. The process appears to have been extremely rapid because of the magnitude of the decay and cooling necessary preceding the formation of the radiohalos.

It appears that the conditions necessary for the formation of Po radiohalos occurred only during global, highly energetic events like Creation and the Genesis Flood. In both events rapid, high-temperature processes occurred, based on the Biblical descriptions of massive cosmological and geological change. The descriptions of both events also suggest accelerated geological processes, and now the RATE group concludes there is evidence for accelerated nuclear decay processes as well. The production of Po radiohalos apparently is not occurring at the present time. It may be possible to find a local geological event today in which small quantities of water in contact with crystallizing magma may allow the slow transport of decay products through the resultant cooling rock, but we believe accelerated decay of the U to rapidly supply enough Po is also a condition for Po radiohalo formation. The rate of nuclear decay is obviously uniformly slow today. In addition, the widespread abundance of Po radiohalos in granites all over the earth would require events of global magnitude. We believe this only happened during Creation and the Genesis Flood.

2.3 Fission Tracks

Another direct evidence of nuclear decay in rocks is the formation of fission tracks by the disintegration of ^{238}U into high-velocity particles which leave small trails of destruction in zircon crystals as they speed away from the decay center. These tracks can be counted using special etching techniques and a computation of nuclear decay rates made in the zircons. *Snelling* [2005b] investigated the densities of fission tracks in several geological formations in Grand Canyon and nearby areas, and found that in most of the zircons the fission track densities matched the expected densities from the amount of radioactive material present in the rock units and their radioisotope "ages." In some of the zircon grains for which the densities did not agree, associated evidence indicated that the tracks had been erased by a process called thermal annealing—the reheating of the rocks enough for the damage trails to be erased by "healing" of the crystal structure. This elimination of the fission tracks may have been due to heating of the zircons by accelerated nuclear decay and during the Laramide uplift to form the Rocky Mountains and the Colorado Plateau at the end of the Genesis Flood.

For those zircons in which the fission track densities and radioisotope ratios agreed, more than 500 million years worth (at today's rate) of nuclear and radioisotope decay had occurred in the past. Taking the Biblical record as historically accurate, this decay must have occurred during the Genesis Flood year about 4500 years ago. Thus, the fission tracks in the zircons are physical evidence of accelerated nuclear decay.

2.4 Do Radioisotope Clocks Need Repair?

Do the different radioisotope clocks provide a consistent picture of the age of a rock or suite of rocks? If concordant ages were obtained, this would lend support to radioisotope dating. Therefore, a major effort of the RATE project was to compare the estimated ages from what would appear to be easily dated rocks by the whole-rock and mineral isochron methods. Rocks selected for radioisotope study were the Beartooth andesitic amphibolite (northwestern Wyoming) and the Bass Rapids diabase sill (Grand Canyon, Arizona). Although *Austin* [2000] has shown previously that rock samples from Grand Canyon give isochron "ages" that conflict with each other and with historical evidence, he collected additional data for the RATE project with more highly controlled processing constraints in order to illustrate this discordance using both the whole-rock and mineral isochron techniques [*Austin*, 2005]. Isochron ages were computed from four different radioisotope pairs within the same rock samples. Yet, the four age determinations differed widely (~0.8 to ~1.4 billion years). If the conventional technique for obtaining "ages" from isochrons was accurate, all four estimates should yield the same "age," at least within small error bounds.

Radioisotopes which disintegrate by α-decay give higher estimates of age than ones that disintegrate by β-decay. *Austin* [2005] documented this strongly from both the Beartooth amphibolite (Wyoming) and the Bass Rapids diabase (Arizona). These well documented cases argue that conventional radioisotope clocks are in need of repair. We ask, "Which of the various radioisotope clocks can be trusted?"

Although the RATE group does not believe these absolute age values are correct, the data provide crucial information about the radioisotope decay process within earth history. In pointing out the disparities and discordances in radioisotope dating the RATE team concluded that radioisotope dating using conventional assumptions is invalid for accurately dating rocks. Not only has the RATE group documented that different radioisotope dating methods disagree with one another, but that the estimated "ages" must be wrong by many orders of magnitude. For example, because Biblical chronology as well as other RATE findings indicate the earth is no more than ten thousand years old, and whereas many rocks are dated more than one billion years old, standard radioisotope dating for such rocks is wrong by at least a factor of 100,000.

2.5 Isochron Discordance

Snelling [2005c] explored a wider sample of rock units for isochron discordance and the role of inheritance and mixing of radioisotopes in the mantle and crust. He collected and analyzed in great detail samples from ten rock units which formed from recent times back to the early Precambrian (pre-Flood period). He tested the reliability of the four major radioisotope systems also used by *Austin* [2005] and similarly found a clear pattern of isochron discordance.

Snelling found that recently formed, often referred to as "young rocks," had inherited the radioisotope signatures of their mantle sources and there was evidence of open-system behavior. Contamination and mixing in crustal rocks had apparently occurred during their ascent from the mantle to the crust and while being intruded and extruded as magma. However, the overall systematic trend of "radioisotope ages" in the rock units in the geologic record indicated that accelerated decay was the dominant factor operating through earth history. Because all three assumptions of conventional radioisotope dating—known initial conditions, closed-system behavior, and constancy of decay rates—were shown to be subject to failure, the radioisotope methods cannot, and should not, be relied upon to produce absolute "ages" for the earth's rock strata. However, if the appropriate corrections are made, the chains of radioisotopes are almost certainly indicative of both the lapse of time and of other historical events, in particular, the Genesis Flood and Creation.

2.6 Composite Isochron Ages

Figure 5 displays a composite diagram of the isochron ages calculated by *Austin* [2005] and *Snelling* [2005c] from their samples in Grand Canyon. The isochron ages are plotted versus atomic weight for the four radioisotope pairs—$^{40}K-^{36}Ar$, $^{87}Rb-^{86}Sr$, $^{147}Sm-^{144}Nd$, and $^{238}U-^{206}Pb$. Note that the α-decayers—^{147}Sm and ^{238}U—give consistently older isochron ages that the β-decayers—^{40}K and ^{87}Rb. The β-decayers have multiple decay paths and so-called forbidden decay modes which may explain part of this discrepancy. Whatever the process involved in speeding up the nuclear decay at various times in earth history, the amount of decay was apparently not the same for all isotopes. A dashed

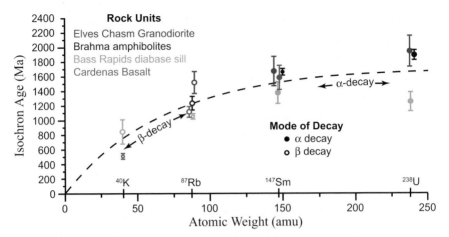

Figure 5. Composite plot of isochron age versus atomic weight for four radioisotope pairs and four Precambrian formations in Grand Canyon from *Austin* [2005] and *Snelling* [2005c].

trend line of isochron age parabolically increasing with atomic weight is drawn by eye on the diagram. The trend may be a hint about the process which causes different isochron ages in the same rock and could lead to a better understanding of accelerated decay. The RATE group recommends that decay rates be investigated for other radioactive elements with different atomic weights and decay modes.

2.7 Theoretical Considerations

Although the geological support for accelerated decay seems persuasive, most physicists will immediately object to positing any major change in nuclear decay rates because both theoretical and experimental considerations have shown that today they change by less than 1% even under extreme variations in temperature, pressure, and chemical conditions. However, some recent reports in the conventional literature show that if radioactive atoms with small energy releases (such as [187]Re with an energy release Q of 0.0025 MeV) are strongly ionized, that is, their electrons are stripped away to alter the electromagnetic field environment of its nucleus in a significant way, the likelihood of decay can be greatly increased [*Bosch et al.*, 1996]. This is not that surprising in terms of current nuclear theory, and it reinforces the conclusion that relatively small changes in the energy structure of the nucleus can alter the stability of the nucleus in dramatic ways.

Experiments to investigate the direct alteration of decay rates under such extreme conditions of temperature and pressure were beyond the financial capability of RATE. Certainly many nuclear experiments are even beyond the ability of the U.S. government at this time. So, the RATE project has focused on feasible studies of the relationship of various model parameters associated with α- and β-decay. For example, *Chaffin* [2005] has studied the shape of the potential energy barrier to α-particles exiting the nucleus of an atom. Because the shape of the potential energy distribution in the nucleus of an atom resembles the cross-section of a well dug in the ground, it is called a "potential well," as shown in Figure 6. Instead of height, the vertical dimension

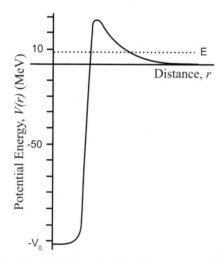

Figure 6. Potential energy seen by the α-particle versus distance from the nuclear center. The nuclear force dominates when the α-particle is inside the nucleus, but is short ranged and gives way to the electrostatic repulsion at large distances.The α-particle typically has a total energy E shown by the dashed line on the figure, and does not have enough energy to cross over the top of the barrier. If the depth of the potential well V_0 should change, then the α-particle's probability of escape is affected.

of a potential well is potential energy inside the nucleus of an atom. Dr. Chaffin has explored the effect of varying the potential well width and depth on α-decay rates. He has found that the quantum mechanical wave function for α-decay which represents a barrier to the escape of particles from the nucleus of an atom is highly sensitive to minor variations in its shape and depth. He has shown that small variations can cause the decay rates to vary by orders of magnitude.

Dr. Chaffin has also studied models derived from string theory and Kaluza-Klein theory and considered how coupling constants in these models (numbers which specify how strongly a particle is associated with a force field it produces or to which it responds) relate to decay rates. These studies show that changes in decay rates may be connected to simultaneous changes in other basic constants. Early indications from double β-decay experiments in progress [Barabash, 1998, 2000, 2003] show that one or more constants involved in calculating β-decay half-lives may be variable. There are indications that any change in decay rate is likely to be dependent upon the type of decay of a given nuclear species. (This is consistent with the pattern of discordance between isochron "ages" of rocks found by Drs. Austin and Snelling.)

Although theoretical studies of nuclear decay are separate from the question of whether accelerated decay has actually occurred, these studies suggest that if certain variables are changed decay rates can be increased significantly. Small changes in some constants appear to be able to produce orders of magnitude changes in the decay rates. On the other hand, we acknowledge that theoretical and experimental studies may never with certainty be able to identify the primary mechanism God actually may have used. Because God is the eternal, all-powerful agent of Creation and the Genesis Flood, then He can simultaneously manipulate many possible variables in His Creation. With all our best efforts we might never discover exactly how or what He did to cause accelerated decay. However, we conceivably might be able from such studies to uncover some relevant interrelationships and estimate the magnitudes of certain parameter variations. We need to remember, however, that God is external and independent of His Creation, and during periods of intervention in the normal operation of His universe

He is not necessarily bound to follow what we call natural law. So, we do well to maintain an attitude of humility and carefulness in our attempts to understand such interventions on His part.

2.8 Radioactive Carbon

Most of the research pursued during the RATE project addressed the physics, geophysics, and geology associated with long half-life isotopes like U, Th, K, Rb, and Sm. Initially, research on short half-life isotopes such as ^{14}C was purposely excluded, because it was believed that the magnitude of the discrepancy between Biblical ages and ages of rocks estimated using long half-life isotopes was the much greater problem. Moreover, the literature revealed that many other young-earth researchers had already expended considerable effort on short-age isotopes. However, before the project had gone far into the research phase Dr. Paul Giem of Loma Linda University informed the RATE group that dozens of high-precision measurements were being reported indicating ^{14}C in coal and other ancient C-rich materials from deep in the geological record. These results were being reported in conventional journals like *Radiocarbon,* but were being interpreted as representing contamination from as yet undetermined sources. He suggested that the RATE project might wish to explore these reports and see if this evidence was relevant to its goals.

The RATE team decided that indeed ^{14}C deserved serious attention, and Dr. John Baumgardner assumed the leadership of this new project. He confirmed that about seventy independent measurements of ^{14}C using a new high-precision technique called accelerator mass spectrometry (AMS) had been reported in the standard radiocarbon literature for samples spanning most of the geological record. This method allows ^{14}C to be measured in much smaller concentrations than had been possible before, by counting ^{14}C atoms directly, rather than waiting for them to decay. *Baumgardner* [2005] collected the reports and graphed the results, as shown in Figure 7.

The average ratio of ^{14}C to total C concentrations in the samples relative to the modern carbon concentration for forty Phanerozoic

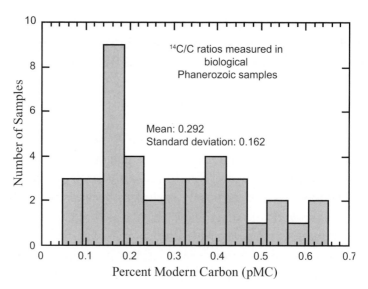

Figure 7. Histogram of measured ^{14}C/C in percent of modern carbon concentration for forty Phanerozoic biological samples as reported in the conventional literature [*Baumgardner et al.*, 2003].

(with uniformitarian ages 0.1 to 545 million years) biological samples was 0.292±0.162 percent modern carbon (pMC). In contrast, the average ratio for thirty Precambrian (greater than 545 Ma according to the conventional time frame) non-biological samples was 0.062±0.034 pMC. The average value of the ^{14}C/C ratio for biological samples would correspond to an age of about 50,000 years, provided one accepts that all the assumptions of conventional ^{14}C dating are valid. Even accepting the uniformitarian assumptions (which likely do not hold, given a recent global Flood), 50,000 years represents a glaring discrepancy with the uniformitarian ages of the reported samples, for example, of 300 million years for Pennsylvanian coal. But, uniformitarian assumptions are almost certainly inappropriate because, not only would a period of accelerated decay in the past have affected ^{14}C levels, but even apart from acceleration in decay rates, the Genesis Flood, by removing so much C from the biosphere, would invalidate the crucial assumption that the initial (pre-Flood) ^{14}C/ C ratio was similar to that of today's atmosphere. The RATE team concluded that even for a short half-life isotope like ^{14}C there is a major disparity between the uniformitarian age estimate and the actual age. The difference from the actual ages may not be as great as for long half-life isotopes, but is still important. In fact, partially because of this finding, the RATE group began to look for a theoretical mechanism of accelerated decay which would produce variable effects dependent upon half-life or possible decay modes (see *Chaffin* [2005]).

Dr. Baumgardner next sought to verify this remarkable result, namely, that samples considered tens to hundreds of millions of years old, given their position in the geological record, actually contain detectable ^{14}C. He obtained ten coal samples from the U.S. Department of Energy Coal Repository and sent them to a highly-regarded commercial laboratory for independent ^{14}C analysis. Moreover, because all of the non-biological samples reported in the literature showed measurable concentrations of ^{14}C as well, he acquired some diamonds and also had them analyzed for ^{14}C. Two criticisms were expected from the scientific community regarding these results from coal. It was expected that many old-age advocates would say that the high level of ^{14}C in the coal was a result of a faulty laboratory technique. However, after over twenty years of careful effort laboratories have reported that most significant sources of possible error have been eliminated. Actually, this process of identifying and correcting the errors in the AMS technique is the main reason for the scores of papers in the radiocarbon literature that deal with samples such as coal which the researchers assumed would be ^{14}C dead according to the conventional timescale. A second, expected criticism was that the source of ^{14}C in coal was *in situ* contamination. Coal has some level of porosity and water percolating through rock formations could conceivably bring some ^{14}C from today's biosphere into the coal seams. Finding measurable levels of ^{14}C in diamond, however, because diamonds are so hard and impervious to contamination, would be a powerful argument that the ^{14}C is actually intrinsic to the sample and not a result of contamination from the modern biosphere.

The average ratio of ^{14}C/C in the ten coal samples analyzed by Dr. Baumgardner was 0.25 pMC. For five diamonds from deep mines it was

0.04 pMC and for seven diamonds from alluvial environments it was 0.12 pMC, all notably greater than the background measurements of which the machines are capable. The independent coal measurements made by the RATE project agree closely with the earlier measurements reported in the radiocarbon literature. However, the new measurements in diamonds add a whole new dimension to the issue. If the level of ^{14}C detected in diamonds holds up as more diamonds are analyzed, the disparity relative to the standard timescale is even greater. Diamonds are thought to have been formed in the earth's mantle 1–3 billion years in the past according to conventional thinking. Yet, if they contain ^{14}C at reproducible levels near to what have been measured thus far, implying an age of 50,000 years or less, what could have been the source? Regardless of the source, it would have had to have gotten there very recently in terms of the uniformitarian timescale. One explanation for the ^{14}C in diamonds is the *in situ* transformation of ^{14}N, a trace contaminant in diamonds, into ^{14}C by bombardment with neutrons. However, the concentrations of neutrons measured in mines and other crustal environments today are many orders of magnitude too small to produce the measured concentrations of ^{14}C. On the other hand, the neutron levels that would have occurred in crustal environments during an episode of accelerated nuclear decay during the Flood do appear to be sufficient to account for the ^{14}C levels in diamonds the RATE project measured.

Because the 5730 year ^{14}C half-life is so short relative to the billions of years of the conventional timescale, the presence of measurable quantities of ^{14}C in coals and diamonds is another compelling indicator that the earth is young. Most of the ^{14}C in coals was probably sequestered when the material which formed the coals was buried during the Genesis Flood. Even with uniformitarian assumptions this had to be less than 50,000 years ago. The source of ^{14}C in diamonds is not yet clear, but whatever its source, it has since been trapped without contamination and the date of its introduction also must be less than 50,000 years ago. Because the Flood likely renders the uniformitarian assumption for the initial ^{14}C level incorrect, this age estimate almost certainly represents an upper bound.

2.9 Historical Reading of Genesis 1:1–2:3

Most of the efforts of RATE were dedicated toward research on rocks and discovering how the radioisotopes in them produced the daughter products observed today. However, because RATE depended so heavily on the Bible as the primary source of information for earth history, some of the effort was spent on evaluating the foundational premise that the primary passages of the Bible text relating to the earth's physical history are to be understood literally.

Recent trends in the evangelical community are troublesome, because an increasing number of conservative Bible scholars are teaching that the Creation and Genesis Flood accounts are mythical in essence and therefore should not be the basis of scientific investigation. To address this issue RATE commissioned Dr. Steven Boyd to conduct a linguistic and statistical study of Biblical Hebrew text to identify characteristics that objectively distinguish narrative passages from poetic passages [*Boyd*, 2005]. Our hope was that from this effort he would be able to demonstrate definitively that the authors of the key Creation and Flood passages were indeed writing literal, historical accounts, not figurative poetry meant merely to convey theological ideas.

He tabulated Hebrew verb forms for numerous narrative and poetic passages throughout the Old Testament. He targeted the preterite, imperfect, perfect, and waw-perfect. In general, narrative passages display high frequencies of preterites and moderate frequencies of imperfect and perfect verb forms. Poetic passages evidence almost the opposite, with low frequencies of preterites and moderate to high frequencies of imperfects and perfects. More particularly—as Figure 8 shows—the relative frequency of preterites for narrative is so different from that for poetry that it alone should be able to classify passages as narrative or poetry.

Dr. Boyd conducted a statistical experiment by randomly selecting a joint sample drawn from the two types of passages from Scripture and testing a distribution of the preterite verb form. He was able to demonstrate from his study, as shown in Figure 9, that the Creation account in Genesis 1:1–2:3 can be objectively identified as a narrative

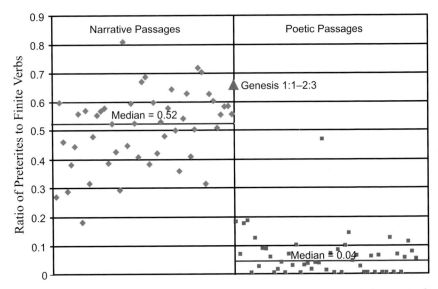

Figure 8. Side-by-side scatter plot of preterite verb forms in narrative passages versus poetic. The green diamonds are the narrative passages of the joint sample. The red squares are the poetic passages. The horizontal blue lines are the median for each sample. Genesis 1:1–2:3 (the blue triangle) is also plotted for comparison.

text with an extremely high statistical confidence level. Furthermore, he showed that Biblical narrative texts compel the reader to believe in their historicity. Genesis 1:1–2:3 should be read therefore as history and taken literally. This study reinforces the underlying premise of the RATE project that building a scientific model from Scripture is consistent with the linguistic character of the texts themselves.

3. Unresolved Problems

There are, of course, many questions and issues which the RATE project has not resolved. Although the problems were discussed at numerous times during project deliberations, adequate time and resources were not available to solve them. Some of them would have led the project astray from its main interests, and some required expertise which the RATE group did not have.

3.1 The Theological Problem

One important issue for many people is the apparent problem of nuclear decay of any sort occurring during Creation week (let alone accelerated decay), given the statement at the end of the sixth day in Genesis 1:31, *"Then God saw everything that He had made, and indeed it was very good."* If nuclear decay occurred at any point during the six days of Creation, it would seem at first that there would be a conflict in the definition of "good." The term "decay" is normally thought to be "bad." So, the issue is, if unstable nuclei of elements such as U or K were "decaying" into Pb, He, and Ar during the Creation week, would this process be compatible with the statement that, *"…*

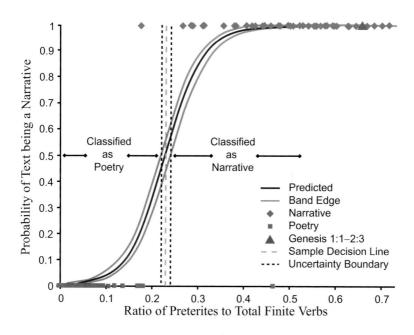

Figure 9. Plot showing the band of possible logistic curves derived from random samples from the total population of texts. The vertical distance between the light blue lines at a given ratio of preterites to finite verbs is a 99.5% confidence interval for the probability that a text with that ratio is a narrative.

everything that He had made ... was very good." The RATE group does not have a conclusive answer to this question, even after eight years of consideration. However, we have several thoughts concerning the issue.

First of all, it is evident from Scripture that indeed physical changes in the earth occurred when God cursed the ground in Genesis 3:14–24. It would seem consistent for nuclear decay to have occurred at any time from the curse onwards, because this passage implies that everything was then no longer "good." So, could it be that all the nuclear decay from which we observe evidence occurred during and following the curse? The most energetic earth processes described in the Bible seem to have occurred during Creation and at the Genesis Flood. If a large amount of nuclear decay occurred at the time of the curse, there is no explicit mention in the Biblical text of major physical disruptions to the earth itself. Of course, this is an argument from silence and the Bible does not always provide all the details. Scripture does indicate that the serpent was cursed, that woman would have pain in childbirth, that man would now have to till the ground, that Adam and Eve were driven from the Garden and away from the tree of life, and that they and their offspring began to die physically. But, nothing is mentioned about tectonic or geological upheavals. If this was indeed the case, then there would be no apparent conflict with Scripture.

However, the magnitude of the nuclear decay and the heat such decay would release seem to the RATE group to be too great to have occurred only since that judgment. A significant portion of the decay could have occurred during the Genesis Flood, but there still seems to be a need for another period of time during which it could have occurred. The only other likely period seems to be early in the Creation week, particularly during the first three days. During the first two days and part of the third day of Creation there was as yet no life on the earth. Any radiation, heat, or other by-products of these nuclear disintegration or transformation processes would not have been a problem for plants and animals.

The processes God used to create and form the earth were probably more energetic than anything we can imagine today, even in light of the May 18, 1980 Mount St. Helens eruption and the December 26, 2004 Asian tsunami. Scripture describes these processes only in very cursory terms. However, there is a sequence to the events. Mass, space, time, and light were formed on the first day, the atmosphere on the second day, and seas, dry land, and plants on the third day. Before the plants were formed there could have been rapid nuclear processes and the transformation of various elements into others.

Is it possible that the apparent conflict here is only semantic? Would the problem go away if we used the term *nuclear transformation* instead of nuclear decay? The basic problem is that we do not have enough information about how God managed these processes. And, even if we had more information, how would we describe them in current scientific terms? All of these events were supernatural, if not in kind, at least in terms of energetics and speed. So, it seems possible to us that some, even most, of the daughter products we observe could have been formed during the early Creation week, and the process was not viewed by God as "bad" at all. Some who still have a problem with the term "nuclear decay" being "bad" could alternatively interpret the considerable quantity of the daughter products we observe today simply to be the result of God's supernatural creative work with no reference to any specific process. What we call daughter elements would have played a "very good" role in the pre-curse period, as well as after the curse. For instance, Pb is a very useful metal.

3.2 The Heat Problem

If God caused a period of accelerated decay during the Genesis Flood, it would have generated a massive pulse of heat in the earth. The RATE group estimates that the heating would have been equal to that produced by about a half billion years of decay at today's rates. But, it would have been generated over the period of only one year of the Genesis Flood. The heat would have melted the crustal rocks many times over unless there was some mechanism for simultaneously removing it quickly. How did the earth survive such a massive dose of heat without vaporizing the oceans and melting the rocks? How did

Noah and his family survive such an environment on the Ark?

A primary piece of Biblical evidence that heat was not a problem is the fact that Noah and his family made it through the year of the Genesis Flood without being cooked! Sometimes we forget the obvious. Or, we choose to ignore the statements of Scripture which can guide our technical considerations. From the simple fact that Noah, his family, and the animals survived and left the Ark at the end of the Genesis Flood we can infer at least one of several possibilities:

- no accelerated decay occurred;
- no large amount of heat was generated by the accelerated decay; and
- God supernaturally protected Noah and his entourage by rapidly removing the large amount of heat that was produced by some unknown mechanism

That accelerated decay occurred during recent earth history was a major conclusion of the RATE project. Evidence provided from several lines of research in this book overwhelmingly supports this conclusion. All nuclear processes we know today generate heat. It is highly likely that accelerated decay generated heat in the crust of the earth proportional to the amount of acceleration. This implies a large amount of heat was generated over a short period of time recently in the crust of the earth. The RATE findings of abundant Po radiohalos in granite implies that a huge amount of nuclear decay took place while this rock was cooling in order to generate the radiohalos. On the other hand, rapid cooling of the granitic plutons in which they are found is also required [*Snelling and Armitage*, 2003]. The implication is that most of the heat from the rapid nuclear decay had to be removed by some extraordinary process.

Baumgardner [2000] earlier had described a long-standing mystery concerning the strong correlation between surface heat flow from crystalline rocks at the earth's surface and the abundance of radioactive elements these rocks contain. He showed that a simple explanation involves a recent burst of radioactive decay such that the surface heat flow is dominated by heat from this event, not from heat conducted from deeper in the earth. Yet, when the actual amount of accelerated decay is taken into account, as indicated by fission track data, for example, the implication is again that most of the heat from this episode of accelerated decay requires removal by some process other than thermal conduction.

The RATE group believes from these arguments that

• a large amount of nuclear decay occurred during the Genesis Flood and during the early part of Creation week as well;

• a large pulse of heat was also generated by this accelerated decay; and

• some mechanism removed this heat as it was being produced.

The removal of heat was so rapid that it likely involved a process other than conduction, convection, or radiation. For example, the cooling of granite plutons would have taken thousands of years by conventional thermal diffusion. Of course, God was directly involved in all of these events, so it is possible that He employed some supernatural process which does not occur today or cannot be detected. However, He commonly uses natural law to do His work on earth, and so we believe it may be possible to discover how He did it.

For example, *Humphreys* [2005] has offered a volumetric cooling mechanism based on relativistic principles. It appears to be consistent with the magnitude of the cooling needed as well as the cosmological language of the *"stretching of the heavens"* contained in Scripture. It involves the stretching in four dimensions of the space we experience in three dimensions and the consequent loss of energy on the part of photons and particles as the expansion of the fabric of space proceeds. Humphreys' postulated explanation represents only a beginning attempt to understanding the complicated events of the Genesis Flood and may not, in fact, be the correct mechanism. But his hypothesis has many attractive explanatory features and only a few known difficulties.

One difficulty is the distribution of volumetric cooling within the earth. The cooling probably could not have been uniform, but instead must have been dependent on some complex function of another variable like absolute temperature. It would have needed to vary strongly in some manner to avoid too much cooling in certain locations such as the oceans. Had the granite plutons with their high concentrations of radioactive elements cooled at sufficiently high rates to form and persist as crystalline rock, then the oceans would have frozen solid had they cooled by the same amount. Likewise, Noah and his family on the Ark would have been in danger of freezing. Of course, the concept of a complex cooling rate being dependent on temperature is not unusual. We know, for example, that Planck's radiation cooling law is a function of the absolute temperature to the fourth power. If such a relationship were to be applied to volumetric cooling, hot objects would cool orders of magnitude faster than cool objects.

The heat problem will eventually, through the research it spawns, actually yield crucial insight as to the mechanism behind accelerated decay itself. For example, the Ice Age following the Genesis Flood or subsurface ice layers may have been results of such an effect. *Baumgardner* [2000] has shown that there is a major problem in explaining the distribution of temperature in and near plutons without invoking some non-conventional heating and cooling mechanism. The RATE project did not have time to pursue this issue to any significant depth. We encourage others with the requisite physics background to investigate this problem and explore these largely uncharted waters.

3.3 The Radiation Problem

If God caused an episode of accelerated decay during the Genesis Flood, how could Noah and his family and all the plants and animals on the Ark have survived the massive dose of radiation such nuclear decay would have unleashed? At first glance, a simple solution to the problem seems to be readily available. The waters of the Genesis Flood covered the entire earth and thereby provided an absorptive layer between the Ark and the crust of the earth where most of the radiation was being generated. The occupants of the Ark would have been protected from the radiation, similar to shielding in a gigantic swimming-pool reactor.

However, at second glance there is a problem. It turns out shielding from the increased radiation dose from outside the Ark is not sufficient. Noah and his family may have had sources of radiation within their own bodies. For example, plants and animals today contain ^{40}K, which is radioactive. If nuclear decay rates were accelerated to the levels the RATE group believes occurred during the Genesis Flood, the radiation dose from similar levels of ^{40}K within Noah's body likely would have been lethal. One solution has been offered that possibly could mitigate this problem—namely, that the ^{40}K we measure in plants and animals today is the result of the Genesis Flood itself. The RATE team believes an attempt should be made to test for ^{40}K in the bodies of pre-Flood insects which were trapped in amber during the Genesis Flood and were thereby protected from subsequent contamination.

4. Conclusions

RATE began its eight-year research project with the intention to investigate radioisotope dating and determine if there was an explanation for the disparity between the conventional estimates of an old earth and the Biblical statements of a young earth. Initially the RATE team had no preconceived ideas regarding what might be found in the data. In fact, because the scientific community is so convinced in the great antiquity of the earth, the team was concerned that it might possibly run up against overwhelming evidence against a Biblical time frame. However, the RATE team was committed to conducting the first major creationist effort to investigate theoretically and experimentally a young-earth explanation of nuclear decay processes, no matter where the evidence led. The RATE team intended to offer a positive, scientific alternative for a thousands-of-years scenario rather than simply critiquing the conventional billions-of-years scenario. The team believed this problem was so important, so central to the current wide-scale defection of society from the literal teachings of the Bible and the creationist model of origins, that the team was willing to stake the scientific reputations of its members on the outcome of this effort. Many supporters agreed with this assessment, based on the widespread prayer support and financial backing the RATE project received.

The first conclusion reached through the literature search and early discussions was that whatever happened in earth history, a large amount of nuclear decay has occurred. The evidence includes the presence of large amounts of radiogenic Pb in minerals that do not normally contain Pb. Large concentrations of fission tracks—linear patterns of crystal damage in rocks caused by high-energy particles ejected from nuclear fission centers—are ubiquitous throughout the rock strata of the earth. Radiohalos—spherical patterns of discolored crystal surrounding nuclear decay centers—are present in most granitic rocks. The formation of radiohalos required a large amount of radioactive decay for the radiohalos to be detectable. And, finally, the measured presence of relatively large quantities of ^{4}He in zircons was, in itself, evidence for a large amount of nuclear decay.

The conclusion that a large amount of decay has occurred had been denied or ignored previously by many creationists. However, the evidence is overwhelming. The magnitude of the nuclear decay indicates that, independent of initial conditions, the equivalent of billions of years worth of nuclear decay has occurred during earth history.

How then should a young-earth advocate proceed? The only remaining avenue available appeared to be to question the assumption that nuclear decay rates have been constant. This approach was adopted by the RATE group as the preferred avenue for research, given the evidence for massive nuclear decay.

Although there were many subprojects to confirm preliminary and auxiliary concepts developed by the RATE group, there were four that provided direct evidence for accelerated decay—

- He diffusion,
- radiohalos,
- isotopic discordance, and
- ^{14}C in coal and diamonds.

These were summarized briefly in the previous section and are discussed in great detail in the appropriate chapters of this book. Three general geophysical conclusions were drawn from the RATE research:

- **A large amount of radioactive decay has occurred.**
- **Nuclear decay processes were accelerated during episodes in earth history.**
- **Conventional radioisotope dates are therefore incorrect by large factors.**

In addition to the geophysical issues, a study was also conducted on the reliability of Scripture as a basis for interpreting earth history.

Passages in the Old Testament were studied regarding their narrative versus poetic content. Because the highly statistically significant results of this study and the findings that the geophysical results were consistent with a literal interpretation of the Bible, two hermeneutical conclusions were also made:

• **Creation and the Genesis Flood are genuine historical events.**
• **Scripture is scientifically reliable.**

5. Recommendations

The RATE project has advanced an entirely new approach to resolving the conflict over the age of the earth. It identified several lines of evidence supporting the case for episodes of accelerated nuclear decay in the earth's past. Such evidence undermines a key assumption that underlies all uniformitarian radioisotope methods for estimating the ages of rocks. However, the experimental and theoretical RATE research needs to be confirmed and extended greatly. For example, trends in isochron "ages" of rocks need to be explored more widely by including additional isotope pairs with different half-lives and types of decay characteristics; He concentrations and the rate of diffusion in zircons need to be measured in a larger suite of rock samples containing a larger range in U concentrations from different geological settings; geological distributions of radiohalos and fission tracks need to be investigated more thoroughly, not only in granites, but also in metamorphic rocks; many more coals, diamonds, and other "old" geologic samples need to be analyzed for their ^{14}C content; and theoretical processes that influence the rate of nuclear decay need to be studied more comprehensively to identify mechanisms by which the decay processes can be accelerated.

Three major problems with accelerated decay pointed out previously, namely "the theological problem," "the heat problem," and "the radiation problem" need further work and consideration. The RATE group is confident that these issues will be solved because the evidence is so strong that accelerated decay has occurred, but at the time when RATE ended in 2005, their resolution had only begun.

There are many other issues and interesting projects which were only begun or considered during RATE which need further work. For example, the abundance of daughter products from long-lived radioisotopes in meteorites from space needs much more attention. These elements are used conventionally to infer cosmological processes involved in the formation of the earth and to estimate its age as a whole. The studies conducted by RATE on rocks from the earth do not yet adequately address the issue of the age of meteorites.

The point is that many of the strands of research started by RATE need to continue. The viability of the concept of accelerated decay has not yet been demonstrated to the satisfaction of many even within sympathetic creationist circles, let alone to the wider scientific community. Although the RATE team has already received some encouragement at technical presentations and hopes to receive more positive response from articles in conventional journals in the future, it does not expect the findings currently in hand by themselves to be adequate yet to precipitate a full-fledged revolution in thinking about the age of the earth. Such ingrained concepts as an old earth and constant rates of nuclear decay will not be overturned merely by the preliminary evidence and explanatory framework RATE has been able to assemble thus far. It will take continued efforts on the part of many more scientists and much greater levels of funding to build an irrefutable case for accelerated decay before it will be entertained with any seriousness by skeptics. This issue is at the core of a naturalistic world-view, not only in the physical sciences but, also, in the life sciences. Many years of additional research and reporting will likely be needed in order to make an enduring impact. The research started by RATE should be continued and expanded.

In the meantime, as the evidence accumulates, initial dissemination of these groundbreaking results should be made in creationist publications and to Christians in general to encourage them regarding the reliability of the Bible. Research on the age of the earth may, with God's help, be one of the most important methods for encouraging the church to work to return recognition and honor back to the Creator and Savior and away from naturalism. Although the technical issues are complex, the concept and implications for belief in the Bible are easily seen by the layman. Confidence in what the Bible says on these matters is important because, as Christ told Nicodemus, *"If I have told you earthly things and you do not believe, how will you believe if I tell you heavenly things?"* (John 3:12).

References

Austin, S.A., Mineral isochron method applied as a test of the assumptions of radioisotope dating, in *Radioisotopes and the Age of the Earth: A Young-Earth Creationist Research Initiative*, edited by L. Vardiman, A.A. Snelling, and E.F. Chaffin, pp. 95–121, Institute for Creation Research, El Cajon, California, and Creation Research Society, St. Joseph, Missouri, 2000.

Austin, S.A., Do radioisotope clocks need repair? Testing the assumptions of isochron dating using K-Ar, Rb-Sr, Sm-Nd, and Pb-Pb isotopes, in *Radioisotopes and the Age of the Earth: Results of a Young-Earth Research Initiative,* edited by L. Vardiman, A.A. Snelling, and E.F. Chaffin, pp. 325–392, Institute for Creation Research, El Cajon, California, and Creation Research Society, Chino Valley, Arizona, 2005.

Barabash, A.S., Does the weak interaction constant depend on time?, *JETP Letters, 68*(1), 1–6, 1998.

Barabash, A.S., Is the weak interaction constant really constant?, *European Physical Journal A, 8,* 137–140, 2000.

Barabash, A.S., Possible evidence of time variation of weak interaction constant from double beta decay experiments, *Astrophysics and Space Science, 283,* 607–612, 2003.

Baumgardner, J.R., Distribution of radioactive isotopes in the earth, in *Radioisotopes and the Age of the Earth: A Young-Earth Creationist Research Initiative*, edited by L. Vardiman, A.A. Snelling, and E.F. Chaffin, pp. 49–94, Institute for Creation Research, El Cajon, California, and Creation Research Society, St. Joseph, Missouri, 2000.

Baumgardner, J.R., ^{14}C evidence for a recent global Flood and a young earth, in *Radioisotopes and the Age of the Earth: Results of a Young-Earth Creationist Research Initiative,* edited by L. Vardiman, A.A. Snelling, and E.F. Chaffin, pp. 587–630, Institute for Creation Research, El Cajon, California, and Creation Research Society, Chino Valley, Arizona, 2005.

Baumgardner, J. R., A. A. Snelling, D. R. Humphreys, and S. A. Austin, Measurable ^{14}C in fossilized organic materials: confirming the young earth Creation-Flood model, in *Proceedings of the Fifth International Conference on Creationism*, edited by R. L. Ivey, Jr., pp. 127–142, Creation Science Fellowship, Pittsburgh, Pennsylvania, 2003.

Bosch, F., *et al.*, Observation of bound-state beta-minus decay of fully ionized ^{187}Re: ^{187}Re-^{187}Os cosmochronometry, *Physical Review Letters, 77,* 5190–5193, 1996.

Boyd, S. F., Statistical determination of genre in Biblical Hebrew: evidence for an historical reading of Genesis 1:1–2:3, in *Radioisotopes and the Age of the Earth: Results of a Young-Earth Creationist Research Initiative,* edited by L. Vardiman, A. A. Snelling, and E. F. Chaffin, pp. 631–734, Institute for Creation Research, El Cajon, California, and Creation Research Society, Chino Valley, Arizona, 2005.

Chaffin, E. F., Accelerated decay: theoretical considerations, in *Radioisotopes and the Age of the Earth: Results of a Young-Earth Creationist Research Initiative,* edited by L. Vardiman, A. A. Snelling, and E. F. Chaffin, pp. 525–585, Institute for Creation Research, El Cajon, California, and Creation Research Society, Chino Valley, Arizona, 2005.

DeYoung, D. B., *Thousands not Billions: Challenging an Icon of Evolution,* Master Books, Green Forest, Arkansas, 2005.

Gentry, R. V., *Creation's Tiny Mystery,* 347 pp., Earth Science Associates, Knoxville, Tennessee, 1988.

Gentry, R., G. J. Glish, and E. H. McBay, Differential helium retention in zircons: implications for nuclear waste management, *Geophysical Research Letters, 9*(10), 1129–1130, 1982.

Humphreys, D. R., Accelerated nuclear decay: a viable hypothesis?, in *Radioisotopes and the Age of the Earth: A Young-Earth Creationist Research Initiative,* edited by L. Vardiman, A. A. Snelling, and E. F. Chaffin, pp. 333–379, Institute for Creation Research, El Cajon, California, and Creation Research Society, St. Joseph, Missouri, 2000.

Humphreys, D. R., Young helium diffusion age of zircons supports accelerated nuclear decay, in *Radioisotopes and the Age of the Earth: Results of a Young-Earth Creationist Research Initiative,* edited by L. Vardiman, A. A. Snelling, and E. F. Chaffin, pp. 25–100, Institute for Creation Research, El Cajon,

California, and Creation Research Society, Chino Valley, Arizona, 2005.

Morris, H.M., *Scientific Creationism*, 281 pp., Master Books, Green Forest, Arkansas, 1974.

Morris, H.M., *The Genesis Record*, 716 pp., Baker Book House, Grand Rapids, Michigan, 1976.

Morris, J.D., *The Young Earth*, 208 pp., Master Books, Green Forest, Arkansas, 1994.

Morris, J.D., and S.A. Austin, *Footprints in the Ash*, 128 pp., Master Books, Green Forest, Arkansas, 2003.

Snelling, A.A., Radiohalos, in *Radioisotopes and the Age of the Earth: A Young-Earth Creationist Research Initiative*, edited by L. Vardiman, A.A. Snelling, and E.F. Chaffin, pp. 381–468, Institute for Creation Research, El Cajon, California, and Creation Research Society, St. Joseph, Missouri, 2000.

Snelling, A.A., Radiohalos in granites: evidence for accelerated nuclear decay, in *Radioisotopes and the Age of the Earth: Results of a Young-Earth Creationist Research Initiative,* edited by L. Vardiman, A.A. Snelling, and E.F. Chaffin, pp. 101–207, Institute for Creation Research, El Cajon, California, and Creation Research Society, Chino Valley, Arizona, 2005a.

Snelling, A.A., Fission tracks in zircons: evidence for abundant nuclear decay, in *Radioisotopes and the Age of the Earth: Results of a Young-Earth Creationist Research Initiative,* edited by L. Vardiman, A.A. Snelling, and E.F. Chaffin, pp. 209–324, Institute for Creation Research, El Cajon, California, and Creation Research Society, Chino Valley, Arizona, 2005b.

Snelling, A.A., Isochron discordances and the role of inheritance and mixing of radioisotopes in the mantle and crust, in *Radioisotopes and the Age of the Earth: Results of a Young-Earth Research Initiative,* edited by L. Vardiman, A.A. Snelling, and E.F. Chaffin, pp. 393–524, Institute for Creation Research, El Cajon, California, and Creation Research Society, Chino Valley, Arizona, 2005c.

Snelling, A.A., and M.H. Armitage, Radiohalos—a tale of three granitic plutons, in *Proceedings of the Fifth International Conference on Creationism,* edited by R.L. Ivey, Jr., pp. 243–267, Creation Science Fellowship, Pittsburgh, Pennsylvania, 2003.

Vardiman, L., A.A. Snelling, and E.F. Chaffin, *Radioisotopes and the Age of the Earth: A Young-Earth Creationist Research Initiative,* 675 pp., Institute for

Creation Research, El Cajon, California, and Creation Research Society, St. Joseph, Missouri, 2000.

Whitcomb, J.C., and H.M. Morris, *The Genesis Flood*, 518 pp., Presbyterian and Reformed Publishing Company, Phillipsburg, New Jersey, 1961.

Index

A

Aaron, 678, 718
Abachi, 556, 573
Abraham, 649, 678, 687
Abramowitz, 95
Abrasion, 248
Abscissa, 40, 54, 59
Absorption, 298, 538-539, 541, 572
Abundances, 12, 124, 144-145, 147,
150, 174-177, 179, 181-182, 187, 191,
345, 355-356, 514, 526, 534, 537-
538, 572
Academia, 734
Academy, 15, 321, 513, 576, 734
Accelerate, 736
Accelerated, 7, 13, 20, 25, 46, 67-70,
73-74, 95-97, 99, 101-102, 109, 111,
135, 142-143, 145, 147-148, 153,
155-156, 158-159, 164, 167, 182-184,
189-190, 199, 210-215, 277, 281-286,
303, 311-312, 317, 322, 384-386,
393-395, 397, 399, 401-403, 405,
432, 434, 454-465, 516-517, 522,
525, 528, 535-538, 541, 556, 563,
566-567, 569, 571, 573, 576, 579,
591, 613, 616, 619-623, 627-629,
729, 731-733, 735-738, 740, 742-744,
746-747, 749-750, 752, 754-756, 759,
761-764, 766-768, 770-771
Accelerator, 544, 547, 557, 560, 587,
589, 591-592, 606, 625-630, 753
Accreted, 402
Accreting, 678
Accretion, 399, 402

Acetone, 341
Acetylene, 606, 608
Achan, 683
Acids, 288
Actinium, 200
Activated, 33, 78
Activation Laboratories, 30, 39, 43, 75-
76, 263, 269-271, 287, 344, 357, 409,
465
Acts, 22, 685, 732
Adah, 688
Adam, 73, 643, 760
Adamellite, 124, 162
Addison Wesley, 197, 578, 581
Additivity, 666
Adelaide, 111, 408
Adhere, 22, 85
Adhesive, 113
Adiabatic, 183
Ad seriatim, 678
Adsorbed, 602
Advection, 155
Advent, 589
Aeolian, 201
Aerts-Bijma, 596-597, 625
Aetiology, 725
African, 610-611
Aggregate, 491
Aggregates, 263, 507
Ahmad, 132, 192
Air, 20, 104, 106, 263, 268-269, 597
Albarède, 395, 397, 429, 509
Albite, 130-131, 202, 490
Albuquerque, 93
Alburger, 565, 573

C

G

S